UNDERSTANDING
TELECOMMUNICATIONS
Systems, Networks, and Applications
Vol. 2

Ming-Chwan Chow

Retired District Manager
AT&T Education Center

Distinguished Member of Technical Staff
Lucent Technologies, Inc.

Andan Publisher
New Jersey

Publisher's Cataloging in Publication Data

Chow, Ming-Chwan
    Understanding Telecommunications: Systems, Networks and Applications/
Ming-Chwan Chow. - - 1st ed.
    v. cm.
    Includes bibliographical references and index.
    LCCN: 99-97227.
    ISBN: 0-9650448-3-1 (Vol. 1)
    ISBN: 0-9650448-8-2 (Vol. 2)

    1. Telecommunications systems.   I. Title.

TK5101.C46 2000   621.382   QBI99-1700

Printed in the United States of America

First edition (2000) by:

Andan Publisher
4 Aufra Place
Holmdel, New Jersey 07733
732-946-4155 (Voice)
732-946-4717 (Fax)

Library of Congress Catalog Card Number: 99-97227

ISBN: 0-9650448-8-2

To my wife, Joann, our children
Anne and Daniel, and their spouses
Robert and Martha, and
the memory of my parents

Books published by Andan Publisher:

- Ming-Chwan Chow, "*Understanding SONET/SDH: Standards and Applications*," 1st ed., 1996, ISBN 0-9650448-2-3

- Ming-Chwan Chow, "*Understanding Wireless: Digital Mobile, Cellular and PCS*," 1st ed., 1998, ISBN 0-9650448-5-8

- Ming-Chwan Chow, "*Understanding Telecommunications: Systems, Networks and Applications (Vol. 1)*," 1st ed., 2000, ISBN 0-9650448-3-1

- Ming-Chwan Chow, "*Understanding Telecommunications: Systems, Networks and Applications (Vol. 2)*," 1st ed., 2000, ISBN 0-9650448-8-2

Contents

Volume 2

CHAPTER 9   Data Communications Fundamental

CHAPTER 10   Network Architectures: LANs and WANs

CHAPTER 11   TCP/IP Voice & Fax over IP (VoIP & FoIP)

CHAPTER 12   Network Management and TMN

CHAPTER 13   Error Control Technologies

CHAPTER 14   Timing and Synchronization

References

Answers to Review Questions

Abbreviations and Acronyms

Index

Volume 1 (A separate book; brief outline shown as follows)

CHAPTER 1 Introduction: Basic Definitions and Terminologies

CHAPTER 4 Signaling Concepts and Applications

CHAPTER 5 Switching Principles and Applications

CHAPTER 6 Transmission Systems and Applications

CHAPTER 7 Optical Fiber Communications

(*) **Further description beyond this level**

Preface

Telecommunications services have evolved from point-to-point connections to global interconnections; and the required communications equipment are no longer just the essential telephones (voice terminals) and simple manual switches, but the software controlled integrated network nodes besides the intelligent customer premises equipment. Engineers were the only group of people had to get involve with telecommunications system design, deployment and maintenance. In modern society, even it is essential for the end users to learn about telecommunications to a certain degree so that they can conduct their daily business effectively.

Telecommunications networks have evolved from all analog, to mixtures of analog and digital, finally to modern digital dominated global networks. Telecommunications applications were originally designed for point-to-point services. Now, multicast, broadcast and global interconnection technologies have brought the world closer. The traffic carried by telecommunications networks is no longer just voice (speech) signals, it has been statistically studied/concluded that half of telecommunications traffic is data, including Internet traffic. The research/development of telecommunications networks must thereby be multimedia and ISDN.

An end-to-end communication link can be viewed as the connection of two networks: the access and the backbone (backhaul) networks. In the US, the backbone networks are no longer plesiochronous digital hierarchy (PDH) dominating networks. The networks have been implemented using SONET standards, such as OC-48 (Optical Carrier signal-48) with a data rate of 2.44832 Gbps (a voice capacity of 32,256 channels). The networks of the Internet have also been implemented using SONET OC-12 signals. For many other countries, SDH STM-16 and STM-4 are used instead of OC-14 and OC-12. The (speed) **bottleneck** of an end-to-end connection is "access networks". Traditional analog (metallic) loops associated with local exchange office are designed to carry one voice signal. Since digital computers was invented in the early 1960s, various modem techniques have been developed for carrying digital data over these analog loops. However, due to the rapid advance of Internet services, broadband access demand is continuously increasing, the present modem technique can no longer meet the increasing speed needs. Therefore, besides intelligent signaling network, high throughput digital switches, and high-speed backbone networks, it is essential to develop broadband access networks. Presently, integrated digital loop carrier systems provided business customers to access the backbone network via OC-3 or OC-12 in North America, and STM-1 and STM-4 in other countries. Cable modems and Hybrid Fiber Coax (HFC) have been deployed for generic applications. In addition, service providers with well-established metallic copper loop plants are seeking for compatible alternate techniques to provide subscribers broadband access capability. Among various techniques, High-speed Digital Subscriber Line

(HDSL), Asymmetrical Digital Subscriber Line (ADSL) and Very high-speed Digital Subscriber Line (VDSL) have potential to be adopted as broadband access standards. HDSL systems may eventually be able to operate on 99% of the copper twisted-pairs that conform to the Carrier Serving Area (CSA) guidelines in the US.

"Understanding Telecommunications: Systems, Networks, and Applications" is a two-volume book. The content of this two-volume is listed as follows:

Volume I: ISBN 0-9650448-3-1:

Chapter

Volume II: ISBN 0-9650448-8-2:

Chapter

Through the years, I have taught several telecommunications courses including: digital transmission, optical fiber, wireless, SONET, SDH and ATM courses [at universities, Bell laboratories, AT&T and Lucent Technologies in the USA, and abroad]. The materials within this book comes from my teaching notes. Without valuable insights and feedback from students who have taken my courses, "Understanding Telecommunications" would not be possible. I would like to give my sincere thanks to all my students and to my colleagues at Lucent Technologies,. Special thanks go to Mr. Carl Mason, who has not only carefully reviewed, and edited the book, but also provided valuable information on several topics. A applause to my wife, as usual, she provides her support in the preparation of this book. She skillfully transformed my hand-written notes and graphs into this final form. My thanks also go to the following people who have contributed their time in review of this book: Ms. Anne Chow, Dr. Daniel Chow, Mr. Robert Moore, Ms. Martha Taylor, and Mr. Mike Seidel.

Ming-Chwan Chow
Holmdel, New Jersey

CHAPTER 8

Digital Wireless Communications

Chapter Objectives

Upon the completion of this chapter, you should be able to:

- Describe several basic telecommunications service environments, service types, the service evolution from Plain Old Telephone Service (POTS) to Personal Communications Service (PCS), define personal and terminal mobility, and service profile management.

- Describe radio transmission: antenna basic (antenna types and characteristics), propagation environment, delay spreading, deep fading, diversity techniques, frequency reuse (cellular and PCS spectra, cellularization, sectorization, frequency ruse factor, and channel assignments).

- Discuss multiple access techniques: Frequency Division Multiple Access (FDMA), Time Division Multiple Access (TDMA), Code Division Multiple Access (CDMA), and their comparisons.

- Describe signal modulation techniques for wireless communications needs: Amplitude Shift Keying (ASK), Frequency Shift Keying (FSK), Phase Shift Keying (PSK), and Quadratural Amplitude Modulation (QAM).

- Describe mobile communications evolution from 1st Generation (1G), into 2G and then into 3G, International Mobile Telecommunications-2000 (IMT-2000), and various IMT-2000 technologies such as the GSM-based W-CDMA 3G, the IS-95-based cdma2000 3G, and the IS-136-based 3G technologies.

8.1 INTRODUCTION

The purpose of any communications service is to transport a signal (i.e., voice, data, or video) to its destination with acceptable quality. The physical media used for signal transport can be either wires (e.g., twisted-pair wires and coaxial cable), optical fibers (see Chapter 7), waveguides (radio signals over a hollow metal tube), or airway (open air) radio wave transmission. This chapter describes the communications over airway (or airlink), but does not include satellite communications (that is beyond the scope of this book).

The evolution of airlink communications can be summarized as follows:

- Analog radio transmission: Figure 8-1 shows the frequency spectrum with several communication system applications. Analog radio communication systems, such as Amplitude Modulation (AM) or Frequency Modulation (FM) are among the earliest technologies used in analog radio transmission.

- Analog satellite communications: This application is operated in the microwave radio frequency range (GHz) as shown in Figure 8-1.

- Digital radio transmission: This type of airway communication systems is typically operated in the microwave radio range (Figure 8-1) [e.g., Digital Radio (DR-11, DR-18), operating at 11 GHz and 18 GHz, respectively].

- Digital satellite communications: This application is also operated in the microwave radio frequency range, but using different modulation and multiplexing methods, compared to analog satellite systems.

- Mobile communication systems: The term "mobile" was adopted because these airway systems were originally intended for mobile units, especially automobiles. Later the term "*wireless*" was introduced. Even though radio and satellite systems are also wireless, the term "wireless" is typically reserved for mobile or cellular systems.

- Paging systems: The original paging service was intended to provide an inexpensive way of contacting subscribers. This service now provides more sophisticated services such as a short message display on the unit. Paging is also a "*wireless*" technology.

- Cordless telephone systems: Another airlink communication system, the cordless telephone, started with analog technology and evolved into digital technology. The primary modifications are in the areas of modulation and multiplexing. Cordless telephony is also referred to as a "wireless" technology.

- Cellular communications systems: As mobile communications systems started to gain popularity, it becomes obvious airway bandwidth would never be sufficient for any practical applications. Therefore, the industry had to find ways of "recycling" the bandwidth. As a result, the term "*frequency reuse*" was introduced. In order to implement frequency reuse, a serving area must be "cellularized". That is, the area is divided into many cells, which re further grouped into clusters (this concept is discussed further in a later section of this chapter). The available bandwidth (i.e., radio channels) used in one cluster of cells can be reused in another clusters, provided a predefined set of rules are followed. As in the case of other airway technologies, cellular communication systems also began as an analog implementation, known as Frequency Division Multiple Access (FDMA). Cellular technology first applied a digital implementation known as Time Division Multiple Access (TDMA), and finally evolved to Code Division Multiple Access (CDMA).

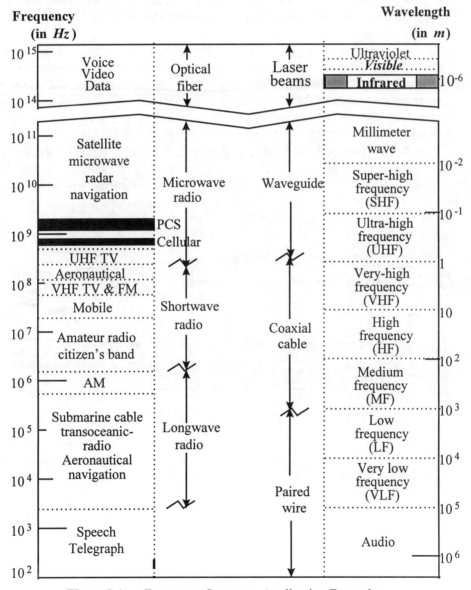

Figure 8-1   Frequency Spectrum Application Examples.

Two frequency ranges are commonly assigned for cellular communication systems: (1) 824 MHz ~ 894 MHz (known as the cellular spectrum); and (2) 1850 MHz ~ 1990 MHz [known as Personal Communication Service (PCS) spectrum].

- Wireless data communications [wireless local area network (LAN)]: This technology is described in Chapter 9. The description includes Wireless In-building Networks (WINs). Associated with this evolution, the "wireless" mouse for PC applications has been implemented by a limited number of vendors.

- Wireless Private Branch eXchange (PBX): The concept of PBX is explained in Chapter 5. The advantage of a wireless PBX is that it is easier to re-configure the network.

- Fixed wireless: This arrangement applies the same principle/technology used in digital cellular (wireless) communications systems. The intention of this application is to implement the subscriber loop system easily in rapid deployment situations. Since there are places in the world where traditional analog (wire) subscriber loop systems are not widely implemented, fixed wireless technology is often the "technology of choice". There are various names used for fixed wireless technology: Airloop®, Wireless Local Loop (WLL), Wireless Subscriber System (WSS), etc.

The network architecture of a digital cellular network is illustrated in Figure 8-2. A cellular network often, if not always, involves a Public Switched Telephone Network (PSTN), commonly referred to as a "landline" or "wireline" network.

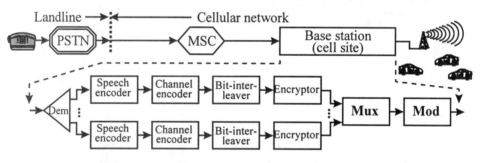

Figure 8-2   A Cellular Communications Network.

The major components of a cellular network (Figure 8-2) are briefly described as follows:

- PSTN: The Public Switched Telephone Network (PSTN) contains three types of Network Elements (NEs). The first type of network elements are switching machines used in local and trunk exchange offices (see Chapter 5). The second type of elements are associated with transmission functions, for example, transmission facilities, pulse code modulation systems, add-drop multiplexers, digital cross-connect systems, integrated digital loop carrier systems, echo cancelers, and regenerators.(see Chapters 6 and 7). The third type of network elements are signaling systems, which are used to perform call related control functions. The most commonly used signaling protocol is signaling system 7 (SS7; Chapter 4 describes signaling).

- Mobile Switching Center or Mobile Telephone Service Switching Office (MSC or MTSO): The primary function of an MSC is call switching (see Chapter 5).

- Base Station or Cell Site (BS or CS): In addition to radio transmission and radio resource management, a base station performs several import functions:

  * Speech encoding: This function converts a speech signal into a digital bit stream for transmission over the digital network. Speech encoding has been previously described in Chapters 1, 6 and 11. Figure 8-2 indicates that speech encoding is implemented in the base station, this approach is not unique. But, speech encoding can also be implemented in the MSC.

  * Channel encoding: When a digital signal is transmitted over an airway, the bits can be corrupted by channel noise and may be restored erroneously. Additional bandwidth is always required to transport additional bits used to perform error detection/correction. Channel error control can be applied for two different purposes: (1) to detect but not to correct channel errors, this application is often used in data signal transport. In transporting data, if errors are detected, "re-transmission" is always executed to insure accurate data information; and (2) to detect channel errors first, and then to correct as many errors as possible. This application is used for the signal that can not tolerate delay if "re-transmission" is executed. Chapter 13 describes error control principle and applications. Bit-interleaving technology is often used to control bursty errors that occur in wireless communications because of its unguided transmission path.

  * Encryption: Encryption is applied to ensure security management in a wireless system. The basic concept is bit scrambling, which is described in Chapter 13. However, a detailed description of encryption is beyond the scope of this book.

  * Multiplexing: Multiplexing allows efficient utilization of bandwidth. That is, "sharing" bandwidth among as many users as possible. Although "bandwidth" is often referred to as "frequency" (Chapter 6 has defined system bandwidth), for wireless communications the definition of bandwidth can be extended beyond frequency. Besides "frequency", "time" and "code" can also be "shared" among users. These techniques are FDMA, TDMA and CDMA.

  * Modulation: It is generally true that a signal in its original form is not suitable for being carried over a transmission media. The signal must be processed before it is compatible with the transmission media. One processor is a modulator at the transmitting end, and another is a demodulator at the receiving end. The common modulation techniques are: AM, FM, Phase Modulation (PM), Amplitude Shift

Keying (ASK), Frequency Shift Keying (FSK), Phase Shift Keying (PSK), and Quadratural Amplitude Modulation (QAM). For wireless mobile or cellular communications systems, one of these modulation methods is typically used.

8.2 TELECOMMUNICATIONS SERVICES

The most common telecommunications services are : (1) Plain Old Telephone Service (known as POTS service); (2) Public (known as coin or pay phone) phone; (3) Calling card service; (4) Airphone used in commercial aircraft; (5) Video teleconferencing; (6) Private Branch eXchange (PBX; Centrex) service; (7) Electronic mail (e-mail); (8) Voice mail; (9) Facsimile signal (Fax) service; (10) Computer data service; (11) Paging service; (12) Mobile fax; (13) Car phone; (14) Voice over internet (VoIP); and (15) Fax over internet (FoIP).

8.2.1 Various Service Environments

The availability of telecommunications services is depends upon the environment. The following list summarizes the services that are available in four common environments:

- **The home environment**: POTS (includes traditional wired phones, cordless phones and answering services), fax, and computer services over voice-grade lines (including Internet service) are typically available in the home environment. [Note that the telecommunications network for "the home" was originally designed for voice applications. Hence, computer data is transmitted over this type of network is known as *voice-grade data*.]

- **The office environment**: In addition to POTS, fax, and computer services, enhanced services such as teleconferencing, PBX, voice mail, and e-mail are often provided in the office environment.

- **The mobile environment**: The most important services in the mobile environment are paging service, cellular car phone, mobile fax, portable computer data, and wireless Internet (not widely adopted yet) services.

- **The outdoor/travel environment**: The services for the outdoor/travel environment include public (coin or pay) phone, credit card calling, paging, cellular (portable) phone, mobile fax, portable computer, and airphone ("air-to-ground" calling).

To provide these services, various facilities for accessing the telecommunications network must be made available to all users. Similarly, the (public) networks covering different parts of the world must be interconnected so that global communications can be implemented. Figure 8-3 shows a simplified configuration for various services and communication environments.

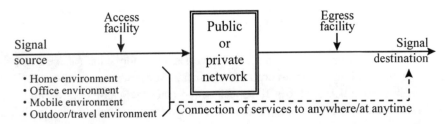

Figure 8-3   Services, Service Environments, Access, Network & Destination.

To allow voice, data and video signals to be transported over a network that is high-speed and highly reliability, requires deployment of access facilities. The selection of access facilities is a function of the service type and the existing network that is available. That is, access facilities evolve along with network technologies. Networks technologies, which are used for voice, data, or video signal transport, have evolved from analog to digital. Similar to the transmission facilities connecting network elements together, have evolved from wire (twisted-pairs and coaxial cable) to wire plus airway (radio and satellite), to optical fiber medium.

For many years, because of technological constraints, Information Movement and Management (IM&M) was implemented with voice signals and data signals being transported over separate networks. The Next Generation Lightguide (Lightwave) Network (NGLN), which is implemented using SONET/SDH standards, will transport voice, data, and video signals over the same network. ATM (Asynchronous Transport Mode) protocol will be applied to this ISDN-type service. In addition to traditional wire access facilities and broadband fiber access facilities, wireless access facilities will also play an important role in the modern communications era.

The transmission facilities of the (backbone) network can be wires, airway, or optical fibers just like the access facilities. However, there are differences between access facilities and network facilities. The major difference is transmission speed (i.e., facility speeds are often much higher than access speeds). Besides network facilities, other components are needed to form a network. These components are transmission terminals (or equipment) and switching machines. The primary transmission systems include digital channel banks (for analog to digital conversion, and vice versa), Add/Drop Multiplexers (ADMs), Digital Cross-connect Systems (DCSs), pair-gain systems, echo cancelers, optical amplifiers, and regenerators. The details of transmission equipment and switching machine functions are described in Chapters 5 and 6. In addition to transmission and switching, signaling network is required for completing telecommunications services (see Chapter 4 for the details of signaling).

When optical fibers are used in high-speed message networks, single-mode fibers (instead of multi-mode fibers) are typically used. Single-mode fibers support much higher speeds than multi-mode fibers. Chapter 7 describes fiber types, characteristics, and applications. Likewise, the other components required to implement a fiber based transmission facility are identified in Chapter 7.

Networks can be classified into two categories: (1) Information (or message) networks, used to perform information transport [i.e., Information Movement & Management (IMM)], and (2) Signaling networks, used to perform call set-up and other call-processing functions. Both networks contain switching machines, transmission terminals, and transmission facilities.

8.2.2 Service Evolution

Analog access facilities have evolved into digital facilities, and networks have made this same transition. Presently, access facilities and their associated networks utilize wires, fibers, and wireless technologies. Multiple (individual) facilities (i.e., voice, audio, data ,and video) have evolved towards integrated access. Similarly, networks have evolved from voice-based low-speed PSTN, separate voice/data, and CCS7/SS7 control, into high-speed SONET/SDH, ISDN, and advanced intelligent network (AIN), respectively.

Therefore, services have expanded from POTS to include fax, computer, paging, voice-mail, electronic-mail (e-mail), and ultimately personal communications service (PCS). Figure 8-4 illustrates the evolution of services towards PCS.

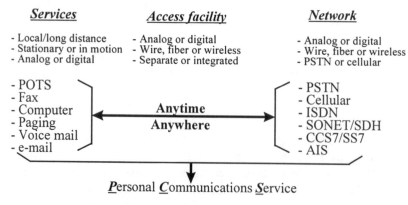

Figure 8-4   Services Evolution into PCS.

8.2.2.1 What is PCS?

Personal Communication Service (PCS) can be considered an integrated extension of current (e.g., POTS voice services, or voice-equivalent services) and emerging (e.g., Internet services) telecommunications services, using both wired (wireline) and wireless networks. It can also be viewed as an expansion of cellular services into a new spectrum, with strong encouragement to generate enhanced features.

Some service providers may initially use PCS to extend the service areas of their existing cellular communication networks. That is, some existing cellular companies are looking at PCS as a means of providing wide coverage areas and filling gaps in their current service offerings. These companies favor using identical standards/protocols in both the cellular and PCS frequency bands. Other companies see PCS as an opportunity to compete with cellular by offering lower costs, additional services, and better quality. These companies favor adoption of new standards/protocols, or extensions of existing standards, to support new services.

Figure 8-5   What is PCS?

The definition of PCS given by the **ANSI-T1P1** committee is: "*PCS is a set of capabilities that allows some combination of* (1) Terminal mobility; (2) Personal mobility, and (3) Service profile management" (see Figure 8-5). However, PCS is interpreted differently based upon individual perspectives:

- **FCC view:** PCS is a broad range of new radio communications services. PCS is any service offered using the FCC's new PCS spectrum. PCS can handle digital wireless voice and data applications, and encourages a diverse array of new services in a highly competitive market.

- **ITU view:** PCS is a "next generation" telephone service that extends from wired networks to wireless networks, to end users. The ITU-T is working on a standard defining PCS network components, while ITU-R is working on a standard defining PCS radio access.

- **ANSI view:** PCS is a next generation telephone services that extends from wired networks to wireless networks. These services are based on any of the seven potential PCS standards (described later in this chapter).

- **Cellular communications view:** PCS is the next (third) generation of cellular communications. It will provide seamless roaming, and improved quality.

- **Cable TV industry view:** Cable TV companies can utilize cable networks to provide PCS and telephone services. New PCS radio ports (i.e., base stations or cell sites), can be deployed along cable routes.

- **User view:** PCS is a new service that provides low cost voice communication, high-speed wireless data applications, mobile fax capabilities, and video services.

8.2.2.2 Terminal Mobility

Terminal mobility means that terminal equipment and its suite of capabilities can be tracked by the network. A user can receive service regardless of whether he/she is stationary or in motion. Similarly, a terminal can access a telecommunications network (e.g., initiate calls) from different stationary locations or while in motion.

In cellular technology, terminal information and user profile data are linked. In contrast, for PCS applications, terminal capability information is not correlated with a specific user. The PCS network can identify and locate "active terminals".

Definition 8-1: An ***active terminal*** is defined as a terminal that is "***powered-up***" but idle, or is "powered-up" and engaged in a call. Terminals that are not powered-up are "***inactive***" and cannot be located or accessed.

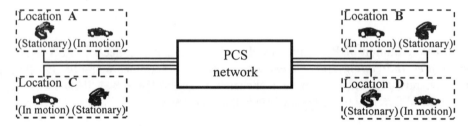

Figure 8-6   Terminal Mobility.

PCS subscribers want the ability to communicate while moving, and they also want to receive and manage special services while in motion. Individuals will have different needs and willingness to pay for these services. Therefore, the same technologies may not be appropriate for any given situation. Some situations justify, and even necessitate, wireless telecommunications, while others do not (see Figure 8-6). Terminal mobility can be further classified as discrete mobility and continuous mobility.

- **Discrete mobility**: Discrete mobility is based on the concept that a subscriber wants to communicate from more than one location within a limited geographical area. Hence, the caller must remain within the coverage area to complete the calls. Examples of services that have discrete mobility are

  * Home: cordless phone
  * Office: wireless PBX
  * Hotel: portable phone
  * Airport: Telepoint service
  * Train station: Telepoint service

Cordless telephones are commonly used in residential applications. In this situation, the telephone cord is replaced by a wireless link that provides terminal mobility to the user within a limited radio coverage area (e.g., a range of several hundred feet). A cordless phone can be analog or digital. The transmission distance of a digital cordless phone is 10 to 20 times greater than an analog cordless phone, and provides improved privacy/security features.

Telepoint service is an extension of cordless telephony which provides short-range access capability via portable radio terminals operating in public areas (e.g., train stations, airports, shopping centers, etc.). The coverage is limited to relatively small zones (typically a few hundred feet), without "handoff" (i.e., the user must remain within the zone to complete calls). The original Telepoint system deployed in the United Kingdom did not allow for incoming calls, but an updated version supports two-way calling.

- **Continuous mobility**: Continuous mobility is based on the concept that a subscriber wants to communicate while in transit between locations. Transit can be at low speeds (e.g., walking) or high speeds (e.g., riding in a car). Low speed continuous mobility is generally thought of as pedestrian speeds in a neighborhood environment or within a building. High speed continuous mobility is generally thought of as vehicular speeds in a wide area environment such as along highways or railroads. Examples of services that have continuous mobility are:

    * Home: cellular phone
    * Car: car phone
    * Car: mobile fax
    * Car: portable computer

With continuous mobility the caller is transferred, by the telecommunications system, to new coverage areas when ever the user is in transit. The process used to maintain the call connection when a mobile subscriber changes coverage areas is called "handoff or "handover". Handoff permits the caller to continue a conversation while moving great distances. A call originated from a location that is different from the mobile unit's current location is delivered automatically (to the mobile unit). This procedure is known as "call delivery".

Cellular radio communication is typically considered the earliest form of wireless "personal communications". It allows the subscriber to place and receive telephone calls over the wireline telephone network wherever cellular coverage is provided. The availability of "roaming", "handoff", and "call delivery" capabilities extends service to users traveling outside their "home" service areas.

A distinguishing feature of *cellular systems* is the use of many base stations with relatively small coverage radii (on the order of 10km). Each frequency is used simultaneously by multiple base/mobile pairs. This "frequency reuse" technique allows a much higher "subscriber density per MHz" of frequency spectrum than offered by previous mobile communication systems. System capacity can be further increased by reducing the cell size (the coverage area of a single base station), to radii as small as 0.5 km. In addition to supporting high subscriber densities, this approach makes possible the use of small, battery-powered portable handsets with lower RF (radio frequency) transmit power, compared to the large vehicular mobile units used in earlier systems. In cellular systems, continuous coverage is achieved by executing a "handoff" (the seamless transfer of the call from one base station to another) wherever a mobile unit crosses cell "boundaries", that is, "roaming" from one base station to another.

8.2.2.3 Personal Mobility

Personal Mobility means that a subscriber can access the network using any of a variety of terminal equipment (i.e., the personal identifier can be used with a variety of terminals). The capabilities of the terminal equipment available to an individual user is based on the user's services profile. Likewise these service features are available from different fixed locations, or while the subscriber is in motion.

The personal identifier indicates the user's service profile to the network. A user can obtain personalized telecommunications services as defined by their personal identifier. Unique phone numbers that serve as links to a personal identifier, are assigned to a user to support inbound service delivery

In cellular applications, a user is assigned a specific terminal that permits them to access the network. In PCS, a user can access and receive network services from any terminal equipment, whether stationary or in motion, by using a personal identifier (e.g., a "smart card"). As a result, users are not required to carry a specific piece of terminal equipment with them in order to access the network.

8.2.2.4 Service Profile Management

The vision for future personal communications services is based on the concept that "*any individual user, whether stationary or in motion, is able to access his or her personalized set of services (from the simplest service, to the most sophisticated services) using any device*". Extending the personal communication vision, any network being accessed via PCS would be able to identify and locate a subscriber, supply the requested services, and maintain continuous connection for the duration of the transaction; regardless of the service requested, the location, or whether the subscriber is mobile.

The personalized set of services are controlled by the user (i.e., the execution of the set of service features is under the subscriber's control). For example, if a subscriber does not want to be reached while roaming (e.g., on the way to a vacation site, or during the entire vacation period), he/she will have the ability to disable call delivery on a selective basis (i.e., screening out all but specific calls).

Service profile management allows the network to provide any service features the subscriber wants and is willing to pay for. Typical service types available for PCS subscribers are listed as follows:

- Phone-call service features

  * 3-way calling
  * Call forwarding
  * Call screening
  * Fast calling
  * Automatic call delivery
  * Call delivery disabling

- Data
- Video conferencing
- Fax
- Multimedia

In the future PCS will introduce new features including: simplified human interfaces, smart card technology, and voice command control.

8.3 RADIO TRANSMISSION

As shown in Figure 8-7, the airlink between the base station and the mobile unit carries a radio signal, which is generated as an analog electrical signal such as an AM, FM, FSK, or QAM signal. Therefore, the radio transmission a digital signal must first be modulated at the transmitting end, and then demodulated at the receiving end.

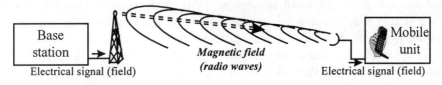

Figure 8-7   Radio Waves: Electrical and Magnetic Fields.

Radio waves propagate through the airway as Transverse ElectroMagnetic (TEM) waves. The energy of the radio signals exists in the form of electric and magnetic fields that vary sinusoidally with time and motion. The electric field and the magnetic field always co-exist because a changing electric field generates a magnetic field, and vice versa. Hence, there is a continuos flow of energy from one field to the other. The polarization of a radio wave plays an important role in radio transmission. The simplified definition of a radio wave is given as follows: "***Polarization describes the behavior of the electric field.***" Detailed coverage of electromagnetic theory is beyond the scope of this book.

8.3.1 Problems, Effects and Solutions

After a digital signal has been modulated, it is ready for transport over the airway. This portion of the end-to-end connection (i.e., the airway) has three major problems as listed in Table 8-1 and described as follows:

(1) **Signal attenuation**: For a typical wireless (radio) transmission, the path loss that a signal experiences is usually between 40 and 70 dB. This is considerably higher than wire facilities or fiber transmission facilities. Thus, the receiver Signal-to-Noise (S/N) performance will be degraded, and speech signal quality may become unacceptable. To ensure signal quality, the transmission path end-to-end power budgeting must be carefully managed.

(2) **Random phase**: Because the environment of radio transmission is continuously changing, the received signal never has a deterministic signal phase at the receiver (with respect to the signal phase at the transmitter). Instead, the phase of the received signal is always random, and causes a random phase shift at the receiver. This condition is especially pronounced if Phase Shift Keying modulation (e.g., 6-FSK, MSK, DPSK, etc.) is used. Phase shift can cause poor or inaccurate receiver detection and erroneous signal restoration. Therefore, the receiver design must have good phase estimation capabilities.

(3) **Multi-path transmission**: Multi-path transmission in wireless connections is a problem that will always exist. A similar problem can also occur in optical fiber transmission systems, especially multi-mode fiber systems. The most serious problem caused by multi-path transmission is delay spread (pulse dispersion), which in turns causes Inter-Symbol Interference (ISI). As a result, the received Bit Error Rate (BER) may become unacceptable. Finally, ISI can limit the digital signal transmission speed. Hence, equalization technology must be applied to minimize delay spreading. In addition to multi-path transmission, "bandwidth limit" can cause further delay spread of the transmission of a logical "1" signal.

Table 8-1   Radio Transmission: Problems, Effects and Solutions.

Problem	Effect	Solution
Signal attenuation	*S/N degradation*	*Power budgeting*
Random phase	*Phase shift*	*Phase estimation**
Multi-path (moving terminal)	*Fading* *Delay spread* *Doppler spread*	*Diversity* *Equalization*

* For coherent detection

Fading or deep fading can be caused by several conditions, such as multi-path transmission, or a blocked signal caused by a physical barrier between the transmitter and the receiver (e.g., building, tunnels, mountains, etc.). Deep fading introduces burst errors in the received digital data stream. Two technologies have been widely used to overcome the deep fading problem: diversity and bit interleaving. The details of these techniques are described later in this chapter.

8.3.2 Antenna Basics

This section describes the types of generic antennas and various antenna characteristics that are often specified for a base station and/or mobile subscriber's equipment. This discussion is intended for readers with a limited background in antenna theory, hence it is a basic review for experienced engineers.

8.3.2.1 Antenna Types

To understand the characteristics of a practical antenna, it is necessary to introduce an artificial theoretical (i.e. reference) antenna model, known as an "isotropic antenna". It is often incorrectly stated that an isotropic antenna is an "idea antenna", that is a perfect antenna without any signal dissipation. It is impossible to create such an antenna.

- Isotropic Antenna: This "antenna" is actually an isotropic radiator, which is an electromagnetic source, radiating equally in all directions. An isotropic antenna is used as a reference for specifying the directional characteristics of a practical antenna. For example, a directional antenna used at a base station may have an antenna gain of:

$$15 \ \textbf{\textit{dBi}}$$

where "i" simply means that this antenna is compared with an "*i*sotropic" antenna that serves as a reference.

- Short Dipole Antenna: A simple but practical type of antennas is known as a "short dipole". The average received power, from a short dipole antenna, is given by the following equations:

$$p_R = \frac{3p_T}{8 \ \pi r^2} \sin^2 \theta \qquad (8\text{-}1)$$

or

$$P_R \text{ (in dBm)} = P_T \text{ (in dBm)} - [9.2 + 20 \times \log r - 20 \log \sin \theta] \text{ (in dB)} \qquad (8\text{-}2)$$

where "*r*" is the transmitting distance, and θ is the angle from the "north pole" of a short dipole antenna (assumed to have a vertical polarization) to the direction of the transmitting path as shown in Figure 8-8(A).

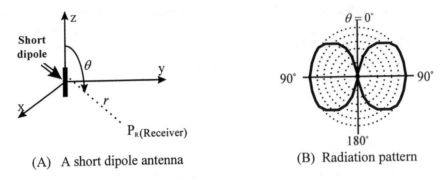

(A) A short dipole antenna   (B) Radiation pattern

Figure 8-8   A Short Dipole Antenna and its Radiation Pattern.

An important characteristic of an antenna is its radiation pattern. This is a graphical representation of the field strength (power density) for an antenna, with the orientation of the measuring point relative to the antenna orientation. For example, the antenna pattern of a short dipole antenna is shown in Figure 8-8(B), which is known as a toroid [it is a three-dimensional graph, not shown in Figure 8-8(B)]. From the pattern, the power strength at various direction from the antenna is clearly illustrated (i.e., maximum power at 90° points, minimum power 0° and 180° points for a short-dipole).

8.3.2.2 Omni (Omni-directional) and Directional Antennas

When an antenna radiates power uniformly in all directions, it is an **omni** or **omni-directional** antenna. When an antenna radiates power non-uniformly in different directions, it is a **directional** antenna. The isotropic antenna is clearly an omni antenna. A short dipole antenna can also be considered an omni antenna because at $\theta = 90°$ the radiation power is equal in all directions surrounding the antenna. However, the radiation power varies with different angles of θ. Therefore, a short dipole antenna (a common, and popular antenna) can also be considered a directional antenna.

Several terms that are associated with a directional antenna (see Figure 8-9) are described in the following section. The **major lobe,** also called the **front lobe,** is the radiation pattern for the desirable direction to the intended receivers. Its radiation power is typically stronger than the radiation power in all other directions. In addition to the major lobe, there are secondary or minor lobes. The minor lobes usually represent undesired radiation or reception. The minor lobes include the **back lobe** and the **side lobes.** In practical applications there can sometimes be more than two side lobes.

Measurements are used to determine if a directional antenna is actually radiating power in the desired direction. These measurements are:

- Front-to-back ratio: The front-to-back ratio is defined as follows:

$$R_{FB} = 10 \times \log \frac{P_M}{P_B} \qquad \text{(in dB)} \qquad (8\text{-}3)$$

where P_M and P_B are the maximum power density of the major lobe (P_M) and the back lobe (P_B), respectively.

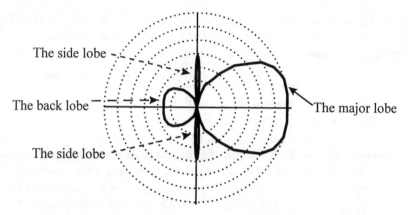

Figure 8-9   The Radiation Pattern of a Directional Antenna.

- Front-to-side ratio: The front-to-side ratio is defined as follows:

$$R_{FS} = 10 \times \log \frac{P_M}{P_S} \qquad (8\text{-}4)$$

where P_M and P_S are the maximum power density of the major lobe and the side lobe, respectively.

Ideally, the larger the ratios (R_{FB} and R_{FS}), the better the directionality of an antenna, because the major lobe will have a larger radiation power. Theoretical requirements of R_{FB} and R_{FS} for an acceptable directional antenna are 25 ~ 30 dB. However, the practical values are typically 20 ~ 25 dB.

8.3.2.3 Antenna Properties

Besides the radiation pattern, the front-to-back ratio, and the front-to-side ratio, a typical antenna system is often specified as follows (note that this is an examples, and may not represent a practical antenna):

- Frequency range: 800 ~ 900 MHz
- Gain: 3 dB typical
- Standard bandwidths (MHz): 806~866; 820~880; 836~896; 896~960

- Horizontal beamwidth (1/2 power points): 105° (typical)
- Vertical beamwidth (1/2 power points): 22° (typical)
- Maximum input power: 500 watts (typical)
- Front-to-back ratio: 25 dB (typical)
- Front-to-side ratio: 25 dB (typical)

One of the most important parameters is the antenna gain, which is not interpreted using the traditional meaning of gain. Antenna gain is always referenced to another antenna (typically an isotropic antenna). The unit of antenna gain can be expressed as *dBi*, or simply *dB*.

Figure 8-10 is used to illustrate the concept of antenna gain of a directional antenna. Assume this directional antenna transmits (radiates) 80 watts of power over the airway, and the input power is 100 watts. At a distance of "*r*" miles away, a mobile subscriber receives a power of 80 μw. To determine the antenna gain of this particular antenna, it is necessary to have a reference antenna. For example, the same arrangement of Figure 8-10(A) is used, but the directional antenna is replaced by an isotropic antenna [see Figure 8-10(B)], and 80 w of power is transmitted by the isotropic antenna over the airway. Assume the received power by a mobile subscriber, who is also at a distance of "*r*" miles" from the transmitting antenna, is 20 μw instead of 80 μw. The antenna gain of the antenna being evaluated [Figure 8-10(A)] can be calculated by using the following equation.

$$G_T = 10 \times \log \frac{P_{R1}}{P_{R2}} = 10 \times \log \frac{80 \ \mu w}{20 \ \mu w} = 6 \quad dB$$

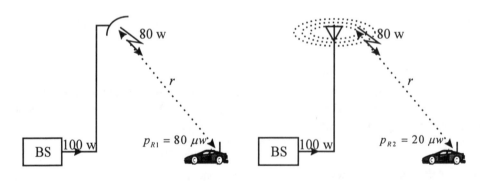

(A) Directional antenna　　　　　　　　(B) Isotropic antenna

Figure 8-10　　Derivation of Antenna Gain.

From this calculation, the antenna in Figure 8-10(A) has a gain (G_T) of 6 dB. The input power to the antenna is 100 w while the output power of this antenna is only 80 w. Hence, there is a 20 w loss from the input port to the output port of the antenna. This is called the dissipation loss of the antenna. Therefore, the concept of "gain", as used in defining "antenna gain", does not have its usual meaning (see Appendix 1-1 in Chapter 1).

Another parameter can be used to specify an antenna. This is the directivity, d. The directivity is related to antenna gain as follows:

$$g = e \times d \qquad \text{or} \qquad G = 10 \times log\, e + D \quad \text{(in dB)} \qquad (8\text{-}5)$$

where e is the antenna efficiency; and e = 1 for a lossless antenna. In this example e = 0.8 [≡ (80 w)/(100 w)]. Hence, the directivity of the antenna in Figure 8-10(A) can be obtained from Eq. (8-5):

$$D = G - 10 \times log\, e = 6 - 10 \times log\, 0.8 = 7 \text{ dB}$$

Note that g (gain) and d (directivity) is unitless numbers, and G (gain) and D (directivity) are number in dB.

8.3.3 Propagation Environment

Airway propagation experiences many environmental problems that are not seen in wireline (twisted-pair or coaxial cable) or fiber communications. These problems are typically caused by "multi-path transmission", "deep fading", and moving receivers. As a result, these problems generate phase shift, delay spread, and Doppler frequency shift of the received signal. The details of these conditions are described in the following sections.

8.3.3.1 Delay Spreading

Delay spreading has many other names (e.g., delay dispersion, pulse spreading). Delay spreading in a wireless environment is caused by two factors: limited channel bandwidth (beyond the scope of this book), and multi-path transmission (shown in Figure 8-11).

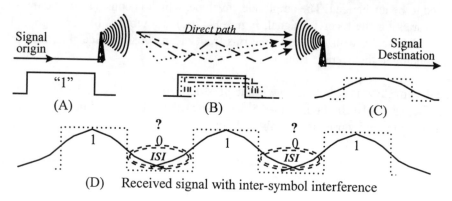

(D)   Received signal with inter-symbol interference

Figure 8-11   Multi-Path Transmission and ISI.

When a digital pulse is transmitted over the airway, there are literally hundreds of paths carrying the information. Each path will reach the receiver at a different instance in time, and with a different signal strength. This condition results in ***pulse spreading***. As shown in Figure 8-11, the signal having the strongest power is usually the direct path transport. In addition to the direct path, there are many reflected paths. Figure 8-11(B) shows the effect of different transmission paths and signal strengths on the information transfer. Some reflected signals may be large enough to contribute to the net signal strength, and can be used to restore the information. Note that the reflected signals are delayed with respect to the direct path signal. Therefore, a single logical "1"'s pulse shape is no longer rectangular [see Figure 8-11(C)] but spreads wider than the original rectangular pulse shape [see Figure 8-11(A)].

Assume the original transmitted bit stream is "101010 ..." as shown by the "dotted" (rectangular) waveform in Figure 8-11(D). The received waveform, because of delay spreading, is no longer rectangular [also shown in Figure 8-11(D) by the "solid" line]. As a result, the energy from a logical "1" will impose interference during the bit interval where a logical "0" resides. Note that the logical "0" interval may receive energy from a preceding "1" as well as from a following logical "1". This type of interference is called "Inter-Symbol Interference" (ISI). If the ISI has an energy level that is higher than the threshold voltage used for signal restoration, the ISI may cause a logical "0" to be detected as a logical "1", thereby generating bit errors at the receiver. Several special techniques can be applied to reduce the effect of ISI, and a commonly-used technology is called "**equalization**".

The appendix at the end of this chapter describes the basic concepts of equalization when applied to control ISI.

8.3.3.2 Deep Fading

Figure 8-12(A) shows the transmitted signal waveform (a sinusoidal wave). The received signal waveform [Figure 8-12(B)] is no longer a sinusoidal wave, but the frequency is assumed to be unchanged. The amplitude envelope, which is constant for the transmitted signal, varies for the received signal. Figure 8-12(C) is a plot of the varying amplitude, using a "dB" scale, with respect to the rms (root mean square) value (i.e., rms value is corresponding to the average value).

When the envelope is below the *rms* value, it is defined as "fading". The fading can be a −5 dB fading, a −10 dB fading, a −15 dB fading, or a −20 dB fading. There are three parameters commonly used to describe fading:

(1) **Rayleigh fading level**: A fading level, l, can be expressed as 0.1, 0.2, 0.5, etc., or, it can be expressed as −20 dB fading ($\equiv 20 \; log \; 0.1$), −14 dB fading ($\equiv 20 \; log \; 0.2$), −6 dB fading ($\equiv 20 \; log \; 0.5$), etc. Depending upon the application, a fading of −10 dB may be considered to be a deep fading. In other cases, a fading of −20 dB is

considered to be a deep fading. The fading level of a typical wireless system has a probability density function that obeys the Rayleigh probability density function. As a result, the fading model used in the design/analysis of wireless system is Rayleigh.

(2) **Average number of fades below a given fading level**: The number of "fades" below a specific level can be used to evaluate the performance of a radio transmission. The average number of fades below the fading level, l, is calculated using the following equation:

$$N_f = \sqrt{2\pi} \times \frac{v \times l}{\lambda_c} = \sqrt{2\pi} \times f_d \times l \qquad \text{fades/s} \qquad (8\text{-}6)$$

where v is the (effective) velocity of the moving receiver, l is the fading level, and λ_c is the wavelength of the transmitted radio signal. Note that f_d is the Doppler frequency shift, which is discussed in Section 8.3.3.3 of this chapter.

(3) **Average duration of a fade below a given level**: This is another method used to express radio transmission quality. It is calculated as follows:

$$\tau = \frac{\lambda_c \times l}{v \times \sqrt{2\pi}} = \frac{l}{f_d \times \sqrt{2\pi}} \qquad \text{sec} \qquad (8\text{-}7)$$

where v is the (effective) velocity of the moving receiver, l is the fading level, λ_c is the wavelength of the transmitted radio signal, and f_d is the Doppler

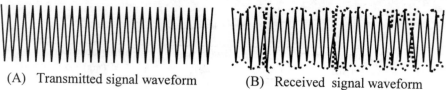

(A) Transmitted signal waveform   (B) Received signal waveform

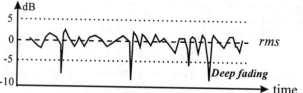

(C) Fading envelope

Figure 8-12   Fading and Deep Fading.

Example 8-1: Calculate the average number of fades and the average duration of a fade, for an application with a fading level of 0.1 (i.e. a −20 dB deep fading) and a carrier frequency of 880 MHz. Assume three cases for the mobile subscriber's speed: (1) 30 mph, (20 50 mph, and (3) 70 mph.

Consider the first case when the speed is 30 mph. First, given that f_c = 880 MHz, and v = 30 mph, the Doppler frequency shift, f_d, is calculated [using Eq. (8-8)] as follows:

$$f_d = \frac{30 \times 0.447 \times 880 \times 10^6}{3 \times 10^8} = 39.336 \ \text{Hz}$$

where the conversion factor between mph and meter per sec has been used (1 mph = 0.447 meter per sec) to derive the effective velocity (v_{eff}), and the speed of light in a vacuum is $c = 3 \times 10^8$ m/s.

By substituting these values (f_d = 39.336, and l = 0.1) into Eqs. (8-6) and (8-7), the average number of fades (N_f), and the average duration of a fade (τ) below the fading level l = 0.1 are calculated as follows:

$$N_f = \sqrt{2\pi} \times 39.336 \times 0.1 = 9.9 \ \ fades / \sec$$

$$\tau = \frac{0.1}{39.336 \times \sqrt{2\pi}} = 1.014 \ \ ms$$

The same procedure is applied for the cases when the mobile subscriber is moving at a speed of 50 mph and 70 mph, respectively. The results of all the three cases are summarized in Table 8-2. It can be seen that the number of fades increases as the mobile unit speed increases (e.g., v = 30 mph, there are 9.9 fades/s, and v = 70 mph, there are 23 fades/s). However, the duration of a fade decreases as the mobile unit speed increases.

Table 8-2   Number of Fades and Duration of a Fade.

Mobile unit speed, v (mph)	Fading rate (fades/s)	Fading duration (ms)
30	9.90	1.014
50	16.4	0.609
70	23.0	0.435

Example 8-2:   Assume that the average duration of a deep fade is an interval of approximately (0.5 ~ 1.0 ms). Determine the average number of bit errors (a burst error) caused during a typical deep fading interval for: (1) a GSM TDMA system, and (2) a IS-136 TDMA system.

Case 1 (for GSM-TDMA):

Assume that 50% (= ½) of the transmitted digital data stream is logical "1s", and the data rate for the GSM TDMA systems is 22.8 kbps at the output of the channel encoder. Note that only the logical "1" is considered in the analysis of deep fading. This is because a logical "1" voltage level is attenuated if a deep fading occurs during the logical "1" time interval. The average number of bit errors (a burst error) caused during a deep fading interval ($0.5 \sim 1.0$ ms) is calculated as follows:

$$\frac{1}{2} \times 22.8 \times 10^3 \times (0.5 \sim 1.0) \times 10^{-3} = 5.7 \sim 11.4 \text{ errors}$$

Case 2 (for IS-136-TDMA):

Assume the same conditions for an IS-136 systems with a data rate of 13 kbps. The average number of bit errors (a burst error) is calculated as follows:

$$\frac{1}{2} \times 13 \times 10^3 \times (0.5 \sim 1.0) \times 10^{-3} = 3.3 \sim 6.5 \text{ errors}$$

The results of these evaluations are important in studying wireless communication systems to determine:

- The types of error control method that should be applied.

- The bit-interleaving technology that should be used to "break-up" burst errors into random (single or double-bit) errors.

- The diversity strategy that should be used to combat deep fading.

These techniques are discussed further in later sections of this chapter.

8.3.3.3 Doppler Shift

When a base station transmits a signal with a carrier frequency, f_c, the received signal, (i.e. received by a mobile subscriber) may not have exactly the same frequency. This phenomenon is known as Doppler (frequency) shift.

By definition, the Doppler frequency shift is given by the following equation:

$$\Delta f = \frac{v_{eff}}{c} \times f_c \tag{8-8}$$

where

$$v_{eff} = \textit{effective velocity} \approx v \quad \textit{if } \theta < 30° \tag{8-9}$$

Example 8-3: Calculate the Doppler frequency shift if a mobile subscriber is moving at speeds of: (1) 30 mph, (2) 50 mph, and (3) 70 mph, respectively. Assume the carrier frequency, f_c, is 880 MHz, and the condition stated in Eq. (8-9) is true.

For the first case, when the mobile subscriber is moving at a speed of 30 mph, using Eq. (8-51) to obtain the following Doppler shift (Δf):

$$\Delta f = \frac{v_{eff}}{c} \times f_c = \frac{30 \times 0.447 \times 880 \times 10^6}{3 \times 10^8} = 39.34 \text{ Hz}$$

Note that 1 mph = 0.447 meter/s has been applied. This calculation has been repeated for the cases of 50 mph and 70 mph mobile unit speeds. The results are listed in Table 8-3.

Table 8-3   Doppler Frequency Shifts.

v (mph)	30	50	70
Δf (Hz)	39.34	65.57	91.79

8.3.4 Diversity

In any airway transport system, a received signal will experience fading and/or deep fading. Figure 8-13 shows a received signal with three deep fading periods, each with a fading level exceeding −5 dB. There are two questions that are often asked about radio transmission deep fading:

- Question 1: "What is the effect of deep fading on transmission quality?"

- Question 2: "What can be done to solve the deep fading problem?"

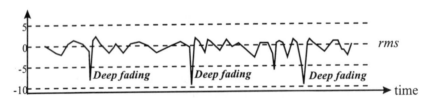

Figure 8-13   Deep Fading with a Fading Level below −5 dB.

The effect of deep fading is poor received signal quality. If the transmitted signal is analog, the received signal will have weak signal strength, but signal degradation may not be serious. However, for digital transmission over the airway, the effect of deep fading is more severe than in an analog signal transport system.

Example 8-2 in the previous section illustrates the average number of bit errors (a burst error) caused by typical deep fading. A special technology known as bit-interleaving can be applied to control burst errors. The purpose of bit interleaving is to break up burst errors into random single-bit or double-bit errors, so that error control codes (e.g., CRC and convolutional codes; described in Chapter 13) can detect/correct single-bit or double-bit random errors.

There are times when bit-interleaving alone cannot completely solve burst error problems. Additional technology must be used to supplement the bit-interleaving method to control burst errors caused by deep fading. One of these additional method is *diversity*.

Definition 8-2: *Diversity is the technique of combining independent fading signals received on several transmission paths to reduce or eliminate the deep fading, and thus to improve the received signal's transmission quality.*

The diversity method is based on at least two transmission signal paths being available at the receiver. All signal paths carry the same message, but will have independent fading statistics (i.e. deep fading does not occur on all signal paths simultaneously). Under this condition, the various signal paths will have different signal strengths (i.e. some will be strong during intervals when others are weak, and vice versa). Properly combining these signals yields a resultant signal with reduced fading, and subsequently better transmission quality.

For the diversity method to be effective, the signals received on different transmission paths (antennas) must **not** be **correlated**. That is, deep fading from various transmission paths cannot occur at the same time. This condition can be met when the receiver antennas (for diversity purpose) are properly separated (antenna positioning is discussed further in a later section of this chapter).

8.3.4.1 Various Diversity Techniques

Early diversity techniques were based on transmitting a signal from a single antenna to several receiving antennas. The distance between the receiving antennas was deliberately made large enough to ensure independent fading on different receive paths. This technique is known as "space-diversity reception".

With the basic principles of the diversity method established, communication engineers quickly realized that the diversity effect could be produced in other ways, rather than only using physically spaced antennas. For example, different transmission paths, different frequencies, and different times are able to achieve diversity under certain conditions. Table 8-4 summarizes various diversity methods, and a brief description of four methods is provided.

- **Space diversity:** This technology has had many applications over the years, and is still widely used in a variety of present-day microwave transport systems. Space diversity is relatively simple to implement, and does not require the expense of additional frequency spectrum. The basic requirement is to provide sufficient physical spacing of antennas so that individual signals are *uncorrelated*. For a Rayleigh fading envelope, uncorrelated signals are independent signals. A variety of techniques are available to perform the combination process that forms a composite signal from the various received signals. The process used to produce a composite signal is described in a later section of this chapter.

Table 8-4   Various Diversity Techniques.

Type	Requirements
Space diversity*	*Receiving antennas must be physically separated sufficiently for independent fading of different signals*
Time diversity	*Sequential time samples must be sent*
Frequency diversity	*Transmitting signals with different carrier frequencies; they must be separated sufficiently for independent fading*
Polarization diversity	*Signals with two orthogonal polarizations for independent fading*

* Widely used technique.

- **Time diversity:** This technology is based on the fact that sequential amplitude samples of a randomly fading signal are uncorrelated, provided these samples are separated sufficiently in time. For mobile radio applications, time diversity is not useful because time separation is inversely proportional to the receiver's speed. Therefore, the separation time would be infinite when the mobile unit was stationary, and would continue to decrease as the mobile unit moved faster.

- **Frequency diversity**: This technique requires the signal to be transmitted over different frequencies, thereby achieving independent diversity branches. These frequencies must be sufficiently separated so that the fading associated with the different frequencies is uncorrelated. The advantage of frequency diversity over space diversity is the reduction in the number of antennas (i.e. only one at each end of the path). However, additional frequency spectrum, which is very expensive for wireless systems, is required. Therefore, this technology is not popular for wireless services.

- **Polarization diversity**: The principle of polarization diversity is based on the fact that *"signals transmitted on two orthogonal polarizations in the mobile radio environment exhibit uncorrelated fading statistics."* This method requires separate antennas. Therefore, polarization diversity is sometimes considered a special case of space diversity. The spacing requirements may be minimized by clever (i.e., smart) antenna configurations that utilize field orthogonality to decorrelate the signals, thereby reducing the space diversity requirement.

8.3.4.2 Combining Techniques for Space Diversity

Among the four diversity techniques, only space diversity has become a mature technology. The space diversity approach has proven to be effective in many modern radio applications. Several combining techniques have been developed to achieve an economical, yet an effective space diversity methodology. Three techniques are shown in Figure 8-14, and described as follows:

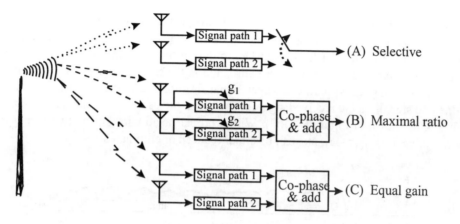

Figure 8-14   Various Combining Techniques for Space Diversity.

- **Selection diversity**: The transmitted signal may be received by two or more receivers, with antennas separated far enough apart to insure independent fading characteristics (i.e., fading positions and fading levels). That is, for a two-receiver diversity scheme, the two antenna can not be too close to each other, otherwise, the deep fading from both receiver will occur at the same time. It is impossible to select a better receiver with a smaller fading. Likewise, if two receivers are too far apart, the phase of the signal from one receiver will be different from the phase of the signal from another path. It is difficult to select a new receiver to replace the existing receiver and has the same phase. The receiver always selects the path with the highest system performance [generally using Signal-to-Noise ratio (S/N) as the performance criteria]. Figure 8-14(A) shows this arrangement.

- **Maximal ratio diversity:** First, the receiver assigns a weight (i.e. preference) to each receiving path. That is, the path with the strongest performance is assigned the largest weight, the path with the weakest performance is assigned the lowest weight. These weighted signals are combined after being co-phased [Figure 8-14(B)]. The co-phase process is used to insure the phase of one path is lined-up with the phase of another path. For example, if the received bit stream from path 1 is "110001010", and the bit stream from path 2 is "11000101", they are *not* co-phased.

    Equal gain diversity is a special case of maximal ratio diversity technique but with equal weight or gain assigned to all different receiving paths [Figure 8-14(C)].

- **Switched diversity:** The strategy for this approach is that the receiver remains with a signal path until the signal power falls below a predetermined level. Once the power threshold is crossed, the receiver switches to another path (not shown in Figure 8-15).

    By applying any of these diversity methods, deep fading can be reduced or eliminated in the resultant combined signal [see Figure 8-15(C)]. Figures 8-15(A) and (B) represent the fading signals received by two different receivers from two different transmission paths. Note that these signals are un-correlated, and have the same average signal power (i.e. they do **not** have deep fading during the same instances). At the time instance $t = t_1$, there is a deep fading on path 1, but at the same instance, the signal from path 2 is very strong the system can select signal from path 2 is the received signal (or combine two signals as the received signal). Therefore, the deep fading can be eliminated or reduced, as shown in Figure 8-15(C). With a proper positioning of the two receivers, the deep fading at $t = t_2$, $t = t_3$, etc. can be either reduced or eliminated.

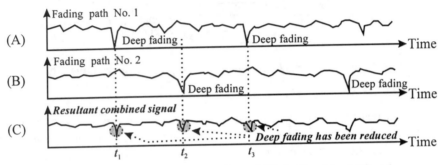

Figure 8-15   Two Fading Signals and Their Combined Signal.

8.3.4.3 Performance Comparison of Different Space Diversity Techniques

Figure 8-16 illustrates the performance comparison of three common space diversity methods, assuming the receiving system has a probability of error of 1%. For each case, the comparison is shown for no diversity, diversity with two receivers (M = 2), three receivers (M = 3), and four receivers (M = 4). These results are also summarized in Table 8-5. A system with an M = 2 implies that two receiving paths are used, and M = 3 implies that three receiving paths are used, etc.

Table 8-5   S/N Improvement for Various Space Diversity Methods.

M	Selective	Maximal ratio	Equal gain
2	10.0 dB	11.5 dB	10.8 dB
3	14.0 dB	16.5 dB	15.5 dB
4	16.0 dB	19.0 dB	18.0 dB

The most pronounced S/N improvement (approximately 10 dB) is between "no diversity" (i.e., M = 1) and a two-receiver configuration (M = 2). If M = 3 is applied, the receiving end will require three receivers. Therefore, receiver costs will be three times (300%) the cost of the system without diversity control (M = 1), compared to an increased cost of 200% for an M = 2 system. Because the S/N improvement between M =

2 and M = 3 is only 4 dB, (see Table 8-5; selective), the M = 2 arrangement is often applied in practical system implementation if the "selective" scheme is chosen.

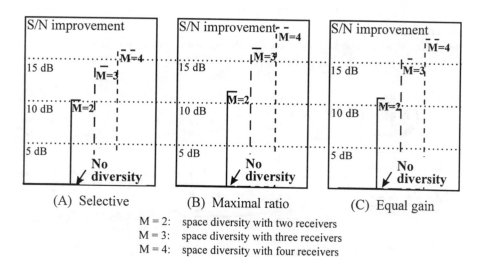

| (A) Selective | (B) Maximal ratio | (C) Equal gain |

M = 2:   space diversity with two receivers
M = 3:   space diversity with three receivers
M = 4:   space diversity with four receivers

Figure 8-16   Performance Comparison for Various Space Diversity Methods.

Another consideration is whether to apply selective, maximal ratio, or equal gain diversity. Assuming the configuration M = 2 is used, for selective diversity the improvement is 10 dB; for maximal ratio diversity the improvement is 11.5 dB, and for an equal gain diversity the improvement is 10.8 dB (see Table 8-5). The best method among these three is maximal ratio diversity, with an improvement of 11.5 dB. However, the implementation costs may not be justified for a 1.5 dB difference in improvement (in comparison between selective and maximum ratio). Therefore, *in practical wireless systems, the two-receiver (M = 2) selective diversity technique has been generally adopted on the basis of "costs versus benefits".*

8.3.5 Smart Antennas

Smart antennas have been used in modern wireless systems to focus the radiated power in a specific direction, providing sufficient received power to achieve a specific level of transmission quality (signal-to-noise ratio). Smart antennas can be grouped into two classes (briefly described as follows):

(1) Switched beam antennas: Switched and fixed beam antennas were the earliest type of "smart antenna" that were used as base station receiving antennas. Figure 8-17 shows a switched (fixed) beam antenna for a 6-sector cellular system, configured for 60° per sector. The receiver samples the received power from each beam, and selects the "best" beam (i.e. the beam with the highest transmission quality; signal-to-noise

ratio). If the quality degrades below a predetermined threshold level, the system automatically switches to another beam. The system can periodically switch the beam as illustrated in Figure 8-17. For example, at the time instance $t = t_1$, antenna beam No. 1 is switched to user No. 3, antenna beam No. 2 is switched to user No. 2, and antenna beam No. 3 is switched to user No. 1; at the time instance $t = t_2$, antenna beam No. 1 is switched to user No. 2, antenna beam No. 2 is switched to user No. 1, and antenna beam No. 3 is switched to user No. 3; etc.

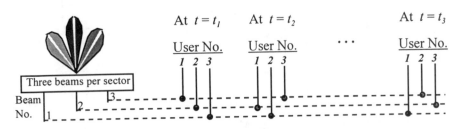

Figure 8-17   Switched Beam antenna.

This switched beam technique was used for wireless systems before 3G (i.e., a new generation of wireless technology; described in Section 8.8 of this chapter). It is used for uplink applications, but is not suitable for downlink use. Frequency Division Duplex (FDD; different frequencies used for uplink and downlink transmission) has been used for practically all cellular systems. Because different propagation conditions exist for different frequencies, it is not appropriate to use the same beam for both uplink and downlink transmission.

Switched beam antennas are not suitable for CDMA wireless systems either. This is because switching beams causes chip errors, disturbs synchronization, and degrades demodulation performance.

(2) Adaptive antenna arrays: Each antenna (per user) contains several elements, each having adjustable gain and phase. By properly adjusting the gain and the phase of each element and them combining them, an antenna can provide an optimum signal for achieving acceptable quality (i.e., signal-to-noise ratio, or bit error rate). This technique is called "forming beams" or "steering beams", and can be used for transmitting. It should be noted that "steering beams" can be used for receiving.

* Advantages: From a "receiving" aspect, adaptive antenna arrays can receive more power from the desired transmitter. At the same time it rejects interference from unwanted signals that inject significant interference. From a "transmission" aspect, this method can focus more power toward the desired receiver, and minimize power that is "wanted".

* Disadvantages: The cost and complexity of array antennas needs to be improved. This is a difficult objective, especially for transmission applications because of higher power levels.

8.4 FREQUENCY SPECTRUM

Various frequency spectra have been assigned for different types of radio transmission systems (e.g., satellite, long-haul transport, radio broadcasting, TV broadcasting, cellular phones, PCS, etc.). Only the frequency spectra for cellular and PCS systems are described in this book.

8.4.1 Cellular Spectrum and PCS Spectrum

Each city in North America typically has two cellular service providers: one is the owner of the local telephone company, and the other is not affiliated with the local telephone company. The affiliated cellular service is known as the wireline carrier, and occupies the B-band frequency spectrum. The unaffiliated service is known as the non-wireline carrier, and occupies the A-band frequency spectrum.

Table 8-6   Original Cellular Spectrum Allocation.

	Non-wireline carrier (A-band)	Wireline carrier (B-band)
Uplink	*825 to 835 MHz*	*870 to 880 MHz*
Downlink	*835 to 845 MHz*	*880 to 890 MHz*

Table 8-7   Expanded Cellular Spectrum Allocation.

	Non-wireline carrier (A-band)	Wireline carrier (B-band)
Uplink	*824 to 825 MHz* *845 to 846.5 MHz*	*846.5 to 849 MHz*
Downlink	*869 to 870 MHz* *890 to 891.5 MHz*	*891.5 to 894 MHz*

The original spectra allocated by the FCC for North American cellular applications are listed in Table 8-6. Note that each carrier has 10 MHz for uplink communications (i.e., the direction from the mobile subscriber to the base station). Another 10 MHz is allocated for downlink communications (i.e., the direction from the base station to the mobile subscriber). For North American cellular network applications, each mobile subscriber is allotted a bandwidth of 30 kHz, thus a 10 MHz spectrum can carry up to 333 subscribers simultaneously.

As cellular traffic increased, the original (spectrum) allocation of 333 channels was insufficient, and FCC expanded the spectrum in 1986. The expansion consisted of allocating an additional 2.5 MHz for the uplink and 2.5 MHz for the downlink. This expansion was granted to both the wireline and the non-wireline bands (see Table 8-7). The North American cellular frequency spectrum allocation is summarized in Figure 8-

18. Band A is the original allocation, and bands A' and A" are the additional spectrum allocations for the non-wireline carriers. For the wireline carriers, band B is the original spectrum, and band B' is the additional spectrum allocation.

The channel assignment for the frequency spectrum used in North American cellular applications (shown in Figure 8-18) is summarized in Table 8-8. The central frequency of each channel (both uplink and downlink) is given. For example, the central frequency of channel No.991 is 824.040 MHz, therefore, this channel occupies the frequency range of (824.025 to 824.055 MHz), which is a bandwidth of 30 kHz.

Both the wireline (A-band) and non-wireline (B-band) have a capacity of 416 RF channels ($\equiv 33 + 333 + 50$, or $\equiv 333 + 83$). Among these 416 RF channels, 395 channels are dedicated for mobile subscribers and 21 channels are set aside for control functions (e.g., call setup). The control channels are Nos. 313 to 333 for the non-wireline spectrum, and Nos. 334 to 354 for the wireline spectrum.

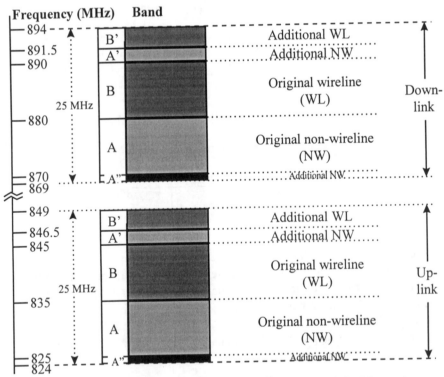

Figure 8-18   Frequency Spectrum Allocation for Cellular Networks.

The central frequency for all cellular channels can be represented by the following equations (for both uplink and downlink communications):

$$f_c = 825.000 + 0.03N \qquad\qquad \text{for} \quad 1 \le N = 866 \qquad \text{down-link} \qquad (8\text{-}10)$$

$$f_c = 825.000 + 0.03(N - 1023) \qquad \text{for} \quad 990 \le N < 1023 \quad \text{down-link} \qquad (8\text{-}11)$$

$$f_c = 870.000 + 0.03N \qquad\qquad \text{for} \quad 1 \le N = 866 \qquad \text{up-link} \qquad (8\text{-}12)$$

$$f_c = 870.000 + 0.03(N - 1023) \qquad \text{for} \quad 990 \le N < 1023 \quad \text{up-link} \qquad (8\text{-}13)$$

Table 8-8 is a summary of channel assignments and the corresponding central frequencies of the cellular band.

Example 8-4: Determine the central, lower and upper frequencies (for both the uplink and downlink transmission) of channel No.200, assuming a 30 kHz bandwidth is used.

Applying Eq.(8-10) for down link transmission, the central frequency is calculated as:

$$f_c = 825 + 0.03 \text{ N} = 825 + 0.03 \ (200) = 831 \text{ MHz}$$

Likewise, applying Eq.(8-12) for up-link transmission, f_c can be obtained as:

$$f_c = 870 + 0.03 \text{ N} = 870 + 0.03 \ (200) = 876 \ \text{ MHz}$$

The frequency bands for channel No.200 are: (1) (830.085 MHz to 831.015 MHz) for down link, and (2) (875.085 MHz to 876.015 MHz) for up link.

The technology of using different frequencies for downlink and uplink (see Example 8-4) communications is known as **Frequency Division Duplex (*FDD*)**.

Table 8-8   Channel Assignment: Central Frequencies.

No. of channels	Channel No.	Uplink (f_c: central f MHz)	Downlink (f_c: central f MHz)
1(Unused)	*(990)*	*(824.010)*	*(869.010)*
33 (A")	*991~ 1023*	*824.040 ~825.000*	*869.040 ~870.000*
333 (A)	*1~333*	*825.030 ~834.990*	*870.030 ~879.990*
333 (B)	*334 ~666*	*835.020~844.980*	*880.020 ~889.980*
50 (A')	*66 7~716*	*845.010 ~846.480*	*890.010 ~891.480*
83 (B')	*717 ~799*	*846.510 ~848.970*	*891.510 ~893.970*
67(Reserved)	*800 ~866*	*849.000 ~850.980*	*894.000 ~895.980*

Similar frequency spectrum assignment algorithm is applied to Personal Communications (PCS) wireless services. The PCS spectrum covers the frequency range of 1850 MHz to 1990 MHz (a total of 140 MHz). From 1850 MHz to 1910 MHz is used for uplink, and from 1930 MHz to 1990 MHz is used for down link transport for licensed service providers. The spectrum range from 1910 MHz to 1930 MHz is assigned to unlicensed service providers. Figure 8-19 represents the PCS frequency spectrum assignments. Note that the spectrum is divided into six bands [A, B, and C (assigned to MTAs) and , D, E and F (assigned to BTAs)]. [for detailed description of PCS see the book "Understanding Wireless: Digital Mobile, Cellular and PCS", ISBN 0-09650448-5-8, published by Andan Publisher (tel. 732-946-4155; fax 732-946-4717)].

Definition 8-3:   Major Trading Areas (MTAs) and Basic Trading Areas (BTAs) were designated by the Randy McNally "Commercial Atlas and Marketing Guide". MTA numbers are provided by Moffet, Larson and Johnson cover large geographical areas. BTAs cover smaller geographical areas. In the US, 51 MTAs and 492 BTAs have been defined (see the reference listed above).

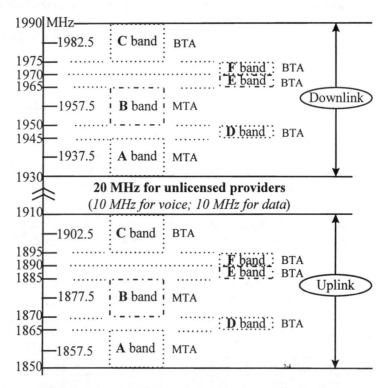

Figure 8-19   PCS Frequency Spectrum Allocation.

8.4.2 Frequency Reuse

During the era of early mobile communications, it was thought that 416 RF channels for cellular applications would be adequate. However, this prediction was incorrect. Therefore, the need for frequency re-use became obvious soon after mobile communications was introduced to the general market in the mid 1980s. Since that time, the technology for reusing the allocated frequency spectrum has advanced rapidly.

To re-use the allocated frequency spectrum for cellular or PCS communications requires two steps:

1. The first step for re-using frequency spectrum is to partition (cellularize) a service area into many individual cells.

2. The second step is to group (clusterize) the cells in the service area into several clusters.

Each cluster of cells will use up all the allocated frequencies: (e.g., 416 RF channels for cellular communications). For implementing these technologies, a drastic change occurred in the base station antenna size and radiated power (see Figure 8-20). The base station shown on the left [Figure 8-20(A)] is used for mobile communications without frequency reuse, while the base station on the right [Figure 8-20(B)] is used for cellular communications with frequency reuse. The height of the antenna is reduced by a factor of 4~5 (i.e., $h = H/5 \sim H/4$). The radiated power from the base station antenna is also reduced considerably (i.e., $P_r \leq P_R /10$). As a result of these changes, the coverage has been reduced from a macro-area to a micro-area (i.e., $r = R/5 \sim R/10$).

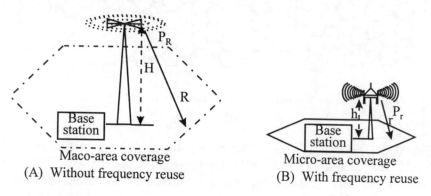

(A) Without frequency reuse   (B) With frequency reuse

Figure 8-20   Base Station Antenna Evolution for Frequency Reuse.

With the transmission coverage reduced to a small area, the frequency used in one area can be reused in another area, within the same serving region. That is, the 416 RF channels can be used to cover a portion (small area) of the entire serving area, and can then be reused many times again in other portions (small areas) of the same serving area. These small areas within the same serving area are known as cells. Therefore, cellular communications are often tied to the concept of frequency re-use. This approach has been used for 800 MHz cellular systems and 1900 MHz PCS systems.

8.4.2.1 Cellularization/Clusterization/Cell and Channel Assignments

A serving area, which can be served by a wireline carrier or a non-wireline carrier, must first be "cellularized" into many individual cells. Theoretically, the cells are assumed to be hexagonal shape for design purposes. The actual cell shapes are completely irregular. In the field, the boundary of a particular cell is defined by experimental data. Since the actual cell shapes are irregular, the serving area (after cellularzing) will have some spots that cannot be served well by any base station. If the cell size is further reduced, the number of these "untouchable" areas will drop considerably. This is one of the concepts of PCS system design. That is, using microcells (rather than standard cells) to permit frequency re-use and achieving better coverage.

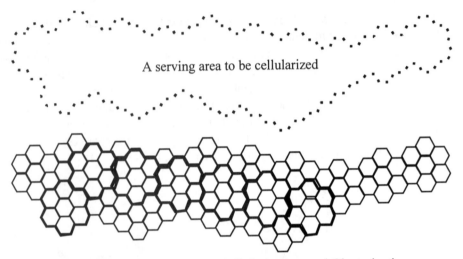

A serving area to be cellularized

Figure 8-21   Serving Area, Cellularization, and Clusterization.

Figure 8-21 shows a serving area having many wireless subscribers than the available 395 RF channels (= 416 − 21). First, the entire serving area is divided into approximately 100 cells. The next step is to clusterize the cells. One cluster of cells may contain 3 cells, 4 cells, 7 cells, 9 cells etc. The cluster size is called the frequency reuse factor, K. In Figure 8-21, the frequency reuse factor is 7 (i.e., groups of 7 cells form a cluster). The available RF channels are **totally** distributed within (each) cluster, hence, the same channels can be re-used in another cluster.

Example 8-2: Describe the meaning of the frequency reuse factor for K = 3 and K = 7.

With the 416 RF channels that are available, 21 channels are reserved for call setup (control). Therefore, 395 RF channels can be used for message transport. For K = 3, there are three cells in each cluster. That is, 395 RF channels will be shared among three cells. For K = 7, there are seven cells in each cluster, and 395 channels are shared among seven cells. This implementation is explained as follows:

Case 1: For K = 3, since 395/3 = 131 + 2/3, the number of RF channels distributed among the three cells within the same cluster are 132, 132 and 131 (132 + 132 + 131 ≡

395). The channel assignments are shown in Table 8-9. The channels are assigned to the cells **in sequence**: channel 1 to cell 1, channel 2 to cell 2, channel 3 to cell 3. Then, starting from cell 1 again: channel 4 to cell 1, channel 5 to cell 2, and channel 6 to cell 3. This procedure is repeated until all of the RF channels are assigned. Note that cell 1 has a total of 132 cells, cell 2 has 132 cells, and cell 3 has 131 cells.

Table 8-9   Channel Assignment (Total 395 Channels) for K = 3.

Cell	Channel No.	Total*
1	1, 4, 7, 10, 13, 16, 19, 22, 25, 28, 31, 34, 37, ..., 391, 394	132
2	2, 5, 8, 11, 14, 17, 20, 23, 26, 29, 32, 35, 38, ..., 392, 395	132
3	3, 6, 9, 12, 15, 18, 21, 24, 27, 30, 33, 36, 39, ..., 393	131

* Total number of channels in each individual cell.

Case 2: For K = 7, since 395/7 = 56 + 3/7, the number of RF channels distributed among the seven cells within the same cluster are 57, 57, 57, 56, 56, 56 and 56. The channel assignments are shown in Table 8-10. The assignment sequence follows the same pattern that was used in case 1.

Table 8-10   Channel Assignment (Total 395 Channels) for K = 7.

Cell	Channel No.	Total
1	1, 8, 15, 22, 29, 36, 43, 50, 57, 64, 71, 78, 85, 92, 99, ..., 386, 393	57
2	2, 9, 16, 23, 30, 37, 44, 51, 58, 65, 72, 79, 86, 93, 100, ..., 387, 394	57
3	3, 10, 17, 24, 31, 38, 45, 52, 59, 66, 73, 80, 87, 94, 101 , ..., 388, 395	57
4	4, 11, 18, 25, 32, 39, 46, 53, 60, 67, 74, 81, 88, 95, 102, ..., 389	56
5	5, 12, 19, 26, 33, 40, 47, 54, 61, 68, 75, 82, 89, 96, 103, ..., 390	56
6	6, 13, 20, 27, 34, 41, 48, 55, 62, 69, 76, 83, 90, 97, 104, ..., 392	56
7	7, 14, 21, 28, 35, 42, 49, 56, 63, 70, 77, 84, 91, 98, 105, ..., 393	56

It should be mentioned that the approach for assigning channels described in these examples is just one of many algorithms that are used to assign RF channels. This is the most commonly-used method, and follows a systematic pattern. From this example, it can be seen that *"the cell capacity increases as the frequency reuse factor decreases."* In addition to cell capacity, the frequency reuse factor also affects system performance as described in Eq.(8-14).

After the serving area has been cellularized (i.e., K cells are grouped into each cluster), the rule for performing clusterization is applied. That is, each cell in a cluster must be assigned a cell number. This numbering system is applied across the entire serving area. If the cell assignment rule is implemented (as suggested), the co-channel interference between neighboring clusters will be minimized.

$$K = i^2 + ij + j^2$$

(8-14)

In Eq.(8-14) i and j are interchangeable, and they are integers (0, 1, 2, 3, ...). The values of K for different pairs of (i, j) are given in Table 8-11 (e.g., K = 19 for i = 2 and j = 3, or i = 3 and j = 2).

Table 8-11   K Values for Different Pairs of (i, j).

	i=0	i=1	i=2	i=3	i=4
j=0	0	1	4	9	16
j=1	1	3	7	13	21
j=2	4	7	12	19	28
j=3	9	13	19	27	37
j=4	16	21	28	37	48

Example 8-6 Cell number assignment in a serving area for all clusters: Illustrate the meaning and the rules that apply to the (i, j) pair for a given value of K (assume K = 7 in this example). Note that this example also explains the algorithm used to assign cell numbers to each cell cluster.

Since it is assumed that K = 7, from Table 8-11, the values of (i, j) are obtained as (2, 1). Note that the values (1, 2) can also be used. The results, from co-channel interference viewpoint, will be the same for either pair of (i, j). For this example, i = 2 and j = 1 have been selected.

Figure 8-22 shows a serving area with 40 cells. Three complete clusters can be formed (each cluster is bounded by bold lines) along with six partially complete clusters (note that it is not necessary to identify the six incomplete clusters after completing the cell number assignment). First, a complete cluster with seven cells is assigned (Example 8-7 will illustrate the algorithm used to assign the initial cluster). In this example, the initial cluster can be any of the three perfect clusters bounded by the bold lines. The cell assignment rule is illustrated by locating the cell 1 positions for the other clusters (after the initial cluster is identified).

Rule for using the value of i: Starting from cell 1 [with a cell radius of "**R**" as shown in Figure 8-22] of the initial cluster, "walk" toward the cell boundary (perpendicular to the cell side). Advance forward for **two (i = 2)** cells to a cell "marked" **6** (the number "6" is not important in the procedure; it is used as illustration only).

Rule for using the value of j: As shown in Figure 8-22 continuing from cell 6, turn 60° left or right (direction does not matter, but it is important to be consistent throughout the entire cell assignment process), and advance **one (j = 1)** cell. The cell located using this procedure is cell **1** of another cluster.

This procedure is applied *six* times for each cell (cell No. 1 in this example) in six directions. The number "six" is based on the hexagon cell shape, which has 6 sides.

After all *six* No. 1 cells (i.e., the No.1 cell positions) in the *six* neighboring clusters have been located, using the (i, j) rules, cell assignments for the remaining serving area can be completed by "*observation*". That is, **(in this example only)** cell 2 is always located above cell 1; cell 3 is always located at the upper right of cell 1; cell 7 is always located at the upper left of cell 1; cell 4 is always located at the lower right of cell 1; cell 5 is always located below cell 1; and cell 6 is always located at the lower left of cell 1.

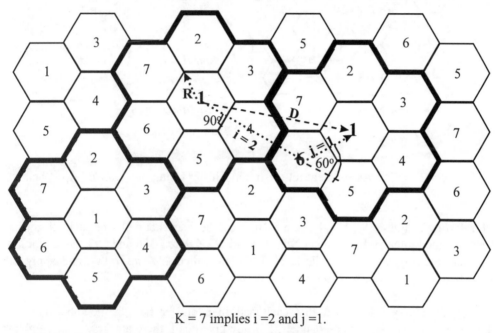

K = 7 implies i =2 and j =1.

Figure 8-22   Clusterization, Cell Number Assignment and K Value (K = 7).

Example 8-7 Cell number assignment for the initial cluster: Describe the cell number assign for starting a new serving area. Assume K = 19.

Any algorithm can be applied to perform the cell number assignment for the initial cluster. Although the techniques may appear different at first glance, after cell number assignments for the entire serving area are complete (from co-channel interference view) the results obtained using different algorithms will be identical, provided the rules for using the (i, j) values described in Example 8-6 are applied.

A common method for assigning cell numbers to the initial cluster is called the "*spiral*" approach. Referring to Figure 8-23, first, arbitrarily designate any cell in the serving area as "*cell 1*". Walk to cell 1's neighbor cell (there are six choices) and designate this cell as "cell 2". In this example, cell 2 is located above cell 1 (this is one choice out of a total of six options). Next, walk clockwise (or, counter-clockwise) around cell 1, assigning cell numbers 3, 4, 5, 6 and 7. Continue walking clockwise past cells 2, 3, 4, 5, 6 and 7 to assign cell numbers 8, 9, 10, 11, 12, 13, 14, 15, 16, 17, 18 and 19.

In summary, all the rules/algorithms used for cell and cluster number assignment are based on systematic methods that minimize co-channel interference to optimize system performance. But, these methods are not unique.

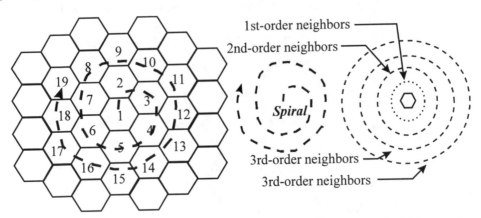

Figure 8-23   Cell Assignment for the Initial Cluster Using the "***Spiral***" Approach.

By referring to Figure 8-21 and Table 8-10, it can be seen that cell 1 of each cluster has been assigned to carry RF channel Nos. 1, 8, 15, 22, 29, ..., 386 and 393. By definition, RF channels assigned to all cells labeled "1" are called "***co-channels***", and apply the same frequency for transmission from the base station.

It should be mentioned that each cell in a cluster has six neighbor clusters, therefore each cell has six co-channels. For any given cell, there are first-order neighbor cells, second-order neighbor cells, etc. (see Figure 8-23) Likewise, for any given RF channel there are first-order, second-order, ..., n^{th} order co-channels. The interference between first-order co-channels [i.e., co-channels that have a distance of "D" between any two adjacent co-channels as shown Figure 8-22] is much stronger than the interference between second-order co-channels. For metropolitan wireless services the 2nd-order co-channel interference may become noticeable because the cell size is much smaller than in rural areas. In summary, as cell size is reduced, higher-order co-channel interference becomes a parameter that must be included in system performance measurements.

8.4.2.2 D/R Ratio and Frequency Reuse Factor, K

Another term, the D/R ratio, can replace the frequency reuse factor K. The distance, D, between two adjacent co-channel cells, and the cell radius, R, are shown in Figure 8-22. The D/R ratio is often used for serving area cell assignment.

- Large D/R ratio case: For a fixed cell size (i.e. R is fixed), D must be large to yield a large D/R ratio. Co-channels are farther apart for a large D/R ratio. Therefore, as the D/R ratio increases, the S/I performance will improve. However, because co-channels are further apart, the total number of RF channels available for a given area decreases as the D/R ratio increases. In summary, cell capacity decreases as the D/R ratio increases (see Figure 8-24).

- Small D/R ratio case: For smaller D/R ratios, there is a corresponding increase in co-channel interference. However, the number of available RF channels for a given area increases as the D/R ratio decreases. In summary, cell capacity increases as the D/R ratio decreases (see Figure 8-24).

The relationship between the D/R ratio and the frequency reuse factor K [given by Eq.(8-14)] is given as follows:

$$\frac{D}{R} = \sqrt{3K} \tag{8-15}$$

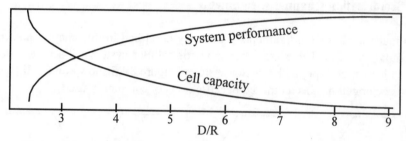

Figure 8-24   Relationship between D/R ratio, Cell Capacity, and System Performance

8.4.2.3 Practical Cell Shapes

Figure 8-25(A) is a typical example of cellularization applied to a serving area. As indicated, the serving area is divided into small areas, called cells, and within each cell a base station is used to serve the cell (see Figure 8-22). Furthermore, several cells are grouped together to form a cluster. All the RF channels available for a given cellular communication system (within a particular frequency spectrum, including the PCS spectrum) are assigned to the cells within a cluster. These RF channels are *repeatedly* re-used for each cluster in the serving area.

It should be noted that a *"hexagon"* is not a practical cell shape. Hexagonal cells are a conceptual method used to simplify cell/cluster design and number assignment. The "hexagon" design algorithm provides a good "starting" cell assignment procedure. Once, the initial cell assignments are complete. Practically every cell must be verified by applying filed trial approach. It is possible, two theoretical hexagon cells may have to combined into one cell. Likewise, a hexagon cell may have to be split into two cells after field trial. The actual cell shape is irregular, and is determined by empirical field trial data. Actual cell shape depends upon the natural terrain and environment of the serving area. The serving area shown in Figure 8-25(A) may have an actual cell arrangement as shown in Figure 8-25(B).

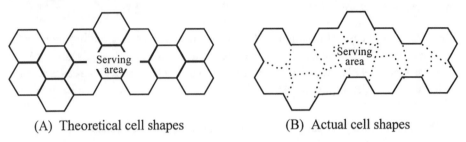

(A) Theoretical cell shapes   (B) Actual cell shapes

Figure 8-25   Theoretical and Actual Cell Shapes a Serving Area.

8.4.2.4 Sectorization/Channel Assignment

Systems that use the cell assignments previously described in this chapter are known as omni cellular systems. There are other types of cellular systems: 2-sector, 3-sector, 4-sector (the least used type) and 6-sector systems. Figure 8-26 shows four cell types (note that the 4-sector cell has been omitted because it is not commonly used).

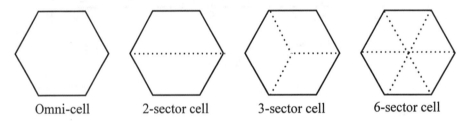

Omni-cell   2-sector cell   3-sector cell   6-sector cell

Figure 8-26   Omni, 2-sector, 3-sector and 6-sector Cells.

A mature cellular network often applies 3-sector cells to improve network performance. Combinations of omni and 3-sector antennas can be found in several metropolitan and urban areas. There are cellular systems that can support sectorized cells, and some that can not. Advanced systems can typically support omni, 3-sector, and 6-sector cells. The 3-sector systems often apply a frequency reuse factor of 7. Therefore, these systems require 21 ($\equiv 3 \times 7$) channel sets (e.g., 21 rows in Table 8-12 of Example 8-8; for example, row No.1 represents cell 1 and the α-face).

Example 8-8:   Describe the algorithm used to perform channel assignment for a sectorized system.   Assume K = 7 and 395 RF channels are available. Draw a serving area with a sufficient number of cells to indicate the cell assignment within a cluster, and the channel assignment for all three sectors within each cell. The channel assignment is shown in Figure 8-27 and Table 8-12.

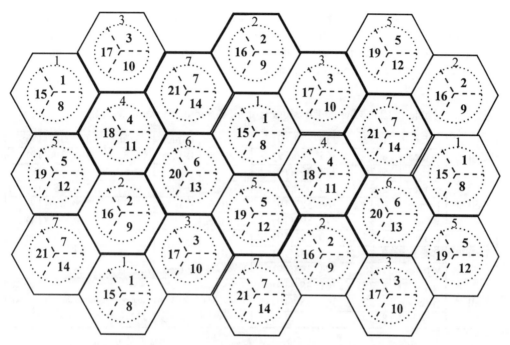

Figure 8-27   Channel Assignment for 3-Sector Systems with K = 7.

Since it is a three-sector system, there are "three faces" in each cell: α, β and γ. Table 8-12 lists the 395 RF channels that are assigned to the three faces of all seven cells. There are many ways to perform channel assignments. The approach shown in Table 8-12 is one of the common systematic methods. The algorithm used is very simple: starting from the α faces, assign channel 1 to cell 1, channel 2 to cell 2, ..., and channel 7 to cell 7. Then, assign the β faces as channel 8 to cell 1, channel 9 to cell 2, ..., and channel 14 to cell 7. The assignment is continued for the γ faces as channel 15 to cell 1, channel 16 to cell 2, ..., channel 21 to cell 7. After finishing the channel assignments for the γ-faces, start over again with the assignments for the α faces, β faces and then γ faces until all the RF channels have been exhausted. In this example, each face has 19 RF channels except the γ faces of cells 4, 5, 6 and 7 which have 18 RF channels [designated by the number inside parenthesis in Table 8-12].

From Table 8-12, it can be seen that the α face of cell 1 has been assigned to carry RF channels 1, 22, ..., 358 and 379. The lowest three channels for cell 1 are channels Nos. 1, 8 and 15 for the α face, the β face and the γ face, respectively (see Figure 8-27 and Table 8-12). Similarly, the lowest three channels for cell 2 are channels Nos. 2, 9 and 16 for the α face, the β face and the γ face, respectively; the lowest three channels for cell 3 are channels Nos. 3, 10 and 17; the lowest three channels for cell 4 are channels Nos. 4, 11 and 18; the lowest three channels for cell 5 are channels Nos. 5, 12 and 19; the lowest three channels for cell 6 are channels Nos. 6, 13 and 20; and, the lowest three channels for cell 7 are channels Nos. 7, 14 and 21 for the α face, the β face and the γ face, respectively.

These channel assignments are shown in Figure 8-27, which does not show any RF channel higher than 21. For example, channel 22 is not shown in Figure 8-27. However, channel 22 is assigned to the same antenna which transmits channel 1 in cell number 1, and the same channel assignment sequence is followed as shown in Table 8-12.

Table 8-12   Channel Assignment for 3-Sector Systems with $K = 7$.

Cell 1	α-face	1, 22, ..., 358, 379(19)	Cell 5	α-face	5, 26, ..., 362, 383(19)
	β-face	8, 29, ..., 365, 386(19)		β-face	12, 33, ..., 369, 390(19)
	γ-face	15, 36, ..., 372, 393(19)		γ-face	19, 40, ..., 376 (18)
Cell 2	α-face	2, 23, ..., 359, 380(19)	Cell 6	α-face	6, 27, ..., 363, 384(19)
	β-face	9, 30, ..., 366, 387(19)		β-face	13, 34, ..., 370, 391(19)
	γ-face	16, 37, ..., 373, 394(19)		γ-face	20, 41, ..., 377 (18)
Cell 3	α-face	3, 24, ..., 360, 381(19)	Cell 7	α-face	7, 28, ..., 364, 385(19)
	β-face	10, 31, ..., 367, 388(19)		β-face	14, 35, ..., 371, 392(19)
	γ-face	17, 38, ..., 374, 395(19)		γ-face	21, 42, ..., 378 (18)
Cell 4	α-face	4, 25, ..., 361, 382(19)	Note: Number inside the parenthesis indicates the total number of RF channels assigned to one sector in each cell.		
	β-face	11, 32, ..., 368, 389(19)			
	γ-face	18, 39, ..., 375 (18)			

8.4.2.5 Other Cell Arrangements

It is often assumed that cell sectorization is used to increase the capacity of a cellular system, but this is **incorrect**. Conversion from the omni-cell arrangement to cell sectorization can improve the system S/I performance, but cell capacity will actually be reduced. Other cell arrangements besides sectorization can be applied to a cellular network for various purposes. Some techniques are "cell splitting", "channel segmentation", and "overlaid cells". These concepts and applications described as follows.

- *Cell splitting:* Cell splitting is often applied when the traffic load carried by the original cell exceeds its capacity. In cell splitting, the distance between adjacent cell sites is typically divided in half (further division can be done if more splitting is required). In Figure 8-28(B), only the central cell has been split. The nominal coverage area of the newly established cell is reduced to a quarter of the area previously covered by the original (i.e., non-split) cell site. The central cell now contains a complete smaller cell, and six half-cells (smaller cells). Thus, the cell site density is quadrupled [Figure 8-28(B)]. Ideally, the new cell site locations are at points midway between neighboring sites. Cell splitting allows four times the traffic to be carried. All the existing cells need not be split at the same time. Only those cells with traffic overloads are candidates for cell splitting. However, if cells are split in only part of the system, serious channel assignment problems may be encountered. That is, if the channel assignment is not done properly, interference between some co-channels may be much worse than others.

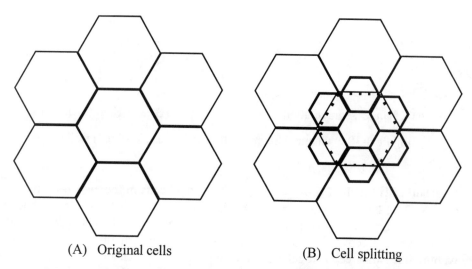

(A) Original cells   (B) Cell splitting

Figure 8-28   Cell Splitting for the Central Cell.

- *Channel segmentation*: Figure 8-29(A) shows a system with a frequency reuse factor K = 7. The shaded cells (with dots) are two co-channel cells. Assume that the area near the boundary of cells Nos. 4 and 7 needs ten (10) extra RF channels since the area has a traffic overload problem. Channel segmentation can be applied as shown in Figure 8-29(B). For US cellular systems with omni cells, cell No. 1 has 57 RF channels assigned to carry 57 subscribers (see Table 8-12). In this example, the "channel segmentation" algorithm is based on sacrificing (i.e., re-assigning) 10 RF channels at two other co-channel cells (i.e. No. 1 cells). That is, ten available channels will not be assigned for use by the No.1 cells. This must be done because reassigning the 10 RF channels to the overload area violates the D/R ratio requirement. Therefore, the 10 RF channels assigned to the overload area can not be used by the No. 1 cells, because the co-channel interference would degrade the system performance to an unacceptable level. Under some extreme circumstances, if the channels in the co-channel cells (e.g. No. 1 cells) must remain in service, the three groups of co-channels (i.e., the 10 RF channels in this example) may suffer performance degradation. This problem can be solved by applying overlaid cells (dual cell) technology.

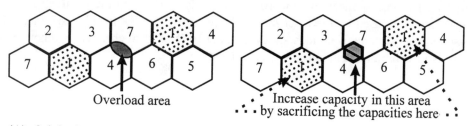

(A) Original system with an overload area   (B) Channel segmentation

Figure 8-29   Channel Segmentation.

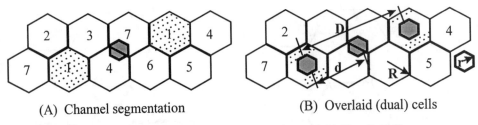

(A) Channel segmentation   (B) Overlaid (dual) cells

Figure 8-30   Channel Segmentation and Overlaid (Dual) Cells.

- **Overlaid cells (or dual cells):** By applying overlaid cells in the two co-channel cells (i.e., No.1 cells) as shown in Figure 8-30(B), use of the 10 RF channels that were sacrificed when channel segmentation was implemented [Figures 8-29(B) and 8-30(A)] can be recovered. As shown in Figure 8-30(B), smaller cells are overlaid within both No. 1 cells (regular large cells). The 10 RF channels are re-gained by restricting the use of the 10 RF channels to within the overlaid areas of the two co-channel cells [i.e., the smaller areas of the No.1 cells shown in Figure 8-30(B)].

For example, in a system with a frequency reuse factor of K = 7, a total of 57 channels is available for the two No. 1 cells. However, 10 of the 57 channels can only be used within the smaller cell (i.e., the overlaid cell). The remaining 47 channels can be used throughout the two No. 1 cells (i.e., they are not restricted to the overlaid cell areas). By restricting the use of 10 RF channels to the small overlaid cells, the co-channel interference between the overlaid cell and the channel segmentation cell is no longer a problem. This is because the D/R ratio requirement is no longer violated, provided the following relationship holds true:

$$\frac{D}{R} = \frac{d}{r} \tag{8-16}$$

where D, d , R and r are the distances and radii as shown in Figure 8-30(B).

For the system with a frequency reuse factor of 7 (k = 7), the 10 RF channels assigned to the three small cells must conform to the d/r ratio, while the remaining 47 RF channels will follow the D/R rule. Therefore, co-channel interference is no longer a problem. In some applications, the 10 RF channels assigned to the overload area may never have been used by the co-channel cells (e.g., No.1 cells). In this case, there is no reason to apply overlaid cell technology (i.e., the 10 reassigned channels will not be used in the No.1 cells, and do not need to be restricted).

8.5 MULTIPLE ACCESS METHODS

It has been mentioned earlier that the "bandwidth" of a system is traditionally refers to the frequency range available for carrying information throughout the system. Therefore, analog systems can be considered "frequency-sharing" systems. The technology of "Frequency Division Multiplexing" (FDM) was developed for sharing the available bandwidth between many users. For radio transmission, a modified term, "Frequency Division Multiple Access" (FDMA), is used to describe this technique. [Figure 8-31(A) shows one user occupying a single frequency range as indicated by individual vertical bars].

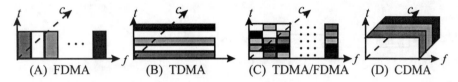

(A) FDMA   (B) TDMA   (C) TDMA/FDMA   (D) CDMA

Figure 8-31   Various Multiple Access Techniques.

The concept of bandwidth can be extended to "time" instead of "frequency". That is, a system can be accessed by many users by "sharing time". Time Division Multiplexing (TDM) technology was developed for this purpose. In wireless applications, the term "Time Division Multiple Access" (TDMA) is used to describe this technique. [Figure 8-31(B) shows one user occupying a single time interval as indicated by separate horizontal bars]. A combination of "frequency sharing" and "time sharing" has been developed for wireless applications, and is known as TDMA/FDMA [Figure 8-31(C) shows each user occupying a separate small rectangle].

Further extension of the bandwidth concept is possible. A third parameter, "code", along with "time" and "frequency" has been used for wireless applications. The addition of "codes" allows a group of users to occupy the same frequency range and the same time interval. This technique is called "Code Division Multiple Access" (CDMA), which is shown in Figure 8-31(D). The principles of CDMA are more complex than FDMA or TDMA. Some later examples can be used to help one to understand CDMA.

The CDMA examples in later sections of this chapter are provided to further explain CDMA concepts/techniques.

8.5.1 Frequency Division Multiple Access

Multiple access is required at the base station (or cell site) where many individual user signals are multiplexed to form one signal that is transmitted using the same antenna (i.e. broadcasted to many mobile units and/or handheld units).

Because FDMA is another term used to indicate "Frequency Division Multiplexing" (FDM), the FDM description given in Chapter 6 is applicable for wireless FDMA systems. Figure 8-32 summarizes the major blocks of the base station transmitter in an FDMA system. Refer to Chapter 6 for additional information regarding FDM techniques, which are directly applicable to FDMA implementations.

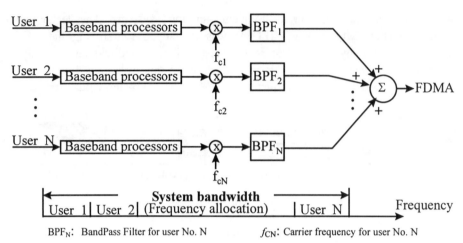

Figure 8-32   FDMA Implementation at the Base Station Transmitter.

8.5.2 Time Division Multiple Access (TDMA)

Three different implementations can be used for TDMA systems: TDMA [pure TDMA as shown in Figure 8-31(B)], TDMA/FDMA (TDMA plus FDMA) which is applied in IS-136 and GSM cellular systems [shown in Figure 8-31(C)], and E-TDMA (Extended TDMA) which has been implemented in some southern areas of the United States.

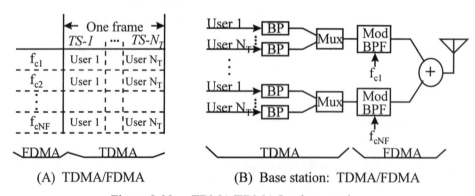

(A) TDMA/FDMA   (B) Base station: TDMA/FDMA

Figure 8-33   TDMA/FDMA Implementation.

"Pure TDMA" technology is identical to Time Division Multiplexing (TDM), which has been previously described in Chapter 6. For wireless services, TDMA plus FDMA is typically used as shown in Figure 8-33. In this example frequency is divided into N_F divisions, using the FDMA methodology, and a frame interval is divided into N_T time slots for N_T users, using the TDMA principle [see Figure 8-33(A)]. In summary, there are N_F radio channels, and N_T users per radio channel as shown in Figure 8-33(A).

The base station architecture can be divided into two sections, as shown in Figure 8-33(B). The first section (TDMA) consists of two major blocks: (1) Baseband Processors (BP; e.g., speech encoding, channel encoding; bit-interleaving, etc.), and (2) time division multiplexer (i.e., mux). These two blocks contain the primary TDMA functions. The second section (FDMA) consists of modulators (i.e., mod) that are connected to BandPass Filters (BPF). The second section implements the primary FDMA functions.

The architecture shown in Figure 8-33(B) has been presented in the IS-54/IS-136 and GSM standards documents. Additional information of interest obtained from the IS-54 standard is provided as general background material:

- IS-54 is the North American dual-mode TDMA cellular standard, developed by the Telecommunications Industry Association (US-Canada) TIA 45.3 committee, based on TDMA/FDD access technology. It specifies the FDMA 30 kHz radio channels. Dual-mode (both analog and digital) operations allow an easier transition from analog to digital cellular communications.

- IS-54 initial release: The initial IS-54 standard was released in January, 1990. The digital speech encoder specification has a rate of 7.95 kbps, with voice quality equivalent to analog FM. It also features mobile assisted handoff, and supports the existing FDMA feature set.

- IS-54 Revision A: Revision A was released in March, 1991. It describes enhanced procedures for timing alignment, synchronization, and associated control channel coding. In addition, it supports features for distinctive alerting and mobile unit information.

- IS-54 Revision B: Revision B was released in March, 1992. Revision B describes authentication, voice privacy, and encryption of signaling/sensitive user data (e.g., PIN and credit card numbers).

- IS-136: IS-136 was released in August, 1994. The specification of a digital control channel increases paging capacity and provides discontinuous reception (sleep mode). Short Message Service (SMS) is also specified for analog voice channels, digital control channels, and/or on digital traffic channels. IS-136 supports asynchronous data and fax, and operation for PCS frequency bands.

8.5.3 Extended TDMA (E-TDMA)

Statistically speaking, the end-to-end connection (wire or wireless) used for voice signal transport does not utilize bandwidth effectively. The speech activity during a typical conversation consists of active periods and quite periods. These two periods are referred to as **spurts** and **pauses**, respectfully. Spurts consist of syllables and words. Pauses include the times in a conversation when one is listening, or both parties are involving in other activities such as looking for information needed to continue the conversation. In a typical conversation, speech spurts last about 1.0 to 2.0 seconds. Figure 8-34 shows an average speech cycle, which typically lasts 3.75 seconds. Therefore, the speech activity factor is approximately 40% (typically 38% ~ 40%).

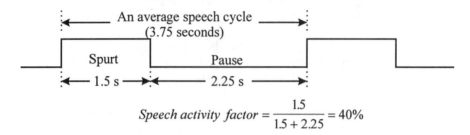

$$Speech\ activity\ factor = \frac{1.5}{1.5 + 2.25} = 40\%$$

Figure 8-34   A typical Speech Cycle and Activity Factor.

Several wireless applications take advantage of pause periods in voice signal transport. The first application is Extended-TDMA (E-TDMA) systems, and the second is Cellular Digital Packet Data (CDPD) transport. Digital Speech Interpolation (DSI) methods evolved from an older technology known as Time Assignment Speech Interpolation (TASI) used for international undersea cable systems in the 1960s. DSI is used to detect spurts and pauses in a speech conversation. Figure 8-35 indicates the DSI improvement factor with respect to reducing the number of traffic channels needed for speech activity factors (N_A) of 35%, 40% and 45%. That is, utilizing pause intervals to carry voice signals from other user conversation, thereby reducing the number of physical facility channels. In other applications, the pause interval can be used to carry different types of signal (e.g., fax or data, which is typically packetized before transporting).

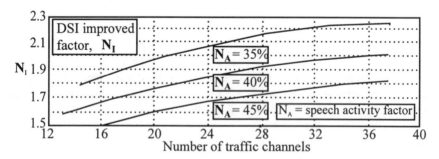

Figure 8-35   DSI Advantage or Improvement Factors.

The application of the DSI improvement factor (N_I) is also shown in Figure 8-35. Assume that the speech activity factor (N_A) is 40%, and 36 end-to-end connections are needed for traffic channels because DSI is **not** used. From Figure 8-35, for NA = 40% and 36 traffic channels, it can be seen that $N_I \approx 2.0$. Applying the formula in Eq.(8-17), a savings of 50% (from 36 traffic channels to 18 channels) can be achieved by using the DSI features available in an E-TDMA system.

$$Required\ traffic\ channel = \frac{Number\ of\ traffic\ channels\ served}{DSI\ improvement\ factor}$$

$$= \frac{36}{2} = 18$$

(8-17)

Similarly, if the speech activity factor (N_A) is assumed to be 35% (i.e., the speech characteristics have larger pause times), and 36 customers need to be served, the DSI improvement factor (N_I) is 2.27 (see Figure 8-35). Therefore, the required number of traffic channels can be reduced to 16 [≡ 36/2.27]. Hence, a savings of more than 55% [≡ = (20 channels saved)/(36 original channels) = 20/36, or = 1− 1/(2.27)] can be achieved.

8.5.4 CDMA Basics

The third type of multiple wireless access technology is Code Division Multiple Access (CDMA), which is classified into three types:

- Fast Frequency Hopping CDMA (FFH-CDMA): For a particular user, the signal amplitude remains unchanged, but its frequency *hops* (i.e., changes) from one value to another at a rate that is typically higher than the user information rate. Figure 8-36(A) shows the frequencies that a user has been hopping between during over many *time chip* (T_C) intervals (defined later).

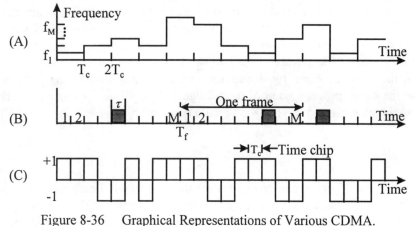

Figure 8-36   Graphical Representations of Various CDMA.

- Fast Time Hopping CDMA (FTH-CDMA): In this scheme, the user signal maintains a constant frequency, but "hops" from one time slot to another time slot during different frame intervals as shown in Figure 8-36(B).

- Direct Sequence CDMA (DS-CDMA; described in the following sections): Based on the signal spectrum of each digital bit as shown in Figure 8-36(C).

The three CDMA types shown in Figure 8-36 are compared in Table 8-13. Since most current commercial CDMA systems utilize DS-CDMA technology, only the details of DS-CDMA are described in this chapter, and the details of other two technologies (i.e. FFH-CDMA and FTH-CDMA) will not described in this book.

Table 8-13   Comparison among FFH-, FTH- and DS-CDMA.

Technology	Advantages	Disadvantages
DS-CDMA	* Best noise and anti-jam * Most difficulty to detect * Best for multipath	⊗ Requires wideband ⊗ Long acquisition time ⊗ Near/far problem
FFH-CDMA	* Greatest spreading * Short acquisition time * Less near/far problem	⊗ Complex freq. Synthesizer ⊗ Error correction required
FTH-CDMA	* High bandwidth efficiency * Simpler than FFH * Near/far avoided	⊗ Long acquisition time ⊗ Error correction required

8.5.4.1 Signal and Signal Spectrum

The DS-CDMA principle is based on the signal (frequency) spectrum of a digital bit (see Figure 8-37). When a digital bit (a logical "1") is plotted in the frequency domain, it is described by a special function known as a *sinc* function (sampling function). That is, the spectrum of a digital bit "behaves" in accordance with a sinc function. When the bit rate of the digital signal $[b(t)]$ is low (i.e. the bit interval T_b is wide) the signal spectrum (in frequency domain) is narrow. In contrast, for a the high rate digital signal $[c(t)]$ the signal spectrum is much wider. When these two digital signals $[b(t)$ and $c(t)]$ are multiplied together, the resultant signal $[y(t)]$ also has a wide spectrum. Assuming $S_b(f)$, $S_c(f)$ and $S_y(f)$ are the signal power spectra of digital signals $b(t)$, $c(t)$ and $y(t)$, respectively, then the approximation given in Eq.(8-18) is a valid conclusion.

$$S_y(f) \approx S_c(f) \tag{8-18}$$

In Figure 8-37, the signal $b(t)$ represents the user's digital bit stream, the signal $c(t)$ represents the PN (Pseudo Noise or pseudo random) sequence of the CDMA system that is assigned to the user, and the signal $y(t)$ represents the composite CDMA signal. From Eq. (8-18) and Figure 7-37, it can be seen that the PN sequence $[c(t)]$ dominates the transmitted CDMA signal's spectrum characteristics. That is, the signal power spectrum of the original digital signal, $b(t)$, has been spread across the wider frequency range of $c(t)$. This technology is known as the *spread spectrum technique*. A question often asked is: "How can the original signal be restored if the transmitted signal does not represent the signal power spectrum of the original signal?" The details of CDMA signal restoration is described in Appendix 8-1 (at the end of this chapter). A simple example is provided in this section to illustrate basic signal restoration concept.

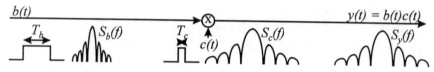

Figure 8-37   Digital Signals and Their Spectra.

Example 8-9: Explain baseband signal spreading/despreading (restoration) techniques used in a DS-CDMA system.

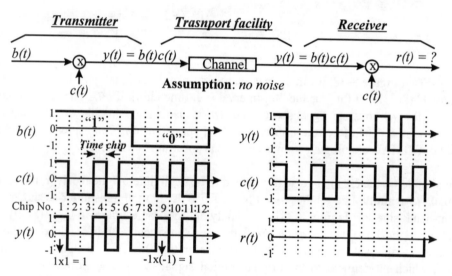

Figure 8-38   Signal Transmitted and Restored Using DS-CDMA.

For simplicity, a 2-bit digital signal, $b(t)$, is assumed to have the pattern "10", and the processing gain (defined later in this section) is assumed to be 6 (i.e., $T_b = 6 \times T_c$). Therefore, the PN sequence, $c(t)$, contains 12 (= 2 × 6) bits, and is assumed to be "100101110101" during the two-bit interval. That is, for 2-bits of information with a gain of 6, since 2 × 6 = 12, a 12-bit PN sequence must be used. The method used to choose the specific 12-bit PN sequence (i.e. 100101110101) is discussed later in this chapter.

In order to illustrate the "spreading" and "despreading" techniques, the following representations must be applied in the CDMA implementation. That is, a logical "1" is represented by a "+1", and a logical "0" is represented by a "−1". Although the purpose of this example is to illustrate signal "spreading" and "despreading" techniques, a more important objective is to explain how the digital signal is restored to the original digital bit sequence of "10".

The transmitted signal, $y(t) = b(t)c(t)$ is obtained, "***chip by chip***". In Figure 8-38 the values of $y(t)$ for the two-bit interval (i.e. 12 time chips) is derived as follows:

$$y(t) = \text{"1"} \quad \text{"-1"} \quad \text{"-1"} \quad \text{"1"} \quad \text{"-1"} \quad \text{"1"} \quad \text{"-1"} \quad \text{"-1"} \quad \text{"1"} \quad \text{"-1"} \quad \text{"1"} \quad \text{"-1"}$$

where the signal is shown "***per time chip***", and the following mathematical rules are applied. For example, during the first chip interval, $b(t) = 1$, and $c(t) = 1$, therefore, the product $y(t) = 1$. During the second chip interval, $b(t) = 1$, and $c(t) = -1$, hence, the product $y(t) = -1$. During the seventh chip interval, $b(t) = -1$, and $c(t) = -1$, accordingly, the product $y(t) = 1$.

$$\text{"1"} \times \text{"1"} = 1; \qquad\qquad \text{"1"} \times \text{"-1"} = \text{"-1"};$$
$$\text{"-1"} \times \text{"1"} = \text{"-1"}; \qquad\qquad \text{"-1"} \times \text{"-1"} = \text{"1"} \qquad\qquad (8\text{-}19)$$

From Figure 8-38, it can be seen that the transmitted signal, $y(t)$, has the same "bit-interval" (i.e. signal rate) as the "bit-interval (i.e. time chip) of $c(t)$. The signal spectrum is wide for $c(t)$, thus the signal spectrum of $y(t)$ is also wide, while the signal spectrum of $b(t)$ is narrow. Therefore, the user signal [$b(t)$] spectrum has been "spread". Therefore, the DS-CDMA technology is known as "spread spectrum" technology.

For simplicity, the channel noise is assumed to be negligible. At the receiver, the received signal $y(t)$ is multiplied by the **same** PN sequence used at the transmitter as shown in the right-hand side of Figure 8-38]. By applying the same rules in Eq. (8-19) when multiplying $y(t)$ and $c(t)$ "***chip by chip***", the received signal, $r(t)$, is obtained as shown in the bottom-right side of Figure 8-38. It can be seen that the received signal, $r(t)$ is indeed "10", which is identical to the original digital signal [$b(t)$]. Therefore, the transmitted signal has been restored accurately at the receiver. In addition, as part of the conversion from $y(t)$ to $r(t)$, the rate has changed from "high" to "low". Thus, the signal spectrum has changed from "wide spectrum" to "narrow spectrum". Thus "spread spectrum" has been "despread" as part of restoring the original signal [$b(t)$] from the received signal [$r(t)$].

8.5.4.2 CDMA Transceiver Building Blocks

Figure 8-39 shows the major building blocks (N multipliers for multiplying user bit sequence with PN sequence, a summing device, a modulator and an antenna) of a DS-CDMA transmitter [Figure 8-39(A)] and receiver (transceiver). The transmitter carries N users, and each is multiplied by its own pseudo noise sequence, PN-j [$j = 1, N$] to obtain $y_1(t), y_2(t), \ldots, y_N(t)$. That is,

$$y_j(t) = b_j(t) \times c_j(t); \quad j = 1, N \qquad\qquad (8\text{-}20)$$

All of these signals [$y_1(t)$ through $y_N(t)$] are summed together (see examples in Appendix 8-1) and then the combined signal is modulated by using a simple technique (e.g. binary FSK) to form the CDMA signal, [$z(t)$] for transmission over the airway.

The received signal [$r(t)$] is first demodulated and then multiplied by a PN sequence. In this example, PN-1 is applied at the receiver [see Figure 8-39(B)] to form a combined signal. The combined signal is then fed to an *"integrate and dump filter"* [this type of filter with its applications is discussed in Appendix 8-1 (Example 8A-2)]. The output of the filter [$v_O(t)$] is sampled to restore the original digital bit stream.

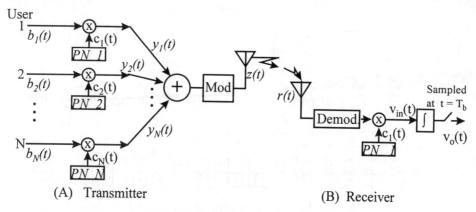

(A) Transmitter   (B) Receiver

Figure 8-39   Simplified Building Blocks of a DS-CDMA Transceiver.

The relationship between the user's digital data stream and the PN sequence is described here. The bit interval of each user digital bit (T_b) is much wider than the (bit) interval (T_c) of the PN sequence as shown in Figure 8-40. That is, the user bit rate is normally much lower than the bit rate of the PN sequence (i.e. $T_b \gg T_c$). Hence, each bit interval (T_c) of the PN sequence is called *"time chip"* of the PN sequence due to its **thin width**. The term processing gain (G; its importance is described in Appendix 8-1), defined as the ratio of user bit interval to the time chip of the PN sequence. That is, processing gain is used to express the relationship between these two waveforms.

$$G = \frac{T_b}{T_c} = \textit{Processing gain} \tag{8-21}$$

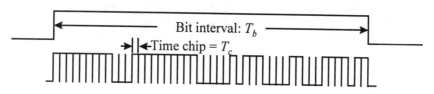

Figure 8-40   Bit Intervals of Digital Signal and PN Sequence.

8.5.4.3 Direct Sequence Generator

The PN sequence (direct sequence) is generated by an *m*-stage maximum-length *pseudo noise* code generator, with a generator polynomial of *g(x)*. A generalized Direct Sequence (DS) generator is shown in Figure 8-41(A). This generator consists of *m* stages of one-bit shift register (or memory device). The first stage has an input from the feedback loop, which is the output of an *N* input Exclusive OR-gate (EOR). The circuit design of the EOR function is determined by the generator polynomial used for the particular DS generator. Example 8-10 describe the design of a PN sequence, and explains why this type of sequence is called a "*pseudo noise* or *pseudo random*" sequence.

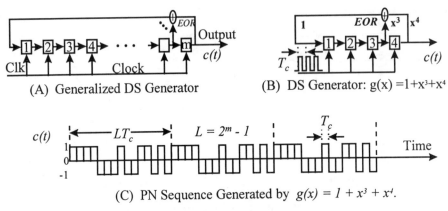

(A) Generalized DS Generator

(B) DS Generator: g(x) =1+x³+x⁴

(C) PN Sequence Generated by $g(x) = 1 + x^3 + x^4$.

Figure 8-41   DS (or PN Sequence) Generator Design.

Example 8-10:   The generator polynomial of a PN sequence is given in Eq.(8-22). Determine the output [*c(t)*] of the DS generator, explain the circuitry used for the EOR function, and discuss the maximum-length of the PN sequence.

$$g(x) = 1 + x^3 + x^4 \qquad\qquad (8\text{-}22)$$

This is a 4-stage DS generator because *m* = 4 [i.e. the degree (*m*) of the generator polynomial is from the term x^4]. The generator requires four single-bit registers. The "1" term in *g(x)* represents the connection from the output of the EOR (the feedback loop) to the input of the first-stage shift register. The polynomial *g(x)* contains two other terms (x^3 and x^4), therefore the EOR requires two inputs. One input is from the output of the third-stage register (corresponding to x^3), and the other is from the output of the fourth-stage shift register (corresponding to x^4). This circuit configuration is shown in Figure 8-41(B) [note that each term in the generator polynomial is indicated in Figure 8-41(B)], and the PN generator is driven by a clock having the rate equal to the time chip, T_c.

The function of the PN sequence generator in Figure 8-41(B) is described as follows. Each shift register is preset to "1", as shown in the second column of Table 8-14.

This table shows all 15 ($\equiv 2^4 - 1$) states of the PN sequence generator. The output of the 4th shift register is the PN sequence [$c(t)$]. That is, row 4 of Table 8-14 contains the following PN sequence. Note that the repeating PN sequence [Eq.(8-23)] is also plotted as a waveform in Figure 8-41(C).

$$c(t) = " 1\ 1\ 1\ 1\ 0\ 0\ 0\ 1\ 0\ 0\ 1\ 1\ 0\ 1\ 0 ... " \tag{8-23}$$

Table 8-14   The 15 Different States for the DS Generator of $g(x) = 1 + x^3 + x^4$.

SR	Clock No														
	1	2	3	4	5	6	7	8	9	10	11	12	13	14	15
1	1	0	0	0	1	0	0	1	1	0	1	0	1	1	1
2	1	1	0	0	0	1	0	0	1	1	0	1	0	1	1
3	1	1	1	0	0	0	1	0	0	1	1	0	1	0	1
4	1	1	1	1	0	0	0	1	0	0	1	1	0	1	0

The generator polynomial of a PN sequence can be different depending on the application. For SONET/SDH, a polynomial of 7th degree is typically used. For ATM, a polynomial of 43rd degree is appropriate. For IS-95, $m = 42$, thus, the maximum length of the sequence is $L = 2^{42} - 1 = 4.4 \times 10^{12}$.

8.5.5 Comparison of FDMA, TDMA, and CDMA

Several aspects of FDMA, TDMA (i.e. TDMA with FDMA, such as IS-136 and GSM) and CDMA technologies are compared in this section. To make these comparisons easier to understand, the following assumptions are made:

- The frequency allocated for the three technologies is the same: 1.26 MHz.

- The user bandwidth [i.e. the RF   (radio frequency) carrier bandwidth] is assumed to be 30 kHz for both FDMA and TDMA.

- The frequency reuse factor, k, is assumed to be 7 for both FDMA and TDMA.

For FDMA, the RF circuits available within the 1.26 MHz bandwidth is calculated as follows:

$$RF\ circuits = \frac{W}{B} = \frac{1.26\ MHz}{30\ kHz} = 42 \tag{8-24}$$

The cell capacity with a frequency reuse factor of 7, is given as follows:

$$Cell\ capacity = N_c = \frac{W}{kB} = \frac{1.26\ MHz}{7 \times 30\ kHz} = 6 \tag{8-25}$$

For IS-136 TDMA/FDMA, there are presently three time slots assigned to each RF channel. Thus the cell capacity is increased three times, $N_c = 18$ (= 3 × 6). Furthermore, in E-TDMA applications, the cell capacity is doubled to become 36 (= 18 × 2).

For CDMA, the cell capacity is calculated [see Appendix 8-1 (Example 8A-2)] to be $N_c = 41$. The results are summarized in Table 8-15, assuming a frequency allocation of 1.26 MHz.

In summary, the DS-CDMA is the best technology among FDMA, IS-136 (TDMA/FDMA), and DS-CDMA, with respect to cell capacity. It is believed that cell capacity of CDMA technology will increase beyond the limits of present technology.

Table 8-15   FDMA, TDMA and CDMA Comparison.

Technology	Carrier bandwidth (B kHz)	RF circuits (W/B)	Cell capacity (N_c)	Frequency reuse factor (k)
FDMA	30	42	6	7
TDMA (IS-136)	30	42	18	7
DS-CDMA	1260	1	41	-

In addition to the cell capacity comparison given in Table 8-15, the speech quality of these three technologies are compared in Figure 8-42 (i.e., different signal-to-interference, S/I, ratios). The S/I comparison is not intended to be exact, but provides a relative assessment of system performance for the different technologies. Under typical conditions (i.e., an environment of S/I = 18 ~ 22 dB), any of the technologies provides acceptable speech quality. Therefore, system capacity and cost will be the primary decision factors used to select the appropriate technology for a particular system. However, it should be noted that both FDMA and CDMA have a better characteristic (i.e., graceful degradation) as the transmission environmental conditions worsen. This is not the case for TDMA-IS-136 or TDMA-GSM (see Figure 8-42).

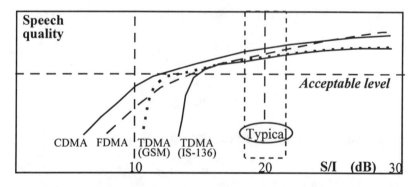

Figure 8-42   Speech Quality Comparison: FDMA, TDMA and CDMA.

Review Questions I for Chapter 8:

(1) Generally speaking, as technology advances a communications system will operate at a _____ frequency, or _____ wavelength.

(2) Among various communications technologies, optical fiber systems operate at the highest frequency range, that is, in the wavelength range known as _____.
The wireless systems are moving towards this range as well, and is referred to as _____ or _____ technology.

(3) In addition to PSTN, a wireless network consists of _____, _____ and _____.

(4) The primary base station functions are: _____, _____, _____, _____, _____ and _____.
However, _____ may be implemented at MSC.

(5) Wireless applications can be found in several environments: _____, _____, _____, and _____.

(6) Personal Communications Service (PCS) allows some combination of _____, _____, and _____.

(7) Unlike guided media (e.g., wire and optical fiber), airway transport technique involves several unique problems/issues such as: _____, _____, _____, and _____.

(8) Several factors must be considered when selecting an antenna for wireless application: _____, _____, _____, _____, _____, _____, and _____.

(9) A typical deep fading (known as Rayleigh fading) can cause about _____ bits bursty errors in TDMA-IS-136 system, and _____ bits bursty errors in TDMA-GSM systems.

(10) To combat deep fading, _____ is used to reduce/eliminate fading, in addition, _____ is used to control bursty errors caused by deep fading. A commonly used diversity technique applies ___-receiver _____ scheme.

(11) The frequency spectrum between 824 MHz and 894 MHz is commonly known as the _____ band, while the frequency spectrum between 1850 MHz and 1990 MHz is called the _____ band.

(12) To overcome the limited airway bandwidth, wireless communications application always adopt _____. To do so, a serving area must be _____.

(13) From performance and cell capacity viewpoint, _____ is superior to _____ and _____.

8.6 SIGNAL MODULATION

The fundamental principles of modulation techniques have been previously described in Chapter 6. This section will highlight the modulation methods used in digital wireless applications, especially the IS-136 (known as π/4-DQPSK modulation) and GSM [known as Minimum Shift Keying (MSK)] standards.

For convenience, the diagram representing various communication technologies (e.g. analog signals transported over an analog system, e.g., voice signals over airway; analog signals transported over a digital system, e.g., digitized voice signal over airway; etc., described in Chapter 6) has been redrawn in Figure 8-43. For *digital wireless* applications, the signal (before being transmitted over the airway) is always in digital format. Therefore, the digital signal must be fed to a modulator using "ASK", "FSK", "PSK", or "QAM" technology, or a modified form (e.g., 16-FSK, 64-PSK, DPSK, 128-QAM, etc.) of these methods.

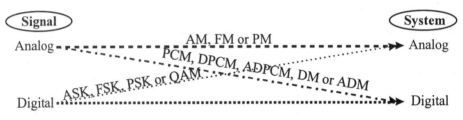

Figure 8-43   Various Modulation Applications.

As described in Chapter 6, the modulation techniques used to change a digital signal to an analog format having the following generic form:

$$x(t) = A_i(t) \bullet \cos\left[\omega_i t + \theta_i(t)\right] \quad i = 1, N \tag{8-26}$$

The definitions, applications and classification of these modulation techniques have been explained in Chapter 6. This chapter will discuss only MSK and π/4-DQPSK modulation techniques.

8.6.1 Variation of Modulation: 4-PSK, 4-QAM and QPSK

A signal constellation can represent many aspects of modulation. Figure 8-44 is used to illustrate this concept (refer to Chapter 6 for additional information).

The definition of 4-PSK is "*a sinusoidal waveform carrying a digital signal that has four possible phases*". These phases can be (0°, 90°, 180° and 270°), (45°, 135°, 225° and 315°), or [(θ, θ + 90°, θ + 180°, θ + 270°); where θ = any angle]. Therefore, both Figure 8-44(A) and Figure 8-44(B) represent a 4-PSK signal constellation.

Figure 8-44(B) also represents a 4-QAM signal (e.g., an M-ary QAM with a value of $M = 4$) constellation. Therefore, it is reasonable to call the constellation of Figure 8-44(B) a QPSK (a combination of 4-*Q*AM and 4-*PSK*) modulation diagram. In addition, the phase of the point in the first quadrant of Figure 8-44(B) is 45° ($\pi/4$), hence, Figure 8-44(B) can also be called a $\pi/4$-QPSK modulation signal constellation diagram. Therefore, the modulation ($\pi/4$-DQPSK) adopted by IS-136 TDMA is similar to Figure 8-44(B). There are some differences between $\pi/4$-QPSK [Figure 8-44(B)] and $\pi/4$-DQPSK modulation. Specifically, the term "*D*", which represents "*D*ifferential", in $\pi/4$-DQPSK is the major distinction. The concept of "differential" is described in the following section.

4-PSK
4-QAM

QPSK
$\pi/4 - QPSK$

(A)   (B)

Figure 8-44   Variation of 4-PSK or 4-QAM.

8.6.2 Differential Phase Shift Keying (DPSK)

When the PSK method is used to modulate a digital signal, there is an issue that must be resolved. For wireless services, the signal phase varies while the conversation (i.e., speech signals) is in progress. In this application, the delay of the signal from the transmitter to the receiver varies, because the receiver is moving and multipath transmission exists. When using the phase of an analog signal [e.g., $A \bullet cos\ (\omega t + \theta_i)$; i = *1*, *N*] to represent a digital signal, the receiver must constantly (regularly) estimate the phase relationship between the transmitter and the receiver. This activity is referred to as **phase estimation**. A common phase estimation technique technologies is Differential Phase Shift Keying (DPSK), which is illustrated in Figure 8-45. The input digital data stream, $d(t)$, is fed to a differential phase shift keying modulator. The feedback signal, $b(t - T_b)$, is a one-bit delayed (T_b) version of the signal $b(t)$ [i.e., by delaying the signal $b(t)$ by a time unit of T_b , as shown by dotted arrows in Figure 8-45, $b(t - T_b)$ can be derived], and is the product of the two signals, $d(t)$ and $b(t - T_b)$, that is:

$$b(t) = d(t) \times b(t - T_b) \qquad (8\text{-}27)$$

In this example the digital data stream is assumed to be "110101001...". **The system assumes *the initial state with b(t) = –1ᵛ* [for – $T_b \leq t \leq 0$]** as shown in Figure 8-45. The formation of the combined signal, $b(t)$ is shown below:

Digital signal $d(t)$:	$+1^v$	$+1^v$	-1^v	$+1^v$	-1^v	$+1^v$	-1^v	-1^v	$+1^v$
$b(t - T_b)$:	-1^v	-1^v	-1^v	$+1^v$	$+1^v$	-1^v	-1^v	$+1^v$	-1^v
$b(t)$:	-1^v	-1^v	$+1^v$	$+1^v$	-1^v	-1^v	$+1^v$	-1^v	-1^v

where the products $(+1^v)(+1^v) = +1^v$; $(+1^v)(-1^v) = -1^v$; $(-1^v)(+1^v) = -1^v$; and $(-1^v)(-1^v)$ $= +1^v$ have been used to obtained $b(t)$.

Once the signal $b(t)$ has been formed, the BPSK modulation (binary-PSK or basic PSK; described in Chapter 6) can be applied. Since a BPSK requires two phases in the carrier signal [Eq.(8-26)], 0° and 180° are assumed. The 1st, the 2nd, the 5th, the 6th, the 8th and the 9th bits of $b(t)$ are assigned a carrier signal with a phase θ_0 of 0°. The 3rd, the 4th and the 7th bits of b(t) are assigned a carrier signal with a phase θ_1 of 180°. Thus, the resultant signal is a DPSK waveform, as shown at the bottom of Figure 8-45.

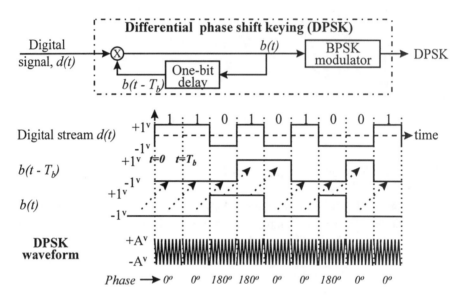

Figure 8-45   Implementation of DPSK Modulation.

8.6.3 π/4-DQPSK for IS-54/IS-136

The implementation of a π/4-DQPSK is shown in Figure 8-46. The top of Figure 8-46 is a block diagram of the modulator circuit, the bottom-left side is the signal constellation diagram of the π/4-DQPSK modulation method, and the bottom-right side chart is the standardized "differential" phase relationship for a pair of binary signals (b_o, b_e).

To implement differential phase shift keying modulation, the digital bitstream is converted from a serial format into a parallel format consisting two components: the odd-number bit stream (b_o) and the even-number bit stream (b_e). The phase change, $\Delta\theta$, required for each signal pair (b_o, b_e) is standardized and listed in Figure 8-46. That is, the digital data bitstream from the digital wireless subscriber is divided into two-bit groups. Each two bit group (b_o, b_e) is represented by a phase change (a standardized value).

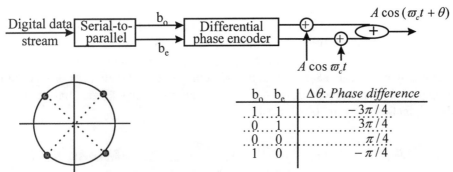

b_o	b_e	$\Delta\theta$: Phase difference
1	1	$-3\pi/4$
0	1	$3\pi/4$
0	0	$\pi/4$
1	0	$-\pi/4$

Figure 8-46 $\pi/4$-DQPSK for IS-54/IS-136.

Before a call is started and the receiver is powered-up and ready to receive a call, the receiver must estimate the received signal's phase with respect to the transmitter's phase. This "phase estimation" procedure must be periodically performed by the system (both the transmitter and the receiver). The phase estimation algorithm is described in Example 8-11.

Example 8-11: Describe the transmitted DPSK signals' phases, and explain how the received DPSK signal is restored to form the original digital data bit stream of: 00100100110011010010100... . Assume each pair of bits (b_o, b_e) is carried by the following sinusoidal waveform:

$$A \cos (\omega_c t + \theta)$$

For simplicity, the initial received signal phase (after the phase estimation process) is assumed to be **0°**. The transmitted signal phase can be calculated as follows:

$\theta_1 = 0° + \Delta\theta = 0° + 45° = 45°; \quad \theta_2 = 45° + \Delta\theta = 45° - 45° = 0°; \quad \theta_3 = 0° + \Delta\theta = 0° + 135° = 135°;$

$\theta_4 = 135° + \Delta\theta = 135° + 45° = 180°; \quad \theta_5 = 180° + \Delta\theta = 180° - 135° = 45°; \quad \dots$

The phase changes $\Delta\theta$'s are obtained from the chart listed in Figure 8-46 and are listed in Table 8-16 (the 2nd row), which also shows the transmitted/received phases (θ_1, θ_2, θ_3, θ_4, θ_5, ...). For example, the first two bits "00" has the $\Delta\theta$ assigned as 45°; the second 2-bit group "10" is assigned a $\Delta\theta$ of −45°; etc. as shown in the second row in Table 8-16. Assuming the channel noise is small (i.e. no errors), the received phases will be restored with the same values as the transmitted phases (Table 8-16; the 4th row). Therefore, the received $\Delta\theta$ is regenerated as follows:

$$\Delta\theta = \theta_1 - \theta_0 = \quad 45° - \quad 0° = \quad 45° \quad \rightarrow \quad (b_o, b_e) = 00$$
$$\Delta\theta = \theta_2 - \theta_1 = \quad 0° - \quad 45° = \quad -45° \quad \rightarrow \quad (b_o, b_e) = 10$$
$$\Delta\theta = \theta_3 - \theta_2 = 135° - \quad 0° = \quad 135° \quad \rightarrow \quad (b_o, b_e) = 01$$
$$\Delta\theta = \theta_4 - \theta_3 = 180° - 135° = \quad 45° \quad \rightarrow \quad (b_o, b_e) = 00$$
$$\Delta\theta = \theta_5 - \theta_4 = \quad 45° - 180° = -135° \quad \rightarrow \quad (b_o, b_e) = 11$$

Where θ_0 is the estimated (reference) phase; θ_1 is the phase of the first received signal; θ_2 is the phase of the second received signal, etc. Taking the difference of θ_1 and θ_0, the phase change, $\Delta\theta$, of the first 2-bit group can be derived as 45°; taking the difference of θ_2 and θ_1, the phase change, $\Delta\theta$, of the second 2-bit group can be derived as −45°, etc. Therefore, by using Table 8-16, it can be found that a $\Delta\theta$ of 45° represents a pair of (00). By applying the same procedure, it can be seen that the received signal has been restored to the original data stream: 0010010011 … .

Table 8-16   Digital Signal, $\Delta\theta$, θ at the Transceiver of a DPSK System.

Digital pair (b_o, b_e)		00	10	01	00	11	…
$\Delta\theta$: at transmitter		45°	−45°	135°	45°	−135°	…
θ: transceiver	0°*	45°	0°	135°	180°	45°	…
$\Delta\theta$: at receiver		45°	−45°	135°	45°	−135°	…
Restored pair		00	10	01	00	11	…

* The initial phase (via phase estimation) is assumed to be 0°.

8.6.4 Minimum Shift Keying (MSK) for GSM

The modulation technology used for GSM (another TDMA protocol) is Minimum Shift Keying (MSK), which can be considered a modified form of Phase Shift Keying (PSK) or Frequency Shift Keying (FSK) modulation.

The principle of MSK modulation is similar to the π/4-DQPSK technique previously discussed. Example 8-12 provides a detailed explanation of MSK modulation.

Example 8-12: Describe the MSK signal phases that are transmitted, and how the received MSK signal is restored as the original digital data stream (01011101010 …). The MSK signal has the sinusoidal waveform: A cos ($\omega_c t + \theta$). The receiver must periodically estimate the received signal phase. The actual phases used at the transmitter (and restored at the receiver) are obtained using the same approach as in π/4-DQPSK systems.

The phase changes ($\Delta\theta$'s) can be obtained by using the GSM standard's requirement shown in Figure 8-47. That is, for a logical "1", $\Delta\theta$ is assigned to be −90°; and for a logical "0", $\Delta\theta$ is assigned to be 90° (as shown in the 2nd row in Table 8-17). For simplicity, the system is assumed to have an initial phase (i.e., estimated or reference phase) of 0°. The phases of the transmitted MSK signal can be calculated as follows:

$$\theta_1 = 0° + \Delta\theta = 0° + 90° = 90°; \qquad \theta_2 = 90° + \Delta\theta = 90° - 90° = 0°;$$
$$\theta_3 = 0° + \Delta\theta = 0° + 90° = 90°; \qquad \theta_4 = 90° + \Delta\theta = 90° - 90° = 90° \quad …$$

Assuming the received MSK signal is error free, the received signal's phases are identical to those transmitted, as shown in Table 8-17. Therefore, based on the received phase changes (which can be derived by using the same procedure used in Example 8-8), the received signal can be restored as the original digital data stream.

The question is often asked: "Why is this modulation technique called minimum shift keying?" The top graph in Figure 8-47 shows the phase diagram (response) of the transmitted signal for Example 8-9. Note that the slope of the phase response results in the frequency response of the signal as shown in the bottom graph of Figure 8-47. It can be seen that there are only two values in the frequency response, Δf and $-\Delta f$. To be able to "*shift*" a signal requires *at minimum* of two different values. This modulation scheme can shift from Δf to $-\Delta f$; or from $-\Delta f$ to Δf. Therefore, the modulation technique described here is named "*Minimum*" Shift Keying (MSK). This method is also considered a phase modulation or a frequency modulation technique (see Table 6-5 in Chapter 6).

Table 8-17   Digital Signal, $\Delta\theta$, θ at the Transceiver of an MSK System.

Digital bit		0	1	0	1	1	...
$\Delta\theta$: at transmitter		90°	−90°	90°	−90°	−90°	...
θ: transceiver	0°*	90°	0°	90°	0°	−90°	...
$\Delta\theta$: at receiver		90°	−90°	90°	−90°	−90°	...
Restored bit		0	1	0	1	1	...

- The initial phase (via phase estimation) is assumed to be 0°.

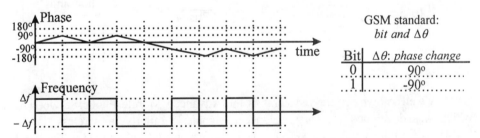

Figure 8-47   The Phase and the Frequency Diagram for Example 8-12.

8.7 PERSONAL COMMUNIATION SERVICE (PCS)

The telecommunications industry first deployed wireless technology (airway) for transmission in dispatch radio business applications during the mid-1930s. These applications were limited, and there were very few users (a total of approximately 3,000 users in the US). Marine radio, one of the few wireless communications applications, was developed in the early 1940s. Consumers, rather than business users, were the major subscribers of marine radio wireless services. Radio paging services were introduced in the mid 1950s, and was accepted by both business users and consumers. The number of users subscribing to radio paging services gradually increased from several thousand to hundreds of thousands. Analog cordless, which evolved into digital cordless, was developed in the early 1970s and was implemented using FM technology. Analog cellular, using Frequency Division Multiple Access (FDMA) methods for airway multiplexing, was introduced in the early 1980s.

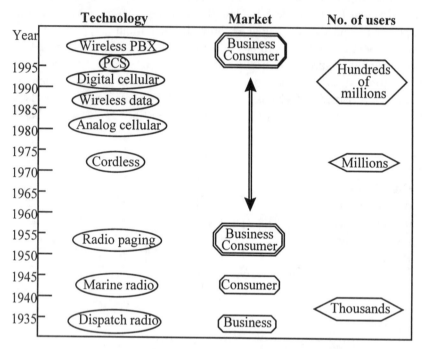

Figure 8-48   Wireless Technology Evolution.

A well known wireless systems is the Advanced Mobile Phone Service (AMPS), which was developed for carrying speech signals. Similarly, a wireless data system known as Cellular Digital Packet Data (CDPD) was initially deployed in the late 1980s. Digital cellular services began applying Time Division Multiple access (TDMA) technology in the late 1980s, and evolved to Code Division Multiple Access (CDMA) by the early 1990s. As a result of these developments, three major standards have been adopted for digital cellular communications: IS-54 (evolving into IS-136, a TDMA-based standard), GSM (a TDMA-based standard), and IS-95 (a CDMA-based standard).

The characteristics of different wireless services are illustrated in Figure 8-48. These technologies can be classified into two groups: (1) Well-established services (dispatch and marine radio, radio paging, cordless phone, and analog/digital cellular phones); and, (2) Emerging services [PCS, wireless PBX, fixed wireless (airloop), Wireless Local Loop (WLL), wireless LANs, Wireless In-building Network (WIN), and optical wireless].

Since the early 1980s, customers demand for various wireless services have led to the broad development of cellular-based services. In addition to wireless capabilities, service providers must allow easy access to the network that connects the user to a desired destination. The basic concept of *"service should also be available anywhere and anytime, with a constantly increasing variety of features"* is rapidly becoming a reality in evolving networks.

There are two areas of general customer (end user) interest:

- **Voice services**: Users require excellent call quality, and good customer support.

- **Image/data services**: These services must be reliable, innovative, feature-rich, and easy to apply.

In addition to enhanced services, customers are also demanding "one-stop shopping" for their communications needs. Likewise, the cost of the services must be relatively low for local calls and roaming. As a result, it is expected that PCS price competition will be fierce. Therefore, PCS service providers must develop "strategic plans" for both marketing and deploying new services and technologies.

8.7.1 Provider Strategic Planning

Since strong competition in the PCS market is expected, PCS service providers must initiate strategic planning in the following areas:

- **Types of services**: PCS services should include voice, data, and/or mobile fax.

- **Types of technology**: PCS technologies can be classified as: (1) cellular-based Time Division Multiple Access (TDMA), (2) cellular-based Code Division Multiple Access (CDMA)], (3) cordless-based, (4) or new technology.

- **Network evolution:** building/expanding the backbone (backhaul) networks.

- **Infrastructure availability**: Meeting "market windows" and satisfying "customer needs" for both new services and increased capacity.

A wide range of enhanced PCS voice services may need to be implemented for both residential and business applications. Likewise, PCS data services may include message applications*, short message services*, in-home health monitoring**, medical alert systems**, home security systems**, child locators**, and telemetry*.

....

Note:

- *Services marked with a "*" indicate data services most likely required by the users at deployment time*

- Services marked with a "**" are potential PCS data services offerings that may be requested by users in the future.

8.7.1.1 Selecting Right PCS Technology

"*Business and customer requirements*" are the driving force for PCS technology. The three major technologies available are: TDMA (IS-136); TDMA (GSM); and CDMA. Factors that a service provider should consider include:

- **Technology capability**

  * What are the system capacity limits?
  * What features are available to the end-users?
  * How good is the voice quality?
  * What is the speed and accuracy of data transport?
  * How soon is the service available for deployment?

- **Interoperability**

  * Can the system inter-operate with cellular networks that are currently deployed and "in service"?
  * Can the system inter-operate with PCS system provided by other vendors?

- **Product availability** (the most critical issue for PCS service providers):

  * What is the interval between placing an order and "turn-over" of a fully operational system?
  * What is the estimated "life span" of the system?
  * Is there a planned upgrade/enhancement program to extend the "life span" of the system?

- **Cost**

  * What is the initial cost for deploying the system?
  * What are the estimated costs for OA&M and upgrading the system?
  * How is the initial investment protected against obsolescence?

If "technical capability" is chosen over "time-to-market", CDMA has many advantages compared to other technologies. In addition, it is important that a PCS service provider select a *widely-accepted standard;* rather than the "**best**" technology because costs, availability, and time to deployment are critical aspects of the PCS business.

8.7.1.2 Building Back Haul Networks

Building a back haul network, including interworking, is a major cost for PCS service providers. A PCS service provider can realize a competitive cost advantage (in-region) for PCS versus the competition, in the areas where traditional wireline facilities and cellular communications services already exist. However, in new areas, PCS business considerations must include:

* What is the cost of initial system deployment?

* What are the estimated costs for OA&M and upgrading the system?

* Is there a planned upgrade/enhancement program to extend the "life span" of the system?

The network architecture can be a "daisy chain", star, or ring topology. Service providers can lease networks from other vendors, or build their own networks (preferably microwave link based networks). The metropolitan back haul network in North America is typically built using T1 digital carrier systems. For rural application, the back haul network is usually a combination of T1 digital carrier, optical fiber, and microwave radio systems. Figure 8-49 illustrates a high level view of an end-to-end connection via a back haul network, which serves both wire and wireless subscribers.

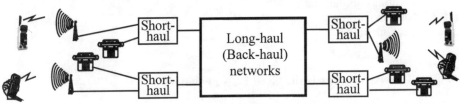

Figure 8-49   An End-to-End Connection.

8.7.1.3 PCS Technical Challenges

Time to market: This is a major concern for all PCS operators, and is also a technical challenge. Rapid deployment of PCS network that meet both current and future customer needs presents a fundamental problem. Availability of "state of art" equipment implies risk and uncertainty. Likewise, deploying mature technology may result in obsolescence.

Obtaining sites: The PCS service provider must initially design for "portable coverage". It will take too long to evolve an existing cellular network to portable coverage. Coverage that is too much or too small can be a competitive disadvantage. Hence, coverage areas must be carefully selected. The costs of PCS sites "built from scratch" (site acquisition and construction) is huge, and can exceed equipment costs. Typically, site acquisition, zoning, design, and construction take six months or more. Therefore, utilizing existing facilities or cost sharing is critical to a successful PCS business.

Clearing the spectrum: The spectrum assigned for PCS communications includes some existing microwave links (that may particularly be true in countries outside the US; and this presents a problem) that may interfere with PCS radio transmission. These microwave links must be relocated. Link relocation depends upon microwave congestion and PCS interference experienced by fixed microwave receivers. Since the majority of microwave paths are likely to be affected by multiple PCS providers, it is possible that microwave relocation costs may be shared by several different service providers.

There are many tasks associated with "microwave spectrum clearing". It may start by negotiations with an existing microwave link owner. Various studies of proposed relocations must be made. These activities can take up to 6 months. Engineering studies, frequency coordination, licensing, ordering, and installing equipment are other aspects of radio link relocation that can take 10 months to a year to complete. The PCS industry has planned for radio link relocation in several phases. That is,

Spectrum clearing will be implemented in 2.5 MHz by 2.5 MHz blocks.

The existing microwave spectrum, which has been allocated for PCS, is occupied by the following businesses:

- Public safety agencies
- Utilities companies
- Railroad industry
- Oil companies

8.7.1.4 Licensed versus Unlicensed PCS Providers

The policies for spectrum clearing depend upon the type of PCS providers. There are *two types of PCS service providers*:

- **Licensed PCS provider**: Microwave users will vacate their spectrum within one to three years. Public safety agencies will take a longer time to vacate their spectrum (i.e. up to five years). In the beginning, PCS licensees will share the spectrum with existing spectrum users, and will pay relocation costs. If the negotiation of relocation fails, the PCS licensee can apply to the FCC for mandatory relocation of existing users to higher frequencies.

- **Unlicensed PCS provider**: In some cases it is not practical to share the spectrum between PCS service providers and existing radio link users. The UTAM (Unlicensed PCS Ad-Hoc Committee for 2 GHz microwave transition and management) is preparing a plan to relocate the spectrum for this service. The costs of relocation will be paid by equipment manufactures.

The following list contains useful steps that may help expedite microwave link relocation by the PCS service providers:

* Apply sophisticated frequency monitoring methods so that spectrum sharing can be implemented effectively, prior to complete relocation of existing microwave radio links.

* Use "frequency agile" radio equipment so that an unassigned frequency can be quickly assigned for another application.

* Apply dynamic channel assignment for allocating channels between the PCS users and existing microwave radio users.

* Use all available bandwidth efficiently (i.e. do not allow any free spectrum to exist at any time).

8.7.2 PCS Attributes and Service Application Types

The key attribute of a PCS system is *"the ability to accommodate mobility of all the intended users."* PCS requires two tiers of services: "high-tier" and "low-tier".

The "high-tier" PCS services can be considered *an extension of traditional cellular services (i.e. downgrading from cellular services to PCS)*. Therefore, "high-tier" PCS service provides more features than "low-tier" PCS service. The terminal mobility for "high-tier" PCS service is expected to be equivalent to traditional cellular services. The coverage area is a broad geographical region, and user mobility can be at any speed. The "high-tier" PCS service provides:

* Roaming
* Call delivery
* Call forwarding
* Three-way calling
* Caller ID
* Speed dialing

Table 8-18   PCS Two Tiers of Services.

Parameter	High-tier service	Low-tier service
Service offering	*Enhanced cellular*	*Limited*
Convenience mobility	*Fully*	*Limited*
Speed mobility	*Vehicle/Pedestrian*	*Pedestrian*
Coverage area	*Broad (macrocells)*	*Short-range (microcells)*

In contrast, a "low-tier" PCS service can be considered *an extension of cordless phone services*. That is, PCS is *an upgrade from traditional cordless service*. The speed mobility for "low-tier" PCS service is limited to pedestrian (i.e. walking) speed, and the coverage area is relatively small. Likewise, "low-tier" PCS features are limited. For example, users may have limited accessibility (or no access at all) to information services, and may not have caller ID. Table 8-18 provides a summary of the operational characteristics of "high tier" and "low tier" PCS services. The technical differences between low-tier and high-tier PCS are as follows:

* Mobility management: There is no mobility management for the low-tier PCS services. However, high-tier PCS services provide full mobility management.

- Power control: The power control for low-tier PCS services is not an issue because of the limited mobility of low-tier services. For high-tier PCS service, a sophisticated dynamic power control is required (i.e. similar to cellular services).

- Feature transparency: High-tier PCS users are able to subscribe to all the service features that traditional cellular users can obtain. The low-tier PCS users are charged at a rate equivalent to cordless phone services, and obtain slightly upgraded capabilities (compared to cordless services).

- Handoffs: Handoff, roaming, and call delivery are available for high-tier PCS services. They are not provided (or required) for low-tier subscribers.

8.7.3 Seven Potential PCS Standards

There are seven potential PCS standards that can be applied to PCS services throughout the world. Eventually service quality and customer satisfaction will determine the "best" standard(s). Three or four standards may outweigh the others, and consequently spread these applications into territories that other technologies previously occupied. Tables 8-20 and 8-21 list seven potential PCS standards, the associated TAG (Technical Ad-hoc Group organized by the Joint Technical Committee), the service tier each standard is designed for, the technology each standard uses, notes, bandwidth requirement, frequency reuse factor, cell type, and vocoder used for each standard.

Table 8-19   Seven Potential PCS Standards.

PCS standard	TAG	Service tier	Technology (based)	Note
IS-95	2	High	CDMA/FDD	US CDMA-based
PCS1900	5	High	TDMA/FDD	GSM-based
IS-136	4	High	TDMA/FDD	US TDMA-based
PACS	3	Low	TDMA/FDD, TDD	TR1313-based
DCT-U	6	Low	TDMA/TDD	DECT-based
PCS2000	1	High	CDMA/TDMA/TDD	Omnipoint
W-CDMA	7	High	CDMA/FDD	Wideband

Table 8-20   Seven Potential PCS Standards (cont.).

PCS standard	Bandwidth (MHz)	Frequency reuse factor/cell type	Vocoder	
IS-95	1.25	1/omni	QCELP	(8/13.3 kbps)
PCS1900	0.200	7/omni or 3/3-sector	RPE-LTP	(13 kbps)
IS-136	0.030	7/omni or 3/3-sector	VSELP	(8 kbps)
PACS	0.300	16/3-sector	ADPCM	(32 kbps)
DCT-U	1.728	9/omni	ADPCM	(32 kbps)
PCS2000	5	3/omni	PCS HC ADPCM PCM	(8 kbps), (32 kbps), or (64 kbps)
W-CDMA	5, 10 or 15	1/omni	ADPCM	(32 kbps)

8.7.4 Service Providers and Systems Selected

Potential PCS service providers include inter-exchange carrier companies (e.g., IXCs; AT&T, MCI, Sprint); local exchange carriers (e.g., LECs; NYNEX, Bell South, Bell Atlantic, etc.); existing cellular licensees; competitive access providers; cable TV providers; and PCS entrepreneurs. Potential PCS equipment vendors include Lucent Technologies, Hitachi, NEC, Sony, Siemens, Casio, Nokia, Nortel, Motorola, Ericsson, and others.

Table 8-21 lists the systems (standards) selected by the top 10 MTA (Major Trading Area) service providers. It should be noted that some of the seven potential systems (standards) have not yet been adopted by any service providers.

Table 8-21 Systems Selected by Top 10 MTA Service Providers.

System/standard	Service Provider
IS-95 based	* *Wireless Co. (now STV)* * *PCS Prime Co.* * *Phillie Co.*
PCS1900 (GSM)	* *Pacific Telesis Mobile Services* * *BellSouth Personal Communications* * *American Personal Communications*
IS-136 based	* *AT&T Wireless PCS*
PACS	* *Not yet selected*
DECT	* *Not yet selected*
PCS2000 (Now, IS-661)	* *Omnipoint*
W-CDMA	* *Not yet selected*

8.7.5 Cellular Technology and PCS

As an introduction for cellular-based PCS technology, this section briefly describes the existing cellular communications network (see Figure 8-50). The three cellular system components and their functions are described as follows:

1. **Mobile-service Switching Center** (MSC): A mobile-service switching center interconnects the cellular system with the public switched telephone network (PSTN). In addition to performing all of the typical call-related functions of a telephone end office, an MSC is also involved with switching calls between different Base Stations (BSs), in real time, as the Mobile Station (MS) moves from the coverage area of one BS (cell area) to another. This is known as **a call handoff**, while the mobile unit is executing "roaming". It also performs a paging function to support call delivery, since the system usually does not know which cell area the mobile station is located in when a call enters the network. After the mobile unit has responded to the paging, and the connection has been complete, call delivery can be executed.

2. **Base Station** (BS): This is the point at which the Mobile Station (e.g., the MS is usually a portable phone) interconnects with the cellular network. The BS contains the radio equipment, and usually manages radio channel resources. A BS typically performs speech encoding, channel encoding, bit-interleaving, encryption, and multiplexing functions.

3. **Mobile Station** (MS): The Mobile Station (e.g., a portable phone) is the end-user's interface to the network. It is an intelligent personal telecommunications terminal with a two-way radio that can access the network on a demand basis.

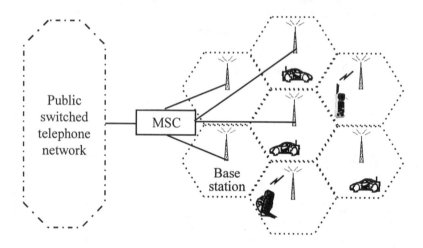

Figure 8-50   Cellular Network: MSC, BS and MS.

An interesting attribute of a cellular system is that it grows almost indefinitely by continuously reusing radio frequencies. As the need for services increases, the radio frequencies are re-used many times within small cell areas. This allows the deployment of many users throughout an area, even though there is a limit to the number of unique radio channels that are available (e.g., in the 800-900 MHz cellular band, only 416 radio channels are available for subscribers and control channels). Digital transmission provides improved security and information privacy, and supports new services. Cellular networks can be interconnected, support automatic roaming, call delivery, and intersystem handoff. Cellular-based PCS applications have several advantages and disadvantages:

- **Cellular technology advantages**: Cellular technology has the largest capacity (compared to other wireless systems). It is suitable for both metropolitan and rural area applications (the coverage area in a metropolitan region can be ≥ 0.5 mile, for rural region, the coverage area can be up to 10 miles). Cellular technology applies frequency reuse to increase capacity in a populated areas. The system uses a high power, thus it is easier to achieve power budgeting. [i.e., a required S/N (Signal-to-Noise) ratio can be implemented easier]. Cellular communications have adopted nation-wide standards, which makes inter-operating between different vendor's systems easier and less expensive (e.g., handoff is also easier). Roaming and call delivery features are available to the users.

- **Cellular technology disadvantages**: Security for an analog cellular network is not easy to implement. In general, cellular services have a high fixed service charge and high "air-time" charges.

Table 8-22 summarizes the cellular technology evolution. The first column lists the various cellular systems that have been adopted for cellular communications. The second column indicates whether the speech signal is an analog or digital signal, and the corresponding cellular frequency in MHz (800, 900 or 450 MHz). The third column indicates the multiple access method: FDMA, TDMA(+FDMA), or CDMA. The geographic location of the initial service offering, and the capacity comparison is also shown in the third column.

Table 8-22   Cellular Technology Evolution.

System	Speech/Freq. (A or D*)/(MHz)	Notes
AMPS	A/800	* FDMA * North America & South America
NAMPS	A/800	* Capacity = 3 × APMS' capacity * FDMA * Motorola * Las Vegas [1992, Centel]
TACS	A/900	* FDMA * U.K. & Hong-Kong
NMT	A/450 or 900	* FDMA * Scandinavia
NTT/JTACS	A/800	* FDMA * Japan
IS-54	D/800	* TDMA/FDMA** * EIA/TIA TR45.3, approved 1990 * First service: 1992 * Evolved to IS-136: 1994 * Capacity = 3 × AMPS' capacity % * E-TDMA: Hughes * Capacity = 6 × AMPS' capacity
GSM	D/900	* TDMA/FDMA * ETSI: 1989 * First service: 1991 * Capacity = 2 x AMPS' capacity %
IS-95	D/800	* CDMA * EIA/TIA TR45.5, approved 1993 * Capacity = (10 ~ 15) × AMPS' %

A/D: Analog or digital;   **: TDMA+FDMA;   %: Doubled in the near future

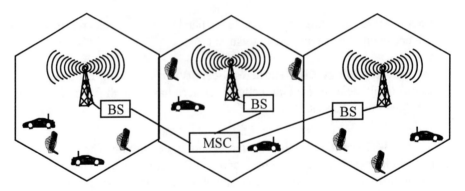

Figure 8-51   Cellular-Based PCS Applications.

One question that continues to be debated is: "**Can cellular technology be used for PCS**?" Some experts answer "**yes**", while other experts answer "**no**". The reasoning behind each answer is given as follows:

- **Yes, cellular technology can be applied to PCS:**

Cellular technology will apply advanced digital technology to implement service privacy and security. It will also provide consistent speech quality. Handoff and roaming features can be easily implemented. Call delivery will be available at least nationwide, and will be available globally in the near future. Handsets are becoming less expensive, smaller, and lighter. Handsets can be transported in automobiles and as handheld luggage, with transmit power as low as 0.6 ~ 3 watts. Cell size will become smaller as capacity requirements increase.

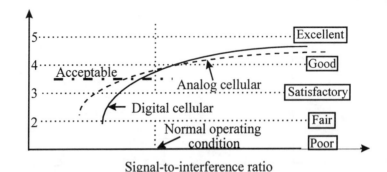

Signal-to-interference ratio

Figure 8-52   Speech Quality for Analog and Digital Cellular Services.

*Microcells are suitable for many reasons: more users per unit area (such as in a city), smaller and lighter handsets will result from the smaller cell size, and microcells can/will "**overlay**" the normal cells in areas with dense population. Therefore, cellular* *technology will be "scaled down" for PCS to provide new capabilities and service features. Figure 8-51 shows a network architecture for a proposed cellular-based PCS applications. This cellular-based PCS technology will add new capabilities and new services to PCS. Handoff capability is definitely a benefit for this technology, and microcells can support coverage up to 2000 ft (as needed).*

- **No, cellular technology will not be applied for PCS**:

Landline "toll speech quality" is not available for cellular communications because of the high degree of speech compression used in the cellular networks. Digital speech quality for cellular technology is not always better than analog cellular speech quality as shown in Figure 8-52. Speech quality is classified into five grades: excellent, good, satisfactory, fair, and poor. For wireless services, a grade of at least 3.5 is required to be acceptable. Under normal operating conditions, both analog and digital cellular services will meet the required speech quality. However, if operating conditions degrade (i.e., S/I ratio is worse), the analog cellular speech quality gracefully degrades, but this is not true for the digital cellular speech quality (see Figure 8-52).

Cellular base station equipment is expensive, which precludes using very small cells (i.e. microcells). Consequently the technology doesn't allow small, low-powered, light weight, and inexpensive handsets needed for PCS applications.

The first commercial available PCS was introduced by Southwestern Bell Mobile Systems and the Panasonic Communications and Systems Co. on March 30, 1993. The system used the existing 800 MHz cellular spectrum. It provided service for wireless business systems, with a flat rate charge of $10~$25 per month for in-building services. The system served fifty-four (54) Southwestern Bell and Cellular-one markets. The handset weight was approximately 8.5 oz, and the system also supported typical cellular services for outdoor applications.

Another PCS-type service, Mercury "One-2-One" PCN (Personal-to-personal Communications Network), was introduced in September, 1993 by Mercury (a joint venture between US West and Cable & Wireless). This system covered London within the M25 Motorway perimeter. It has been extended to Southeast England, and is expected to cover 99% of the UK population by the end of the year 1999. This system uses DCS1800 technology (based on GSM), and allocates 50 MHz of clear spectrum at 1800 MHz. This system offers smart cards, known as Subscriber Identity Modules (SIMs), so that multiple users can share the same equipment (phone). The services available from this system include: basic calls, voice mail, call forwarding, and others. Local calls during "off peak" hours and weekends are free. Fees for personal use are $18.75 (and up)/month depending on the different services subscribed, and business use is $35 (and up)/month.

Three standards (out of seven potential PCS standards) have been proposed for cellular technology: IS-95-based, PCS1900 and IS-136-based (see Table 8-19). Table 8-

23 summarizes the comparison of cellular, microcell cellular, and PCS technologies. The fist column lists the characteristics (speech quality, mobility, cell radius, service security, coverage area, radio port size, and handset transmission power). The remaining columns list the corresponding attributes for the three standards.

Table 8-23   Cellular, Microcell Cellular and PCS Comparison.

Characteristic	Cellular (current)	Cellular (microcell)	PCS
Speech quality	* Adequate * Not landline quality	* Adequate * Not landline quality	* Landline quality – Toll quality – Business quality
Mobility	* Vehicular	* Pedestrian	* Vehicular * Pedestrian
Cell radius	* ≤ 10 miles	* ≤ 2000 ft	* ≤ 2000 ft
Security	* Vulnerable * Encryption	* Vulnerable * Encryption	* Landline security encryption
Coverage	* > 90%	* > 99%	* > 99%
Radio port size	* Small building; (3000 ft³)	* Breadbox (10 ft³)	* Breadbox
Handset trans. Power	* 600 mw for portable	* 600 mw for portable	* ≤ 200 mw

8.8 3G WIRELESS MOBILE COMMUNICATIONS

As previously mentioned in this chapter, the cellular communication era started with the introduction of the Advanced Mobile Phone Service (AMPS). Since the late 1970s, wireless services have grown rapidly. As in the case of landline technologies, wireless technologies originated as analog services and evolved into digital services (e.g., from FDMA to TDMA, and then CDMA). Table 8-24 summarizes the historical milestones for wireless services milestones.

As the technologies advance, it is common practice to classify various stages of development into "generations". For wireless technologies, the industry has adopted the following groupings:

- *The first generation*: The first generation wireless services applied analog-based technologies. There were several technologies used in this era throughout the world: (1) US, Canada, Austria, S. Korea, Brazil, Taiwan, Thailand, and Mexico (using AMPS and NAMPS technologies); (2) UK & China (using TACS technology); (3) Japan (using J-TACS and N-TACS technologies); (4) Italy (using RTMS technology); (5) Germany (using C-Netz technology); (6) Sweden, Finland, Norway, and Denmark (using NMT technology); and (7) France (using NMT and RC2000 technologies).

- *The second generation*: The second generation wireless services applied digital-based technologies. The technologies used in this era are: (1) US, Canada, Mexico, and Hong-Kong (using IS-136 TDMA); (2) UK, Germany, and Australia [using GSM TDMA, and CDMA (IS-95)].

- *The third generation (3G)*: The third generation wireless technologies are being planned for global applications by vendors and wireless service providers to support the ITU's International Mobile Telecommunications-2000 (IMT-2000) standards.

Table 8-24   Wireless Services Historical Milestones.

Year(s)	Service events
1920's	The first mobile radio units installed in police vehicles (Detroit & NY)
1930s/40's	Mobile radio adopted frequency modulation technique
1946	The first commercial mobile telephone service introduced (St. Louis)
1947	Cellular concept proposed by Bell Laboratories for mobile telephone
1950's	VHF and UHF bands adopted for mobile radio systems
1964	Mobile Telephone Service (MTS) with automatic dialing introduced
1969	Improved MTS (IMTS) introduced
1974	FCC allocated 40 MHz (800 MHz band) for mobile communications
1975-78	A full scale cellular system (approved by FCC in 1977), Advanced MPS (AMPS) was operational in 1978
1980	FCC created two "new" 20 MHz allocations (wireline and non-wireline)
1980's/90's	TDMA (IS-54/136 and GSM), CDMA (IS-95) and PCS introduced

Definition 8-4 (cdmaOne/cdma2000): cdmaOne is a term used for the family of standards and products based on IS-95 technology. It include cellular, PCS, and Wireless Local Loop (WLL, fixed wireless and airloop). The term is used for marketing the IS-95 technology. The term "cdmaOne" is a registered trademark of CDMA Development Group (CDG). The term "cdma2000" is the name/logo applied to the 3G evolution of cdmaOne. The major 3G technologies are summarized as follows:

- cdma2000: It is a wideband-CDMA based technology. It provides backward network and service compatibility with cdmaOne (IS-95). The original bandwidth requirement is 3.75 MHz. Other associated parameters (e.g. bit rate) have not been be finalized.

- W-CDMA: It is supported by European Telecommunications Standard Institute (ETSI) and NTT of Japan. It is a wideband-CDMA based technology. It provides backward network and service compatibility with GSM. The present bandwidth requirement is 5 MHz.

- UWC-136 (Universal Wireless Communications) or IS-136 High-Speed (HS): It is a TDMA based technology. It provides backward network and service compatibility with IS-136. The present bandwidth requirements are 30 kHz for IS-136 services, 200 kHz for IS-136 HS outdoor/vehicular services, and 1.6 MHz for IS-136 HS indoor services.

8.8.1 IMT-2000 (International Mobile Telecommunications-2000)

The motivation for developing IMT-2000 is the need for new high bit rate wireless services: wireless multimedia, intranet, internet, high quality speech, and videoconferencing. In addition, it is expected that the capacity for speech services will be doubled with the introduction of new service capabilities and features.

Definition 8-5 (a direct quote from ITU ***IMT-2000***; ***http://www.itu.int/imt***):

"IMT-2000 is an initiative of the ITU. It will provide wireless access to the global telecommunication infrastructure through both satellite and terrestrial systems, serving fixed and mobile users in public and private networks.

It is being developed on the basis of a 'family of systems' concept, defined as a federation of systems providing IMT-2000 service capabilities to users of all family members in a global roaming offering.

The ITU vision of global wireless access in the 21st century, including mobile and fixed access, IMT is aimed at providing direction to the many related technological developments in this area to assist the convergence of these essentially competing wireless access technologies. "

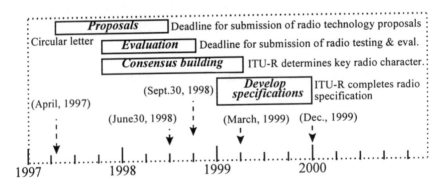

Figure 8-53   IMT-2000 Key Activities.

- IMT-2000 activities: The key activities are illustrated in Figure 8-53. This includes the **proposals** (The original circular letter was issued April 4, 1997, and, all radio technology proposals were submitted on June 30, 1998), **evaluation** [Radio testing and EVALuation (REVAL) was submitted before Sept. 30, 1998], **consensus building** [the deadline for ITU-R to complete (determine) key radio characteristics is March, 1999], and **specifications development** (ITU-R radio specifications are due by Dec., 1999).

- IMT-2000 radio rec.: The following is a list of applicable recommendations associated with TMT-2000 radio.

*	M.687-2	Future Public Land Mobile Telecommunications Systems (FPLMTS)
*	M.816	Framework for services supported on FPLMTS
*	M.817	FPLMTS network architecture
*	M.818-1	Satellite operations within FPLMTS
*	M.819-2	FPLMST for developing countries
*	M.1034-1	Requirements for the radio interfaces
*	M.1035	Framework for the radio interfaces and radio sub-system functionality
*	M.1078	Security principles
*	M.1079	Speech and voice band data performance requirements
*	M.1167	Framework for satellite component of FPLMTS
*	M.1168	Framework of FPLMTS management
*	M.1223	Evaluation of security mechanisms
*	M.1224	Vocabulary of terms
*	M.1225	Guidelines for evaluation of Radio Transmission Technologies (RTT) for IMT-2000 (REVAL)

- IMT-2000 standard organizations: Here is a list of prominent organizations.

*	ITU-T	International Telecomm Union - Telecomm Standardization sector
*	ITU-R	International Telecomm Union - Radiocomm Standardization sector
*	ETSI	European Telecomm Standards Institute
*	SMG2	ETSI Special Mobile Group 2 (includes 3G standards)
*	EC	European Commission
*	ANSI	American National Standards Institution
*	T1	ANSI Telecomm Standards Committee
*	TIA	Telecomm Industry Association
*	ATIS	Alliance for Telecomm Industry Solutions
*	TR-45	TIA Committee for Mobile and Personal Comm at 800 MHz
*	TR-46	TIA Committee for Mobile and Personal Comm at 1800 MHz
*	ARIB	Association of Radio Industries and Business (Japan)
*	TTA	Telecomm Technology Association (Korea)

- IMT-2000 data rates: The proposed *minimum* IMT data rates are (1) 2.048 Mbps for indoor/office/home applications; (2) 384 kbps for local area applications; (3) 144 kbps for regional applications; and (4) 9.6 kbps for global applications. Note that higher data bit rates are required for microcells/picocells, and this high bit rate service requires higher handset power.

- Universal Mobile Telecommunications Systems/services (UMTS) and UMTS Forum: UMTS is the European designation for IMT-2000 proposals, which are based on contributions and collaborative work among several European countries. The UMTS Forum [Forum is formed by telecommunications service providers, manufacturers, and governmental organizations (countries from Europe and other regions)], is an industry association for defining and promoting UMTS.

8.8.2 IMT-2000 Radio Transmission Technology (RTT)

There are many RTT proposals to ITU: (1) 10 terrestrial RTT proposals (**7** wideband CDMA, from 1 MHz to 20 MHz; **1** wideband TDMA/CDMA, 1.2 MHz; **1** wideband TDMA, 30 kHz, 200 kHz and 1.6 MHz; and **1** wideband TDMA, 1.728 MHz); and (2) 5 satellite RRT proposals. These proposals are summarized in Table 8-25.

Table 8-25   IMT-2000 RTT Proposals to ITU

Proposal	Description	Environment	Source
UTRA:W-CDMA	UMTS terrestrial radio access	I/P/V#	ETSI SMG2
DECT	Digital enhanced cordless Telecomm TDMA	I/P #	ETSI DECT
W-CDMA/NA	North American wideband CDMA	I/P/V#	T1P1-ATIS
cdma2000	Wideband CDMA (IS-95)	I/P/V#	TIA TR45.5
WIMS W-CDMA	Wireless multimedia and messaging services	I/P/V#	TIA TR46.1
UWC-136	Universal wireless communications TDMA	I/P/V#	TIA TR45.3
TD-SCDMA	Time-division synchronous CDMA	I/P/V#	CATT
W-CDMA	Wideband CDMA	I/P/V#	Japan ARIB
CDMA II	Asynchronous DS-CDMA	I/P/V#	S Korea TTA
CDMA I	Multi-band synchronous DS-CDMA	I/P/V#	S Korea TTA
SW-CDMA	Satellite wideband CDMA	S#	ESA
SW-CTDMA	Satellite wideband hybrid CDMA/TDMA	S#	ESA
SAT-CDMA	49 LEO satellites in 7 planes at 2000 km	S#	S Korea TTA
ICO RTT	10 MEO satellites in 2 planes at 10,390 km	S#	ICO GC
Horizons	Horizons satellite system	S#	Inmarsat

I/P/V/S: Indoor/Pedestrian/Vehicular/Satellite;   CATT: China Academy of Telecommunication Technology
MEO: Medium Earth orbit;   LEO: Low Earth orbit;   ICO: Independent company;   ESA: European Space Administrator

The 3G radio technologies listed in Table 8-25 can be grouped into three categories as follows:

(1) <u>European region 3G RTT proposals</u>: There are two major proposals that apply to European and some other regions. These proposals and characteristics are described as follows.

* W-CDMA was adopted by the ETSI as the UMTS Terrestrial Radio Access (UTRA) technology.

* W-CDMA is based on a compromise that is a combination of W-CDMA and TDMA options.

* W-CDMA is backward compatible with GSM core networks.

* W-CDMA is supported by worldwide GSM carriers, NTT of Japan, and many Asian carriers.

* W-CDMA has a bandwidth of 4.8 MHz or higher.

(2) <u>North American 3G RTT proposals</u>: There are four major proposals that apply to North America. These proposals and their characteristics are described as follows.

* W-CDMA/NA: North America wideband-CDMA is based on IS-95 (cdmaOne evolving to wideband). This effort is led by TIA TR45.5 and CDMA Development Group (CDG).

* cdma2000: This is a GSM based (PCS1900 evolving to wideband) technology. This effort is led by ATIS T1P1.5 (PCS1900) in North America, and ETSI and GSM carriers worldwide. It is supported by the PCS1900 carriers in the US.

* WIMS W-CDMA: Wireless Integrated Multimedia and messaging Services (WIMS) is a wideband-CDMA technology, proposed by TIA TR46.1. It is supported by several carriers in the US.

* UWC-136: This is a IS-136 based proposal that includes IS-136 high speed services. It was developed by the Universal Wireless Communications Consortium (UWCC) and TIA TR 45.3. This technology is supported by several carriers in the US.

(3) <u>Asian regional 3G RTT proposals</u>: There are four major proposals that apply to Asian region. These proposals and characteristics are described as follows:

* W-CDMA: This technology is aligned with the ETSI UTRA concept, which was developed by the ETSI SMG2. It is based on R&D conducted by NTT in close cooperation with Nokia and Ericsson, and is supported by several carriers in Asia.

* cdma2000: This technology provides backward compatibility with IS-95 based cdmaOne networks, that have been implemented by several carriers in Asia (e.g., Japan and South Korea).

It is expected that 3G technologies for wireless services will be implemented in the year 2000. Among 3G supporters, NTT is most aggressive in promoting 3G services. One important factor is that 3G is clearly the choice of emerging wireless technologies. The reasons for this are listed as follows:

• It is important to protect the huge investment in existing second generation wireless technologies (e.g., GSM, IS-54/136, and cdmaOne) that are currently in service.

• It is important to capitalize on global GSM market presence. It is essential to preserve a "single" evolution path for GSM based networks.

• Many manufacturers want to avoid paying royalties to Qualcomm for the use of cdmaOne patents. Note that there are still some patent issues associated with 3G technologies that need to be resolved.

• It is important for service providers to continuously adopt new and emerging technologies to meet the customers' needs, and for equipment manufacturers to maintain their market leadership. The following activities reflect these aggressive positions:

* NTT (Japan): NTT will most likely be the first service provider to deploy 3G networks using wideband CDMA technology by the year 2000.

* SK Telecom (S. Korea): SKT is planning to deploy 3G networks using cdma2000 technology to provide services for the World Cup competition in the year 2002.

* Nokia and Ericsson: These vendors are positioning want to assert manufacturing leadership for 3G (W-CDMA) in Europe and other regions.

* CDG (CDMA Development Group): CDG wants to assert manufacturing leadership for 3G technology using cdma2000.

The details of three 3G radio transmission technology proposals (IS-95-based cdma2000; GSM-based W-CDMA; and IS-136-based UWC-136) are described in subsequent sections. However, before discussing these three 3G technologies, several basic 3G network and technology concepts are presented as background material.

8.8.3 3G Networks, Network Components, and Technology Concepts

From technical viewpoint, the architectures, components, and functions of different cellular communications networks (including 3G networks) are similar. The discussion in this section covers a Wireless Intelligent Network (WIN), its functional blocks, interfaces, and various WIN characteristics.

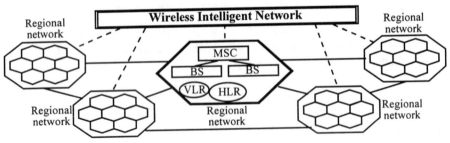

Figure 8-54   (Regional) Network Interworking.

8.8.3.1 WIN Functional Blocks/Interfaces

The components of a wireless network and their functions are discussed in this section. The major components are mobile switching centers, base stations, mobile units (user terminals), wireless intelligent networks, and the appropriate operations systems. Figure 8-54 shows the interworking of several regional networks. In this example, five regional networks are connected together. As shown one regional network has been enlarged to illustrate the major internal components, which include: a Mobile services Switching Center (MSC), Base Station (BS), Home Location Register (HLR), Visitor Location

Register (VLR), etc. The Wireless Intelligent Network (WIN) ensures the seamless interworking of the five regional networks (see Figure 8-54).

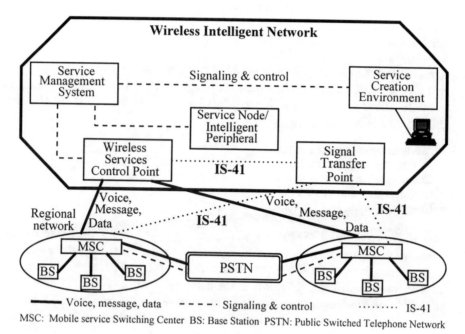

Figure 8-55   WIN Functional Blocks and Interfaces.

The WIN provides unique telecommunication services for individual subscribers. The functions performed by a WIN can be implemented by five functional blocks, as shown in Figure 8-55. This WIN is connected to two regional networks (for example only) via data links (indicated by dotted lines representing IS-41 protocol) for communications (i.e., for administrating network). Similarly, the WIN and regional networks have message links [indicated by solid lines] for transporting subscriber voice, message, and data signals. Note that a Public Switched telephone Network (PSTN) is required to connect the regional networks together. The PSTN is also connected to each MSC using two links (i.e., a data link for carrying control signals, and a message link for carrying subscriber voice, message, and data signals). The five functional blocks of a WIN are described as follows:

- *Service Management System (SMS):* An SMS is a WIN service administration system used to implement all Operations, Administration, Maintenance and Provisioning (OAM&P) functions. The SMS enables service providers to exercise sophisticated data manipulation (e.g., the recent change). It also provides the management capabilities for the wireless Service Control Point (SCP) and Service Creation Node (SCN). When the SMS is coupled with a Service Creation Environment (SCE), the SMS provides the ability to construct, configure, and manage newly-generated services.

- *Wireless Service Control Point (WSCP):* A WSCP provides the capability to support Home Location Register (HLR) services for up to 1 million subscribers. A WSCP centralizes service logic software and data. It is used to introduce new wireless services, and host standalone Home Location Registers. In addition, a WSCP performs subscriber authentication functions.

- *Service Node/Intelligent Peripheral (SN/IP):* SN and IP are external adjunct nodes that provide specialized wireless network functionality. Their capabilities are similar to the functions provided by a Service Creation Node. However, SN/IP also supports call processing services such as:

  * Advanced messaging services
  * Automatic call distribution
  * Customized announcement
  * Calling name and profile delivery
  * Integrated voice and fax message delivery

- *Signal Transfer Point (STP):* An STP is used to support SS7 message routing and specialized address translation. It is important to note that Signal Transfer Points (STPs) are always deployed in "mated pairs" (i.e. STPs are duplicated). This implementation provides *reliability* in the network. That is, if one STP fails, the other is capable of handling all the message traffic routed to the pair. An STP handles the routing of messages via the SS7 signaling network (described in Chapter 4) which is briefly reviewed in the next section.

- *Service Creation Environment (SCE):* An SCE is an optional component in the Wireless Service Control Point (WSCP). An SCE is a software development workstation used for independently generating and testing new service packages. An SCE gives service providers a state-of-the-art software development platform that contains a service control language used to customize advanced services rapidly and with a great flexibility. By using the "point-and-click" ease of the SCE, service providers can rapidly create unique services for any subscriber, and then modify that service for reuse by other subscribers.

Figure 8-56 shows additional functional blocks and interfaces within a WIN. These functional blocks and interfaces are described as follows:

- *Service Switching Point (SSP):* An SSP identifies calls that require special processing. It is used to generate a request or query that is sent o an external network database to obtain handling and routing information. An SSP can also execute the instructions found in the handling and routing information.

- *Signaling System 7 (SS7) network*: An SS7 (or CCS7) network provides access to external databases, the Service Control Points (SCPs), and the SSPs. The SS7 network administers call handling and routing information. [Note: SS7 refers to the signaling protocol, but can also refer to the actual network that uses SS7 signaling protocol.]

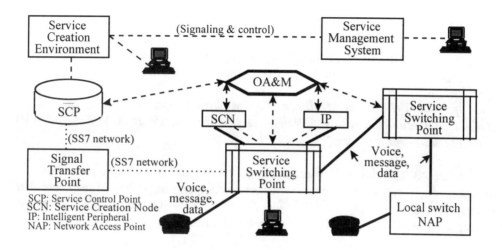

Figure 8-56   Interfaces of a Wireless Intelligent Network (WIN).

- **Network Access Point (NAP):** A NAP can recognize requests for service, and then apply interoffice signaling to transfer the call to the appropriate Service Switching Point (SSP) to handle a particular call.

    Note that the SS7 signaling network (shown as dotted lines in Figure 8-56) provides call handling and routing instructions for the intelligent network services that are stored in the network database or Service Control Points (SCPs). The SS7 network is used to process call control information (signaling), as well as queries and responses that are derived from the network database. The signaling and database information is routed over the SS7 signaling network in the form of "digitally-formatted" messages, which are typically carried by the T1 digital carrier system (discussed in detail in Chapter 6) in North American applications. In other countries the E-1 (2.048 Mbps) digital carrier system (also discussed in Chapter 6) performs this function. Each network element or Signaling Point (SP) that can transmit or receive SS7 messages has a unique address, and these messages are routed to the correct location by a Signal Transfer Point (STP).

- **Service Control Point (SCP):** The SCP contains a large database that stores call handling and routing instructions that are executed by the SSPs. The "mated pair" configuration enables the network to support load sharing of message traffic. The mated pair configuration also provides redundancy for rapid disaster recovery. However, if redundancy for reliability is not required, then single (non-mated) SCP can be deployed.

- **Service Creation Node (SCN):** The SCN, which is supported by the SMS, supports call-processing activities such as advanced messaging services, automatic call distribution, and customized announcements.

8.8.3.2 WIN Triggers

The Wireless Intelligent Network (WIN) provides the infrastructure for implementing wireless cellular services and PCS. The **"WIN trigger"** is a **software feature,** that:

"provides the cellular Mobile or PCS Switching Center (MSC or PCSC) with the ability to communicate with a Wireless Service Control Point (WSCP) using IS-41 protocol features/procedures."

Using "WIN triggers", wireless networks can provide service transparency to roaming subscribers. That is, the service executes properly regardless of the subscriber's geographical location. The "WIN triggers" allow the MSC and/or PCSC to transfer control to the WSCP during call processing, thereby activating WIN service logic.

The WIN uses high reliability platform computers in a *duplicated* configuration, and interfaces with the Wireless service Switching Point (SSP) utilizing WIN/IS-41C based trigger protocol. It also supports Multiple Switching Centers (MSCs or PCSCs) with a centralized standalone Home Location Register (HLR) database. The HLR function combines information about a subscriber's roaming patterns, terminal characteristics, and service requirements to allow increased subscriber capacity, while also simplifying network administration.

The Wireless services Switching Point (WSSP) resides in the MSC or PCSC, and supports the trigger capabilities along with the necessary interfaces required by the Service Control Point (SCP) and Service Node/Intelligent Peripheral (SN/IP).

The WIN triggers are designed to be compatible with Home Location Registers (HLRs), Service Control Points (SCPs), and MSC/PCSC adjuncts that communicate via IS-41 Reversion C protocol. Three major WIN triggers are:

- *Origination trigger*: It allows the MSC/PCSC to query the Wireless Service Control Point (WSCP) for call control instructions, when a call is originated from a mobile unit.

- *Dialed number trigger*: It allows the MSC/PCSC to query the WSCP for call control instructions, when a particular dialed number sequence is identified in an originating call from a mobile unit.

- *Termination trigger*: It allows the MSC/PCSC to query the WSCP for call control instructions, when a call arrives at the MSC/PCSC that is destined for a mobile unit.

8.8.3.3 Signaling System 7

A wireless network can be modeled as a two-layer network having a *transport layer* and a *signaling layer*. Figure 8-57 shows this type of wireless network architecture. The transport layer in a wireless/cellular network consists of mobile switch centers, base stations, a trunk network (i.e. public telephone network), and local (fixed) exchange switches. The transport layer is connected to the signaling layer via an interface such as Signaling System 7 (SS7). Figure 8-57 is a simplified diagram that only shows the Service Signaling Point (SSP), Home Location Register (HLR), Visitor Location Register (VLR), and Equipment Identity Register (EIR) elements in the signaling layer.

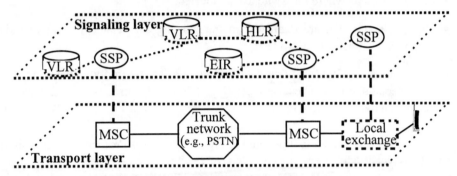

Figure 8-57   Transport and Signaling Layers.

The call-related control information, known as signaling, is transmitted on the same type of facilities that carry the subscriber's data signal. SS7 is a set of signaling protocols that handle the transfer of all call-related control information over the signaling network. The signaling network consists of Signaling Transfer Points, Service Signaling Points, and Service Control Point as shown in Figure 8-58. The signaling network uses a packet switching network architecture, rather than a circuit switching network architecture (which is used in the transport network). The SS7 signaling protocol is an international standard recommended by the ITU-T (formerly, CCITT). The corresponding protocol and system used in the North American network is called CCS7.

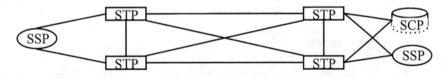

Figure 8-58   Network Elements of a SS7 (or CCS7) Network.

Prior to SS7 or CCS7 signaling technology, several signaling schemes were developed and implemented. These schemes were known as "in-band" signaling, "out-of-band" signaling, and "separate facility" signaling. Signaling information (i.e., call-related control signals) that occupies the same frequency spectrum as the subscriber's signal is called **"in-band signaling"**. This was the first generation signaling protocol. This technology subsequently advanced to "out-of-band" signaling, and has further evolved to systems that carry signaling information on entirely *separate facilities*. Out-of-band signaling uses a "bandwidth-on-demand" transmission technique. The "signaling" information carries call setup and other call-related control signals. Like all communication networks, SS7 and CCS7 contain many network elements (nodes) that are known as Signaling Transfer Points (STPs). These nodes are interconnected by long-distance transmission facilities (i.e., special digital facilities). The nodes of the signaling network are called Signaling Points (SPs), which include:

- Central offices where toll switches are located.

- Special nodes that are dedicated to transporting call-related information [i.e., Signaling Transfer Point (STP)].

- Special systems that provide database services to the various switching nodes for special services. These services (e.g., "800" calls, credit-card calls, etc.) are called Network Control Points (NCPs).

The SS7 protocol model is illustrated in Figure 8-59. This protocol model is similar to the OSI 7-layer model. The seven layers of the OSI protocol are: the Application Layer (layer 7), the Presentation Layer (layer 6), the Session Layer (layer 5), the Transport Layer (layer 4), the Network Layer (layer 3), the Data Link Layer (layer 2), and the Physical Layer (layer 1).

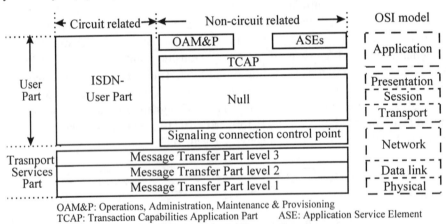

OAM&P: Operations, Administration, Maintenance & Provisioning
TCAP: Transaction Capabilities Application Part   ASE: Application Service Element

Figure 8-59   SS7 Architecture (Protocol Model) and OSI Model.

The SS7 protocol is divided into two parts: the transport service part, and the user part. The function of these parts is described as follows:

- **Transport services part**: This function consists of the Message Transfer Part level 1, level 2, and level 3 (*MTP 1, MTP 2* and *MTP 3*). The MTP provides routing services. The three MTP levels perform operations that involve the physical layer, the data link layer, and the network layer (partially). Each MTP uses level-3 header and level-3 address information, along with Signal Point Codes (SPCs) or Point Codes (PCs) to forward the "upper" part messages to appropriate destinations in the network. In summary, the MTP selects the next data link that is used to forward the message.

Every network entity (e.g., STP, 4ESS, 1AESS, 5ESS or NCP) that can generate or receive a SS7 message, is labeled with a Signaling Point Code (SPC). If the SPC is a destination, it is called a *Destination Point Code* (DPC). Similarly, if the SPC is the origin of a level-3 MTP message, it is called an *Originating Point Code* (OPC).

- **The user part** (UP): The second part of the SS7 protocol is the User Part (UP). The UP is divided into two sections: the circuit-related and non-circuit related parts. The circuit-related part is also called the ISDN User Part (ISUP), and includes the Telephone User Part (TUP) and the Data User Part (DUP). The non-circuit related part includes: the Operations, Administration, Maintenance & Provisioning (OAM&P) functions, the Application Services Elements (ASEs), and the Transaction Capabilities Application Part (TCAP). The non-circuit related UP implements OSI layer 4 to layer 7 functionality, however these operations are not limited to OSI functionality. Two additional parts are included in this UP: the null part (currently undefined) and the signaling connection control point.

For mobile applications, the Application Service Elements (ASEs), plus the OAM&P is known as *the mobile application part*. This mobile application part, combined with the Transaction Capabilities Application Part (TCAP) form *the Mobile Application Entity* (MAE). The protocol used for the MAE is called the *Mobile Application Protocol* (MAP), which defines the following functions:

- * Location registration and cancellation
- * Handover (handoff) procedures
- * Handling supplementary services
- * Retrieval of user parameters during call set-up
- * Authentication procedures
- * Operations, Administration and Maintenance (OA&M)

Figure 8-60 shows the relationship (data links connections) between location areas (LAs), Mobile Switch Centers (MSCs), Home Location Registers (HLR), and Visitor Location Registers (VLRs). A Wireless Intelligent Network (WIN), based on the SS7 signaling protocol, integrates the HLR and all the VLRs that are linked to various LAs. In this example only three VLRs are shown. In actual applications one wireless intelligent network can support many more than three VLRs. One Visitor Location Register (VLR) can serve one or more MSC areas, for example, the VLR No. 1 and VLR No. 3 (see Figure 8-60) each serves only one MSC area (i.e., MSC_1 and MSC_4, respectively), while VLR No. 2 serves two MSC areas (i.e., MSC_2 and MSC_3).

An MSC can serve many Location Areas (e.g., LA_1, LA_2, LA_3, ...) as shown in Figure 8-60. When a mobile subscriber is roaming [e.g., moving from Local Area 4 (LA_4) of MSC_3 toward LA_1 of MSC_4 as shown in Figure 8-60]. The roaming process is controlled by the visitor location register in charge of the area that the mobile subscriber is *roaming toward* (i.e., VLR_3 controls the roaming process in this example). When the mobile unit first appears in an area (LA_1 of MSC_4 in this example) it performs a registration procedure (most of the areas are now using automatic registration, but there are still areas where registration must be performed manually) so that the mobile unit's home location register is notified along with all the associated network components. Then the MSC in charge of the area (i.e., MSC_4) will acknowledge this registration, and transfers messages (e.g. the identity of the location area where the mobile subscriber is now situated) to the VLR (LA_1 in this case). An up-to-date service profile of the mobile subscriber is maintained in a centralized database (i.e. a stand-alone HLR) provides the subscribed services. Note that one HLR can serve multiple MSCs, however an HLR can also be distributed over multiple locations.

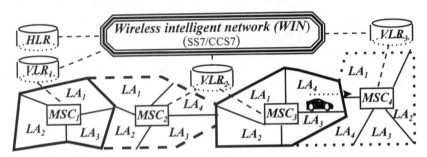

Figure 8-60   Relationship among Location Area, HLR and VLR.

8.8.3.4 Home Location Register

A *Home Location Register (HLR)* is a data base used to manage a mobile subscriber. All administrative activities concerning a given mobile subscriber are recorded by the HLR. The HLR is the location register to which a user identity is assigned for record keeping purposes. The HLR database contains all of the subscriber information [e.g., the Electronic Series Number (ESN) of the subscriber device, the subscriber's Directory Number (DN), the International Mobile Subscriber Identity (IMSI) profile information, the mobile unit's current location, the service validated period, etc.]. This data base is used for routing calls to the mobile subscribers managed by this HLR. However, the HLRs have no direct control over the mobile switching centers.

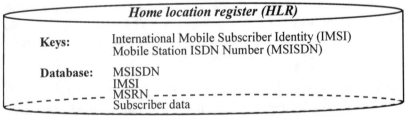

Figure 8-61   Keys and Data Base Contents of a HLR.

A Public Land-Mobile Network (PLMN) for a serving area may contain one or more HLRs. The number of HLRs required in a serving area depends upon:

- The number of mobile subscribers
- The capacity of the equipment
- The organization of the network

For security reasons, two **"keys"** are required to **access** the information stored in the HLR. These " keys" (Figure 8-61) are the Mobile Station ISDN Number (MSISDN) and the International Mobile Subscriber Identity (IMSI).

The most common information stored in a HLR includes:

- A permanent copy of the mobile subscriber's subscription information
- Location information enabling the routing of calls toward the MSC where the mobile unit is located [e.g. the Mobile Station Roaming Number (MSRN), VLR address, the MSC address, etc.]
- The International Mobile Subscriber Identity (IMSI)
- The Mobile Subscriber ISDN Number (MSISDN)
- Teleservices and bearer services subscription information
- Service restrictions (e.g., roaming limitations, and supplementary service parameters)

Features typically supported by a stand-alone HLR includes:

- Call delivery
- Message waiting notification
- Call forwarding
- Remote feature control
- Call transfer
- Subscriber PIN intercept
- Call waiting
- Call Conference (3-way calling)
- Voice message retrieval

8.8.3.5 Visitor Location Register

A *Visitor Location Register (VLR)* is used by an MSC in conjunction with the HLR to retrieve information for handling calls to/from a visiting mobile subscriber (i.e., a subscriber that is roaming). The VLR is a functional unit that *dynamically* stores subscriber information [e.g., Electronic Series Number (ESN) of the user unit device, user's Directory Number (DN), and user profile information obtained from the user's HLR] when a mobile subscriber is located in the area covered by the VLR. That is, when a mobile subscriber enters an area not served by their home MSC, the "visiting" mobile subscriber is temporarily registered (usually automatically, but may be manual in some areas) with the VLR via the "new" MSC. The "new" MSC requests all the subscriber's information from the HLR located in the subscribers home MSC. A VLR is a temporary copy of the subscriber's information that is accessed by the MSC. A VLR is only active when the mobile subscriber is roaming. Once a mobile subscriber has roamed beyond the serving area of the VLR, their information is removed from the VLR database. The information contained in the VLR data base is shown in Figure 8-62, and listed as follows:

- Mobile Station ISDN Number (MSISDN)
- International Mobile Subscriber Identity (IMSI)
- Temporary mobile subscriber identity (TMSI)
- Mobile Station Roaming Number (MSRN)
- Location Area Code (LAC) of mobile unit
- A copy of the subscriber information from their HLR

The **keys required to access** to the VLR information are IMSI, TMSI and MSRN (see Figure 8-62). It should be noted that for GSM applications, a mobile unit is **always** viewed as a "visitor". Therefore, when the mobile unit initiates call requests in its home Mobile Switching Center (MSC) area, the subscriber is simply "visiting its home".

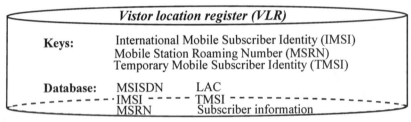

Figure 8-62   Keys and Data Base Contents of a VLR.

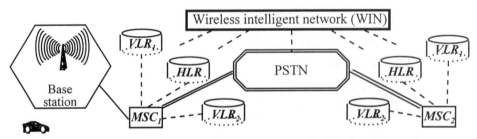

Figure 8-63   Major Network Components of a Wireless Network.

In summary, the HLR is a subscriber database and can be implemented as part of the Mobile service Switching Center (MSC) or as a centralized function handled by the network (Figure 8-63). The SS7 signaling network is used to transport control messages to/from the HLR. In contrast, the VLR is a temporary user's database that contains a subset of the HLR information for the duration of the mobile unit's visit. The mobile features, which are typically implemented in software, can be stored in the MSC or in the network. A WIN allows software features to execute in an intelligent network node such as a Service Control Point (SCP).

The Wireless Intelligent Network (WIN), defined by TIA TR-45.2.2.4, supports intelligent network capabilities for wireless applications (e.g. incoming call screening, calling name presentation, voice controlled services, short message services, single number services, etc.). Additional WIN capabilities are: enhanced wireless emergency services, wireless number portability, over-the-air service provisioning, enhanced billing options, "calling party pays", 3G "virtual home environment", etc. With the WIN capabilities, it has been proposed that 3G (IMT-2000) should provide several types of wireless services including:

- All 2nd generation core fixed and mobile services: Examples of these services are registration, paging, authentication [these three services are User Identity Module (UIM)-based services], encryption, dispatch, short message service, emergency calling services, legally authorized electronic surveillance, and supplementary services.

- Support for circuit switched channels: The channel bit rates are 32 kbps and 56/64 kbps for "dial-up" access to computer services, "2B+D" ISDN access, and video conferencing at 64 kbps, 128 kbps or 384 kbps.

- Support for packet data at various bit rates: packet data bit rates are 9.6 kbps for global applications, 144 kbps (or higher) for high mobility traffic or regional applications, 384 kbps for pedestrian traffic or local area applications, and 2.048 Mbps for indoor/office/home applications.

- Common billing, charging, and user profile management: These capabilities include sharing usage and rate information between service providers, recording standardized call details, and managing/sharing standardized user profiles.

- Supports for multimedia services: These services include fixed/variable rate traffic, bandwidth on demand, asymmetric links, call/connection separation, multiple bearers, multimedia mail store and forward, broadband access (up to 2 Mbps), and Quality of Service (QoS) negotiation and provisioning.

- Supports for geographical position finding of mobiles: It identifies geographical position, and reports this information to both the network and the mobile unit.

- Supports for interoperability and roaming: This capability applies to all the 3G family of systems.

- Supports for future services: Examples of future services are Universal Personal Telecommunications (UPT), internet access, and satellite access.

8.8.4 The GSM Based W-CDMA 3G Technology

Two major Time Division Multiple Access (TDMA) standards are commonly used in 2G mobile applications: GSM (Global System for Mobile communications) and IS-54/IS-136. In addition, three well-known GSM based technologies are: GSM, DCS1800, and PCS1900. They use 200 kHz (x2) carrier bandwidth, and up to 8 calls per carrier with one time slot allocated per call. The full-rate (13 kbps) or "enhanced full rate" vocoder is specified, and frequency re-use is based on 4-cell/12-sector (4 cells/cluster; 3 sectors/cell) or better scheme.

- GSM was standardized in the early-1990s for digital cellular applications (occupying approximately in spectrum of 800~900 MHz) and is used in more than 100 countries.

- DCS1800 (Digital Cellular System at 1800 MHz; see Figure 8-19 for frequency spectrum) is an "upbanded" version of GSM, and is called Personal Communications Network (PCN) or Personal Communication Service (PCS) in some areas. It has been adopted by many countries in addition to the European region.

- PCS1900 (PCS at 1900 MHz) is the ANSI standard used in North America, and is also called "GSM-North America".

The 3G GSM-based technology adopts the wideband (i.e., any bandwidth higher than the IS-95 CDMA bandwidth; approximately 1.23 MHz) CDMA multiple access method. The following reasons justify using W-CDMA instead of IS-95 based CDMA:

- The technology provides flexible high bit rate services (see Figure 8-64).

- The scheme is dynamically adaptable, and can be used to
  * provide a wide range of bit rates (from low to high) with a small granularity.
  * multiplex several users with different bit rates and services.
  * optimize the bandwidth resource usage.

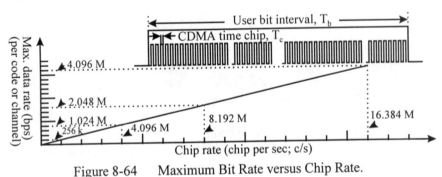

Figure 8-64   Maximum Bit Rate versus Chip Rate.

- It utilizes soft handover to improve quality, while also providing additional diversity.

- It allows universal frequency re-use.

- It can capitalize on multipath, the traditional nemesis of mobile communications. (i.e., "RAKE" receivers can achieve signal diversity from three or more paths using "time diversity technique" to overcome the digital bit error rate due to deep fading.)

- The technique applies "pilot bits" rather than "pilot channels" to allow coherent reception for both uplink and downlink communications. A W-CDMA channel is divided into 0.625-ms slots that contains two parts: (1) pilot bits, and (2) a payload field for carrying voice/data and/or control messages. In addition, this technique is well suited for "smart antenna" application.

- The technique utilizes inter-cell asynchronous operation. The system may not need Global Positioning System (GPS) synchronization. The cdmaOne technology requires every cell to be synchronized to within 10μs of one another. This allows the same short Personal Number (PN) code to be re-used by different sectors, but the method requires a GPS receiver near every cell. This GPS requirement can be burdensome and difficult to achieve. Thus, the GSM-based W-CDMA 3G technology applies inter-cell operation to avoid the need of using GPS. However, it requires different PN codes for each sector, and fast acquisition of these PN codes (e.g., when roaming/handover/call delivery is performed).

- GSM network architecture, functional elements/capabilities, GSM messages and protocol supports 2G GSM services [i.e., GSM Subscriber Identity Module (SIM) cards, and 2G GSM vocoders].

Table 8-26   Major Characteristics of W-CDMA and WIMS.

	W-CDMA			WIMS		
Nominal bandwidth (Hz)	5 M	10 M	20 M	5 M	10 M	20 M
Chip rate (M-chips/sec)	4.096	8.192	16.384	4.096	8.192	16.384
Max user bit rate (kbps)* #	~480*	~960*	~1920*	16	16	16
Max user bit rate (Mbps)* @	~2	~2	~2	2.4*	6.144*	12.288*
Backward compatibility	GSM			ISDN		
Coherent demod. For both links	Yes, applying time-multiplexed pilot bits					
Frequency re-use	Universal (1/1)					
Inter-cell synchronization?	No%; applying inter-cell asynchronous operation					
Frame time (msec)	10					

* This rate is only achievable under ideal conditions;   % (For W-CDMA) Yes, if TDD operation
\# For single code or channel   @ For multicode

- The technology is compatible with Wireless Integrated Multimedia and messaging Service (WIMS; as shown in Table 8-26).

8.8.5 The IS-95 Based cdma2000 3G Technology

The term "cdmaOne" is a general term for IS-95 based standards and products including: cellular (800 MHz, Figure 8-18), PCS (1800 MHz, Figure 8-19), Wireless Local Loop (WLL) etc. It is a registered trademark of the CDMA Development Group (CDG).

The characteristics of cdmaOne (IS-95 based CDMA technology) are:

- "Soft" handover is available (e.g., it has the ability to acquire a new Base Station (BS) for handover before relinquishing the present BS). It also provides the ability to communicate simultaneously with three or more cells/sectors for extended time periods. Handover typically does not disrupt voice or data transmission.

- It applies multiple correlators such as "RAKE' receivers to achieve robust performance in multi-path environments.

- Single chip [i.e., Very Large Scale Integrated (VLSI) devices] implementations are available from several semi-conductor vendors.

- Variable rate speech encoding services are available. A maximum rate of 8 kbps (out of 13 kbps) can be selected as the nominal rate. One half, one quarter, or one-eighth rates can be provisioned during "silent" intervals with commensurate power reductions.

- It requires a fast and rigorous handset with dynamic power control to solve the "near/far" problem of maintaining transmission quality.

- Plans for supporting up to 64 kbps data services using ANSI-95-B (by the year 1999) requires new handsets and infrastructure upgrades.

- Currently some non-standard W-CDMA ($\geq$ 5 MHz) systems exist that support up to 144 kbps (or higher) data rates. These systems are primarily used for non-mobile applications such as Wireless Local Loop (WLL) systems.

Table 8-27   Major Characteristics of cdma2000 Technology.

Nominal bandwidth (Hz)	1.25 M	3.75 M	7.5 M	11.25 M	15 M
Chip rate (M-chips/sec)	1.2288	3.6864	7.3728	11.0592	14.7456
Max user bit rate (kbps)* #	307.2*	1036.8*	2073.6*	2457.6*	2457.6*
Max user bit rate (Mbps)* @	For further study				
Backward compatibility	cdmaOne (IS-95) and ANSI TIA/EIA-41				
Coherent demod. For both links	Yes, applying continuous pilot channels				
Frequency re-use	Universal (1/1)				
Inter-cell synchronization?	yes				
Frame time (msec)	20 typically; 5 optional for control				

For single code or channel   @ For multicode
* This rate is only achievable under ideal conditions;

The technology of cdmaOne is evolving into cdma2000, and can be divided into two phases. The phase I cdma2000 is standardized as TIA/EIA-95-C (ANSI-95-C). The target publication date is the second quarter of 1999, and commercial services will be available in the year 2000. Two modes of operation are planned [i.e., (1X at 1.25 MHz), and (3X at 3.75 MHz)]. The data rates for both packet-switched and circuit-switched services can be up to 144 kbps. Voice capacity enhancements are approximately doubled.

Phase II is known as TIA/EIA-95-D (ANSI-95-D) with target publication set for 4Q99, and commercial services in the year 2001. Three additional modes, besides the two operational modes available in Phase I standard have been added [i.e., (6X at 7.5 MHz), (9X at 11.25 MHz), and (12X at 15 MHz)]. Circuit and packet data rates up to 2 Mbps will be supported. The technology will support advanced multimedia services. Table 8-27 summarizes the major characteristics of cdma2000 technology.

8.8.6 The IS-136 Based UWC-136 3G Technology

IS-54/IS-136 is one of the two major TDMA standards used in 2G mobile applications (i.e., GSM is the other one). The IS-136 standard is also called D-AMPS (Digital Advanced Mobile Phone Service), TIA/EIA-627, or TIA/EIA-136. IS-136 uses 30 kHz carrier bandwidth (instead of 200 kHz) six time slots at 8 kbps per carrier (i.e., 48 kbps total in 30 kHz; each call uses two time slots). The frequency re-use adopts 7-cell/21-sector (i.e., 7 cells/cluster, and 3 sectors/cell) or better scheme. The term UWC-136 (Universal Wireless Communication) is the name adopted for evolving IS-136 into a 3G wireless standard. The Universal Wireless Communications Consortium (UWCC) is an organization representing over 80 carriers and vendors that support IS-136 evolution. Table 8-28 shows the UW-136 major characteristics. UW-136 is a family of technologies, based on TDMA-technology, including the following:

- IS-136: It uses 30 kHz per carrier. The rate for voice is 30 kHz, and up to 22.8 kbps data service is available.

- IS-136+: It also uses 30 kHz per carrier. The rate for voice is 30 kHz, and up to 64 kbps data with higher level modulation methods is available.

- IS-136 HS (High speed) outdoor/vehicular: It uses 200 kHz per carrier for 30 kHz voice, with rates up to 384 kbps for data only.

- IS-136 HS (High Speed) indoor: It uses 1.6 MHz per carrier for 30 kHz, with rates up to 2 Mbps for data only.

Table 8-28   Major Characteristics of UWC-136.

	IS-136+	IS-136 HS outdoor/vehicular	IS-136 HS indoor
Nominal bandwidth (Hz)	30 k	200 k	1600 k
Max user bit rate (kbps)*	~ 64 k*	~ 384 k*	~ 2 M*
Backward compatibility	IS-136 and ANSI TIA/EIA-41		
Coherent demod. For both links	No	Yes (both forward and reverse)	
Frequency re-use	7/21 (typically)	1/3	3 cell omni
Inter-cell synchronization?	No (except TDD operation)		
Frame time (msec)	40	4.615	

    * This rate is only achievable under ideal conditions;

Review Questions II for Chapter 8:

(14) Analog wireless technology converts analog subscriber's signals into a signal that is suitable for airway transport by using either _____, _____ or _____ modulation. Likewise, digital wireless technology converts digital subscriber's signal using _____, _____, _____ shift keying, or _____ schemes.

(15) Modulation used in TDMA IS-136 systems is _____, and in GSM systems is (   ) _____.

(16) Since PCS service competition is expected to be furious, service provider must initiate strategic planning in the areas of _____, _____, _____, and _____. Several technical challenges that PCS service providers need to face are: _____, _____, and _____.

(17) Presently, seven proposals have been accepted as PCS standards. Among them, most promising technologies are: _____, _____, _____ and _____.

(18) (True, False) Most vendors and service providers believe that a cellular technology can be applied to PCS systems.

(19) Several advantages can be achieved if cellular technology is applied to PCS systems, such as _____, _____, _____, _____, _____, etc.

(20) The first generation (1G) wireless technology is referred to: _____, _____, _____, _____, _____, and _____. The second generation (2G) technology is referred to _____, _____ and _____. The third generation (3G) wireless technology supports _____.

(21) The term used for the family of standards and products based on IS-95 CDMA technology is _____. The term _____ is the name/logo applied to the 3G evolution of _____.

(22) Three major 3G technologies are: _____, _____, and _____.

(23) (True, False) Quoted from ITU-T: "IMT-200 provides wireless access to the global telecommunications infrastructure through both satellite and terrestrial systems, serving fixed and mobile users in public and private networks.

(24) From technical viewpoint, the network architecture, components, and functions of different cellular wireless communications networks (including 3G networks) are similar. The major network components are (1) _____, (2) _____, _____, _____, _____ (within a regional network), and (3) _____.

APPENDIX 8-1   CDMA Implementation

8A-1. Direct Sequence Characteristics: Auto- and Cross-Correlation

In a CDMA system applications, it is often stated that *"to minimize interference between CDMA users, it is necessary that every pair of Pseudo Noise (PN) sequences [$c_i(t)$ and $c_j(t)$] has small cross-correlation."* A CDMA system with a 13-bit PN code ($m = 13$, $L = 2^{13} - 1 = 8,191$) can accommodate a maximum of 630 users with distinct codes, each having a small cross correlation with each other.

Definition 8-6 of **Autocorrelation:** A measure of similarity between a signal and its delayed version, that is, $c_i(t)$ and $c_i(t+\tau)$:

$$R_{ii}(\tau) = \frac{1}{MT_c} \int_{-MT_c/2}^{MT_c/2} c_i(t) c_i(t + \tau)\, dt \qquad (8A-1)$$

Definition 8-6 of **Cross-correlation:** A measure of similarity between two signals, that is, $c_i(t)$ and $c_j(t)$:

$$R_{ij}(\tau) = \frac{1}{MT_c} \int_{-MT_c/2}^{MT_c/2} c_i(t) c_j(t + \tau)\, dt \qquad (8A-2)$$

Example 8A-1: Derive the autocorrelation of the PN sequence $c(t)$ in Table 8A-1 [i.e., a 15-chip PN code: c(t) = " 111100010011010 ...", with logical "1" = +1 and "0" = -1].

Table 8A-1   Autocorrelation Calculation.

Original, $c_i(t)$	1 1 1 1 -1 -1 -1 1 -1 -1 1 1 -1 1 -1	**Average**
No shift, $c_i(t)$	1 1 1 1 -1 -1 -1 1 -1 -1 1 1 -1 1 -1	
$c_i(t) \times c_i(t)$	1 1 1 1 1 1 1 1 1 1 1 1 1 1 1	15/15 = 1
Original, $c_i(t)$	1 1 1 1 -1 -1 -1 1 -1 -1 1 1 -1 1 -1	**Average**
1 shift, $c_i(t+T_c)$	-1 1 1 1 1 -1 -1 -1 1 -1 -1 1 1 -1 1	
$c_i(t) \times c_i(t+T_c)$	-1 1 1 1 -1 1 1 -1 -1 1 -1 1 -1 -1 -1	(7-8)/15 = -1/15

"1" × "1" = "1";   "1" × "-1" = "-1";   "-1" × "1" = "-1";   "-1" × "-1" = "1"

In Table 8A-1, without any shift, by multiplying the first and second rows one can obtain the third row. There are 15 "1s" out of 15 time chips in $c_i(t) \times c_i(t)$. This results in an average of $15T_c/15T_c = 1$ as shown in row No. 3 in Table 8A-1. By definition, the autocorrelation of $c(t)$ has a value of 1 when $\tau = 0$. With one shift, there are 7 "1s" and 8 "-1s" in $c_i(t) \times c_i(t+T_c)$ as shown in row No. 6 in Table 8A-1. The average is $(7-8)/15 = -1/15$. By definition the autocorrelation of $c(t)$ has a value of $-1/15$ when $\tau = T_c$.

This procedure is continued for two-shifts, three-shifts, four-shifts, five-shifts, ... , up to 14-shifts (= 15 time chips − 1). The average is −1/15 for each case. Therefore, the autocorrelation of the PN sequence [given $c(t)$ as shown in Figure 8A-1] indicates four bit intervals each having 15 chips (four bits implies 2^4 − 1 time chips). Within each bit interval, the autocorrelation at $\tau = 0$ has a value of "1", and the autocorrelation at any chip time is −1/15.

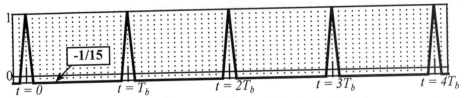

Figure 8A-1   The autocorrelation for the 15-Chip PN Sequence.

The question "How does a CDMA system actually work?" is often asked. In a CDMA system each individual user signal (digital bit stream) is multiplied by its own PN sequence at the transmitter. The resultant signal is combined with many other users' signals, and then transmitted via an antenna as shown in Figure 8-39(A). This combined signal is transmitted to **all potential** receivers. Every receiver receives the same signal, which is a composite of all the information transmitted for every user. Example 8A-2 explains how each user receives the intended information as a separate signal.

Example 8A-2: Assume three users signals are transmitted by the transmitter shown in Figure 8-39(A). The **processing gain is assumed to be "6",** and the PN sequences and payload information (user bit streams) are given as follows:

- User No. 1: $c_1(t)$ = "*1111-1-1* -11-1-111 *-11-1111* 1-1-1-11-1 *-111-11-1*..." is the PN sequence, and $b_1(t)$ = "10011..." is the user bit stream.

- User No. 2: $c_2(t)$ = "*11-11-11* 111-1-1-1 *1-1-111-1* 1-11111 *-1-1-11-1-1*..." is the PN sequence, and $b_2(t)$ = "10110..." is the user bit stream.

- User No. 3: $c_3(t)$ = "-1-11-1-11 *1-11-111* 11-1-1-11 *-1-111-11* -11111-1..." is the PN sequence, and $b_3(t)$ = "11011..." is the user bit stream.

Show that by applying $c_1(t)$ at the receiver, the bit stream $b_1(t)$ can be restored; by applying $c_2(t)$ at the receiver, the bit stream $b_2(t)$ can be restored; and by applying $c_3(t)$ at the receiver, the bit stream $b_3(t)$ can be restored from the transmitted signal $z(t)$ [see Figure 8-39(A)].

First, find $y_1(t)$, $y_2(t)$ and $y_3(t)$ as follows [Note that a logical "0" in the information bit stream is treated as "−1"; while a logical "1" in the information bit stream is treated as

"+1" for the operation illustrated in Figure 8A-2]. The transmitter forms the multiplied signal $y_1(t)$, $y_2(t)$, and $y_3(t)$ as follows:

$y_1(t)$ = $b_1(t) \times c_1(t)$ = "10011..." × "*1111-1-1*-11-1-111-*11-11111*-1-1-11-1 -*111-11-1*..."
$\qquad\qquad\quad \equiv$ "*1111-1-1* 1-111-1-1 *1-11-1-1-1* 1-1-1-11-1 -*111-11-1*..."

$y_2(t)$ = $b_2(t) \times c_2(t)$ = "10110..." × "*11-11-11*111-1-1-1*1-1-111-11*-11111-1-1-*11-1-1* ..."
$\qquad\qquad\quad \equiv$ "*11-11-11* -1-1-1111 *1-1-111-1* 1-11111 *111-111*..."

$y_3(t)$ = $b_3(t) \times c_3(t)$ = "11011..." × "-1-11-1-11*1-11-11111*1-1-1-11-*1-111-11* -11111-1..."
$\qquad\qquad\quad \equiv$ "*-1-11-1-11* 1-11-111 *-1-1111-1* -1-111-11 -*11111-1*..."

Next, add $y_1(t)$, $y_2(t)$ and $y_3(t)$ to obtain the transmitted signal [$z(t)$] as follows:

$$z(t) = y_1(t) + y_2(t) + y_3(t)$$

$$= \text{"1111-311-311111-3111-31-31111-133-13-1..."} \qquad\qquad (8A\text{-}3)$$

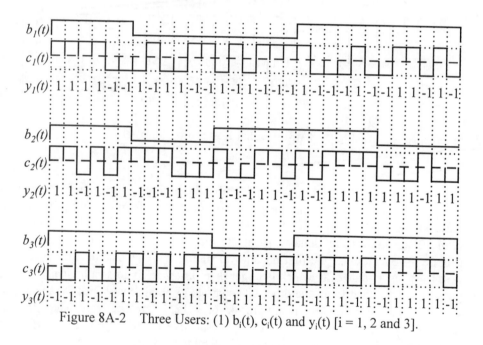

Figure 8A-2   Three Users: (1) $b_i(t)$, $c_i(t)$ and $y_i(t)$ [i = 1, 2 and 3].

The signal, $z(t)$, is received by each user who has its own PN sequence used to restore the respective information. Before describing how the signal restoration is implemented, it should be understood that each user applies an integrate-and-dump filter. The principle of this filter is summarized as follows:

For the integrate and dump filter: (1) if at the end of one-bit interval the integrated value is greater than "0", the bit will be restored as a logical "1"; and (2) if the integrated value is less than "0", the bit will be restored as a logical "0".

- **Case 1** (user 1): For user No.1 to restore information from the received signal $z(t)$, the receiver will multiply the PN sequence $c_1(t)$ with $z(t)$. Then by feeding the result to an integrate and dump filter, obtain the values at the output of the filter at the end of each bit-interval (i.e. six-chip intervals in this example because the processing gain is assumed to be 6) as shown in Figure 8A-3.

    In Figure 8A-3 the top waveform, $z(t)$, is the transmitted CDMA signal from the base station. This signal is received by all users, assuming the channel noise is negligible. It has values of -3, -1, 1 and 3. This signal is multiplied by the PN sequence, $c_1(t)$, which is the second waveform in Figure 8A-3, and has values of -1 and 1. The multiplication is performed on "chip by chip" basis, and the result is ($z \times c_1$); shown in Figure 8A-3: 1, 1, 1, 1, 3, -1; -1, -3, -1, -1, 1, 1; -1, -3, -1, 1, 1, -3; 1, 3, -1, -1, 1, -1; 1, 3, 3, 1, 3, 1, ...

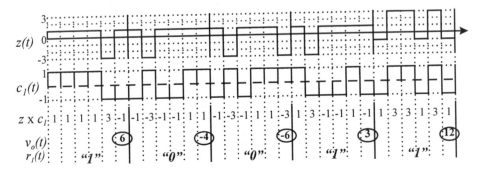

Figure 8A-3   Signal Restoration for $b_1(t)$.

    For each group of six consecutive chips, the multiplication values are summed (since the first function of the integrate and dump filter is **integrating** or summing these values). For example, the sum of the first six chips is 6 (= 1+1+1+1+3-1), which is the first value of the signal $v_0(t)$ at the output of the integrate and dump filter (Figure 8A-3). Because the first bit interval (the first six chips: since the processing gain is 6) has a value of 6, which is <u>larger than 0</u>, it is restored as a logical "1". This procedure is applied to all the other bit intervals to obtain the values for the 2nd, 3rd, 4th, 5th, ... intervals , and the result are -4, -6, 3, 12, ..., respectively. Thus, they are restored as logical "0", "0", "1", "1", ..., respectively. Finally, the received signal, $r_1(t)$, is restored as "10011...", which is identical to the transmitted signal, $b_1(t)$.

$$v_0(t) = (+6; \ -4; \ -6; \ +3; \ +12; \ ...) \qquad \Rightarrow \qquad r_1(t) = \text{"10011..."} \equiv b_1(t)$$

- **Case 2** (user 2): The same approach used in case 1 is applied for case 2. That is, by multiplying $c_2(t)$ and $z(t)$ and then feeding the result to an integrate and dump filter, the values at the output of the filter at the end of each bit-interval (six-chip interval) are derived as shown in Figure 8A-4.

$$v_o(t) = (+4; \ -4; \ +8; \ +8; \ -12; \ ...) \qquad \Rightarrow \qquad r_2(t) = \text{``10110...''} \equiv b_2(t)$$

The output voltage at the end of the *first* six-chip interval is +4, which is larger than 0, therefore, this bit is restored as a logical "1". This is also true for the third and the fourth bit intervals, which are decoded as "1". The output voltages for the second and the fifth intervals have negative values, -4 and -12, and are restored as logical "0s". Thus, the received signal $r_2(t)$ is restored as "10110...", which is identical to the transmitted signal, $b_2(t)$.

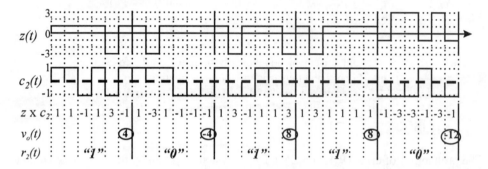

Figure 8A-4   Signal Restoration for $b_2(t)$.

- **Case 3** (user 3): As in cases 1 and 2, multiplying $c_3(t)$ and $z(t)$, and then feeding the result to an integrate and dump filter, the values at the output of the filter is the restored signal, $r_3(t)$, which is identical to the transmitted signal, $b_3(t)$, as shown in Figure 8A-5.

$$v_o(t) = (+2; \ +6; \ -8; \ +4; \ 10; \ ...) \qquad \Rightarrow \qquad r_3(t) = \text{``11011...''} \equiv b_3(t)$$

The restored signal is $r_3(t) = \text{``11011...''}$, which is identical to $b_3(t)$.

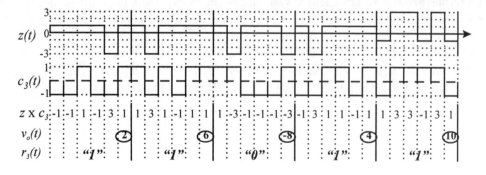

Figure 8A-5   Signal Restoration for $b_3(t)$.

8A-2 CDMA Uplink Performance

A DS-CDMA base station receives the signal from N users. It is assumed that the base station will analyze the performance of user No. 1. The Signal-to-Interference ratio (S/I) can be derived as shown in Eq.(8A-4). The ratio, E_b/N_T is the performance measure, which is the received bit Energy divided by the received interference Noise power. This measurement is equivalent to the signal-to-noise ratio.

$$\frac{E_b}{N_T} = \frac{A_1^2 T_2 / 2}{N_s + \sum_{i=2}^{N}(A_i^2/3)T_c} \approx \frac{A_1^2/2}{\sum_{i=2}^{N}(A_i^2/3)} \times \frac{T_b}{T_c} = \frac{Signal\ power}{Interference\ power} \times \frac{T_b}{T_c} \qquad (8A\text{-}4)$$

where N_S = channel noise, which is typically smaller than the co-channel
                    interference and thus is ignored in the equation
           A_1 = Received carrier level of the desired signal (user No. 1)
           A_i = Received carrier level of the interfering signal (i = 2, N)
           T_b/T_c = processing gain

The probability of error (P_e) of a DS-CDMA system is given by the following equation:

$$P_e = (\frac{1}{2})\ erfc\ \sqrt{\frac{E_b}{N_T}} \qquad (8A\text{-}5)$$

where erfc(a) is the complementary error function, erfc(a) = 1 – erf(a). For practical applications, the following approximation is adequate:

$$erfc(a) \approx \frac{e^{-a^2}}{a \times \sqrt{\pi}} \qquad if\ a \geq 1 \qquad (8A\text{-}6)$$

Example 8A-3: A DS-CDMA system has an E_b/N_T ratio of 7 dB. Calculate the probability of error for the system.

An E_b/N_T ratio of 7 dB yields E_b/N_T = 10(7/10) = 5.012 [**Caution:** *do not use the numerical dB value of E_b/N_T directly in the formula*]. Substituting the E_b/N_T ratio (E_b/N_T = 5.012, **not** 7 dB) into Eq.(8A-5), obtain the probability of error as follows:

$$P_e = (\frac{1}{2})\ erfc\ \sqrt{\frac{E_b}{N_T}} = (\frac{1}{2})\ erfc\ \sqrt{5.012} = 0.5\ erfc\ (2.23875)$$

$$\approx 0.5\ \frac{e^{-(2.23875)^2}}{2.23875 \times \sqrt{\pi}} = 8.4 \times 10^{-4}$$

Example 8A-4: The performance requirement of a DS-CDMA system is to have (at the base station) a maximum probability of error, $P_e = 10^{-3}$. Assume that the system noise has much weaker power than the interference signal power, the processing gain is 128, and all the mobile units send out the same power level signals to the base station [i.e. $A_1 = A_i$ ($i = 1, N$) as indicated in Eq.(8A-4), that is, the base station receives the same voltage A_1 from every mobile unit]. Determine the maximum number of users this system can support.

From Eq. (8A-5), by substituting $P_e = 10^{-3}$ and using trial and error method, the E_b/N_T ratio is derived as follows:

$$P_e = (\frac{1}{2}) \, erfc \sqrt{\frac{E_b}{N_T}} = 10^{-3} \qquad \Rightarrow \qquad E_b/N_T = 4.852$$

Substituting this value into Eq.(8A-4) results in:

$$\frac{E_b}{N_T}[= 4.852] = \frac{A_1^2/2}{\sum_{i=2}^{N} A_i^2/3} \times \frac{T_b}{T_c} = \frac{3}{2(N-1)} \times 128 \qquad (8A-7)$$

Therefore, N = maximum number of users can be calculated to be 41 (i.e. the system can support a maximum of 41 users).

Example 8A-5: The area served by the system described in Example 8A-4 has a temporary need to increase the number of users from 41 to a higher number. Discuss the performance trade-off (degradation) when the number of users is increased beyond 41. It should be noted (as shown in Figure 8-24) that in any wireless system:

"System performance degrades as the number of users increases."

To solve this problem, first apply Eq.(8A-7), for a given N (the maximum number of users), to obtain E_b/N_T, which is then substituted into Eq.(8A-5) to calculate the probability of error performance, P_e.

The system (as derived in Example 8A-4) was designed to carry up to 41 users, with a performance level of $P_e = 10^{-3}$. Assume the number of users is increased to 45 (an approximate 10% increase from the original designed capacity). By applying Eq.(8A-7) to compute the E_b/N_T ratio, and by applying Eq.(8A-5) the value of P_e; and a value of $P_e = 1.7 \times 10^{-3}$ can be calculated (this value is plotted in Figure 8A-6).

This procedure is repeated for N = 50 (a 20% increase from the original designed capacity), N = 55 (a 30% increase), N = 60 (a 40% increase), N = 65 (a 50% increase), and N = 70 (a 60% increase). The results are plotted in Figure 8A-7. It can be seen in Figure 8A-7 that the system performance of a DS-CDMA system **degrades gracefully** as the number of users increases. When the system is overused (i.e. at 60% in excess of the designed capacity) the performance is approximately one order of magnitude worse than the required performance specification. This is a very attractive characteristic of the DS-CDMA technology, with respect to network operations and loading.

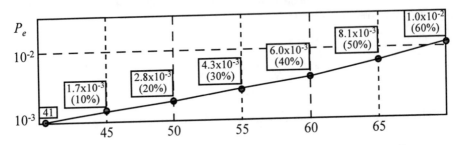

Figure 8A-6   (CDMA) Graceful Degradation as the Number of Users Increases.

Example 8A-6: Signal degradation due to a lack of dynamic power control by CDMA users (or base station). For the CDMA system designed in Example 8A-4, signal degradation will occur if the radiated power of one of the 41 users is not well controlled. Assume that a user radiates a voltage level seven times higher than the other 40 users. Examine the resulting impact on system performance.

First, by applying Eq.(8A-4) with $A_1 = A_2 = A_3 = A_4 = \ldots = A_{40}$, and $A_{41} = 7\,A_1$, the E_b/N_T ratio can be obtained as 2.43. Next, substituting this value into Eq.(8A-5) to calculate the probability of error. The result can be obtained as follows:

$$P_e = 1.4 \times 10^{-2} \equiv 14 \text{ x (the designed } P_e)$$

Clearly, this system's probability of error performance is 14 times worse than what is designed for. Therefore, when the radiated power of one or more users is not well controlled, the system degrades rapidly. It suggests that:

"Dynamic power control must be carefully implemented by system software in a CDMA system."

Appendix 8-2   Demodulation and Equalization

In addition to demodulating the received signal (the inverse function of modulation) two additional important functions are performed by the receiver: (1) filtering, and (2) equalization. These two functions are briefly described in this appendix.

8B-1 Filtering to Control Channel Noise

As the modulated signal is transported over the airway it is corrupted by channel noise, which in turn degrades the system performance [i.e. Signal to Noise ratio ($\equiv$ S/N)]. The degradation of S/N result in an increased the bit error rate for digital services. To improve the S/N of a wireless system, the first action is to add a channel filter at the receiver.

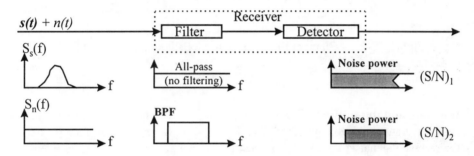

Figure 8B-1   S/N Performance With and Without a Channel Filter.

The channel noise, which represents all the noise sources in the end-to-end connection, is represented as a white Gaussian noise model (proof of this concept is beyond the scope of this book). White noise has a nearly flat spectrum across the entire frequency range used in practical communication systems. The noise power at the receiver is simply the area under the noise spectrum curve. If a channel filter is not applied, the $(S/N)_1$ is smaller than the $(S/N)_2$ for a receiver with a channel filter (that has a smaller received noise power as shown in Figure 8B-1). Hence, a receiver of any communication system is implemented by using a channel filter.

Four generic types of filters are available for different applications: Low-Pass Filter (LPF), High Pass Filter (HPF), BandPass Filter (BPF), and notch (band-stop, band reject) filter. For wireless receivers, the received signal is "bandpass" and occupies the frequency range of ($f_l \sim f_u$). Therefore, bandpass filters are commonly used in wireless receivers. The filter shown in Figure 8B-1 is a generic BandPass Filter (BPF). Many different filters have been developed to perform the BPF function. Two commonly-seen filters (matched, and integrate-and-dump filters) are briefly described as follows:

- **Matched filters**: This filter's spectrum is designed to be adaptable to an incoming signal spectrum. That is, the received signal power is maintained at its maximum value, while the received noise power is reduced to a smaller value. As shown in Figure 8B-2, the received noise power is smaller when a matched filter is used instead of a generic BPF. The S/N performance without a filter $(S/N)_1$, with a generic BPF $(S/N)_2$, and a matched filter $(S/N)_3$ are related as follows:

$$\left(\frac{S}{N}\right)_3 < \left(\frac{S}{N}\right)_2 < \left(\frac{S}{N}\right)_1$$

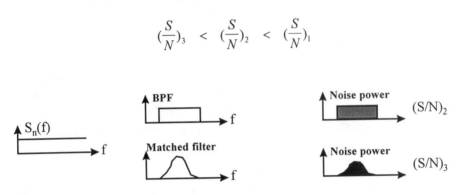

Figure 8B-2   Channel Filters: a Generic BPF and a Matched Filter.

- **Integrate and dump filter**: This filter's design is based on the fact that Gaussian noise has an average noise voltage of "0" (i.e., $E[n(t)] \approx 0$). Instead of sampling (or detecting) the received signal at the middle of each bit interval, a receiver using an integrate and dump filter samples the signal at the end of each bit-interval (i.e., $t = n \times T_b$).

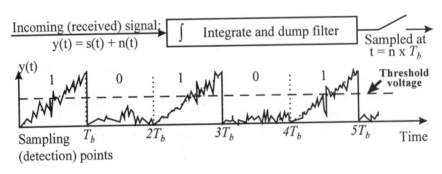

Figure 8B-3   An Integrate and Dump Filter.

For the bit intervals where a logical "1" has been transmitted, the integrated signal power at the end of the bit interval should be greater than the threshold level (see Figure 8B-3). This is because the average noise power is approximately "0" over the bit-interval, and the accumulated power at the end of the bit interval contributed by the incoming signal (e.g., during the intervals $0 \leq t \leq T_b$, $2T_b \leq t \leq 3T_b$, $4T_b \leq t \leq 5T_b$, ..., as shown in Figure 8B-3) will be restored as a logical "1".

In comparison, for the time intervals $T_b \leq t \leq 2T_b$ and $3T_b \leq t \leq 4T_b$ (see Figure 8B-3), the integrated signal power (or voltage) at the end of the bit interval is almost "zero". This is because the averaged noise power is approximately "0", and the signal power contributed during the interval is also "0", hence the accumulated power at the end of the interval will be restored as logical "0".

An advantage of using an integrate and dump filter is the reduced effect of impulse noise which may occur during the interval when the receiver is sampling the incoming signal. For example, during the interval $4T_b \leq t \leq 5T_b$ there is impulse noise with a large negative voltage spike in the middle of the bit interval (see Figure 8B-3). If the receiver sampled the incoming signal at the mid-point of the interval, this bit would have been erroneously restored as a logical "0" (instead of a logical "1") because the impulse noise spike was large enough to cross the threshold voltage.

8B-2 Inter-Symbol Interference (ISI)

When transmitting a digital bit stream over a communication channel, the signal pulses representing logical 1's will be spread over a larger interval than the interval allocated for a single digital bit. This phenomena is known as dispersion, pulse distortion, delay spread, delay dispersion, or pulse dispersion. Pulse dispersion causes **Inter-Symbol Interference (ISI),** and can introduce bit errors at the receiver. There are two major contributors to ISI in wireless systems: (1) bandlimiting, and (2) multi-path transmission.

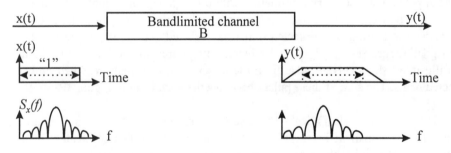

Figure 8B-4   Bandlimiting Effect: Pulse Dispersion.

(1) **Bandlimiting**: A wireless system used to transport a digital data stream is always bandwidth-limited. That is, the available bandwidth for carrying the digital data stream is never sufficient because the bandwidth of a digital signal is infinite. The result is that a restored digital "1" is never a rectangular shape, but is actually "spread out" as shown in Figure 8B-4. From a signal spectrum viewpoint, an ideal

digital pulse has a sinc function, sinc(f), with equally spaced side lobe zero-crossings and a main lobe with a zero-crossing twice as large as the side-lobe zero-crossing space. With pulse dispersion, the spacing between two adjacent zero-crossings are no longer equal [see Figure 8B-4, or Figure 8B-6(A)].

- **Multi-path transmission:** When a digital pulse is transmitted over the airway, there are literally hundreds of paths carrying the information. Each path will reach the receiver at a different time instance with a different signal strength. This condition also results in a pulse spreading effect that is similar to bandlimiting.

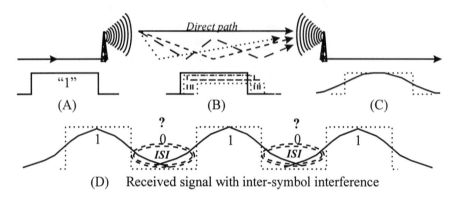

(D)   Received signal with inter-symbol interference

Figure 8B-5   Multi-Path Transmission and ISI.

As shown in Figure 8B-5, a receiver typically receives a signal with the strongest power from the direct path transport. In addition to the direct path, there are many reflected paths that also carry information with different signal strengths. Some reflected signals may be large enough to contribute to the net signal strength, and can be used to restore the information. The reflected signals are delayed in time with respect to the direct path signal. Figure 8B-5(A) is the pulse representing a transmitted logical "1". Figure 8B-5(B) illustrates the received pulse from the direct path, and many received *pulses* from reflected paths. The sum of these pulses becomes the waveform in Figure 8B-5(C).

Therefore, a single logical "1" pulse (transmitted from the far end) is no longer rectangular, as shown in Figure 8B-5(C). Combining the effect of channel bandwidth limitation with multi-path transmission, produces the received data stream shown in Figure 8B-5(D). As indicated, the energy from a logical "1" will impose interference during the bit interval where a logical "0" resides; thus causes Inter-Symbol Interference (ISI). Note that the logical "0" interval may receive energy from a previous "1" as well as from a following logical "1". If the ISI has an energy level that is higher than the threshold voltage used for signal restoration, the ISI can force a "0" to erroneously become a "1", and will result in a poor bit error rate at the receiver. Special techniques can be applied to reduce the ISI effect. A commonly-used technology is "**equalization**".

8B-3 Equalization: Concept and Implementation

The effect of pulse spreading is illustrated in Figure 8B-5(D). To explain the concept and implementation of equalization, the signal power spectrum is analyzed. A received signal in a wireless system, with inter-symbol interference and equalization, typically has a signal spectrum as shown in Figure 8B-6(A). This sinc(f) pattern has irregular zero-crossing spaces and theoretically, it is no longer a sinc function. The zero crossings are **not** occurring at t = ±T, ±2T, ±3T, ±4T, etc. However, after this distorted signal is fed into an equalizer, the output signal is restored as shown in Figure 8B-6(B), with evenly spaced zero crossings occurring at t = ±T, ±2T, ±3T, ±4T, etc. Hence, the signal has been transformed into a "true" sinc function.

"A sinc function in the frequency domain represents a logical "1" (or rectangular pulse) in the time domain, and vice versa."

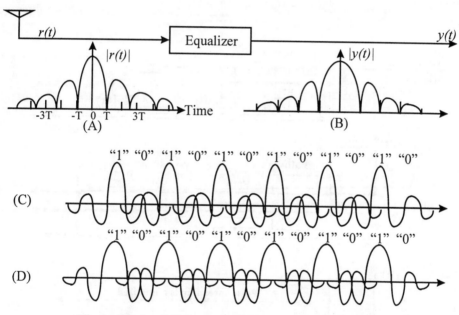

Figure 8B-6   Effect of Equalization: ISI Improvement.

The effect of equalization substantially improves inter-symbol interference. If a digital data stream of "10101010..." has been transmitted, the received signal waveform shown in Figure 8B-6(C) results when a receiver does not use an equalizer. It can be seen that the bit intervals where a logical "0" resides, are affected by the signal energy from adjacent logical "1" signals. This ISI may be strong enough to cause the restored signal to be decoded erroneously (i.e. interpreted as a logical "*1*" in this case). In comparison, when a receiver uses an equalizer [Figure 8B-5(B)], there is a minimum energy level during the logical "*0*" intervals, therefore the "0" bits will be restored correctly.

A common design method used for implementing equalization is a "delay line". As shown in Figure 8B-7, there are N taps of one-bit delay elements (Ds) connected to gain devices (g_0, g_1, g_2, ...). It should be noted that a gain device can be either positive or negative (i.e. larger than 1, or less than 1).

This example uses multi-path transmission to illustrate how a delay line (an equalizer) reduces pulse spreading. The received signal has 6 paths, as shown in Figure 8B-7, and is connected directly to a gain device with a gain of g_0. The received signal is delayed by one delay unit (T seconds) and fed to a gain device with a gain of g_1 (a negative number in this example). This procedure is continued for N times, and all of the signals are summed to yield a composite signal $y(t)$. For an automatic equalizer, the least square error criterion is applied to achieve an optimal result so that $y(t)$ will have a minimum pulse spreading.

$$y(t) = z_1(t) + z_2(t) + z_3(t) + \dots \qquad (8B-1)$$

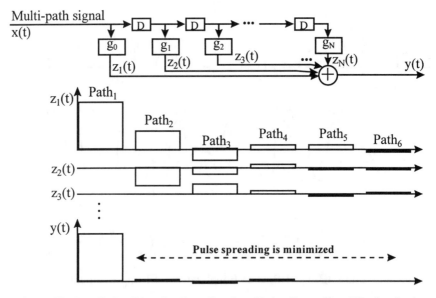

Figure 8B-7   Delay Line for Equalization (Pulse Spreading Elimination).

Note that, with an equalizer, the signal strengths for those intervals shown as "path$_2$", "path$_3$", "path$_4$", "path$_5$", "path$_6$", etc., are properly "equalized", that is, an approximately "0" level. Therefore, the only signal strength appears at the output of the equalizer is from the "direct" path. The "delay spread (dispersion, pulse spreading) has been reduced or eliminated.

CHAPTER 9

Data Communications Fundamentals

Chapter Objectives

Upon the completion of this chapter, you should be able to:

- Describe several basic terms used in the data communications industry (e.g., simplex; half duplex vs. full duplex; point-to-point vs. multi-point communications; serial vs. parallel transport; skew; synchronous vs. asynchronous transport, etc.).

- Describe the Open System Interconnection (OSI) Reference Model (RM) and its structure (layers 1 to 7; definitions, and functions), the concepts of layered architecture, entities, protocol, and interfaces. Describe electrical interface standards: (e.g., parallel-to-serial/serial-to-parallel conversion; EIA-232-D; V.24; V.28; V.35; X.21; X.21bis; EIA-422-A; EIA-423-A; EIA449; and EIA-530).

- Discuss data transmission fundamentals (e.g., various transmission media; signal rate vs. bit rate; channel and bandwidth; data encoding; and data modulation), and several commonly-used modem standards.

- Describe data link protocols (e.g., functions and types; Automatic Repeat & reQuest (ARQ); error control; bisync overview; and HDLC).

- Describe network interfaces [e.g., ITU-T X.25 (protocols, call setup, call termination, call request, etc.); ISDN/B-ISDN (standards, rate interfaces, etc.); frame relay packet switching (evolution, standards, networks, protocols, applications, etc.)].

9.1 INTRODUCTION

The purpose of a communication system (see Figure 9-1) is to carry a signal (voice, video, image, or data signals) from its source to its destination with a specific level of transmission quality. An information transmitter (i.e., a "source") encodes the information in a message format that is compatible with the communications network. These messages are carried by a transmission medium over the communications network. The medium can be wire (twisted-pair wires or coaxial cables), airway (radio, wireless, or satellite systems), or optical fibers. In addition to the transmission medium, a network contains transmission terminals, transmission equipment, switching machines, and signaling network. The destination point in a network is equipped with a receiver (i.e., a "sink") which decodes the received signal and restores the message.

Both the information source (transmitter) and sink (receiver) can be human beings, or devices (e.g., computers, printers, sensors, etc.). The information carried by a communications network can be four different types:

(1) Audio signals (e.g., speech signal or music)

(2) Visual signals (e.g., still pictures or textual information in the form of alpha-numeric characters, or in computer data files)

(3) Parametric signals (e.g., readings from meters, gauges, or sensors)

(4) Multi-media signals (e.g., a combination of voice, video, and data; moving pictures/television; or computer graphic simulations).

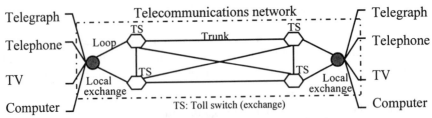

Figure 9-1   An End-to-End Communication.

9.1.1 Terms Used in Signal Communications

Several terms/concepts used in communications will be briefly reviewed. An understanding of these terms will simplify the introduction of data communications fundamentals.

- Simplex, half duplex vs. full duplex communications

    Communications can either one-way or two-way. If the signal is always transmitted by one party and other parties can only receive it, it is "one-way communication". For example, TV or radio broadcast is this type of operation, and is referred to as "*simplex*" communication. Similarly, if both parties are "transmitting" and "receiving", it is referred to as "two-way" or "***duplex***" communication. As shown in Figure 9-2, there are two methods that can be used to implement "two-way" (duplex) communication:

(1) Half-duplex (or two-way alternate) communication: In this approach if one party is sending messages, the other party can only receive messages (i.e., both parties cannot send message at the same time). Thus, both parties can send and receive messages, but they must "take turns". Typically, the "telegraph" is implemented for half-duplex communication. For voice communications, it is not practical to use the half-duplex approach. However, for computer-to-computer communication, it can be negotiated whether system requires half-duplex of full-duplex capabilities.

(2) Full-duplex (two-way simultaneous) communication: This approach implies that both parties can simultaneously send and/or receive messages. It is clear that voice communication between humans is naturally a full-duplex communication method. Hence, telecommunications system designers must consider this factor.

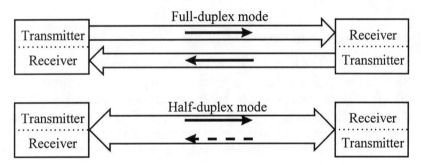

Figure 9-2   Half-Duplex versus Full-Duplex Communications.

- Point-to-point vs. multi-point communications

Another way to classify communication scenarios is to consider the number of devices that share a physical communication link. If only two devices share a particular physical link, the link is referred to as a "point-to-point" link. This is shown in Figure 9-3(A), where the two devices are a transmitter and a receiver.

In the contrast, if more than two devices share a physical link, it is called a multi-point link. Figure 9-3(B) show three examples of multi-point links:

* The bottom-left illustrates a "star" multi-point link used in a Local Area Network (LAN). A Transmitter (T) broadcasts (or multi-casts) signal to several Receivers (Rs).

* The center illustrates a mobile communication system. The Base Station's (BS) antenna radiates signals to multiple mobile receivers via airlinks.

* The bottom-right illustrates a satellite system that communicates with multiple earth stations via airlinks.

(A) Point-to-point transmission

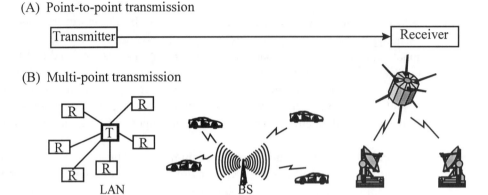

(B) Multi-point transmission

Figure 9-3   Point-to-point and Multi-point Links.

* Analog vs. digital communications:

As it previously in Chapter 1, an analog signal may possess any voltage level within a specific limit. For example, if a system has voltage limits between -10^v (volts) and $+10^v$, an analog signal generated by this system could possess a voltage of -10^v, -9.5^v, -9^v, -8.7^v, ..., $+7.6^v$, $+8.4^v$, $+9.2^v$, or, $+10^v$ at any given instance in time. Technically speaking, an analog signal is considered to be a continuous signal. In comparison, a digital signal is considered to be a discrete signal. That is, a digital signal can only possess a finite set of voltages. For example, a digital signal may be represented by a unipolar waveform with voltage levels of $(-5^v, 0^v)$; a polar waveform with voltage levels of $(-5^v, +5^v)$; or a bipolar waveform with voltage levels of $(-5^v, 0^v, +5^v)$, as previously defined in Chapter 1.

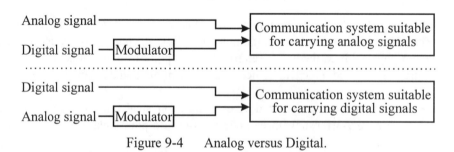

Figure 9-4   Analog versus Digital.

There are communication systems which are suitable for carrying digital signals over long distances (see Figure 9-4, bottom section). In this configuration, digital signals can be sent directly over the system. However, analog signals must be modulated [e.g., using Pulse Code Modulation (PCM) for voice digitization; described in Chapter 6] before being carried by the system. Similarly, there are systems designed to carry analog signals over long distances (see Figure 9-4, top section). An analog signal can be carried directly over the system. However, digital signals must be modulated [e.g., Amplitude Shift Keying (ASK); Frequency Shift Keying (FSK; 16-FSK; 32-FSK; 128-FSK, etc.); Phase Shift Keying (PSK; 16-PSK, 32-PSK, 128-PSK, etc.); or Quadrature Amplitude Modulation (QAM), described in Chapter 6] before being carried by the system.

- Data coding:

It is important in modern communication systems to store and transport user data (information). In addition, the communication system must also allow users to exchange data in a reliable, efficient, and intelligible manner.

User data is generally organized and stored in computing machines as "files" (e.g., a computer program, a document, or numerical readings from an experiment). The information (data) stored inside a machine is always represented (or coded) by a unique bit patterns. That is, each "character" of a file is stored as an "n-bit" codeword.

Example 9-1: Using the ASCII code (see Appendix 9A-1 at the end of this chapter) and "even parity-check" 8-bit codewords, verify the following character encoding for the message "Example 9-1.":

E	x	a	m	p	l
11000101	01111000	11100001	11101101	11110000	01101100

e		9	-	1	.
01100101	10100000	00111001	00101101	10110001	00101110

The Least Significant Bit (LSB) indicated by a bold digit is the additive parity-check bit for implementing the even-parity algorithm for the ASCII code of each character obtained from Figure 9A-1 in Appendix 9-1.

The resulting coded information bitstream (11000101   01111000   11100001   11101101   11110000   01101100   01100101   10100000   00111001   00101101   10110001   00101110) can be transmitted from one Data Terminal Equipment (DTE) to another DTE via different waveform formats (NRZ unipolar, RZ unipolar, polar, NRZ bipolar, or RZ bipolar; described in Chapter 6).

Regardless of the waveform format used to carry the information, the bit order sequence of transmission can be Most Significant Bit (MSB) first through Least Significant Bit (LSB) last, or vice versa (i.e., LSB first through MSB last). (Note that, previously stated in Chapter 6, for SONET/SDH standards, MSB is transported first).

- Serial versus parallel communications:

The coded information in "Example 9-1" can be transmitted as a serial or in parallel signal. Using the serial transmission methodology (assuming the MSB is transmitted first), the sequence of transmission will be (10100011), (00011110), (10000111), ..., (01110100), appearing as a continuous bitstream on a single port.

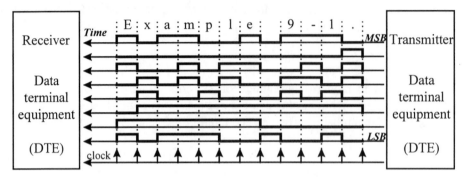

Figure 9-5   Parallel Transmission with Eight Ports.

In comparison, a system with multiple ports can be used to carry data in parallel as shown in Figure 9-5. Port No. 1 is used to transport the first bit (i.e., the MSB) of each character, port No. 2 carries the second MSBs, port No. 3 carries the third MSBs, ..., and port No. 8 carries the LSBs. At the first clock pulse, all of the eight bits (11000101) of the character "E" are sent simultaneously; at the second clock pulse, all of the eight bits (01111000) of the character "x" are sent; ...; and at the 12th clock pulse, all of the eight bits (00101110) of the character "." are sent.

The clock signal is critical in a digital communication system. It is essential that all bits be transmitted at the same instance so that they can be restored correctly at the receiver. The decoded bit stream can then be restored accurately as user information at the final destination. Two aspects of the clock signal must be considered in a digital communications system: (1) the accuracy of a clock (e.g., 10^{-11}), and (2) clock synchronization (i.e., timing at the receiver with respect to the transmitter; Chapter 6 and Chapter 14).

- Signal skew:

For parallel communication, a clock with good accuracy at the transmitter will generate a signal with a constant bit interval between any two adjacent bits (Figure 9-5). That is, the bits for the same character are generated at the same time by a clock pulse. However, after long-distance transmission the received bits (for the same character) will often arrive at slightly different time instances. This phenomena is called *skew*. When the skew is "bad" (i.e., a large timing offset), the bit decoding may not be the same as was transmitted. Consequently, the restored character will be different from the original character transmitted. Skew may alleviated in several ways. One way is to slow down the transmission speed, because slow speed data has greater tolerance for skew. However, speed reduction defeats the purpose of using a parallel system, which is designed to have high transmission speed.

Another method for alleviating skew is to install repeaters (amplifiers) or regenerators in the transport network to restore (i.e., re-time) bits before the skew is too large to decode the bits accurately. Therefore, the designed system speed can be maintained. This approach obviously results in increased overall system cost.

Example 9-2: Assume the third bit of each character is skewed so that the 3rd bit is moved to the 4th bit position, and the characters are erroneously decoded. Determine the characters that will be restored if the original message transmitted was "Data".

From Figure 9A-1 in Appendix 9-1, the message "Data" is encoded as (*0*100*0*100 *1*110*0*001 *0*111*0*100 *1*110*0*001) at the transmitter, using "even-parity". The italicized bit is the even parity-check bit, and the LSB, which is assumed to be transmitted last in the 8 bit sequence of each character. The bold bit is the 3rd bit transmitted, and the decoded (skewed) value for the 3rd bit is indicated by the "underlined" bit.

The decoded bits are (0100000) for the transmitted sequence (01000100), because it is assumed that the 3rd bit has been skewed to take on the value of the 4th bit. As previously indicated, the skew may be caused by two major reasons: (1) the distance, or (2) the receiving clock is not quite synchronized with the transmitting clock. Similarly, the decoded bits for the 2nd, the 3rd, and the 4th characters are (11100001), (01110000) and (111000001), respectively.

Assuming that, for simplicity, parity-checking is not performed, the restored message from the decoded bitstream, according to Figure 9A-1 will be "@apa", which is obviously different from the message that was originally transmitted (i.e., "data").

In practical applications, since the 1st and the 3rd decoded characters have violated parity-check rule (i.e., even-parity has not been maintained), the receiver will request re-transmission.

Table 9-1 summarizes the applications, the advantages and the disadvantages of serial and parallel transmission of a data bitstream.

(1) Serial transmission: Practically all long distance systems apply serial transmission because of the skew caused by "long" distance can be severe if parallel transmission were adopted. One primary disadvantage is speed tradeoff.

(2) Parallel transmission: Parallel transmission method is used in the digital computer environments, either internal or peripheral. The primary reason is the needs for "high" throughput required by a computer. However, a system with a moderate distance may require additional equipment such as amplifiers.

Table 9-1   Comparison between Serial and Parallel Transmission.

Parameter	Serial transmission	Parallel transmission
Applications	• *Data Terminate Equipment to DTE* • *Long distance transmission*	• *CPU-peripheral* • *Computer internal applications* • *Short distance transmission*
Advantages	• *Easy to implement* • *Device independent*	• *High throughput* • *Match internal architecture*
Disadvantages	• *Low speed (throughput)* • *P/S conversion required*	• *Limited distance due to skew* • *Increased costs: (clock, amplifiers, etc.)*

It should be mentioned that there is another type of skew in communication systems which carry both audio and video signal simultaneously on the same medium (e.g., broadcast TV or video services). When the received audio signal does not match exactly the associated video signal exactly, the signal is defined as having "skew". This may also occur in ATM multimedia services.

9.1.2 Synchronous versus Asynchronous Communications

The definitions of synchronous and asynchronous transmission are different from an application viewpoint. Asynchronous, bit-synchronous, and byte synchronous signals have been previously defined in Chapter 6. The definition of synchronization, with respect to data transmission, is discussed in this section.

9.1.2.1 Definitions: Asynchronous and Synchronous Data Transmission

Figure 9-6 illustrates the definition of asynchronous [Figure 9-6(A)] and synchronous [Figure 9-6(B)] data transmission as follows:

- Asynchronous data transmission: The transmission of each individual character within a data message is totally independent of the transmission of the previous characters. Asynchronous transmission has the following characteristics:

  * Each character must be framed: At least two framing bits are required per character, one indicating the beginning of a character and the other indicating the end of the character. Because of the added framing bits, the line efficiency for an asynchronous system is very low (e.g., 80% efficiency for an 8-bit character system). That is, additional overhead bits used as "flags" must be inserted regularly into "information" bitstream to identify the beginning and end of a character. This reduces transmission efficiency to a value less than 100%.

  * The timing of each bit is specified within a character.

  * Inter-character time intervals are typically non-uniform.

- Synchronous data transmission: The transmission of all characters within a data message block is contiguous (i.e., one character after another). Synchronous transmission has the following characteristics:

  * Each message block (rather than each character) is framed: The framing bits (characters) typically consist of several bits, and are used to indicate the beginning and end of each message block. The line efficiency can be 99% or even higher.

  * Within a message block, all characters must be transmitted contiguously.

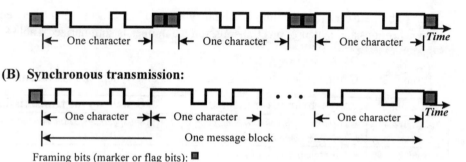

(A) Asynchronous transmission:

(B) Synchronous transmission:

Framing bits (marker or flag bits): ■

Figure 9-6   Synchronous and Asynchronous Data Transmission.

9.1.2.2 Applications: Asynchronous and Synchronous Data Transmission

The applications, advantages, and disadvantages of asynchronous and synchronous transmission are described in this section.

- Asynchronous transmission: This method is commonly used for communications between terminals and computers. Terminal users are relatively slow when entering data, typically generating no more than 15 characters per second (e.g., keyboard entry). In addition, the user at the terminal generates a small number of characters at a time, and usually checks the characters on the screen prior to sending subsequent characters, or entering "new" data.

     The user always participates in the error detection/correction task. For example, if errors have been detected, the user may choose to ignore them if they are not important (e.g., minor spelling errors), or the user may apply the <DEL> or <BACKSPACE> key as often as necessary to correct errors, or inserting additional characters, prior to sending a message.

     The cornerstone of error recovery in an asynchronous transmission system is a concept known as "echoplex". If a terminal is provisioned for in the "echoplex mode", a character entered at the terminal is not displayed until it is "echoed back" from the host. That is, after a key is struck, the appropriate bit coding for that character is sent to the computer, then the computer sends the character back to the terminal to be displayed. This process allows the user to be involved in the end-to-end error recovery process to improve system performance (i.e., data transmission accuracy).

- Synchronous transmission: This method is commonly used for computer-to-computer message communications. The error recovery technology used in a synchronous transmission system is discussed later in this chapter. There are synchronous terminals that support synchronous transmission to and from a host computer.

The comparison (applications, advantages and disadvantages) between the asynchronous and synchronous transmission techniques is summarized Table 9-2.

Table 9-2   Comparison between Asynchronous and Synchronous Transmission.

Parameter	Asynchronous transmission	Synchronous transmission
Applications	• *Terminal equipment to computer* • *Low-cost computer-to-computer*	• *High-speed device interconnection*
Advantages	• *Easy to implement (low cost)* • *Clock re-synchronizes with each character*	• *High throughput* • *High line efficiency*
Disadvantages	• *Low speed (throughput)* • *Low line efficiency*	• *Automatic error detection required* • *High accuracy timing required* • *Relatively complex (high cost)*

Asynchronous transmission is simpler to implement, and therefore has a lower cost than synchronous transmission. For this mode of transmission, "synchronization" between the transmitter and the receiver is relatively simple since each character is sent as an independent entity with its own framing information. However, asynchronous operation has a relatively low efficiency. In addition, the system speed is relatively low (typically, less than 20 kbps) comparing to a synchronous transmission.

In a synchronous transmission system, the line efficiency is much higher than asynchronous transmission. Framing characters are added to the line data bitstream between two adjacent message blocks, with each block containing many message characters. For example, if the message block has a length of 16,000 character (e.g., Digital Equipment Corps' DECNet), the line efficiency is as high as 99.99%. The transmission speed is also relatively faster (typically up to 100 Mbps). However, synchronous systems require automatic error detection/correction since the transmission speed is high. In addition, it requires sophisticated timing methods. The receiver must accurately determine all character and bit boundaries. This is necessary to allow the restoration of messages with a minimum number of erroneous bits. This can be implemented with very accurate clocks at both the transmitter and the receiver; and these clocks must also be synchronized. Due to this "overhead", a synchronous transmission system is usually much more expensive than an asynchronous transmission system.

9.1.2.3 Asynchronous Data Transmission Format

Figure 9-7 shows the character format used in an asynchronous transmission system. The line state is in either the "high" or "low state" (e.g., "mark" or "space"; $+3^v$ or -3^v; $+3^v$ or 0^v; etc.). In a typical system, the "mark" (a logical "1") is transmitted with a line voltage between 3 and 5 volts, while a "space" (a logical "0") is transmitted with a line voltage of zero. The asynchronous character is preceded by a framing bit (shown as the starting bit in Figure 9-7) known as the "start bit", which is typically in the "space" state (i.e., logical "0"). The asynchronous character is followed by a "stop" interval, which may occupy one or two-bit intervals. The "stop" interval always returns the line to the "mark" state (i.e., logical "1"). This is done so that there is always a *"mark-to-space"* transition between two adjacent characters. By using this arrangement, the receiver can determine when a character is coming by detecting a "mark-to-space" transition. This transition can also be used to synchronize the receiver clock with respect to the transmitter clock.

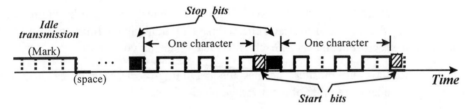

Figure 9-7   Asynchronous Character Format.

When there is no data to be transmitted on the line, idle characters must be transmitted. An idle line is kept in the "mark" state (i.e., logical "1") to distinguish a lack of transmission activity from a "cut wire" [i.e., a cut wire would lose power and present itself as the "space" state (logical "0")].

For a successful asynchronous transmission, the transmitter and the receiver must agree upon:

- The number of data bit per character: A system typically uses 8-bit characters. This type of data has a built-in error detection/correction capability (described in Chapter 13). For ASCII code, the data message is represented by a 7-bit character, and an 8th bit is used for the purpose of performing a parity-check function over the 7 character bits.

- The length of a bit interval: This is the same as defining the data rate (e.g., 2.5 kbps, 100 Mbps) also called the transmission speed.

- The length of the "stop" interval must be defined: The "stop" interval can be one-bit interval or longer, and may consist of several bit intervals.

- The sequence (order) of bit transmission must be defined: The sequence of transmission can be the Most Significant Bit (MSB) first, and the Least Significant Bit (LSB) last; or vice versa.

- The digital data coding must be specified: A standard coding scheme such as ASCII (see Figure 9A-1 in appendix A9-1) may be used. ASCII code is only one of many character codes that can be applied to code data message characters.

- The electrical signal level must be defined: A 3^v level (or a 5^v-level) is commonly used to represent the "mark" state, while a 0^v-level can represent the "space" state.

9.1.2.4 Synchronous Data Transmission Format

Figure 9-8 shows a synchronous message format, which is often referred to as a message block or frame. A synchronous message is sent as a contiguous data bitstream with no breaks between any message characters. The message block consists of the following fields:

- Synchronous characters field: The "synchronous characters" are used by the receiver to prepare for the arrival of message characters. This field also defines an 8-bit block pattern so the receiver can decode each individual character correctly.

- Message header: The "header" defines the beginning-of-message frame, and may include the sequence number of the message block (frame).

- Data (payload) field: The "payload" contains user information. All data characters are sent as part of a continuous transmission block.

- Message trailer: The "trailer" is the end-of-message frame indicator, and may include error detection information (typically CRC).

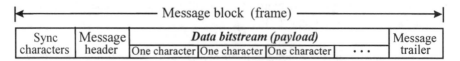

Figure 9-8   Synchronous Message Format.

For successful synchronous transmission, the transmitter and the receiver must agree upon:

- Transmission format
- Length of bit interval (data rate)
- SYNC characters

- Size and contents of header
- Size and contents of trailer
- Digital data encoding

9.1.3 File Transfer

Figure 9-9 illustrates the steps required in the case when a user on host A (e.g., computer system A) is transferring a file to a user on host B. The steps are described as follows:

- The user at host A creates a file (e.g., "file.txt") using a suitable text processing editor on the host A.

- The file (e.g., "file.txt") is stored as a collection of logical "1s" and "0s". This unique collection of "1s" and "0s" represents information contained in the file. The character code is typically a popular format (e.g., ASCII and EBCDIC).

- A data bitstream is then transmitted as a signal over a physical medium (the choice of signal format and medium is independent of the character code).

- The data can be transmitted either in parallel or in serial (as previously described in this chapter).

- If serial transmission is chosen, the option of asynchronous or synchronous transmission must be selected (as previously described in this chapter).

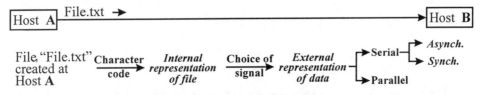

Figure 9-9   Steps in a File Transfer.

For successful transmission of the file, some agreements must be met. These agreements include: error recovery techniques, connection establishment and release, and file format. To facilitate these agreements, national and international standards organizations were formed. The standards organizations clarify interface requirements and protocols.

9.1.4 Standard Organizations Associated with Data Communications

It is important for data engineers, managers, and users to recognize relevant standards organizations. Standards are important since they allow different vendors to build compatible devices without necessitating that they share internal design information.

More importantly, standards will tend to reduce the cost of many devices since equipment will be more mass produced (rather than replying on small quantities of customer designed systems). Anyone who is technically qualified and interested in participation can become a member of a standards organization, and can participate in relevant standards activities. Some primary national and international standard organizations, with respect to data communications, are briefly described as follows:

- International Telecommunications Union - Telecommunications Standards Sector (ITU-T)

  * ITU-T was formerly called CCITT, an agency of the U.N. since 1948.
  * The State Department is the U.S. representative to ITU-T.
  * ITU-T develops recommendations for access to public networks.
  * ITU-T formally issues new recommendations every four years.
  * ITU-T plays an important role in developing (standard) recommendations for data communications.
    ♦ ITU-T Rec. I-series: Related to ISDN (e.g., I.122, I.430, I.43, ...).
    ♦ ITU-T Rec. V-series: Related to data communications over telephone networks (e.g., V.32, V.34, V.35, ...).
    ♦ ITU-T Rec. X-series: Related to data communications networks (e.g., X.21, X.25, X.31, ...).
  * ITU-T supports subcommittees or Study Groups (e.g., SG4, SG7, SG13, SG15, ...).

- American National Standards Institute (ANSI)

  * ANSI is responsible for U.S. national standards in many areas [ranging from safety clothing (boots, helmets, jackets, ...) to aircraft].
  * Accredited Standards Committees (ASC): Perform and administer technical work and development of standards. ASC operates according to the regulations established by ANSI.
  * ASC divides the areas of work among Technical Committees. Two important data communications Technical Committees are:
    ♦ ANSI-T1 committee: Address issues concerning telecommunications (e.g., T1D1 committee develops standards for ISDN architecture, services, switching and signaling). ANSI Recommendations are T1.105, T1.106, etc.
    ♦ ANSI-X3 committee: Address issues concerning information processing (e.g., X3.66).

- International Organization for Standards (ISO)

  * ISO can be considered as an international version of ANSI.

- * ISO sets international standards in many areas (e.g., environmental requirements, quality control, manufacturing process, development, and telecommunications interfaces).

- * ISO major contribution: Open Systems Interconnection Reference Model.

- * ISO standards for computer networking: Joint Technical Committee (JTC-1) subcommittee 6 (SC6), and Technical Committee 97.

- Institute of Electrical and Electronics Engineers (IEEE): A professional society that is involved in a number of standards-making activities. One activity involves Local Area Networks (LANs) (e.g., IEEE 802 committee).

- Electronics Industries Association (EIA): An organization comprised of vendors and users of electronics equipment. The EIA members also address a number of standards (e.g., the electrical interfaces between computing equipment; EIA-232-D).

- Federal Information Processing Standards (FIPS), U.S. Federal Government Standards (FED-STD), U.S. Military Standards (MIL-STD), Department of Defense Standards (DOD-STD) and National Bureau of Standards (NBS): These agencies set standards that must be met by vendors that deal with U.S. government organizations.

- De facto industry standards: Recognized standards or interfaces that have been established by prominent vendors, service providers, or customers (e.g., AT&T, IBM).

9.2 OSI REFERENCE MODEL

In the early 1990's, the rapid proliferation and wide variety of protocols, modems, signaling methods, and network architectures caused difficulty for users attempting to access telecommunications networks. In addition, users had to purchase expensive and redundant equipment. As a result, the standards organizations decided to define common structures and integrated networks for data processing to alleviate some of these problems. The layered network architecture, known as the Open Systems Interconnection Reference Model (OSI-RM), was proposed by the International Organization of Standardization (ISO) in 1978. This model, which was approved in 1983, makes it possible for data processing machines from different vendors to communicate and inter-change data efficiently.

The OSI standards allow service providers to build standardized data networks, and benefits both users and vendors. In the OSI environment complicated communications tasks are divided into a set of manageable functions called layers. Each layer performs a subset of the tasks which are required for a system to communicate with another system. *This (layered) OSI basic reference model is defined in ITU-T Rec. X.200.*

Definition 9-1:   A **real system** is a computer (together with its associated software, peripherals, terminals, human operators, physical processors and subsystems) that is responsible for information transfer. In comparison, an **open system** is a "representation" (i.e., an external interface) of a real system that complies with the architecture and protocols defined by OSI. In other words, an **open system** is that portion of a real system that is visible to other open systems, and functions to transfer and process information jointly.

OSI addresses interconnection, exchange of information (i.e., transmission), and "cooperation" (i.e., inter-process communications) between open systems. OSI standards define:

- Data representation
- Data storage
- Resource management
- Integrity and security
- Program support (i.e., compilation, linking, testing, storage, etc.)
- Information exchange
- Synchronization between activities

9.2.1 Concepts of Layered Architecture

Real systems are interconnected by using a physical transmission medium (see Figure 9-9). The overall objective of all hardware and software components that form an open system is to enable interconnection between application processes.

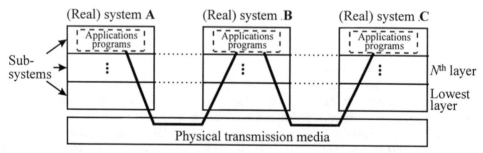

Figure 9-9   Concepts of A Layered (System) Architecture.

Application processes are an abstraction of user programs which implement certain users functions. Note that not all aspects of an application program are required to comply with OSI standards. Only the aspects of an application that concern communication or cooperation between open systems are of interest. To design/implement complex mechanisms for information transfer and cooperation, the entire network must be viewed as a series of layers. Each open system is logically divided into a collection of subsystems, each subsystem implements a specific set of functions. A layer is a collection of all the subsystems from different open systems which perform similar functions.

9.2.2 Layers, Services, and Functions

A network of computers may be viewed as a series of layers, with each layer cutting across several systems as shown in Figure 9-9. Each layer provides a set of services for the subsystems in a higher layer. The services include the ability to move data across the network, and the ability to enable users to exchange data without concern for its representation (i.e., the original data format).

Each layer, in addition to provide a set of services to the next higher layer, also implements additional functions, over and above the service made available by the lower layers, thereby enlarging the overall service or improving its quality.

By applying the layer structure, large problems are divided into smaller manageable problems. For example, providing a service that allows a user to transfer data reliably across a network, without concern for representation of information. This problem is solved by implementing specific functions in different layers to perform each aspect of the overall task. This process is a top-down approach, which leads to modularity and independence from the actual implementation of underlying functions. Hence, the design of a layer can be changed to incorporate new technology, without having to change other layers.

The concept of layering is "transparency". That is, a given layer transfers user data without concern regarding content or format. In addition, data in any form can be transferred by the supporting layer.

The functions implemented within a layer "close the gap" between the services needed (i.e., from a lower layer) and those to be provided for use by a higher layer. Once the services provided by each layer are defined, it is easy to implement the functionality of each layer.

9.2.3 Entities, Protocols, and Interfaces

A subsystem consists of one or more entities that are hardware or software modules (see Figure 9-10). In other words, a computer network may be viewed as a collection of entities.

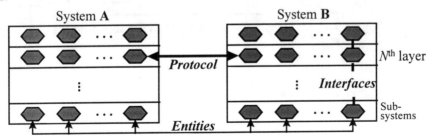

Figure 9-10   Entities, Protocols, and Interfaces.

Two entities in different systems may interact or communicate with each other, provided they belong to the same layer. Such entities are defined as "*peer entities*". The interaction between peer entities is governed by protocol, which specifies the nature of the information that may be exchanged, with respect to both contents and representation. Protocol also specifies the conditions required for an entity to send or receive information.

Two entities that belong to two *adjacent* layers within a real system can interact with each other. Interaction across a layer is consistent with a service being made available (by an entity) to the next higher layer. The specification is dependent upon the collection of primitive operations that either entity is capable of supporting. These operations are called "primitives", which indicate they cannot be further broken down. Associated with each primitive is a collection of parameters that can be changed to take advantage of improved technology.

Aspects pertaining to the implementation of the service primitives and the representation of parameters are not parts of the architectural specification. An implementation of the service is referred to as an "interface", because it accesses services across an interface within the same system, that are across a layer boundary. Services are made available by an entity in the Nth layer at Service Access Points (SAPs; see Figure 9-11). An entity provides services at one or more SAPs, and entities in higher layers may access services at one or more SAPs. There is one restriction: two entities within the same subsystem may not access services at a common SAP.

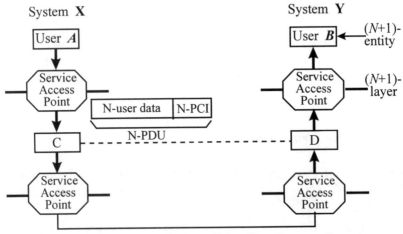

Figure 9-11   Transmission of User Data between Systems.

9.2.4 Transmission of User Data

Figure 9-11 shows the flow of user data from one system to another. Assume that user A at system X needs to send data to user B at system Y. First, user A hands over data to the supporting layer. This can be done by using a service primitive that corresponds with the data transfer service, and by supplying the identity of user B (i.e., B's address). It is the responsibility of this layer to deliver the contents to its destination (i.e., user B). The entity C, which supports data transfer at the corresponding Service Access Point (SAP), sends the user data to the corresponding supporting entity, D, which is located at the remote end (i.e., the destination). The data is sent with control information that pertains to the protocol between the two supporting entities (i.e., C and D), and is known as Protocol Control Information (PCI). The PCI typically contains a sequence number and CRC information. The user data and PCI together are called a Protocol Data Unit (PDU).

The entities transfer the Protocol Data Unit (PDU) in the following manner. The entity uses services provided by the lower layer to transmit the PDU. It typically hands over the PDU to the lower layer as user data. The lower layer may need to append its own protocol control information. At the remote end, the receiving entity "strips off" the Protocol Control Information (PCI), interprets the PCI, and delivers only the user data to the final destination (i.e., user B, in this example).

The transparency property of data transfer is an important concept in a layered architecture. The concept of transparency is summarized as follows:

- The supporting layer does not, in any way, constrain the kind of data that is transferred across the layer, with respect to both the contents and its encoding.

- The supporting layer is not required to examine the user data as part of performing its functions. For example, a layer does not compare the contents of two user messages to determine whether or not they are duplicates.

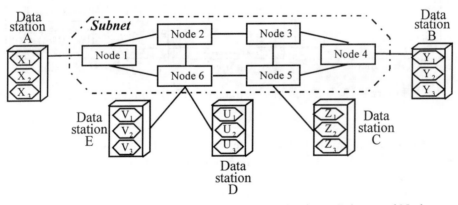

Figure 9-12   A Computer Network with Data Stations, Subnet and Nodes.

Figure 9-12 shows a computer network consisting of several data stations (i.e., host computers) and many nodes that forms subnet. These stations can communicate with each other over the subnet by using store-and-forward methods. The host computers contain the application program processes (e.g., X_1, X_2, X_3, Y_1, Y_2, Y_3, Z_1, Z_2, Z_3, …). The subnet provides the communication facilities, and consists of several nodes connected by high-speed trunks. Each node in the subnet is a specialized computer that performs the following functions:

- Accepts data from a link, and temporarily stores the data for later transfer.

- Determines the link on which the data will be delivered (i.e., sent).

- Sends the data on the selected link.

9.2.5 OSI Reference Model Layer Structure

Figure 9-13 shows the OSI reference model that supports an application program X in data station A, to communicate with an application program Y in (a remote) data station B. The connection between X and Y is indicated by the "bold dotted" line in Figure 9-13.

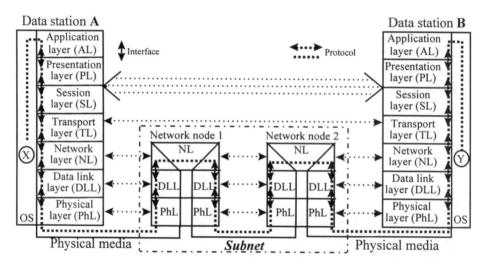

Figure 9-13   Seven Layer-structure of OSI Reference Model.

There are seven layers in the OSI reference model. The lower three layers (i.e., physical layer, data link layer, and network layer) are called the "chained layers", which exist in both the nodes (i.e., the subnet) and the host computers (i.e., data stations). These layers are responsible for transporting data packets over the subnet.

The upper four layers (i.e., transport layer, session layer, presentation layer, and application layer) are called the "end-to-end layers", which exist in the host computers only. The upper layers have information processing-oriented capabilities and deal with the way the application programs communicate. The transport layer is a liaison between the lower layers and the upper layers, and provides an end-to-end reliable path between the applications.

Each layer provides services to the layer above it, and receives services from the layer below. A layer requests services from the layer beneath it through an interface.

Each entity converses with its peer entity, which resides in a network node or another data station. "Peer-to-peer" communication is governed by a standard protocol. The services and the protocols at each layer are specified by the ISO and ITU-T. The peer entities communicate with each other via a virtual connection (i.e., a logical connection). The physical connection exists at the physical media layer, which can be twisted-pair wires, coaxial cables, digital radio signals, or optical fibers.

Figure 9-14 shows how the user X in system A transfers data to user Y in system B within an OSI environment. The data is presented by user X to the application layer, which adds Protocol Control Information (PCI) in the form of a header that is attached to the user data. The header contains a message number, date, time, etc. and is only meaningful to the application entities (i.e., this information is treated as data by the presentation layer). The user data plus the PCI is known as the Protocol Data Unit (PDU).

The application layer sends the PDU, which is treated as data, to the lower layer (i.e., to the presentation layer). In turn, the presentation layer adds its PCI to the received data to form the presentation layer PDU, which is then sent to the session layer. The same process is repeated until the user data reaches the physical layer, where the resulting message is transmitted as a series of bits via the transmission media.

At the receiver, each layer strips off the overhead information and interprets its header (i.e., the respective PCI), and then deliver the data to the higher layer. Note that in the receiving direction, the data at a particular layer is the "data plus the PCI" of its higher layer. For example, the session layer strips of its overhead (PCI) bits and delivers the data to the presentation layer. This "data" includes the "data" and the "PCI of the presentation layer". Eventually the user Y receives the data from user X via the application layer. The functions of the seven OSI layers are described the following sections.

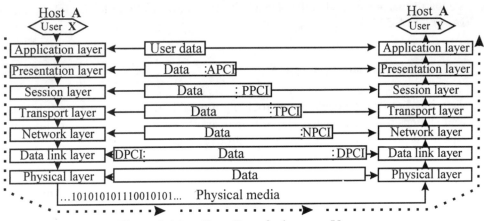

Figure 9-14   Data Transfer between Users.

9.2.5.1 Layer 1: the Physical Layer

This layer defines the physical interfaces between devices, and defines the rules by which the message data bitstream is passed from one device to another. Four important characteristics of the physical layer are described here.

(1) Electrical characteristic: It describes the voltage level representation of the data bitstream [e.g., unipolar, polar, or bipolar waveform; and Return-to-Zero (RZ) or Non-Return-to-Zero signal (NRZ); previously described in Chapter 6]. It also defines the data transmission rate (e.g., 64 kbps, 1.544 Mbps, 100 Mbps, etc).

(2) Functional characteristic: It specifies the functions performed by the individual circuits of the physical interface that connects a system to the transmission medium. The major functions are listed as follows:

   * To activate the physical connection
   * To maintain the physical connection
   * To deactivate the physical connection
   * To transmit the data bitstream
   * To multiplex the data (if needed)
   * To perform "point-to-point" data transport
   * To perform "point-to-multipoint" data transport

(3) Mechanical characteristic: It specifies the physical properties of the interface to the transmission medium. The specification includes the physical connector that joins one or more conductors (known as circuits) together.

(4) Procedural characteristic: It specifies the sequence of events that occur in the physical layer, and determines the methods used to exchange data bitstreams across the physical medium.

The standards that are applied to the physical layer are: EIA-232-C, EIA-232-D, EIA232-E, EIA-449, EIA-530, V.35, and X.21.

9.2.5.2 Layer 2: the Data Link Layer

The data link layer is responsible for providing a reliable (i.e., error-free) path between adjacent stations to higher layers. The principal service performed by the data link layer for higher layers is error detection and control. The data link layer delimits the data transmission units (i.e. frames), and performs an error and sequence check on the frames. It should also be noted that the content of the information is not relevant. Acknowledgments sent to the transmitter (by the receiver) confirms that the frames have been received. If the data frames are not acknowledged, the transmitter re-transmits the frames. The functions of the data link layer are summarized as follows:

- To establish the data link connection
- To release the data link connection
- To perform delimiting/synchronization
- To control message sequencing
- To perform error detection and error recovery
- To perform flow control
- To exchange identification and parametric information

The standards that applied to the data link layer are: ISO HDLC (a superset of several data link protocols), LAPB (layer 2 of the ITU-T X.25 packet switching interface), LAPD (layer 2 of the ITU-T ISDN), ANSI X3.28, IEEE802.2 (for LAN), and IBM's BISYNC.

9.2.5.3 Layer 3: the Network Layer

The network layer is responsible for transferring information between end systems across a communications network (e.g., the subnet). Note that in the subnet in Figure 9-13, there are two network layers, two data link layers, and two physical layers. The network layer relieves higher layers from the need to address issues associated with underlying data transmission and switching technologies. At the network layer, the computer system engages in a dialogue with the network to specify the destination address, request network facilities, and set priority. The functions of the network layer are:

- To route/relay data
- To establish network connection
- To transfer data
- To perform error detection and error recovery
- To perform flow control
- To reset network connections

The standards that applied to the network layer are: ITU-T X.25 (packet layer protocol), ITU-T Q.931 (layer 3 of ISDN), ITU-T X.213 (network layer protocol), ISO 8473 (connectionless network protocol), and DOD-IP (Department of Defense Internet Protocol).

9.2.5.4 Layer 4: the Transport Layer

The transport layer is responsible for providing reliable and cost-effective end-to-end data transfer between the end system entities. The functions of the transport layer are:

- To establish and release transport connections
- To detect end-to-end errors
- To monitor transmission quality
- To perform end-to-end error recovery
- To multiplex transport connections to form network connections with improved quality and increased throughput
- To perform flow control

The standards that applied to the transport layer are: DOD-TCP (Internet), ISO 8072 and ITU-T X.214 [transport layer service definitions for transport protocol classes 0, 1, 2, 3 and 4 (TP0, TP1, TP2, TP3 and TP4)], ISO 8073 and ITU-T X.224 (transport layer protocol specification).

9.2.5.5 Layer 5: the Session Layer

The lowest four layers (i.e., the physical, data, network and transport layers) of the OSI model provide the means for a reliable exchange of data and expedite data services. For some applications, this basic service in insufficient. For example, (1) a remote terminal access application might require a half-duplex dialogue; (2) a transaction-processing application might require checkpoints in the data-transfer stream to permit backup and recovery; or, (3) a message-processing application might require the ability to interrupt a dialogue in order to prepare a new portion of a message, and later resume the dialogue where it was left off. All of these functions could be embedded in specific applications at layer 7 (i.e., the application layer). However, since these capabilities have wide-spread applicability, it is appropriate to have a separate layer: known as the session layer.

The session layer provides the methods for controlling the dialogue between applications in end systems. It supports organized and synchronized data transfer. The services provided by the session layer are:

• Defines dialogue discipline: The dialogue can be two-way simultaneous (i.e., full duplex), or two-way alternate (i.e., half duplex).

• Defines data grouping: The data can be grouped for transfer to several end systems.

• Performs error recovery: The session layer provides a "checkpoint mechanism". If a failure occurs between checkpoints, the session entity can re-transmit all the data accumulated since the most recent valid checkpoint.

The functions performed by the session layer are summarized as follows:

• To map the session connection to the transport connection
• To provide the session connection
• To release the session connection
• To manage the data exchange
• To enforce dialogue disciplines
• To act as a synchronization point
• To provide expedited data transfer

The standards that applied to the session layer are: ISO 8326 and ITU-T X.215 (session layer service definition), and ISO 8327 and ITU-T X.225 (session layer protocol specification).

9.2.5.6 Layer 6: the Presentation Layer

The presentation layer provides services that pertain to the representation of user data in a form that can be understood. The meaning of the information is preserved, while format and language differences (i.e., the syntax) are resolved. The functions performed by this layer are summarized as follows:

- To request session establishment and termination
- To request data transfer
- To perform syntax transformation
- To transfer syntax negotiations
- To perform code conversion (e.g., ASCII to EBCDIC)
- To perform data encryption
- To perform data compression

The standards that applied to session layer are: ISO ASN.1 and ITU-T X.409.

9.2.5.7 Layer 7: the Application Layer

The application layer provides services that are directly accessible by the application programs and end users. These services reflect the accumulation of all the services performed by lower layers. That is, the application layer contains all the functions which implement communication between open systems that are not already performed by the lower layers. The application layer establishes the association between the application entities, and allows for identification and authorization of communication users. The application layer performs virtual terminal management.

The standards that applied to the application layer are: Standard for File Transfer, Access and Management (FTAM), Message Handling System (MHS), airline flight reservations protocols, credit check protocols, etc.

Example 9-3: Map the OSI reference model to the TCP/IP model (Figure 9-15).

Although it was developed before the definition of the OSI model, TCP/IP and its services fit very closely into the OSI architecture (Figure 9-15). The best match between the OSI architecture and TCP/IP is between ISO 8473 (i.e., connectionless network protocol), CLNP, and IP (both datagram layers), as well as TP4 and TCP (both virtual circuit). However, each stack uses different concepts of Internet addressing. Internet Protocol (IP) has a 32-bit fixed address space, while CLNP is an extensive NSAP (Network Service Access Points) global address. TCP also uses port addresses, while TP4 uses Transport Service Access Points (TSAPs). Note that both CLNP and IP are considered to be layer 3, despite the fact that they may be implemented on top of other network layers, like those of X.25 and frame relay.

The architecture of the OSI application layer benefited from early development of the Internet Protocol (IP). The presentation layer and the session layer represent refinements of the Internet architecture. That is, they group functions together which are common across a wide range of applications.

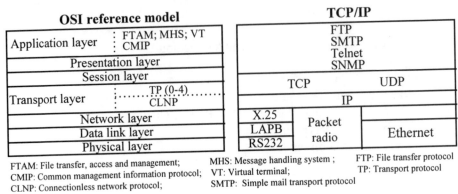

Figure 9-15   OSI Reference Model and TCP/IP.

The following describes the mapping of TCP/IP and OSI reference models:

- FTAM versus FTP: File Transfer Access and Management (FTAM) is built on the session and presentation layers used for handling dialogue establishment, maintenance, and syntax representation. In comparison, File Transfer Protocol (FTP) uses Telnet (a TCP application level protocol) for dialogue establishment and control, and provides a syntactical representation of data. FTP supports fewer functions than FTAM, hence it is easier to implement.

- MHS versus SMTP: Message Handling Service (MHS) offers multimedia services and many options for sending, handling, cataloging, and filing electronic mail. For example, MHS provides message encoding for both voice and fax services. The representation of data is handled by the presentation layer using ASN.1 encoding rules. MHS can also offer a delivery report service, probe service, priority message service, delayed delivery etc. In comparison, Simple Mail Transport Protocol (SMTP) embodies the services of the session and presentation layers. SMTP supports fewer functions than MHS, hence it is easier to implement.

- VT versus Telnet: Virtual Terminal (VT) uses abstract data types (objects) to model the functions of terminal access methods and communications services. VT has greater functionality than Telnet, and is also more flexible. In comparison, Telnet uses a fixed (parametric) coding scheme for each terminal.

- CMIP versus SNMP: Common Management Information Protocol (CMIP) uses virtual circuit service via TP4, while Simple Network Management Protocol (SNMP) uses the datagram service of User Datagram Protocol (UDP).

9.3 DATA TRANSMISSION FUNDAMENTALS

Several data transmission topics are briefly reviewed in this section: (1) transmission media; (2) signal rates and bit rates; (3) definitions of channel, bandwidth, and passband (or bandpass) filters, and bandlimited channel; (4) noise; and (5) a subscriber loop.

(1) Transmission media: There are three major types of transmission media used in modern communication networks. They are: (1) wires, (2) fibers, and (3) airway. However, these media types are classified in different ways, from a development and implementation viewpoint:

- Twisted pair wires: This type of transmission media is the oldest type, and still popular for modern data communication networks. Twisted pair consists of two insulated copper wires arranged in a spiral pattern that reduces interference (known as cross-talk) between two adjacent wire pairs.

  In some applications, one wire of the twisted pair provides the ground potential, and this arrangement is known as an "unbalanced line". Similarly, a balanced line is one in which both wires of the twisted pair wire carry signals with equal amplitudes, but opposite phases. Balanced lines are specified for some electrical standards (e.g., RS-422).

  Twisted pair wires are typical used for the following cases: (1) to connect phones, fax machine, etc. to central office equipment (known as local loop); (2) to connect phones to Private Branch eXchanges (PBXs); (3) to connect printers and terminals to Local Area Networks (LANs); and, (4) to transport multiplexed digitized voice signals.

  Twisted pair wires can be used to carry analog or digital signals. When carrying an analog signal, repeaters spaced 5~6 km (about 3.1~3.7 miles) must applied along the transmission path. For digital signal transmission, regenerators spaced 2~3 km (about 1.2~1.8 miles) are required. The functions of analog repeaters and digital regenerators are discussed in Chapter 6.

  Compared to other transmission media, twisted pair wires are limited in distance, data rate, and bandwidth. Another factor to consider for twisted pair wires is that attenuation increases as the signal frequency is increased. Therefore, transmission performance is degraded for high frequency signals.

- Coaxial cables: A coaxial cable consists of two copper conductors, similar to twisted pair wires, but having a different physical arrangement. The inner conductor (i.e., the core) can be either a solid or stranded copper wire that is covered with an insulting material. Surrounding the core conductor is an "outer conductor" that can be either solid (i.e., copper foil) or braided (i.e., multi-stranded) copper wire. Finally a protective layer of insulation (i.e., the jacket) covers the entire cable. Because both conductors have a common axis, this type of media is called "coaxial" cable.

Coaxial cables can be used to transmit analog or digital signals. Traditionally, they are used for long-distance telephone transmission since they have the capacity to carry hundreds of digitized voice signals. Coaxial cables have been also been used for cable TV distribution, LANs, and high-speed I/O channels in computer networks.

Coaxial cables are much less susceptible to cross-talk and interference than twisted pair wires. They are also more effective for long-distance transmission because they can carry higher frequency signals (i.e., support higher data rates). However, more expensive than twisted pair wires with respect to both initial installation and long term maintenance.

- Optical fibers: Chapter 7 is devoted to a detailed discussion of optical fibers because this type of media is so important for high-speed (e.g., 560 Mbps, 10 Gbps) and long-distance (e.g., trans-oceanic undersea systems) applications.

Optical fiber cables have an enormous bandwidth, and thus they can support data rates in Gbps over hundreds of miles. The fibers have very low signal attenuation characteristics. Fibers with 0.1 dB/km loss (i.e., attenuation) are common in modern communications systems. Optical fibers have excellent Bit Error Rate (BER; or Bit Error Ratio) performance, typically three-to-six orders (10^{-3} *to* 10^{-6}) of magnitude better than wireline media because electrical interference is minimum. As an added security benefits, eavesdropping (e.g., wire tapping, etc.) is practically impossible in fiber applications.

Optical fiber can be used for long-haul transmission, Metropolitan Area Networks (MANs), Local Area Networks (LANs), and short-distance equipment interconnection (i.e., inter-frame within the same central office, and intra-frame; here frame is referred to equipment frame; note that this type of applications reduces the design complexity besides cutting the system costs).

- Airway: Airway transmission has been described in Chapter 8. Communications systems using airway media are satellite systems, microwave radio system, cellular systems, PCS, optical wireless, wireless PBX, Wireless Local Loop (WLL), etc. Several important advantages of this type of transmission media are quick deployment, broad coverage, and user and terminal mobility.

(2) Signal rates and bit rates: Two terms are commonly used to indicate the speed of a digital signal transmitted over any transmission media: (1) baud rat, and (2) bit rate.

- Baud rate: The baud rate is used to indicate the number of signaling elements (i.e., symbol) transmitted per second.

- Bit rate: The bit rate is used to indicate the number of bits (i.e., binary digits) transmitted per second.

Example 9-4: Determine the baud rate and bit rate of the signal that has the waveform shown in Figure 9-16. Note that the system allows eight different voltage levels (i.e., 0 volts to 7 volts; note that these voltages are not the ones used in practical systems, and used for example only) to represent the codewords in the digital bitstream. The voltage level corresponding to each of the eight possible 3-bit codewords is shown in Table 9-3.

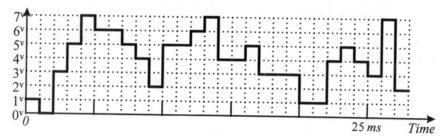

Figure 9-16   The Signal Waveform of a Multi-level Digital Signal.

Table 9-3   Codewords versus Voltage Levels.

Codeword	000	001	011	010	110	111	101	100
Voltage	0v	1v	2v	3v	4v	5v	6v	7v

As shown in Figure 9-16, twenty-five 25 signal elements (symbols, or voltage levels) are sent in 25 ms (i.e., one symbol or voltage level per millisecond). Each symbol (voltage level) lasts for an interval of 1 ms. Therefore, by definition, this signal has a baud rate of:

$$Signaling\ rate = \frac{1}{Symbol\ interval\ (in\ s)} = \frac{1}{1 \times 10^{-3}} = 1,000\ baud \qquad (9\text{-}1)$$

Each symbol (i.e., voltage level) represents 3 bit codeword, as shown in Table 9-3. Therefore, by definition, the signal has a bit rate of:

$$Bit\ rate = 1,000 \times 3 = 3,000\ bps$$

It should be noted that the bitstream carried by the waveform (see Figure 9-16) is 001 000 010 111 100 101 101 111 110 011 111 111 101 100 110 110 111 010 010 010 001 001 110 111 110 010 100 011 … .

(3) Channel, bandwidth, passband (bandpass) filters, and bandlimited channel: There are several definitions for "channel". First, a channel, sometimes is known as a circuit, is a conduit through which an information signal passes. Channels can exist in any of the transmission media described earlier in this chapter. In some applications, "channel" is one timeslot assigned within a 125-µs frame intervals. For example, a T1 digital carrier system has 24 voice channels. Another application of "channel" is

cellular wireless services. In cellular system, the frequency spectrum range of 825.015 MHz to 825.045 MHz is assigned as "channel 1" for a mobile unit to send information to the base station. Besides the definition of "channel", two other terms are defined here: passband (or bandpass) and bandwidth.

Review: In order to understand the term "passband", examples of four generic (i.e., ideal) filter types are shown in Figure 9-17.

- A Low-Pass Filter (LPF) allows signals with frequency values up to f_c to pass through. Practical LPF filters allow a small portion of a signal with a frequency higher than f_c to pass through.

- A High-Pass Filter (HPF) allows signals with frequency values higher than f_c to pass through. Similarly, practical HPF filters allow a small portion of a signal with a frequency lower than f_c to pass through.

- A BandPass (or passband) Filter (BPF) allows signals with frequency values between f_1 and f_2 to pass through.

- A notch filter (band-stop, stop-band, or band-rejected filter) prevents signals with frequency values in a very narrowband around f_s from passing through. This type of filter is designed for specific systems that have an impulse noise sensitivity around f_s. By using a band-stop filter, the impulse noise can be removed from the received signal and thus reduce the noise power considerably. Even the received "signal" will be reduced around f_s, therefore the received overall signal power will be reduced by a small amount, and the Signal-to-Noise ratio (S/N) will be improved.

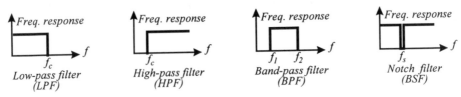

Figure 9-17   Four Generic (Ideal) Filter Types.

From Figure 9-17, it can be seen that a bandpass filter has a frequency range of (f_1, f_2) with $f_1 \neq 0$ Hz. That is, it has a passband of (f_1, f_2). Based on this definition of a bandpass (or passband) filter, a signal and a system with a frequency response shown in Figure 9-18 is called a passband signal and a passband system, respectively. Note that the dotted line is the ideal response, while the solid line is the practical case. The passband (f_1, f_2) or (f_3, f_4) are the 3-dB points in the frequency response curves. This passband channel (system) is also called a bandlimited channel (system).

Generally speaking, after the voice signal has been modulated, the modulated signal is a "bandpass (passband)" signal. For example, if a voice signal is modulated and carried by a system with a bandwidth of (60 kHz to 108 kHz), a bandpass voice signal will occupy at the frequency range of (60 to 64 kHz), (64 to 68 kHz), (68 to 72 kHz), etc. The unmodulated voice signal occupying the frequency spectrum of (0 to 4 kHz) is called a "baseband" signal because the frequency range of (0 to 4 kHz) is the voice base frequencies.

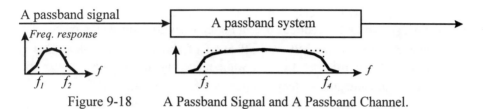

Figure 9-18   A Passband Signal and A Passband Channel.

Bandlimited channel (Nyquist theorem): For a bandlimited channel that has a bandwidth of **B** ($\equiv f_4 - f_3$), the maximum number of discrete signal elements (or symbols) that can be transmitted is equal to **2B** baud (previously described in Chapter 3).

(4) Noise and system performance: A signal transported from its source to its destination is always corrupted by noise. There are many noise sources: thermal noise, shot noise, background noise, amplifier noise, impulse noise, cross-talk, etc. Noise is any unwanted signal that degrades signal transmission quality. In order to understand system performance, several noise characteristics are considered: (1) is the noise a Gaussian noise? and (2) is the noise a "white" noise? If the noise is a "white Gaussian" noise signal, then the analysis becomes easier. That is, if the channel noise can be modeled as white Gaussian noise, it is possible to derive the system performance, and the signal-to-noise ratio.

Figure 9-19 is a model for a communication system used to carry analog or digital signals. Figure 9-19(A) represents the system model. A additive "white Gaussian" noise corrupts the channel. At the receiver, the system performance must be evaluated to check if the system can provide a specific quality requirement. If the channel is used to carry an analog signal, the system performance is the Signal-to-Noise ratio (S/N), which is always expressed as in dB (e.g., 18 dB, 21 dB, etc.). Likewise, if the channel is used to carry a digital signal, either the S/N ratio or the BER (Bit Error Rate, or Bit Error Ratio) can be used to express system performance. BER is always expressed in "power of 10" (e.g., 10^{-6}, 10^{-8}, etc.). It should be noted that the higher the S/N ratio, the better the BER, which translates into improved system performance. The BER requirements are different for different services.

Note that in designing/analyzing long-distance transport systems, the "Gaussian" model [Figure 9-19(A)] is often adopted. A Gaussian noise has a "bell-shape" noise voltage distribution as shown in Figure 9-19(B) and has expectation value of 0. That is, the noise voltage has an average noise voltage of 0 volt. The voltage distribution of a Gaussian noise has a probability density function (pdf) as shown in Figure 9-19(B). That is, the probability that the noise voltage level of 0 volts is the highest. The probability decreases as the noise voltage level increases in the positive voltage end, and as the noise voltage level decreases in the negative voltage end. In summary, a Gaussian noise voltage level oscillates around 0 volts. More often the voltage levels are closer to 0 volts, and rarely has a very high voltage.

A "strict-sense" white noise signal has a "constant" (N_o) power spectral density function, shown by the "dotted" line in Figure 9-19(C). However, a practical channel contains noise with the 3-dB roll-off point of about $f = 10^{14}$ Hz. This type of channel is still considered to be a white-noise channel because almost all long-distance communication systems operate at frequencies below 10^{14}.

(A) A Communication channel with additive "white Gaussian" noise

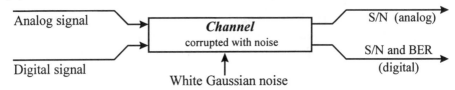

(B) Noise voltage distribution   (C) Noise power spectral density

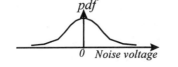   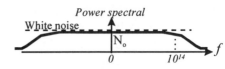

Figure 9-19   Signal, Noise and Channel Performance.

(5) The subscriber loop: The subscriber loop is the typical (traditional) method that a user accesses a public communication network. Network access technology has been previously described in Chapter 3. Similarly, the connection of data signals from a PC or a terminal to a computer network often involves a subscriber loop. A typical subscriber loop has a bandwidth of 3,000 Hz (as previously described in Chapter 3), and a S/N ratio of 25~30 dB. Since data communication often replies on subscriber loop, it is important to know what data rate can be transmitted over the loop.

Example 9-5: The signal baud rate of a typical subscriber loop (see Figure 9-20) can be derived by applying the Nyquist theorem:

$$\text{Signal rate} = 2 \times 3,000 \text{ baud} = 6,000 \text{ baud}$$

The Shannon Capacity theorem: This theorem describes the relationship between the channel capacity (C) and the channel performance [bandwidth (B) and S/N ratio]:

$$C \le B \times \log_2 (1 + \frac{S}{N}) \tag{9-2}$$

Example 9-6: Given a subscriber loop with a bandwidth (B) of 3,000 Hz, and a S/N of 30 dB, determine the maximum channel capacity (C) by applying the Shannon theorem.

$$C \le 3,000 \times \log_2 (1 + 10^{30/10}) = 30,000 \quad bps$$

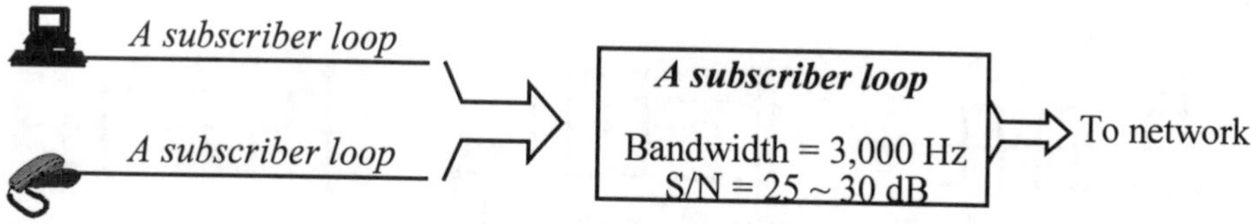

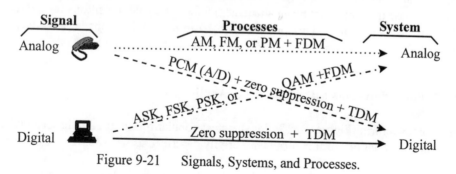

Figure 9-20   A Typical Subscriber Loop.

9.4 DATA ENCODING/MODULATION

As previously discussed in Chapter 6, signal sources (i.e., the user's signal) are generally categorized as either analog or digital signals. These signals may or may not be compatible with the available channels, which are also classified as analog or digital channels. Figure 9-21 represents a summary of the methods to transport various signals over different systems. That is,

- Analog signals transported over analog systems
- Analog signals transported over digital systems
- Digital signals transported over analog systems
- Digital signals transported over digital systems

Figure 9-21   Signals, Systems, and Processes.

For the study of data communications, digital signals transported over analog system (e.g., a subscriber loop, or airway) is described in details in the following sections. The output of a computer (i.e., user data) is known as the baseband signal, and it has a digital signal format. The following sections describe the characteristics of these signals, formats, and processes:

- Baseband signals: Unipolar, polar, and bipolar waveforms
- BandPass signals: ASK, FSK, PSK, and QAM waveforms

9.4.1 Baseband Signals

Three signal waveforms: (1) unipolar, (2) polar, and (3) bipolar (see Figure 9-22), are commonly used as data baseband signals. The characteristics of each signal type is discussed in the following sections.

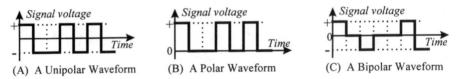

(A) A Unipolar Waveform   (B) A Polar Waveform   (C) A Bipolar Waveform

Figure 9-22   Three Waveforms used to Represent Digital Signals.

9.4.1.1 Unipolar Waveform: Baseband Data Applications

A Non-Return-to-Zero unipolar waveform [Figure 9-22(A)] is often called a "NRZ-L" signal, where "L" represents level. That is, if there is a data bit of "1", the signal will be transmitted as a "+" voltage level (e.g., 3 volts or 5 volts), and this voltage level will last for the entire bit interval. NRZ-L is typically used in Transistor-to-Transistor Logic (TTL) devices in data processing and terminal equipment. TTL devices are also used to generate and interpret digital data signals.

A unipolar baseband signal (waveform) is not appropriate for performing timing synchronization functions, especially if the signal source has a long string of "1s" or "0s". This is because there may not be an adequate number of signal transitions for the receiver to reliably recover timing. This problem can be improved by using a 50% duty cycle Return-to-Zero (RZ) unipolar signals (previously described in Chapter 6).

9.4.1.2 Polar Waveform: Baseband Data Applications

The polar waveform [Figure 9-22(B)] is the most popular format used in baseband data applications. Variations of this format are briefly described as follows:

(1) Polar signal for EIA-232-D application: This waveform has a non-return-to-zero format since there are two allowable voltage levels ($-A^v$ and $+A^v$) without a 0^v voltage to return to. This baseband signal is not appropriate for performing timing synchronization functions, especially if the signal source has a long string of "1s" or "0s". The limited number of signal transitions, as in the unipolar signal case, may not be sufficient for reliable timing recovery.

(2) NRZ-I for magnetic tapes and IBM's SNA applications: This is another non-return-to-zero format, polar baseband signal. The "I" in NRZ-I, designates that the principle of "differential encoding" has been applied. The rule is that a polarity change (i.e.,

from + to −; or from − to +) implies a logical "0" is being transmitted (see Figure 9-23). If the polarity remains unchanged, a logical "1" is being transmitted. This encoding method is excellent for a string of "0s", but, represents problems for a long string of "1s". That is, a receiver may lose synchronization if the signal source contains a long string of "1s" because of the limited number of signal transitions in this case. Another name for this signal is NRZ-S (where "S" represents space).

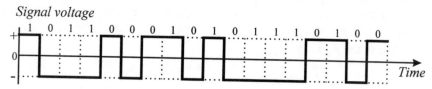

Figure 9-23   An NRZ-I Baseband Data Signal.

(3) Manchester code: This coding scheme [see Figure 9-24(A)] is used for Ethernet applications: Every bit, regardless of whether it is a logical "1" or "0" has a signal transition. That is, the waveform for a logical "1" consists of 50% of the bit interval starting at a low voltage level, followed by the remaining 50% of the bit interval being held at a high voltage level. The waveform of a logical "0" is the exact reverse order (i.e., 50% of the bit interval starts at a high voltage level, followed by the remaining 50% of the bit interval being held at a low voltage level). Because this format guarantees a signal transition during every bit interval, it is known as "fully self-clocking" coding technique. In addition to Ethernet applications, this format is also recommended by the IEEE standard 802.3 (a carrier-sense, multiple access collision detection bus for local area networks). Another name for this technique is "digital biphase" or "diphase" coding.

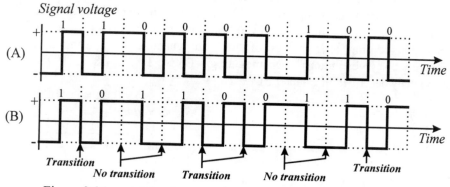

Figure 9-24   A Manchester and a Differential Manchester Code.

(4) Differential Manchester code: This coding scheme is used for token ring LANs and IEEE standard 802.5 applications. Every bit interval of this code also possesses a transition (at the mid-bit point) for timing synchronization purposes [Figure 9-24(B)]. At the beginning of each bit interval, the following rule is applied:

* For a logical "1", there is no transition from the preceding bit. For example, in Figure 9-24(B), the first bit is a logical "1", which is encoded as in Manchester code. The third bit is a logical "1", since the preceding bit ends with a "high" voltage level, the third bit ***does not*** have a transition at the starting point of the bit interval. The same procedure is repeatedly applied to the 4th, 7th, and 8th bits.

* For a logical "0", there is a transition from the preceding bit. The first bit ends with a "high" voltage level, the second bit is a logical "0" that ***requires*** a transition at the starting point of the bit interval. This procedure is repeatedly applied to the 5th, 6th, and 9th bits.

9.4.1.3 Bipolar Waveform: Baseband Data Applications

Two bipolar waveforms have been widely applied for transporting baseband data signals. Both waveforms, the BiPolar Return-to-Zero code (BPRZ), and the pseudo-ternary code, utilize three voltage levels: +, 0 and –. They are described as below.

* BPRZ code: This coding method is sued for DS1, DS2, DS3, E1, E2 and E3 applications. The BPRZ technique is based on encoding logical "1s" as "+ voltage levels", and "– voltage levels" in an alternating sequence. That is, the respective voltage level (+ or –) persists for 50% of the bit interval representing a logical "1", and then returns to the 0 voltage level [see Figure 9-25(A)]. Therefore this coding scheme is known as a 50% duty cycle RZ bipolar signal, and is also called an Alternate Mark Inversion (AMI) code. All logical "0s" are coded as 0 voltage levels. The disadvantage of this code is the need to transmit three different voltage levels, instead of two as in other coding schemes. However, the advantages of BPRZ are: (1) it is a DC-balanced signal that reduces static electricity interference and allows easier inductor/capacitor coupling, and (2) an abundant number of signal transitions are provided for timing functions, even for long strings of "1s" and "0s". Signal transitions during long strings of "0s" are guaranteed by using special "zero suppression (substitution)" schemes (e.g., B3Zs, B6Zs, B8Zs, HDB3, etc. as previously described in Chapter 6).

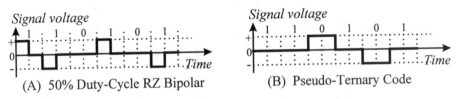

   (A) 50% Duty-Cycle RZ Bipolar   (B) Pseudo-Ternary Code

      Figure 9-25   Two Alternate Mark Inversion Codes.

* Pseudo-ternary code: This coding method is used for ISDN applications. The pseudo-ternary technique is another form of AMI coding [see Figure 9-25(B)]. In this approach, alternating "+" and "–" voltage levels are used to encode logical "0s".

Similarly, all logical "1s" are coded as 0 voltage levels (the exact opposite scheme that is used for AMI coding). Pseudo-ternary coding has the same characteristics of AMI coding. This coding scheme is used in the basic rate interface for ISDN standards (ITU-T Rec. I.430).

9.4.2 Modulation Methods for Digital Signals

As shown in Figure 9-21, a data signal (e.g., unipolar, polar or bipolar) is not suitable for transport over an analog system such as a subscriber loop or airway. The digital bitstream must be converted into an analog signal before being transmitted over an analog channel. Chapter 8 describes this type of communications for airway applications. The modulation principle used for carrying data signals over a traditional subscriber loop is identical to the method used to transport digital signals over the airway medium. Chapter 8 describes the modulation methods summarized in Table 9-4. It should be noted that any data bit stream carried by an analog system (e.g., the traditional subscriber loops, or airway) must be represented by an analog signal, expressed as follows:

$$x(t) = A(t) \times sin\ [\omega t + \theta(t)] \tag{9-3}$$

By changing the amplitude $[A(t)]$, the frequency (ω), or the phase $[\theta(t)]$ in the above analog signal results in different modulation methods (see Table 9-4; and Chapter 8).

Table 9-4   Various Modulation Methods for Data Communications.

Changing amplitude	Changing frequency	Changing Phase	Changing both amplitude & phase
ASK	*FSK (or BFSK)*	*PSK (or BPSK)*	*QAM*
Multi-level	*M-FSK*	*M-PSK*	*M-QAM*
	32-FSK	*32-PSK*	*32-QAM*
	128-FSK	*64-PSK*	*128-QAM*
	MSK	*MSK*	*256-QAM*
		DPSK	
		QPSK	
		DQPSK	

Table 9-5   Analog versus Digital Modulations.

Analog signal over analog system		*AM*	*FM*	*PM*	*X*
Digital signal over analog system		*ASK*	*FSK*	*PSK*	*QAM*

The modulation methods: ASK, FSK, PSK and QAM can be applied to digital signals that are transmitted over an analog system. They are equivalent to AM, FM and PM methods used for analog signals transmission over an analog system (see Table 9-5).

Definition 9-2: ASK (Amplitude Shift Keying) - The **amplitude** of the carrier [$A(t)$ in Eq. (9-3)] is changed (i.e., modulated) according to the (amplitude) of the (message) signal (i.e., the modulating signal).

Definition 9-3: FSK (Frequency Shift Keying) - The **frequency** of the carrier [ω in Eq. (9-3)] is changed (i.e., modulated) according to the (amplitude) of the (message) signal (i.e., the modulating signal).

Definition 9-4: PSK (Phase Shift Keying) - The **phase** of the carrier [$\theta(t)$ in Eq. (9-3)] is changed (i.e., modulated) according to the (amplitude) of the (message) signal (i.e., the modulating signal).

Definition 9-5: QAM (Quadrature Amplitude Modulation) - Both the amplitude [$A(t)$ in Eq. (9-3)] and the phase [ω in Eq. (9-3)] are changed (i.e., modulated) according to the (amplitude) of the (message) signal (i.e., the modulating signal).

Typical applications for these modulation methods are listed in Table 9-6, along with the modulation properties of each method. (The TCM modulation in Table 9-6 was previously described in Chapter 3).

Table 9-6   Properties and Applications of Various Modulations.

Modulation	Properties	Applications
FSK	*Simple*	*Low/moderate-speed modems*
PSK	*Self-clocking*	*Moderate-speed modems*
QAM	*Self-clocking & error-detection*	*High-speed & error-checking modems*
TCM*	*Error correction*	*High-speed & error correction modems*

* Trellis coded modulation (TCM): see B. Sklar, "Digital Communications: Fundamentals & Applications", Prentice Hall

9.5 ELECTRICAL INTERFACE STANDARDS

Before describing electrical interface standards (e.g., EIA-232-D), it is important to understand the concepts of transmission between Data Terminal Equipment (DTE; Figure 9-26). The transmission between two DTEs is a serial bitstream. However, within the DTE parallel data processing architectures are commonly used, and the transmission distance between two adjacent DTEs is typically limited (i.e., short). Hence, a parallel-to-serial and a serial-to-parallel converters must be provided, and Data Circuit Equipment (DCE) (e.g., a modem) are used to extend the physical transmission distances. Table 9-7 provides a summary of the standards that apply to modem applications (e.g., V.22bis, V.29, V.32, V.32bis, V.34, etc.).

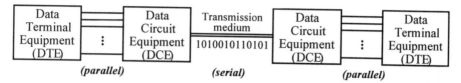

(parallel)   **(serial)**   **(parallel)**

Figure 9-26   DTE and DCE Connections.

Table 9-7   Modem Standards.

Modem type	Bit rate (bps)	Baud rate	Modulation	Full/Half-duplex
V.22bis	2,400	600	QAM	HDX
V.29	9,600	2,400	M-QAM	HDX
V.32	4,800/9,600	2,400	QAM; M-QAM	FDX/EC
V.32bis	14,400	2,400	QAM; TCM	FDX/EC
V.32terbo	19,200	2,400	QAM; TCM	FDX/EC
V.34	28,800	2,400; 2,743; 2,800; 3,000; 3,200; 3,429; ...	QAM; TCM	FDX/EC
V.34bis	33,600	2,400; 2,743; 2,800; 3,000; 3,200; 3,429; ...	QAM; TCM	FDX/EC

TCM: Trellis coded modulation;   FDX: Full-duplex;   HDX: Half-duplex;   EC: Error control

9.5.1 Parallel-to-Serial/Serial-to-Parallel Converters

As shown in Figure 9-26, a parallel-to-serial conversion is used to allow data transmission in serial form over long distances. In the receiving direction, serial-to-parallel conversion is used to present the data in a parallel format for internal processing (i.e., within a DTE). The hardware elements used to implement the converters are typically shift registers.

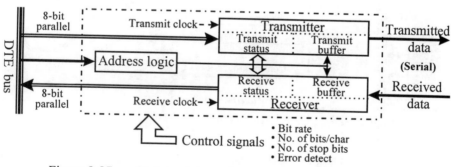

Figure 9-27   Universal Asynchronous P/S and S/P Converter.

Figure 9-27 is a block diagram of a universal asynchronous parallel-to-serial (transmitter) and serial-to-parallel converter (receiver). This function is commonly called a Universal Asynchronous Receiver-Transmitter (UART) and is often implemented as a

Very Large Scale Integration (VLSI) device. There are two internal status registers that can be read or written by an external processor, to monitor overrun errors, framing errors, and parity errors (i.e., a test that detects transmission bit errors). These registers also contain "interrupt enable bits" and "flag bits" used to indicate a character has been received, or the UART is ready to transmit a new character.

Control signals are provided for data error indication, character length selection, and stop bit length selection, along with other functions depending upon the device. The clock signals are typically externally generated, and establish the bit rates for transmission and reception. The UART may used in either "program-controlled" or "interrupt-driven" systems. In the case of program-controlled systems, an external processor reads the status register to determine whether a character has arrived, or a character is ready to be transmitted. Hence, the processor is only performing I/O control functions. In comparison, in an interrupt-driven system the UART notifies the processor, via an interrupt signal, that an action is required. In this arrangement the processor controls I/O functions, and performs maintenance activities.

Example 9-7: Describe the DTE-to DEC connections for a UART application.

A typical Universal Asynchronous Receiver-Transmitter (UART) application (DTE-to-DCE connection) is shown in Figure 9-28. The Data Terminal Equipment (DTE) is the Personal Computer (PC), and the Data Circuit Equipment (DCE) is the asynchronous modem. The DTE contains I/O Controller (IOC), Central Processing Unit (CPU) and memory. These devices communicate over an internal parallel bus. The IOC also communicates with the UART by taking data from memory and placing it in the data into the UART's (transmit) buffer for transmission. Similarly, the IOC takes the data from the IOC receive buffer, and places the received data into memory for processing.

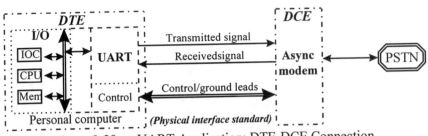

Figure 9-28   UART Application: DTE-DCE Connection.

The DTE (via the UART) communicates with the DCE over the serial transmit and receive lines. Control signals are also passed between the DTE and the DCE. These signals are flow control, permission to transmit, and timing information. The signals passed between the DTE and the DCE use digital formats. The asynchronous modem converts the digital signals into analog signals for transmission over the telephone network (i.e., PSTN), and vice versa. The electrical connection between the DTE and the DCE is specified by the physical interface standard EIA-232-D.

9.5.2 Physical Interface Standard: EIA-232-D

The physical interface standard, EIA-232-D, that specifies the connection between the DTE and the DCE (Figure 9-28) has the following characteristics.

- Electrical properties: The standard specifies the type of signaling, voltage levels and functions. It also describes whether the interface is electrically balanced (i.e., both wires are above ground potential, and carry signals with equal amplitude but opposite phase) or unbalanced (i.e., one wire is at the ground potential and the other carries the signal).

- Mechanical properties: It specifies the type of connector, pin sizes, and cable type.

- Interchange circuit functions: As indicated earlier, the serial interface is actually composed of many leads for data transfer, electrical grounding, timing, and other control functions. Interchange circuits that perform each of these functions are defined in the standard.

- Interfaces between devices: The interchange circuits allow the exchange of information between the DTE and the DCE. The function of each circuit is defined, and the action a device takes when certain events occur is also described in the standard.

- Subset functions for specific uses: The interface standards contain many options and features used to support different application environments. Subsets of these numerous circuits are defined for specific applications. For example, a full-duplex application does not require the signals that control half-duplex applications.

9.5.2.1 EIA-232-D Overview

The Electronic Industries Association (EIA)-232 standard is the most commonly used serial DTE to DCE interface standard in the Unites States. It was original introduced in the early 1960s as RS-232. The third version, RS-232-C, was released in August 1969, and remained the standard until early 1987 when EIA-232-D was introduced. These two versions are similar, but the differences are highlighted in the subsequent sections. The electrical characteristics of EIA-232-D are listed in Table 9-8.

Table 9-8   Key Electrical Properties of EIA-232-D.

Characteristic	Specification
Maximum open-circuit voltage	± 25 *volts*
Maximum short-circuit current	± 0.5 *amps*
Driver slew rate (*dv/dt*)	<20 *volts* / *µs*
Maximum capacitance	2,500 *pf*
Maximum distance (assuming 50 pf/ft)	50 *ft*
Maximum data rate	20 *kbps*
Signaling	*Polar*

9.5.2.2 EIA-232-D Voltages

Figure 9-29 shows the voltage requirements defined in EIA-232-D. As indicated in Table 9-8, the maximum open-circuit voltage is ±25 volts.

Since the signaling specified in EIA232-D is a polar waveform, the logical "0" or "space" is transmitted by a voltage between +5 volts to +15 volts with a noise margin between +3 volts and +5 volts. The logical "1" or "mark" is transmitted by a voltage between −5 volts to −15 volts with a noise margin between −3 volts and −5 volts. The transition zone is between −3 volts and +3 volts. In the control circuits, "ON" is a positive signal, and "OFF" is a negative signal.

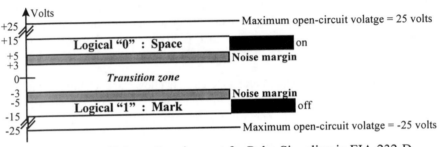

Figure 9-29   Voltage Requirement for Polar Signaling in EIA-232-D.

9.5.2.3 EIA-232-D Timing Operation

When two computers (A and B) are linked together using an EIA-232-D interface, a sequence of events is required to establish the connection (shown in Figure 9-30). Assume that computer A is the sending terminal (DTE) and its associated modem is the DCE. Likewise, the receiving terminal is computer B (the DTE)with its modem (DCE).

The sequence of events to be discussed here corresponds to the "circled" numbers in Figure 9-30.

1. Communication is initiated with a "handshake" between terminal A (DTE) and modem A (the DCE). Terminal A will turn on the "data ready" pin [pin No. 20] informing modem A that a data exchange is beginning. This pin [pin No. 20] will stay "ON" throughout the exchange interval. Terminal A then transmits a phone number via the "transmit data" pin [pin No. 2] to start the modem dialing sequence.

2. After receiving the phone number, modem B (DCE) alerts its terminal B (the DTE) via the "ring indicator" pin [pin No. 22]. Terminal B turns on its "data ready" pin [pin No. 20], and generates a carrier signal used by terminal B to exchange data with terminal A. It also turns on its "data set ready" pin [pin No. 6] indicating (to modem B) that it is ready to receive data.

3. After detecting a carrier signal, modem A alerts terminal A via the "received line signal detector" pin [pin No. 8]. The modem also informs the terminal using pin No.6 (i.e., the "data set ready" pin) that a circuit has been established. If modem A has been configured, it will also send an "on line" message to the computer screen via the terminal's "received data" pin [pin No. 3].

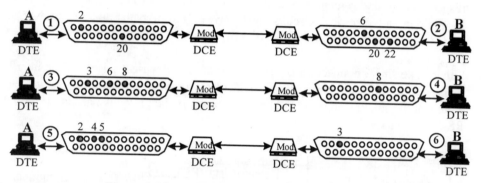

Figure 9-30   EIA-232-D Timing Operation.

4. Terminal A generates a carrier signal that is sent from modem A to modem B. Modem B detects this carrier signal via its "received line signal detector" pin [pin No. 8].

5. When a terminal (e.g., terminal A) wants to send data, it activates its "request to send" pin [pin No. 4]. Modem A responds by activating the "clear to send" pin [pin No. 5]. Terminal A sends data (in the form of pulses representing logical "1s" and "0s") to modem A on the "transmit data" pin [pin No. 2]. Modem A modulates these pulses, and sends the data on an analog carrier signal to modem B.

6. Modem B converts the data signal to a digital format, and sends it to terminal B on the "received data" pin [pin No. 3].

9.5.2.4 EIA-232-D Interchange Circuits

As it is shown in Figure 9-30, the EIA-232-D standard specifies the use of a 25-pin D-shaped subminiature (DB-25) connector. The standard defines the use of 24 pins (two of the 24 pins are reserved for test circuits) and one pin is unassigned. However, not all 24 pins are required in every application. The minimum subset of pins for the EIA-232-D standard connector is shown in Figure 9-31. To exchange data between two devices (computers), at least three circuits are required. They are the Transmitted Data (TD), the Received Data (RD), and the Signal GrouND (SGND) as shown in Figure 9-31. A brief description of these connections follows.

- Transmitted Data (TD): The TD is the serial data output generated by the DTE that is transmitted by the DCE [pin No. 2].

- Received Data (RD): The RD is the serial data that is sent to the DTE from the DCE (pin No.3).

- Signal GrouND (SGND): The voltage levels on the TD and RD leads must be between +25 volts and −25 volts (see Figure 9-29). This voltage is measured with respect to a ground reference, and the SGND lead (pin No.7) provides this reference. In addition, all electrical circuits must have a return path, and the SGND lead provides a common return for all EIA-232-D circuits.

- Shield: The shield connection is essential because it electrically isolates the interface to protect it from abnormal electrical incidents (e.g., electrostatic discharge, etc.). Note that the shield lead (pin No.1) is also known as the protective ground lead in the RS-232-C standard.

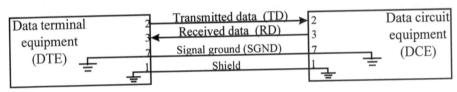

Figure 9-31   Minimum Subset of EIA-232-D Connections.

Example 9-8: Describe the EIA-232-D lead assignments for half-duplex applications.

The EIA-232-D lead assignments for half-duplex applications is shown in Figure 9-32. In addition to the minimum subset of leads shown in Figure 9-31, two leads (RTS and CTS), are required for this application. The Request-To-Send (RTS) and the Clear-To-Send (CTS) leads are controlled by the DTE and DCE, respectively. If the DTE is ready to transmit, the "RTS" lead is turned "ON"; and when the DCE grants permission for the DTE to transmit, the "CTS" lead is turned "ON".

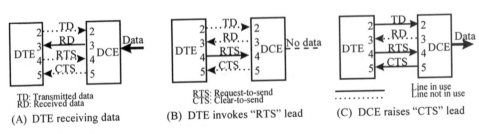

Figure 9-32   EIA-232-D Half-Duplex Applications.

The half-duplex scenario using the "RTS" and the "CTS" leads is described as follows. When the DTE is receiving data, the DCE is in the receive mode and sends data to the DTE via the RD lead [pin No. 3; Figure 9-32(A)]. During this time interval, the TD lead is in the idle state, and the other control leads are "OFF" (i.e., in the low voltage state). This is indicated by dotted lines in Figure 9-32(A).

When the DTE indicates it is ready to transmit data, it places the "RTS" lead (pin No.4) in the "ON" condition as shown in Figure 9-32(B). The DCE is responsible for seizing the communication channel. That is, in the half-duplex mode the DCE must send the carrier signal.

After the DCE has seized the line, it is in the transmit mode, and places the "CTS" lead in the "ON" condition. When the DTE detects the "CTS" lead (pin No.5) is in the "ON" state, the DTE starts sending data via the "TD" lead [pin No.2; Figure 9-32(C)].

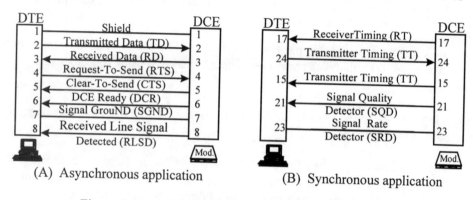

(A) Asynchronous application   (B) Synchronous application

Figure 9-32   Asynchronous/Synchronous Applications.

Example 9-9: Describe the connection between a DTE and a DCE using the EIA-232-D standard for an asynchronous leased-line case application.

There are eight connections [Figure 9-33(A)] required for the subset of the EIA-232-D to provide asynchronous leased-line communications. Six leads (shield, TD, RD, RTS, CTS and SGND) have been previously described. DCR and RLSD are discussed as follows:

- The DCE Ready (DCR; pin No.6): It indicates the DCE is not in the test mode, and is ready to operate. This lead is controlled by the DCE. [note that in RS-232-C it's called Data Set Ready (DSR)].

- The Received Line Signal Detect (RLSD; pin No.8): It indicates the DCE is receiving a valid carrier signal from the remote DCE. This lead is also controlled by the DCE. [note that in RS-232-C, it's called Carrier Detect (CD)].

Example 9-10: Describe the connection between a DTE and a DCE using the EIA-232-D standard for a synchronous leased-line case application [see Figure 9-33(B)].

Additional leads are required in the EIA-232-D interface using synchronous communications. These leads are described as follows:

- The Signal Quality Detector (SQD; pin No. 21): This lead is used by the DCE to indicate is a high probability the received data contains error. It is used to indicate low signal quality, and is used in some systems to request re-transmission of the data.

- Some synchronous modems have dual rate capabilities. The "Signal Rate Selector" (SRD; pin No. 23) is provided to allow the selection of the appropriate data rate. This lead can be controlled by either the DTE or the DCE.

- Transmitter Timing (TT; pin Nos.15 and 24): In the DTE-DCE equipment pair, a master clock is required. This clock can be either in the terminal (DTE) or the modem (DCE). Pin Nos. 15 and 24 are both available to carry the transmitter timing information; but only one is needed.

- The Receiving Timing (RT; pin No. 17): It is used by the receiver modem to notify its associated DTE that data should be sampled (detected) using this clock rate.

Example 9-11: Describe the EIA-232-D application for DTE to DTE direct connection (*null modem*) using Figure 9-34.

Generally EIA-232-D specifies the interface standards for connections between a DTE and a DCE. However, there are circumstances in which two DTE devices are connected together. For example, connecting a local terminal directly to a computer. A "null modem" is used to permit direct DTE-to-DTE connections.

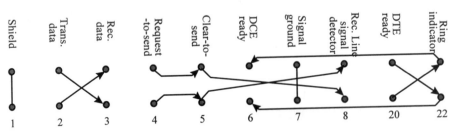

Figure 9-34   Connection of Asynchronous Null Modem.

The "null modem" provides a means of generating the control signals usually provided by a modem. Pins 2 and 3 are "cross-connected" to provide the needed transmit/receive functions. Pins 4 and 5 are "jumpered" and connected to pin 8, and, pins 6 and 22 are "jumpered" and connected to pin 20; to provide the necessary control signals. Note that the ring indicator signal is the method used by the DCE to inform the DTE that the device (phone) is ringing. The DTE ready signal gives the modem permission to answer the incoming call in the case of a switched line application. It should be noted that EIA-232-D may also be used over a dial-up connector or for synchronous applications, typically in applications requiring < 20 kbps.

Example 9-12: A functional diagram of a typical asynchronous input/output circuit of a Personal Computer (PC) is shown in Figure 9-35. (There are two basic parts of this I/O circuit: the generic part and the PC-specific part).

This board uses an EIA-232-D serial interface. The EIA-232-D port is controlled by a Universal Asynchronous Receiver-Transmitter (UART). The UART contains the transmitter buffer and the receiver buffer. These are part of the generic functions of the I/O PC circuit. All serial I/O circuits contain these functions.

The PC-specific interface characteristics include the I/O control ROM (Read-Only Memory), the address and control logic, the PC backplane connector, and the physical size and shape of the circuit board itself. These components vary depending upon the specific PC systems.

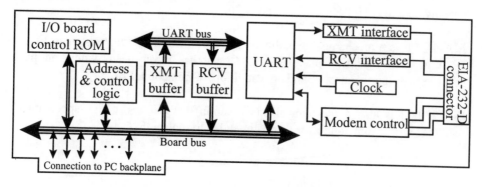

Figure 9-35   A Typical Asynchronous I/O Circuit for a PC.

9.5.3 Other Physical Interfaces

Besides the EIA-232-D interface standard, there are a number of other important physical interface standards. A brief discussion on these standards are given in this section.

- ITU-T Rec. V.24 and V.28: These standards provide mechanical and electrical definitions, respectively, that are essentially identical to EIA-232-D. They are used to define the common serial physical interface used in Europe. The only difference between V.24/V.28 and EIA-232-D is that the ITU-T Rec. is more specific in handling some circuits. Note that V.24/V.28 also specify a DB-25 connector.

- ITU-T Rec. V.35: It is commonly applied to 48 kbps services in Europe. It is also used for 56 kbps and 64 kbps in North America. V.35 is electrically similar to V.28

with the exception that its data and clock signals are electrically balanced. However, V.35 uses a square 34-pin connector instead of a DB-25 connector.

- ITU-T Rec. X.21 and X.21bis: X.25 is the recommended physical interface for X.25 services. It is used for switched digital networks, and provides more functionality than EIA-232-D, but requires fewer pins. X.21 may be used in the United States for services with rates up to 10 Mbps, and distances up to 3,333 ft. This standard is not commonly used. X.21 specifies a 15-pin connector, and X.21bis specifies a 25-pin connector.

- EIA-422-A: It is an electrical specification only, and defines an electrically balanced interface. Because of the protection from noise, which an electrically balanced interface provides, EIA-422-A may be used for services with rates up to 10 Mbps, and distances up to 4,000 ft. EIA-422-A is equivalent to ITU-T Rec. V.11 and V.27.

- EIA-423-A: It is an electrical specification only, and defines an electrically unbalanced interface. It may operate at speeds up to 20 kbps in an EIA-232-D compatible mode; or at rates up to 100 kbps, and distances up to 4,000 ft. EIA-423-A is equivalent to ITU-T Recs. V.10 and X.26.

- EIA-449: It is a mechanical specification that defines more functions than EIA-232-D. It was intended to replace RS-232-C, but has never been widely adopted. It specifies a 37-pin connector, and an a additional 9-pin connector.

- EIA-530: It is also a mechanical specification that defines a high-speed interface using the DB-25-pin connector, and is intended to replace EIA-449.

9.5.4 Physical Interface Protocols

All communications are based on "agreements". A protocol is a set of agreed-upon rules that facilitate the communication process. For example, EIA-232-D described in the previous section is a protocol. Provided device manufacturers comply with the "rules", devices can "talk to each other" (i.e., communicate) without difficulty.

Protocols define the external (i.e., visible) behavior of communicating parties, and can be implemented in either hardware or software.

EIA-232-D, V.24, V.28, and V.35 are physical interface protocols. They pertain to the transmission of bits over a communication channel. For example, the EIA-232-D protocol specifies interface between a DTE and a DCE for serial transmission. It is used for services with speeds up to 20 kbps, and distances up to 50 ft. The connector has 25 pins, with all pins (except one), defined. Besides physical interface protocols, other types of protocols are needed for data communications.

Review Questions I for Chapter 9:

(1) (True, False) Simplex communication system allows one party to transmit signal, and the other part can only receive not transmit, for example, TV broadcasting.

(2) Half-duplex allows both parties to transmit and receive, but they have to _____ to transmit. That is, they can transmit at the same time. But, _____ communication systems allow two parties to transmit simultaneously.

(3) Multicast and broadcast modes are different. Multicast is the method that a transmitter sends information to _____ parties, and broadcast is the method that a transmitter sends information to ____ parties.

(4) Transmitting bitstream from one location to another can be either "serial" or "parallel". For long distance transport, _____ scheme is typically used. For computer or system "internal" transport, _____ scheme is used to reduce _____.

(5) In data communication, asynchronous transport requires to _____ each character by adding _____ bit(s) before the character know as _____ bits, and adding _____ bit(s) after the character known as _____ bits. In comparison, synchronous communication, _____ bit(s) are added before and after each _____, which contains more than one _____.

(6) Synchronous message format typically contains the following four fields: _____, message _____, payload which consisting many _____, and a message _____.

(7) Name some major data communications standard organizations: _____, _____, _____, _____, _____, FIPS, FED-STD, MIL-STD, DOD-STD, and NBS.

(8) OSI layered reference model is defined in ITU-T Rec. _____. The lower three layers (i.e., _____, _____, and _____ layers) of the seven-layer model are called the _____ layers. Likewise, the upper four layers (i.e., _____, _____, _____, and _____ layers) are called the _____ layers.

(9) In transporting data, the data is sent with control information that pertains to the protocol between two supporting entities, and is called _____ (PCI). A PCI typically contains a _____ and ____ information. The user data and PCI together are called a _____ (PDU).

(10) (True, False) In the OSI layer, each layer provides services to the layer above it, and receives services from the layer below. A layer requests services from the layer beneath it through an *interface*.

(11) (True, False) Although it was developed before the definition of the OSI model, TCP/IP and its services fit very closely into the OSI architecture.

(12) The most commonly electrical interface standard is _____.

9.6 DATA LINK PROTOCOLS

EIA-232-D protocol is not sufficient to implement reliable transmission for data communications. Besides the physical interface protocol (e.g., EIA-232-D), a second class of protocols (e.g., data link protocols) are required to provide reliable transmission of user information between adjacent machines. To achieve a reliable transmission, the data link protocols must be able to recover from bit errors (by detecting errors and re-transmit error-free data), and maintain message synchronization.

There are many causes of errors in communication systems. During data bitstream transmission, the bits are occasionally restored with errors. That is, a logical "1" may be restored as a logical "0", and vice versa. For high quality data transmission, that offers relatively error-free data transmission, an error control method must be implemented. An error control method may utilize one of the following two approaches:

- Error detect only:

    The data bitstream is transmitted along with extra bits, known as parity-check bits, so that the receiver has enough information to determine whether the restored data bitstream is "error free" or not. Once the receiver detects an error (within it capability; described further in Chapter 13), the receiver requests re-transmission of the message.

- Error detect and correct:

    In some applications, after the receiver has detected erroneous bits, it will further attempt to correct the errors. Clearly, more parity-check bits must be transmitted along with the data bitstream to accomplish this task (i.e., error correction).

9.6.1 Automatic Repeat/Request (ARQ: Error Detect Only) System

In Automatic Repeat/reQuest (ARQ) systems, the receiver typically indicates the acceptance or rejection of a block of user information. If a block is rejected (i.e., a negative acknowledgment is received by the transmitter) the transmitter re-transmits the block in question. ARQ schemes may be either of the following two approaches:

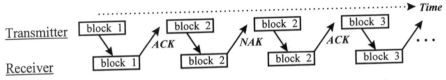

Figure 9-36   Stop-and-Wait Automatic Repeat/Request (ARQ) System.

(1) Stop-and-wait ARQ: In this approach (Figure 9-36), the transmitter must wait after each transmitted block for an acknowledgment or rejection signal (ACK or NAK).

After the 1st block is received, the receiver will send a ACK to indicate this block is acceptable. The transmitter must wait for this ACK signal before it sends out the 2nd block. Figure 9-36 illustrates an example in which the 2nd block is not acceptable. The receiver sends an NAK (Negative AcKnowledgment) message to the transmitter. After receiving this NAK message, the transmitter automatically re-transmits the 2nd block.

(2) Continuous ARQ: In this arrangement, the transmitter continues to send blocks of information while the acknowledgments or rejections (i.e., NAK) arrive on a separate return channel. There are two different ways to implement continuous ARQ:

* Selective continuous ARQ: Using this approach, the transmitter only re-transmits blocks reported to be in error. In Figure 9-37(A), assume blocks 1 to 3 are acceptable while the 4th block is rejected. The NAK_4 message is returned to the transmitter after it has sent out block number 7 (B_7). As a result, the transmitter sends out block number 4 (B_4) again. Note that a means of identifying and recording whether a specific block is accepted or rejected is required. This approach minimizes the amount of data retransmitted (i.e., bandwidth utilization is optimized). However, the receiver must also process blocks in an out-of-sequence order. In this example, the received sequence is B_1, B_2, B_3, B_5, B_6, B_7, B_4, B_8, ... (note that the first B_4 block was rejected). The "out-of-sequence" problem can be solved by applying the go-back-N approach.

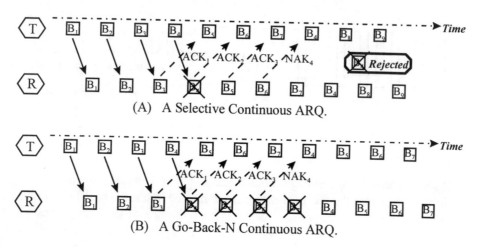

(A)   A Selective Continuous ARQ.

(B)   A Go-Back-N Continuous ARQ.

Figure 9-37   A Selective and a Go-Back-N Continuous ARQ.

* Go-back-N continuous ARQ: In Figure 9-37(B), it is also assumed that block number 4 is rejected. After the transmitter has received NAK_4 (indicating that block number 4 has been rejected), it will automatically re-send B_4, B_5, B_6, and B_7 before it sends out B_8. Since a NAK_4 message was sent to the transmitter, the receiver will record that B_1, B_2, and B_3 have been accepted and all the blocks after

B_4 (inclusively) will be rejected until new blocks are received. Therefore, as shown in Figure 9-37(B), the received sequence is B_1, B_2, B_3, B_4, B_5, B_6, B_7, and B_8, ...

The deciding factor for implementing either the "selective" or "go-back-N continuous" ARQ is the consequence of re-transmitting a potentially large number of blocks, versus the complexity of rearranging the blocks after they have been received out of sequence. In the selective continuous ARQ approach, the transmitter must buffer all allowable outstanding (i.e., unacknowledged) blocks, and the receiver must also buffer all blocks as they may be received out of order. In comparison, in the go-back-N arrangement, the transmitter must also buffer all allowable blocks, but the receiver only has to buffer the current block. Therefore, the "go-back-N" approach is more common. However, in an extreme noisy environment, the re-transmitted N blocks may again be corrupted by noise and declared unacceptable. Therefore, retransmission may occur many times, which increases overhead considerably.

9.6.2 Error Control in Synchronous Communications

The ARQ protocols previously described require the receiver to have the ability of determining whether a received block is error free or not. This implies that the transmitted block must provide error detection capability.

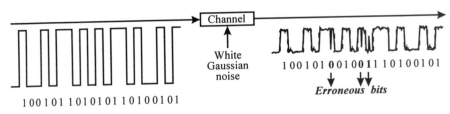

Figure 9-38   A Noisy Channel and Erroneous Bits.

Both synchronous and asynchronous transmission systems are susceptible to noise, which in turn can cause the received data bitstream to be in error. The effect of noise on bit error rate (BER, or bit error ratio) depends upon the rate of the data bitstream. The speed of synchronous transmission systems is often higher than that of asynchronous transmission systems. In addition, an asynchronous transmission system contains a great deal of idle line time, whereas synchronous data systems have contiguous data streams. Therefore, the consequence of noise is more severe in synchronous systems. Figure 9-38 shows three (bit) positions where the restored bits may be in error (shown by the "bold digits"). The errors were caused by significant noise voltages (e.g., impulsive noise) at the detecting (sampling) points. The noise on a transmission channel is typically bursty. Hence, in very short time intervals, noise may cause many bits to be restored erroneously. For example, in a 9.6 kbps data stream transmission a burst of noise might destroy 960 bits, or 120 consecutive characters (assuming 8 bits per character is used).

There are many methods for performing error detection. There are odd parity-check, even parity check, Vertical Redundancy Check (VRC), Horizontal Redundancy Check (HRC), VRC + HRC, single-error detecting CRC (Cyclic Redundancy Check) code, double-error error detecting CRC code, multiple error detecting CRC, Hamming codes, Reed-Solomon codes, BCH codes and convolutional codes. These techniques are described in Chapter 13 of this book.

9.6.3 Function and Types of Data Link Protocols

The basic function of data link protocol for data transmission is to provide reliable transfer of the data bitstream between machines. Reliability means the received (restored) characters are error free, without loss of data, without duplication of data, and received in proper order. Data link protocols can be grouped into three general types:

(1) Character-oriented protocols: This type of protocol utilizes special characters to frame messages. A classic example is IBM's "BInary SYNChronous communications (BISYNC) protocol. In this scheme, the user information is transmitted as a series of blocks (i.e., packets).

(2) Byte-(count) oriented protocols: In this type of protocol, a count field at the beginning of a message is used to indicate the number of characters that constitute the message. An example is Digital Equipment Corp's (DEC's) "Digital Data Communication Message Protocol (DDCMP)".

(3) Bit-oriented protocols: In this type of protocol, a special bit pattern is used to frame the bits that constitute a message. This framing pattern (i.e., flag) hardly ever appears in the actual message. This protocol treats all messages as bit streams. Theoretically, this protocol can be implemented in any machine, even though it might use different codes. There are several bit-oriented protocols, for example:

- IBM's "Synchronous Data Link Control (SDLC)"
- ISO's "High Level Data Link Control (HDLC)"
- ITU-T's "Link Access Procedure-Balanced (LAPB)"
- ITU-T's "Link Access Procedure on the D channel in ISDN (LAPD)"
- LAN "Logical Link Control (LLC) and Medium Access Control (MAC)"
- Frame relay.

9.6.4 BISYNC Overview

BISYNC, which was introduced by IBM in the 1960s, is one of the oldest data link protocols still in use. It is a "stop-and-wait" character-oriented protocol ,and supports the Transcode, ASCII and EBCDIC character codes. The data blocks are not explicitly sequenced. Acknowledgments utilize an alternating bit scheme, using ACK0 or ACK1. Bit error detection employed for BISYNC is either Cyclic Redundancy Check (CRC), or Vertical Redundancy Check (VRC) plus Horizontal Redundancy Check (HRC) technology.

The frame structure of BISYSNC is shown in Figure 9-39. A frame consists of eight fields, two of them [i.e., header and Start Of Header (SOH)] are optional.

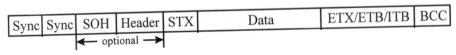

Figure 9-39   BISYNC Frame Structure.

- Sync characters: All message blocks start with two Synchronization (Sync) characters.

- Header: The header is optional. If it is present, the header will be preceded by a "Start-Of-Header" (SOH) character.

- Start-of-TeXt (STX) and data: The starting point of the data bitstream is delimited by a "Start of TeXt" (STX) character. The end of the data bitstream is delimited by either an "End of TeXt" (ETX), "End of Transmission Block" (ETB), or "Intermediate Transmission Block" (ITB) character. ETB indicates the end of a block of characters. ETX performs the same function of ETB and also indicates the end of message. ITB is used to separate a message for error-detection purposes, without causing a reversal of transmission direction.

- Block Check Character (BCC): The BCC character is used at the end of each message block for performing error detection, typically using CRC.

9.6.5 High Level Data Link Control (HDLC) Overview

HDLC is a "go-back-N" or "selective continuous and bit-oriented" data link protocol, which is the current ISO data link protocol standard. Other bit-oriented data link protocol are often described in terms of how they compare to HDLC. Normally, HDLC operates in the Automatic Repeat reQuset (ARQ) mode. However, it can also operate as a "Positive Acknowledgment or Retransmission" (PAR) protocol, which in the absence of acknowledgment automatically initiates a retransmission.

9.6.5.1 HDLC Frame

Figure 9-40 shows the HDLC frame structure, which consists of six fields: flag, address, control, data (information/payload), frame check sequence and another flag.

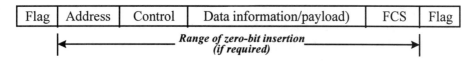

Figure 9-40   HDLC Frame Structure.

- Flag: The frame bit pattern is "01111110" (7D hex), and this code is used to delimit both the beginning and the end of a HDLC frame.

- Address: This field can serve two purposes-

  (1) In a multipoint environment, this address octet (note that this field may be one or more octets) indicates the address of the secondary station on the line.

  (2) In the point-to-point environment, it indicates whether the message following the address field is a command or a response to a received command.

- Control: This field is used to indicate the frame type. It may also carry sequencing information and acknowledgment. Typically, it consists of a one- or two-octet field.

- Information (data payload): This field can carry any number of bits, which is constrained by the amount of buffer space and/or the transmission line. Some systems require this field to be composed of an integer number of octets.

- Frame Check Sequence (FCS): This field has a length of two octets. CRC error control technology is used in this field. The generator polynomial for the CRC code is given as follows:

$$g(x) = 1 + x^5 + x^{12} + x^{16} \tag{9-3}$$

which is known as ITU-T CRC code. The applications CRC error control technique is described in Chapter 13 of this book.

9.6.5.2 HDLC Data Transparency

Definition 9-6: In data link protocol, transparency is the ability of the protocol to send "control" information (message) as data.

Applying transparency in HDLC protocol can create a problem (refer to Figure 9-40) which occurs when a control signal is being transmitted. In HDLC protocol, the framing pattern is unique ("01111110"), and is used to delimit the beginning and the end of a frame (i.e., using flag fields). After the frame boundaries have been established, the "control" signal within a frame can be extracted. However, the framing pattern ("01111110") appears within a frame, the system will not be able to differentiate whether this pattern is the actual flag or data that is carrying a control signal.

This problem can be solved by applying a scheme called zero-bit insertion (also known as bit stuffing) to implement transparency in bit-oriented protocols. As indicated in Figure 9-40, between the two flag fields, the transmitter inserts a "0" after every block of five contiguous "1s". This guarantees that there will not be six contiguous "1s" that might form a "flag look alike" pattern (01111110) between two legitimate flags. As a result, a "0" must be inserted after "5" contiguous "1s" have been transmitted. For example, if the original "control" signal between two flags consists of the following bitstream:

$$...0010011111111111111110101011111111110101...$$

that is,

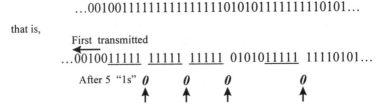

The actual bitstream that is transmitted will be:

$$...0010011111011111011111001010101111011110101...$$

Note that four "0s" have been inserted to eliminate the strings of six contiguous "1s", which might be mis-interpreted as framing pattern.

At the receiver, after detecting five contiguous "1s", the receiver makes a decision based on the value of the next bit. If it is a "0", the receiver assumes that this is a "stuffed bit" and removes it from the bitstream. If it is a "1", the receiver assumes the bitstream is a flag, and uses it for synchronization.

9.6.5.3 HDLC Frame Types

The ISO HDLC data link protocol defines three different frame types by using the control field (see Figure 9-40). They are:

(1) Information frame (I-frame): This type of frame is used to transport user data back and forth between two machines. For this application, the control field carries the sequence number of the I-frame and a response field (i.e., the sequence number of the next expected I-frame).

Example 9-13: Describe the HDLC I-frame structure and its applications.

The control field of the HDLC I-frame may contain one or two octets. It contains the sequence number of the I-frame being transmitted, and the sequence number of the next expected I-frame. For the latter application, the sequence number is used to serve as the acknowledgment of the previously received I-frame. This scheme of sending as sequence number as the acknowledgment is known as "piggy backing". The NS field is the sequence number of the I-frame, and contains 3 or 7 bits. The NR is the sequence number of the next expected I-frame, and contains 3 or 7 bits. This allows 127 ($\equiv 2^8 - 1$) frames to be outstanding at any given time for the "go-back-N" continuous Automatic Repeat/reQuest (ARQ) application. This feature is powerful for transmission links with a relatively long round-trip propagation delay (e.g., international connections on the order of 50 to 100 ms; satellite links on the order of 250-270 ms for one hop).

Flag	Address	Control				Data	FCS	Flag
		0	NS	P/F	NR			

Figure 9-41   The Control Field of the HDLC I-Frames.

(2) Supervisory frame (S-frame): This type of frame is used to control the exchange of I-frames. All S-frames carry a response field. There are four types of S-frame: (1) the Receive Ready (RR) frame used to serve as a positive acknowledgment for an I-frame; (2) REJect (REJ); (3) Selective REJect (SREJ); and (4) Receive Not Ready (RNR) for flow control frame. Both REJ and SREJ frames serve as a negative acknowledgments for "go-back-N" and selective retransmission, respectively.

(3) Unnumbered frame (U-frame): This type of frame is used to control the link. For example, U-frame can be used to establish and terminate a link, exchange station identification information, and/or indicate the reception of an unrecognized frame. Note, there 18 types of U-frames defined by the HDLC protocol (the description of these frames is beyond the scope of this book).

9.6.5.4 Other Bit-Oriented Data Link Protocols

Besides HDLC data link protocol, several other bit-oriented data link protocols are commonly used. They are:

• Synchronous Data Link Control (SDLC) protocol: It was the first bit-oriented data link protocol, developed by IBM, and supports "modulo 8" sequencing only.

• Advanced Data Communication Control Procedure (ADCCP; ANSI X3.66): IBM's proposal of SDLC to ANSI as a national standard resulted in the adoption of ADCCP. Similarly, ANSI's proposal of ADCCP to ISO as an international standard resulted in ISO's adoption of HDLC. Therefore, ADCCP is essentially identical to ISO's HDLC, and is very versatile.

• ITU-T X.25: X.25 may adopt one of two bit-oriented data link protocols, specifically Link Access Procedures (LAP) and Link Access Procedures Balanced (LAPB). Both LAP and LAPB are "go-back-N" protocols, and use a one-octet address field over point-to-point and full-duplex links. However, these protocols only distinguish commands and responses.

- ITU-T I.441 (ISDN): For ISDN applications, the link access procedures on the D-channel (LAPD) is used. It is a bit-oriented, "go-back-N" ARQ protocol, and uses full-duplex links on a point-to-point applications, with a two-octet address field.

9.7 COMMUNICATION RESOURCE SHARING

Long-haul (long-distance) communications facilities are typically expensive, and require large bandwidth (for analog applications) or high speed (for digital applications). A single user is not typically willing to pay for the sole use of facilities because of high costs. In addition, single users will never need such a broad bandwidth. However, communication resource sharing becomes necessary in modern telecommunications systems. For example, a twisted pair of wires is used as a local loop in a telephone network, it has a typical bandwidth of 3 kHz and a data speed of about 30 kbps using binary technology, (according to Shannon's capacity theorem). However, a twisted pair of wires can have a bandwidth of up to 10 MHz (theoretically) which could be used for many personal computer applications.

The techniques that can be applied for communication resource sharing are shown in Figure 9-42. This chapter describes data communications, therefore wireless data links are not included. Another multiplexing technology known as Code Division Multiple Access (CDMA) (discussed in Chapter 8) is not included in Figure 9-42 for simplicity.

- Multiplexing: Allows many devices (e.g., computers) to share a single, high-capacity, point-to-point transmission facility.

- Polling/contention: Allows many devices to share a broadcast network simultaneously.

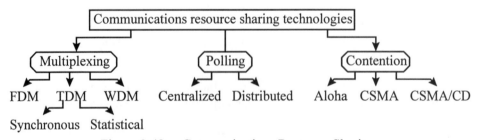

Figure 9-42   Communications Resource Sharing.

9.7.1 Multiplexing Technologies Overview

A large bandwidth or high-speed transmission facility can be shared by many users by utilizing one of three multiplexing techniques. This section provides a simplified overview of these techniques.

(1) Frequency Division Multiplexing (FDM): For analog signals (user data), frequency division multiplexing is always used to share the large bandwidth of the transmission facility with many customers. Figure 9-43 shows a transmission facility with a bandwidth of $B = f_{N+1} - f_1$. This bandwidth is divided into N equal portions ($f_2 - f_1$ = $f_3 - f_2 = f_4 - f_3$ = ... = W) allocated for each user. Note that the available bandwidth is not always divided into equal segments. In this example (Figure 9-43), the transmission facility is said to have "N channels for N users".

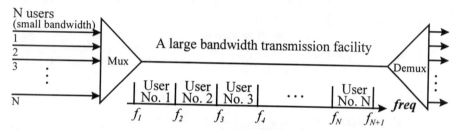

Figure 9-43   Frequency Division Multiplexing (FDMA).

(2) Time Division Multiplexing (TDM): As previously defined, a digital system is a "time-share" system. Time is first divided into pre-determined intervals (typically 125-μs segments) known as individual **frames**. A "frame" is then subdivided into smaller portions, called time slots (channels). To implement communications resource sharing, these timeslots are shared by many users. This technology is TDM, and is used for digital applications [e.g., computer data or digitized voice (speech) signals]. There are two different TDM techniques being used in modern communications networks. They are briefly described as follows.

(A) (Synchronous) TDM:

    User No. 1 2 3 4 5 $\cdots$ N 1 2 3 4 5 $\cdots$ N

(B) (Asynchronous) TDM (or, statistical multiplexing):

    User No. 1 1 6 4 7 $\cdots$ N 5 1 2 2 8 $\cdots$ 9

Figure 9-44   Synchronous and Asynchronous TDM.

- Synchronous TDM: In the digital systems using synchronous TDM, channel No. 1 of each frame is repeatedly assigned to the same user (i.e., user No. 1). Similarly, channel No. 2 is repeatedly assigned to user No. 2; ...; and, channel No. N of each frame is repeatedly assigned to user No. N [see Figure 9-44(A)]. Synchronous

TDM is also known as Synchronous Transfer Mode (STM). The digital systems carrying DS1, DS1C, DS2, DS3, DS3C, DS4 (the μ-law signals), E1, E2, E3, E4 (the A-law signals), STS-1, STS-3, ... (SONET signals), STM-1, STM-4, ... (SDH signals) all utilize synchronous TDM technology (also known as STM).

- Statistical multiplexing (asynchronous TDM, modified TDM): In asynchronous TDM channel assignments are dynamic and based on user bandwidth needs. For example, in Figure 9-44(B) both channel Nos. 1 and 2 of frame No.1 are assigned to user No.1, channel No. 3 is assigned to user No. 6, etc. In frame No. 2, channel No. 1 is no longer assigned to the same user (i.e., user No. 1) as in frame No. 1, and has been reassigned to user No.5. It is clear that the channel assignment is based on "bandwidth on demand" (i.e., based on the users' statistical needs). Thus this technique is called statistical multiplexing, also known as Asynchronous Transfer Mode (ATM) as distinguished from STM. All packet switched services (e.g., X.25 packet-switched, frame relay, and ATM; which described in Chapters 5 and 6) apply statistical multiplexing technology.

(3) Wavelength Division Multiplexing (WDM): WDM is only used in optical fiber networks. It is similar FDM of Figure 9-43. In an optical system that does not use WDM, one "hair" of fiber is used to carry one signal (e.g., 2.5 Gbps), and the system operates at the central (nominal) wavelength of λ_c. In a WDM system, an optical fiber carries many wavelengths, λ_{c1}, λ_{c2}, λ_{c3}, ..., and λ_{cN} as shown in Figure 9-45 (details of WDM technology are previously provided in Chapter 7). Using WDM, one "hair" of fiber can carry many multiplexed signals (i.e., $N \times 2.5$ Gbps).

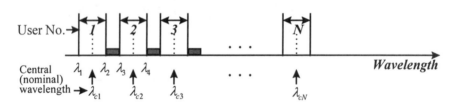

Figure 9-45   Wavelength Division Multiplexing (WDM).

9.7.2 Polling and Contention

Polling and contention are techniques used to share communication resources in a broadcast network, which implies that every device in the network can "hear" every transmission sent by every other device. Figure 9-46 shows two broadcast network examples: one is a Local Area Network (LAN) for a small geographical area, and another is a satellite network for an extremely large geographical area. In this chapter, the polling and contention technique will be described for LAN applications only. When multiple machines share the same transmission link, a pre-determined algorithm must be used so that all machines can gain access to communicate on the channel. There are two approaches (Figure 9-47) which have been used to allow several machines to access the communications link.

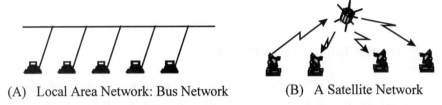

(A)   Local Area Network: Bus Network   (B)   A Satellite Network

Figure 9-46   Broadcast Network Examples.

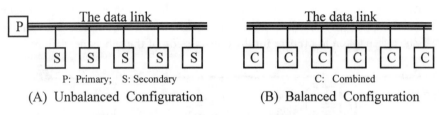

(A) Unbalanced Configuration   (B) Balanced Configuration

Figure 9-47   Multiple Machines on a Link.

- Unbalanced configuration: In this approach [Figure 9-47(A)], one station is designated the "Primary" (P) station while all other stations are "Secondary" (S) stations. It is the primary station's responsibility to poll each secondary station to determine if the secondary is ready to transmit or receive. All communication on the link is between a secondary station and the primary station. The system applies centralized control, and an example of this configuration is IBM's BISYNC.

- Balanced configuration: In a balanced configuration [Figure 9-47(B)], each station is called a "combined" (C) station. All stations are peers and may communicate with each other, thus they have attributes in "common". This configuration applies a distributed control algorithm, and practically all LANs use the balanced approach.

The principal techniques used to share communication resources in a broadcast network are centralized polling, distributed polling, and contention. Centralized polling applies a centralized controller to control each device according to a pre-determined strategy (e.g., round-robin polling). Due to the bursty nature of computer communications, centralized polling is not appropriate because when most devices are polled they have nothing to communicate to the link. In contrast, some devices will have a large quantity of data to transmit and are restricted (i.e., slowed down) if they wait for the entire polling cycle between transmission intervals. An alternative to centralized polling must be applied for bursty data communications. The most common alternatives are variations of distributed polling or pure contention. In a pure contention system, any device can transmit without any restrictions, therefore, collisions always occur. When a collision occurs, one device has to "back-off" and try later. A method must be applied to randomize the "back-off" period, or an infinite string of collisions will result. In comparison, the distributed polling approach utilizes a token passing principle.

9.7.2.1 Distributed Polling: Token Passing

In a "token passing/polling" system, there are two types of tokens: a free token and a busy token. Whenever a station is ready to transmit data on the link, it changes a free token into a busy token. A busy token is placed at the beginning of a data frame, and the user's data immediately follows the busy token.

When a station (device) observes a free token, the station is allowed to change it into a busy token, and then transmit data. After transmission is complete, the transmitter must re-issue a free token to prepare for the transmission of the subsequent frame.

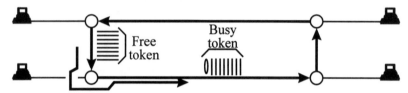

Figure 9-48   Distributed Polling: Token Passing.

When a station observes an incoming free token, the station can change the free token into a busy token. This is done by simply inverting the value of the Least Significant Bit (LSB). Each station receives all the transmitted bits, and then regenerates them. Token passing networks are relatively new. Some examples are: IBM Token Ring, Manufacturing Automation Protocol (MAP), IEEE 802.4 token bus, and IEEE 802.5 token ring standards.

9.7.2.2 Pure Contention

Most bus (shared media) networks control access between all stations and the bus by applying contention methodology. When more than one station during the same timeslot are ready to transmit frames, a collision will occur. The pioneer contention network is ALOHANET, which was introduced at the University of Hawaii in the late 1960s. The contention scheme used for this network was called "pure Aloha", which is illustrated by the example shown in Figure 9-49. During timeslot No. 1, station No. 1 is ready, and transmits its data. During the timeslot No.2, station No. 2 is ready, and transmit its data. However, before the second station finishes its transmission, the 3rd station is ready. Since all stations can transmit at will, the 3rd station will collide with the 2nd station (near the end of the transmission of the 2nd station). The result is that both frames (from the 2nd and the 3rd stations) are destroyed.

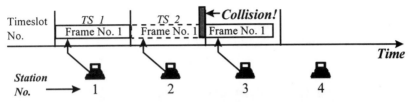

Figure 9-49   Pure Aloha Contention.

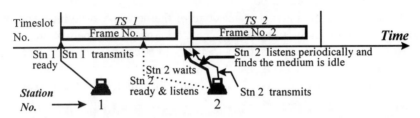

Figure 9-50   Carrier Sense Multiple Access (CSMA).

9.7.2.3 Carrier Sense Multiple Access (CSMA)

The CSMA contention algorithm is a refinement of pure contention that uses a "Listen-Before-Talk" (LBT) approach. If a station is ready to transit, it first listens to the medium. If the medium is idle (i.e., no other station is transmitting), then the station will transmit. If the medium is busy (i.e., another station is transmitting data), then the station must wait until the medium is idle. While waiting, the station listens to the medium periodically. When the medium becomes idle, the station having waited will begin transmitting its data.

9.7.2.4 CSMA with Collision Detection (CSMA/CD)

A commonly used contention scheme is CSMA with collision detection, and stations that utilize "Listen-While-Talking" (LWT). That is, stations that are transmitting continue to monitor the link.

If a collision is detected, the transmitting stations stop transmitting. This decreases the amount of time lost during collisions. There is a minimum amount of time required to detect a collision, called the "contention interval". If a station transmits for the duration of the contention interval without detecting a collision, then the transmitter is guaranteed that no collisions will occur. After the contention interval has elapsed, all stations on the link have heard the station transmit.

Detecting a collision is a straight forward approach. If the information on the link is not identical to the information that is being transmitted, then a collision has occurred.

CSMA/CD networks also apply a randomized "back-off" algorithm so that two stations do not continue to collide. Ethernet (adopted by Xerox, DEC and Intel) was the first CSMA/CD network introduced in the mid 1980s. Other examples of CSMA/CD networks include AT&T's StarLAN and the IEEE 802/3 CSMA/CD bus standard.

9.8 NETWORK INTERFACES

A network interface is the access point for a user to enter the network. Specifying the network interface allows the internal architecture of the network to be independent, with respect to the user. That is, the user doesn't need to know the internal architecture of the network that transports the user's data. The network interface provides a "point-to-point" link between the user and the network, and a network interface is required at each end of the network. Therefore, the network can be viewed as an information link between two hosts.

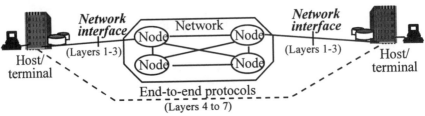

Figure 9-51   Network, Network Interfaces, and User Relationships.

It should be noted that a network interface does not define end-to-end procedures. It only defines the layers of the OSI reference model (i.e., layers 1 to 3). The choice of end-to-end protocol is selected by the users, and is transparent to the network (see Figure 9-51) just like the internal operations of the network is transparent to the user. The details of two specific network interface types are described in this chapter: ITU-T X.25 and Integrated Service Digital Network (ISDN).

9.8.1 ITU-T Rec. X.25

Digital computers were first introduced in the early 1960's, and since that time many common carriers (service providers) throughout the world have realized the need to provide a Public Data Network (PDN), to carry computer data. The PDN is a companion to the Public Switched Telephone Network (PSTN) that carries speech signals. The PDN provides local and long-haul **data-carrying** services, just as the PSTN provides local and long-haul voice-carrying services.

During the sane time period, packet switching technology was proving itself to be a viable technology for data transmission. In the 1970s, PDN and packet switching concepts came together, and a number of Packet Switched Public Data Networks

(PSPDNs) were implemented. Common carriers recognized the need for compatibility, and ITU-T Rec. X.25 was defined. That is, the interface between a user and a PSPDN was standardized. ITU-T Rec. X.25 has been a reference since 1976, and X.25 is a common protocol throughout the world. Some examples of X.25 networks are: U.S. Sprintnet, Tymnet, AT&T Accunet Packet Switched Service (using No.1 PSS) which were implemented in US, Datapac (Canada) and Transpac (France).

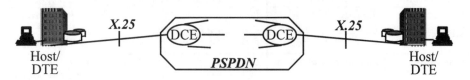

Figure 9-52   PSPDN and X.25 Interfaces.

Figure 9-52 shows a generic PSPDN and X.25 interfaces. The end users (hosts) are Data Terminal Equipment (DTE), and the PSPDN boundary node is Data Circuit Equipment (DCE). ITU-T X.25 defines the DTE-DCE interface. The DTEs operate as packet mode, are synchronous, and include upper OSI layer (4-7) software. In comparison, the DCEs use only the lower OSI layer (1-3) software/hardware. In the following sections, the X.25 protocols, call setup, call request packet, incoming call packet, data packet, call termination, clear request packet, and clear indication packet are described in detail.

9.8.1.1 X.25 Protocols

The ITU-T X.25 DTE/DCE interface is composed of three layers of protocol. The responsibility, protocol type, functions, data transfer, and other specifications for each layer, are summarized in Table 9-9.

- Layer 1 (physical layer; corresponding to the OSI physical layer): This layer defines the procedure for the physical connection. It also specifies the physical, mechanical, and electrical aspects of the interface. The data transfer mode is serial, synchronous, full-duplex, and point-to-point. X.25 specifies ITU-T Rec. X.21bis or X.21 be used as the physical interface. This requirement is not adhered to in the United States. ANSI recommends EIA-232-C, EIA-449, and V.35.

- Layer 2 (link layer; corresponding the OSI data link layer): This layer provides error-free communication over the physical path connecting two adjacent data stations. For this layer, the framing and operational procedures are a subset of High-level Data Link Control (HDLC). The Link Access Procedure (LAP) was defined in the 1976 version of X.25, while a balanced version (LAPB) was defined in the 1980 version. Although LAP is still supported by X.25, it is not recommended for the new systems.

LAPB provides data link establishment/termination, and supports full-duplex, point-to-point transmission of frames with flow control.

Table 9-9   The X.25 Three Layer Protocol.

	Layer 1 (physical)	Layer 2 (Link)	Layer 3 (Packet)
Responsibility	*Bits transport*	*Reliable path for frames*	*Packet transfer*
Protocol type	*X.21bis, X.21 EIA-232-C, EIA-449 V.35*	*Link access Procedure balanced, LAPB*	*Packet layer protocol (PLP)*
Functions	*Physical connection*	*Data link*	*Virtual circuit Assign logical channel*
Data transfer	*Point-to-point, Full duplex, Synchronous, Serial*	*Point-to-point, full-duplex, Error-free, Sequential delivery*	*Point-to-point, Full duplex, Sequential delivery*
Other specifications	*Physical spec, Electrical, spec, Mechanical spec.*	*Frame structure, Error control, Flow control*	*Packet format, Fragment/recombine, Flow control, Multiplexing*

- Layer 3 (packet layer; corresponding to the OSI network layer): This layer segments (fragments) the data bitstream into packets at the transmitter, reassembles packets into a data bitstream at the receiver, and assigns logical channel identifiers. It also establishes, resets and clears virtual calls (i.e., calls on virtual circuits).

The packet layer multiplexes logical channels into the data link. It should be noted that only virtual circuit service is provided. That is, datagram services are **not** supported in X.25 (Datagram services were added in the 1980 version of X.25, but this feature was dropped from the 1984 version of X.25). The X.25 Packet Layer Protocol (PLP) does not include routing functions, which are supported by the OSI network layer, because routing is not needed for a point-to-point link applications.

9.8.1.2 X.25 Call Setup and Call Termination

To illustrate the call set-up of an X.25 virtual call, assume that the connection is a full-duplex end-to-end connection between two DTEs, and a logical channel is identified as the virtual circuit across the DTE/DCE interface. The call set-up consists of the following steps (note that the steps described below correspond to the circled numbers in Figure 9-53).

1. The calling DTE (No. 1234) sends out, via interface protocol, a "call request" packet to request a Virtual Circuit (VC) connecting to DTE No. 567 (the called party). The VC has a Logical Channel Identifier (LCI; across the DTE/DCE interface) number of 22, which is chosen by the calling DTE.

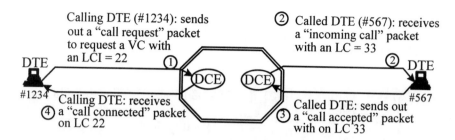

Figure 9-53   Four Major Steps for X.25 Call Setup.

2. At the remote site (the DTE/DCE interface), the called DTE (No. 567) receives a "incoming call" packet, which indicates a call is coming from DTE No. 1234 on LCI No. 33 (the second LCI is chosen by the called DTE).

3. After deciding to accept the call, the called DTE (No. 567) sends out a "call accepted" packet on LCI 33. It should be understood that it is not necessary to have a full address because the LCI provides unambiguous address information.

4. The calling DTE receives the "call connected" packet on LCI 22. This packet indicates a logical channel has been established, and data can be exchanged between two DTEs (the calling and called DTEs).

It should be noted that address information is not mandatory in the "call accepted" and the "call connected" packets. However, address information is included in these packets for redundancy and error checking purposes.

At the conclusion of sending data, the DTE must perform a "clear the call" function. First, the DTE sends a "clear request/clear indication" packet to remove the logical channel number assignment at both X.25 interfaces. This packet also "frees-up" buffer memory and removes the routing table entries that were created by the PSPDN to establish the virtual circuit. All these actions are part of the call-clearing procedure. Similarly, the "clear channel" request is confirmed by a "clear confirmation" packet.

9.8.1.3 X.25 Call Request, Incoming Call, and Other Packets

Figure 9-54 illustrates a X.25 "call request" (sent by a DTE) and "incoming call" (sent by a DCE) packet format. This format is described as follows: the first three octets are the same for all packets, but the remaining octets are specific for the "call request/incoming call" packet. The "call accepted/call connected" packets have a similar format.

*   General Format Identifier (GFI): Bits 5 to 8 of the first octet is assigned as GFI, and has a value of "0001" (see Figure 9-54). Note that bit 8 is the MSB of the octet.

- Logical Channel Identifier (LCI): It has a length of 12 bits, and occupies bits 1 to 4 of the first octet and bits 1 to 8 of the second octet. It is used to identify the logical channel used for the connection, and has a value between 0 and 4,095 ($2^8 = 4,096$).

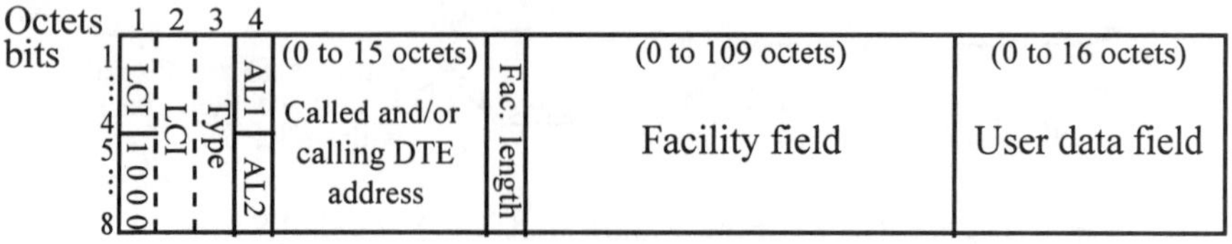

Figure 9-54   X.25 Call Request/Incoming Call Packet Format.

- Packet Type Identifier (PTI): The 3rd octet is used to identify the packet type.

- Calling DTE Address Length (AL2): Bit Nos. 5 to 8 of the 4th octet indicate the number of digits in the calling DTE's address. It has a value between 0 and 15.

- Called DTE Address Length (AL1): Bit Nos. 1 to 4 of the 4th octet indicate the number of digits in the called DTE's address. It has a value between 0 and 15.

- Called and/or calling DTE addresses: A called DTE address (if present) will be followed by a calling DTE address. Each address is coded into Binary-Coded Decimal (BCD) with two BCD symbols per octet. This field can be between 0 and 15 octets.

- Facility length: This one-octet field is used to indicate the number of octets in the facility field and has a value between 0 and 109 (i.e., the maximum number of octets allowed in the facility field is 109). Facilities are optional capabilities that a user may want associated with a given call (e.g., large packet sizes or reverse charging).

- Facility field: This field contains the optional user facility request, if any. The maximum number of octets allowed in the facility field is 109.

- User data field: This field contains any additional required information that is needed to setup the call (e.g., a password). This field is also optional, but if used the maximum length is 16 octets.

Figure 9-55 shows the X.25 "clear request/clear indication" packet has the format. A "clear request" packet is sent by a DTE, while a "clear indication" packet is sent by a DCE. The first three octets of the packet are identical to the a "call request/incoming call" packet (see Figure 9-54). Two additional octets are used for this process:

- Clear cause field: The 4th octet is the clear cause field used to indicate the reason the call was cleared (e.g., the remote DTE was busy, or the network is congested).

- Diagnostic code field: The 5th octet and contains additional details about the conditions that caused the call to be cleared.

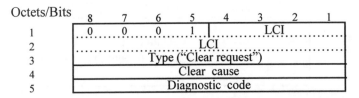

Figure 9-55   A X.25 Clear Request/Clear Indication Packet.

9.8.1.4 X.25 Data Packet

A X.25 data packet has the format shown in Figure 9-56. As shown, the overhead required for this data packet is relatively small. In summary, once a call has been established, the packet requires only the Logical Channel Identifier (LCI).

- Octet Nos.1 and 2: They are the same as the "call request" packet (see Figure 9-54).

- The packet type: Bit No.1 of the 3rd octet indicates the packet type.

  * If the packet is a "data" packet, this bit is set to logical "0".
  * For other types of packets, this bit is set to logical "1".

- Packet sequence number: Bits Nos. 2, 3 and 4 of the 3rd octet indicate the sequence number of the data packet. Since there are three bits in this field, eight numbers ($2^3 = 8$) can be used. The sequence number can be repeatedly assigned as "0 1 2 3 4 5 6 7 0 1 2 3 4 5 6 7 0 1 2 3 4 5 6 7 …".

- More indicator: The 5th bit of the 3rd octet is used to indicate whether there are more data packets.

  * If there are more data packets following, this bit is set to logical "0".
  * If no additional data packets are following, this bit is set to logical "1".

- Acknowledgment number: The value occupying bits Nos. 6 to 8 of the 3rd octet is used to indicate the sequence number of the next expected data packet. Combining these three bits with the three packet sequence number bits, provides an error checking capability.

- User data field: This field can have a length up to 4,096 octets. However, the default size of this field is 128 octets. The factors used to determine data field size are: (1) the buffer size of the data stations, (2) the channel characteristics, and (3) the error-detection capability of the data link layer.

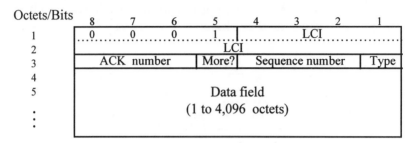

Figure 9-56   A X.25 Data Packet Format.

Example 9-14: Describe the call scenario of a X.25 call between two DTEs.

Figure 9-57 shows a X.25 call scenario involving a calling DTE (#1234), a local DCE, a PSPDN, a remote DCE and a called DTE (#567). The steps described below corresponds to the circled number in Figure 9-57.

1. The calling DTE (#1234) sends out a "call request" packet on Logical Channel # 22 (LC22) to establish a virtual circuit to DTE #567 (the called DTE). The called DTE receives an "incoming call" packet from DTE #1234 on incoming LC33, which was chosen by the called DTE.

2. The called DTE (#567) sends out a "call accepted" packet on LC33, after accepting the call. This packet, originated from the called DTE as a "call accepted" packet, but it is delivered as a "call connected" packet to the calling DTE on LC22.

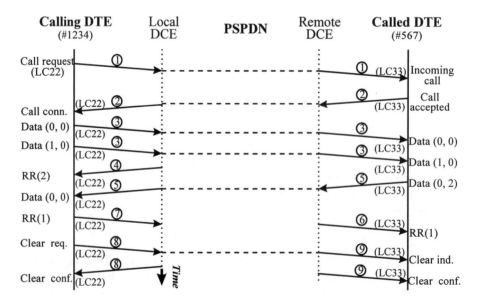

Figure 9-56   Complete a X.25 Call Connection.

3. The calling DTE (#1234) is ready to send data. In this example, two packets are sent: data packet 0 (0, 0) and data packet 1 (1, 0) consecutively on LC22.

4. The local DCE acknowledges data packet 1 by sending a "Receive Read RR(2)" packet to the calling DTE.

5. The called DTE (#567) sends a data packet 0, indicating reception of data packets 0 and 1 from the calling DTE (the next expected packet will be 2).

6. The remote DCE acknowledges this packet by sending RR(1) packet.

7. The calling DTE acknowledges the local DCE's packet by returning an RR(1) packet.

8. After the exchange of data packets having complete, the calling DTE sends a "clear request" packet on LC 22 to clear the channel. The PSPDN clears the call at the local DTE/DCE interface and sends a "clear confirmation" packet to DTE #1234.

9. The PSPDN is responsible for clearing the call through the entire network, including the remote DTE/DCE interface. The called DTE (#567) receives a "clear indication" packet on LC33 and the remote DCE responds with a "clear confirmation" packet. The call is now completely cleared.

Example 9-15: Describe the resetting and restarting procedures of a X.25 call between two Data Terminating Equipment (DTEs).

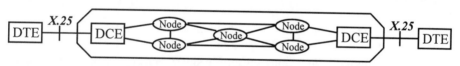

Figure 9-58   A Generic X.25 Interface Connection.

The X.25 interface provides a virtual circuit service to the user even if the pathway connecting users, via the network, is not perfect (i.e., error free). If channel noise is severe and causes bit errors or other problems, it is possible that the Packet Layer Protocol (PLP) may lose packets. Packet retransmission can be requested by a DTE by sending a "reject" packet. However, some networks do not support the "reject" packet option. In those cases, errors at the PLP can be resolved by _**resetting**_ the virtual circuit (i.e., sending a "reset" packet).

The "reset" packet can be used to _**reinitialize**_ the virtual circuit. The reset procedure involves: (1) sending a "reset request/indication" packet, (2) resetting the sequence numbers on both ends to zero, (3) invoking higher-layer procedures to recover the lost data, and (4) allowing recovery errors on the virtual circuit.

If the PLP fails (due to software errors or DTE failure) or if the data link goes down, then all virtual circuits in the DTE/DCE interface are at risk. When this type of "fatal error" occurs, the packet layer at the DTE/DCE interface is ***restarted***. The restart procedure involves: (1) initializing/reinitializing the packet layer interface, (2) sending a "restart request/indication" packet, (3) resetting all permanent virtual circuits, (4) clearing all switched virtual circuits, and (5) allowing recovery errors on the interface.

9.8.2 Integrated Services Digital Network (ISDN)

An Integrated Services Digital Network (ISDN) is typically a public network, that is implemented entirely using digital technology. An ISDN can provide a wide variety of telecommunications services, including circuit-switched voice and data, packet-switched data, high quality audio (i.e., non-speech signals), video, multimedia, and teletext.

9.8.2.1 ISDN Evolution, ISDN Services and ISDN Standards

The basic concept of Integrated Services Digital Network (ISDN) is the reduction or elimination of analog technology from the telecommunications network. This is essentially a shift from the older technology of analog signals to completely digital data transfer methods. While it will always be necessary to provide an analog interface for human speech (i.e., a speaker and microphone to convert electrical signals to acoustic sound, and vice versa), ISDN is focused on eliminating the wide spread use of analog facilities (i.e., traditional loop plant connections between end-users and the central office switching exchange).

Although a large portion of the telecommunications network is already operating within the scope of digital transport, the deployment of ISDN technology will eventually provide high-speed digital connections to both business and residential subscribers that supports a full range of services, including voice, data, video, and multimedia.

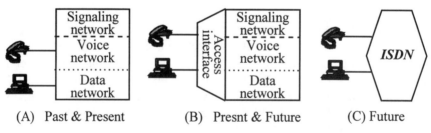

(A) Past & Present   (B) Presnt & Future   (C) Future

Figure 9-59   Access and Networking Evolution.

ISDN services are accessed by users through a "universal socket". Therefore, a single standard interface is provided for all ISDN-compatible devices. These devices can be telephones, data terminals, televisions, stereos or other equipment. Hence, ISDN is a natural step in the evolution toward a fully digital telecommunications network. This network consists of **wire** (twisted-pair wires and coaxial cables), **air** (fixed wireless, cellular, digital microwave radios and satellite), and **fiber** transmission facilities.

Telecommunications services have evolved rapidly since the mid 1960's, especially from an access and networking perspective. Figure 9-59(A) shows three individual networks: voice, data, and signaling. In past and some current applications, different services require separate networks, and different access interfaces. Figure 9-59(B) shows the first step toward ISDN. In this interim arrangement, the data, voice, and signaling networks are still separate entities. However, users can access these networks via a single access interface. Eventually, true ISDN will have one access interface and one network for all services (voice, audio, data, image, and video) as shown in Figure 9-59(C).

The evolution from the configuration in Figure 9-59(A) to 9-59(B) is known as "***not-transparent***", because is equipment are changing from analog to digital. This includes the conversion of traditional analog loops into digital carrier loop systems.

In contrast, the evolution from the configuration in Figure 9-59(B) to 9-59(C) is "***transparent***". The conversion to ISDN can progress without affecting the user (i.e., the user should not even know that the evolution has occurred). This transparency is a result of using the same access interface, while the network is invisible to the user.

Figure 9-60 shows several services that an ISDN can provide, and indicates the large number of different devices the ISDN supports.

- A multimedia terminal, incorporating voice, data and audio features, may interface to an ISDN from a business or residential users site.

- DTEs supporting X.25 or other non-ISDN equipment may access the ISDN via a device called a Terminal Adapter (TA). A TA enables a non-ISDN device to present as an ISDN-compatible device.

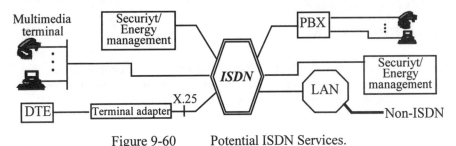

Figure 9-60   Potential ISDN Services.

- A PBX (Private Branch eXchange) acts as an intermediate device for the connection of telephones, personal computers, ISDN devices, and non-ISDN devices in a business environment.

- Non-ISDN devices can interface the ISDN via a compatible station or a LAN.

- A home or business security/energy management system can send data packets to a monitoring station via ISDN.

Several organizations are involved in the development of ISDN standards. ISDN is one of the most active areas of current network standards bodies. Specifically, the user-network interface (S and T) is defined in the ITU-T *I*-series recommendations (first published in 1984), and other related recommendations are in the E-, G-, Q- and X-series.

In the US, an ANSI T1D1 (sub-committee) task group contributes to the ITU-T ISDN recommendations and US ISDN standards/applications. Other service providers (e.g., AT&T, Bellcore, Northern Telecom and Siemens) have developed their own ISDN standards. Figure 9-61 shows the equipment and reference points in a generic ISDN configuration. The user-network interface may use the U reference point, and the non-ISDN user-network interfaces may use the R reference point, which applies public standards such as X.21, V.35, EIA-232-D, or EIA-530. The ISDN reference points are described further in the next section. Note that ITU-T views the U reference point as being internal to the network. The U reference point is considered to be beyond the scope of ITU-T recommendations, but, the FCC views the U reference point as the network boundary. Many other organizations also believe the U reference should be studied by the ANSI T1D1 standards group.

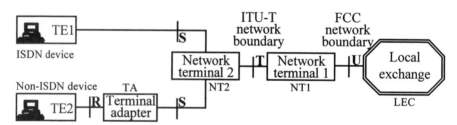

Figure 9-61   ISDN Equipment and Reference Points.

9.8.2.2 ISDN Reference Points

Since the introduction of the ISDN standards, many new ISDN-related technologies have been developed. The two important ISDN concepts (equipment and reference points; Figure 9-61) are used to implement ISDN technologies are described as follows:

(1) ISDN equipment: The Local Exchange (LE; the central office) provides ISDN services. Network Terminal 1 (NT1) performs the termination function for the network and the LE. The NT1 is analogous to the DCE in X.25 (see Figure 9-58). Network Terminal 2 (NT2), if present (see the S reference description point below), is customer premises equipment (e.g., PBX) that provides on-site distribution. User

equipment can be classified as two groups: Terminal Equipment 1 (TE1) ISDN devices, and TE2 non-ISDN devices. Thee TE2 devices access the ISDN via a Terminal Adapter (TA), which may be integrated into the TE2.

(2) ISDN reference points: The four ISDN reference points are defined as follows.

*   U reference point: As shown in Figure 9-61, the U reference point is the link between the local exchange and the network terminal 1 (i.e., the transmission line). The ITU-T views this reference point as being part of the network, hence the ITU-T recommendations do not describe this interface. However, the FCC views this point as the network boundary, and ANSI is actively defining standards for this interface.

*   T reference point: This point is considered the network boundary by the ITU-T, and is analogous to the DTE/DCE X.25interface (see Figure 9-58).

*   S reference point: This is the interface between two CPEs (e.g., between NT2 and TE1, or between NT2 and TA). It is possible that an NT2 may not be present. In this case, the "S/T" reference point is the network boundary.

*   R reference point: This point is specific to certain TE2 devices and an associated TA. That is, the R reference point is a "vendor specific" point. The TE2 equipment manufactured by any vendor must have an appropriate R interface so that the TE2-TA equipment presents itself as a TE1 device (i.e., the TE2 equipment interface is equivalent to a standard ISDN device).

9.8.2.3 ISDN Rate Interfaces, B- and D-Channels

Several ISDN rate interfaces have been defined by ISDN standards. These rates consist of two basic ISDN channels: the B-channel and the D-channel.

Definition: The B-channel (**_B_**earer channel) is used for all forms of telecommunications services: voice, audio, image, video, and data. The B-channel is granted in response to a request for service that is sent over the D-channel

ISDN carries only digital bitstreams. Therefore, all signals (voice, audio, image and video) must be digitized so they can be carried "transparently" over the ISDN network. It should be noted that all B-channels operate at the 64 kbps ($\equiv$ 8 bits per sample $\times$ 8,000 samples per second) clear channel mode. That is, all bits in the B-channel must be used to carry user information, rather than signaling or other network related information.

In addition to the B-channel, there are other ISDN channel types: the H0, H11, the H12, H31, H32 and H4 channels. Their rates are shown in Table 9-10. The H-channels are provided for services that require higher bit rates (e.g., video, fast facsimile, high-speed data, high-quality audio, etc.).

Table 9-10   Various ISDN Channels and Their Associated Rates.

Channel	Rate	Channel	Rate
B	64 kbps		
H0	384 kbps		
H12	1.92 Mbps	H11	1.536 Mbps
H31	32.768 Mbps	H32	43~45 Mbps
H4	132.032~138.24 Mbps		

Definition: The D-channel (**D**ata-link channel) operates at 16 or 64 kbps, and is primarily used for network signaling. Whenever a user requests an ISDN service, the D-channel carries this service-request message.

For example, anytime an ISDN user lifts up the handset (i.e., initiates an off-hook condition), the telephone automatically sends a service request message (on the D-channel) to obtain an outgoing voice line. It should be noted that the signaling carried on the D-channel has a bandwidth that is less than a D-channel. Therefore, packet-mode data may be sent on the D-channel.

Example 9-15: Describe applications of the ISDN B-channels and D-channels.

Table 9-11   ISDN Applications on B- Channels and D-Channels.

Channel	Applications		
B-channel	Digitized voice	High-speed data	Others
	64 kbps PCM	*Circuit switched*	*Facsimile*
	32 kbps ADPCM	*Packet switched*	*Slow-scanned video*
D-channel	Signaling	Low-speed data	Telemetry
	Basic	*Videotex*	*Emergency services*
	Enhanced	*Teleletex*	*Energy management*

There are several applications for ISDN B-channels and D-channels. Table 9-11 summarizes the types of traffic that can be carried by B-channels and D-channels.

Two fundamental ISDN services, the Basic rate and Primary rate interfaces have been defined (see Table 9-12). These services are described as follows:

- Basic Rate Interface (BRI): The BRI is composed of: two 64-kbps B-channels, one 16-kbps D channel, and overhead bits (for framing and synchronization). The user rate is 144 kbps, and the signaling/overhead rate is 48 kbps. The applications for this "2B + D" (i.e., two Bearer channels + one Data link channel) interface is designed to be used by residential customers, and small business customers that have needs for voice, facsimile, and low-speed data services. These services can be accessed through a single multifunction terminal, or via several separate terminals with a single physical interface. Most existing twisted-pair (two-wire) local loops can support a "2B+D" interface.

Table 9-12   The Basic and the Primary ISDN Rates/Structures.

Interface	Rate	Structure
Basic rate access	*192 kbps*	*2B + D16*
Primary rate access	*1.544 Mbps*	*23B + D64* *3H0 + D64* *H11*
	2.048 Mbps	*30 B + D64* *31B* *5H0 + D64* *H12 + D64*

- Primary Rate Interface (PRI): The PRI is intended for large business customers, and has a much higher capacity than the BRI interface. There are two different PRIs: one for μ-law, and the other for A-law applications (see Chapter 6). The PRI for μ-law hierarchy operates at a rate of 1.544 Mbps, which corresponds the T1 digital carrier system using the DS1 signal format. Within the 1.544 Mbps signal, the user data occupies 1.536 Mbps, and has a structure of 23B + D [(23 + 1 =) 24 × 64 kbps ≡ 1.536 Mbps]. The PRI can also support multiple 384 kbps H0 channels [e.g., (3H0 + D) and 4H0, and one 1.536 Mbps H11 channel; Note that (1) an ISDN capacity of 6 DS0-channels (i.e., 64 kbps) or 384 kbps rate is defined as a H0 ISDN channel, an ISDN service of 1.536 Mbps is defined as H11]. In addition, it can support mixtures of B and H0 channels [e.g., (3H0 + 5B + D) and (3H0 + D), (2H0 + 11B + D), etc.].

In contrast, for the A-law PRI operates at a rate of 2.048 Mbps (the signal rate of E1, CEPT1, or PS1 signals). The structure of this PRI can be a 30B + D64, or 31B. It can also support H0 channels (e.g., 5H0 + D64), the H12 channels (e.g., H12 + D64), and the mixture of B channels and H0 [e.g., (5H0 + D), (4H0 + 6B + D), (3H0 + 12B + D), etc.]. Note that two data link rates are available for ISDN applications: 16 kbps and 64 kbps (known as D16 and D64).

9.8.2.4 ISDN Layer Protocol

ISDN contains three layers (layer 1, 2 and 3) described as follows:

- ISDN Layer 1: Layer 1 corresponds to the OSI physical layer (layer 1). The functions of this layer are defined in ITU-T Rec. I.430 for the Basic Rate Interface (BRI) and ITU-T Rec. I.431 for the Primary Rate Interface (PRI).

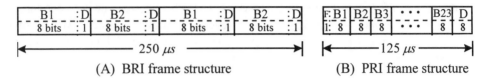

(A) BRI frame structure   (B) PRI frame structure

Figure 9-62   ISDN Layer Frame Structures.

Two schemes (BRI and PRI) are used for the ISDN Layer 1 (physical layer) frame structures. The structures are described as follows:

For the BRI application, a pseudo-ternary signal (see Figure 9-25) is used to transport the data. The frame structure for BRI is shown in Figure 9-62(A). In this interface, a frame is defined as an interval of 250 μs. Thus, there are 4,000 frames per second. Each frame contains two groups having an 8-bit B1-channel followed by a one-bit D-channel, and two groups having an 8-bit B2-channel followed by a one-bit D-channel. Therefore, a BRI frame is composed of 16 bits from each B-channel (B1 and B2; yielding a rate of 64 kbps ≡ 16 bits/frame × 4,000 frames/sec) and a four bit D-channel (yielding a rate of 16 kbps ≡ 4 bits/frame × 4,000 frames/sec). As previously mentioned, in addition to the "2B+D" channels, the BRI contains overhead capacity for synchronization and framing (i.e., for physical layer signaling). There are 48 bit total in one 250-μs frame: 32 bits for the B-channels, 4 bits for the D-channel, and 12 bits (i.e., 48 kbps) for the overhead. Thus, the basic rate is 192 kbps (≡ 2 × 64 + 16 + 48).

The PRI frame structure [Figure 9-62(B)] is identical to the extended superframe T1 structure discussed in Chapter 6, and is commonly call a "23B+D" structure.

- ISDN Layer 2 (link layer): Layer 2 is equivalent to the OSI data link layer (layer 2). The link layer is defined in the ITU-T Recs. I.440 (Q.920) and I.441 (Q.921). The ISDN data link protocol is called the Link Access Procedures on the D-channel (LAPD), which is a "go-back-N" "bit-oriented" protocol (a subset of HDLC).

  LAPD provides the following three types of service to layer 3: (1) By using the call control procedure, the D-channel can provide circuit-switched services for voice or data on the B-channel; (2) The D-channel can provide packet-switched service on the B- or D-channel; and (3) The D-channel can provide operation, administration and maintenance (OA&M) service on the D-channel.

  There is no protocol specified for the B-channel because the user can send any type of information over the B-channel. Therefore, the frame format of the B-channel is determined by the service and/or protocol that the user has requested at call set-up time.

- ISDN Layer 3: Layer 3 is defined in ITU-T Recs. I.450 (Q.930) and I.451 (Q.931). RecommendationI.451 defines the set of network signaling messages used on the D-channel. There is no ISDN Layer 3 definition for the B-channel because it can carry any information in any format. The ISDN signaling is similar to the signaling used in POTS (Table 9-13). Note that the ISDN telephone, instead of the network, generates a dial tone and the ringing sound for the user.

Table 9-13   Signaling for ISDN vs. POTS.

ISDN signaling	**POTS signaling**
ISDN phone sends SETUP message	*POTS phone sends off-hook signal*
Network sends setup ACK message, ISDN phone generates dial tone	*Network replies with dial tone*
Phone sends INFO message	*User dials telephone·number*
Network sends ALAERTING message, ISDN phone generates ringing sound	*User hears audible ringing or ringing*

Example 9-16:   Describe a generic ISDN voice call.

An ISDN voice call scenario (i.e., , how a voice cal is established) is described as follows:

1. The user picks up the ISDN telephone handset or activates a "call" button. The ISDN phone sends a "setup" message to the ISDN network. This message requests a B-channel for a voice call.

2. After receiving the call setup request, the network replies with a "setup ACK" message that is sent to the ISDN phone.

3. The "setup ACK" message causes the ISDN phone to generate a dial tone, which directs the user to dial the called party's telephone number. The dialed number is sent to the network in an "INFO" message.

4. The Local Exchange (LE) establishes the call through the ISDN. It also sends an "alerting" message that causes the ISDN phone to generate a ringing sound heard by the user.

5. The called party answers the call by lifting his/her handset. The ISDN then sends a "connect" message indicating that a B-channel is ready to carry the conversation.

6. The two users may now start their conversation, which remains active until one of them "hands up" the handset. This action indicates the conversation is to be terminated, and a "DISConnect" (DISC) message is sent over the D-channel.

7. The ISDN responds with a "release" message, and the ISDN phone replies with a "RELease COMPlete" (REL COMP) message on the D-channel. The B-channel is now available for another call.

Note that throughout this scenario signaling information is sent on the D-channel while voice conversation occupies the B-channel.

Example 9-17:   Describe an X.25 data call on an ISDN B-channel.

A scenario for establishing an X.25 data call on an ISDN B-channel is described as follows:

1. The user data terminal (device) sends a "setup" message on the D-channel to request a packet-switched mode data connection on the B-channel. This message also specifies the X.25 level 2 (LAPB) and level 3 (PLP) frame and packet formats.

2. The ISDN responds with a "connect" message on the D-channel indicating that a B-channel is ready to carry data.

3. The user (an X.25 DTE) establishes an X.25 logical link with the network line equipment (LE; an X.25 DCE) on the B-channel. The user sends a LAPB Set Asynchronous Balanced Mode (SABM) frame to the network LE, which responds with a LAPB Unnumbered Acknowledgment (UA) frame. The data link between the DTE (the user) and the DCE (the network) has been established.

4. The user sends an X.25 "call request" packet on the B-channel to obtain a virtual circuit connection to the destination DTE. The network LE responds with an X.25 "call connect" packet on the B-channel. The virtual circuit connection is established.

5. The X.25 data packets are exchanged between the DTEs.

6. When one user "hangs-up", this indicates the call is complete. This action sends a "clear request" packet on the B-channel to "clear" the virtual circuit. The ISDN replies with a "clear confirmation" packet.

7. The X.25 data link on the B-channels is cleared after the user sends a LAPB "disconnect" frame, and the ISDN replies with a LAPB UA frame.

8. Although, the user has cleared the virtual circuit and the data link, the B-channel is still in use. Therefore, the user must send a "disconnect" message on the D-channel. The ISDN responds with a "release" message, and the user replies with a "release complete" message. The B-channel is released, and available for another user.

Note that throughout this scenario, signaling is carried on the D-channel and X.25 data is carried on the B-channel. It should also be noted that all X.25 packets are exchanged between two DTEs via LAPB I-frames on the B-channel.

9.8.3 Broadband-ISDN (B-ISDN)

The definitions of narrowband, wideband and broadband services have never been clearly defined for general applications. This is because of rapid changes in digital technology. However, from an ISDN services viewpoint, the definition of broadband is defined in ITU-T Recommendation I.113 as: "*A service or a system that requires transmission channels capable of supporting rates greater then the primary rate.*"

B-ISDN is a packet-switched mode [Asynchronous Transfer Mode (ATM)] network that supports integrated services. ISDN supports circuit-switched channels. In contrast, B-ISDN does **not** support circuit-switched channels, but it emulates circuit switching functions by using packet-switched technology.

B-ISDN information transport is not provided via traditional link-layer variable octet frames. Instead, it is provided by small fixed size link-layer entities, ATM cells (ATM packets). The TDM used for B-ISDN is known as statistical multiplexing.

Table 9-14   ISDN Services and Required Rates.

	Service	Required speed
Residential	CAD/CAM	64 kbps ~ 50 Mbps
	Teleconference	64 kbps ~ 50 Mbps
	Facsimile	1.2 kbps ~ 1.5 Mbps
	Inter-computer	1.3 56 kbps ~ 150 Mbps
Business	CATV (TV)	50 Mbps ~ 150 Mbps
	CATV (HDTV)	150 Mbps ~ 600 Mbps

Starting in the early 1980's, the demand for greater bandwidth to transport information started, and has been constantly increasing. Entertainment and business video-based applications (Table 9-14 lists different data rates needed for typical ISDN services.) is leading this demand. Other applications such as high-resolution image communication, HDTV (High Definition TV) distribution, video/document retrieval, and high-speed file transfer, also require high bandwidth services. The availability of high-speed semi-conductor technology (reducing signal processing time and equipment costs), optical fiber technology (with transport speeds in the Gbps range, and high reliability) and other technological advancements continue to support this demand. For faster speeds and higher capacity services

9.8.4 Frame Relay

The term of "frame relay" has different meanings in the data communication industry, depending upon the specific application.

- Frame relay (from one perspective) is a technology that is based on "routers", which are used to interconnect Local Area Networks (LANs).

- Frame relay (from a different perspective) is a method to get a higher throughput from an existing data network (e.g., a slow X.25 protocol). For the customers seeking improved throughput for Wide Area Networks (WANs), frame relay is an OSI-based "smart" approach applied to the Data Transfer Phase (DTP) of a circuit-mode call, and is positioned as replacement for expensive (leased) private lines.

- Frame relay can also be considered an enhancement to the ISDN protocol. In this case, frame relay is effectively another data service capability.

9.8.4.1 X.25, Frame Relay and ATM

Frame relay is a new and improved (compared to X.25) data transfer technology, and an expedited frame transmission technology. Frame relay provides high-speed services (up to 1.544 Mbps for μ-law; or 2.048 Mbps for A-law). The service can be dedicated or switched , and transported over a public or private network. This section briefly compares the different technologies used for data transfer (refer to Figure 9-63).

- X.25: This technology is based on the concept of data transport over voice-grade lines. X.25 is considered a narrowband technology, which applies connection-oriented switching., and has data transfer speeds up to 56 kbps.

- Frame relay: This technology takes advantages of high quality transmission facilities to implement enhanced ISDN services. It is a wideband technology, but it still applies connection-oriented switching, and is specifically intended or data applications.

- ATM: This technology utilizes optical transmission (high capacity and greater quality for broadband and multimedia transport), fast signal processing and low cost memory devices to provide improved data and voice-band information transfer services.

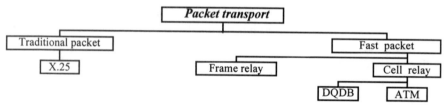

Figure 9-63   X.25, Frame Relay and ATM.

9.8.4.2 Why use Frame Relay for Data Transfer?

Data transfer over a voice-grade lines using X.25 services has been widely accepted in the data industry for many years. Hence, the question "Why is frame relay being positioned as replacement for X.25?" First, the data throughput rate of 56 kbps (X.25) is insufficient for many customers. A clear 64 kbps channel with 1.544 Mbps or 2.048 Mbps throughput has become the minimum requirement for commercial customers. Secondly, wide-area connectivity of LANs (running at approximately 10 Mbps) by using frame relay could provide a viable means for internetworking machines running at 1.544 Mbps in μ-law applications (or 2.048 Mbps in A-law applications).

Customers and vendors have reached a similar conclusion: "Frame relay will do the job they want, and at the right price." In addition, frame relay can be offered on existing facilities by simply deploying software modifications in routers and switching equipment. Hence, the data industry fully supports frame relay technology.

As shown in Figure 9-63, frame relay is designated as an ISDN packet-mode service which makes acceptance in the market place easier. Frame-relay related ISDN standards are relatively complete, and have evolved faster than any ISDN standard. This condition has also encouraged a rapid acceptance of frame relay technology.

9.8.4.3 Frame Relay Evolution and Standards

From the mid 1970's through the early 1980's X.25 transmission speed was limited to 9.6 kbps, with a rather high Bit Error Rate (BER), and a relatively slow, rigid protocol.

In the mid 1980's, X.25 customers recognized the need for data networking. This brought about the introduction of high-speed data transmission, with data rates from 64 kbps up to 1.544 Mbps. With increased speed, reliability became more important because of the larger quantity of data being handled.

LAN customers with private networks that are based on bridges and routers, have pushed high-speed data transport to become a reality. This technology is called frame relay. Frame relay is a high-speed data transport technology with flexible protocols.

Figure 6-64   Frame Relay Key Standards.

The primary ITU-T Recommendations that contain standards associated with frame relay are indicated in Figure 9-64. ITU-T Recs. I-222, I-233 and I-370 deal with frame relay architecture and services. ITU-T Recs. Q.922 and Q.933 specify the frame relay User Network Interface (UNI) signaling, data transfer protocols, and procedures. Standards dealing with the internetworking between frame relay networks and other networks (e.g., ISDN, B-ISDN, etc.) are defined in the ITU-T Rec.I.5xy series of documents (e.g., I.555).

9.8.4.4 Frame Relay Network: Private and Public

A frame relay network can be either private [(Figure 9-65(A) or public [Figure 9-65(B)]. A private frame relay network can be designed as a point-to-point mesh of routers, whose main functions are to provide connectivity and to perform protocol conversion. Figure 9-65(A) is an example of this type of network based on locating routers in several major cities. Note that these network interconnections are logical links (i.e., switched connections). Many data users have deployed private networks made up of bridges and routers. Frame relay can easily be supported on existing networks as a retrofit function, or old devices can be replaced with new routers that have built-in frame relay functions. This approach may be the most expeditious way of implementing frame relay technology, but can become uneconomical in the long run because of the large number of routers and interconnections

Another, and perhaps better arrangement is a public frame relay network, with several frame relay nodes [see Figure 9-65(B)]. The frame relay nodes are the access points for users. A host computer can be tied to the public frame relay network via a Front-End Processor (FEP), that is connected to a Private Line (PL). In North America, the private line is typically a leased T1 digital carrier circuit (described in Chapter 6). A host can also be connected to the network via a token-ring LAN. PCs can be connected using an Ethernet LAN to the frame relay network via a router.

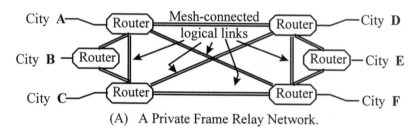

(A) A Private Frame Relay Network.

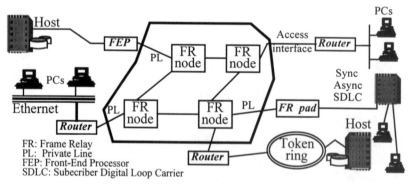

(B) A Public Frame Relay Network.

Figure 9-64   Private and Public Frame Relay Networks.

9.8.4.5 Frame Relay Interworking

Frame relay can support a multiplicity of "connection-oriented" and "connectionless" protocols at the network and higher layers. The protocol stack (PHY, MAC, LLC, CLNP and TP4) is shown at bottom right and left of Figure 9-66, and is used when a "connectionless" protocol is transported over a frame relay network. Local Area Networks (LANs), Metropolitan Area Networks (MANs) and frame relay networks are actually implemented as multiple subnetworks. An internetworking protocol combines these subnetworks, and can be deployed in routers and end systems. As shown in the protocol stack, the ISO Transport Protocol class 4 (TP4) layer, located above the ConnectionLess Network Protocol (CLNP), is used to provide many functions including: (1) end-to-end reliability; (2) regulating flow control functions; and (3) detection/correction of errors. When using the frame relay bearer service, the ConnectionLess Network Service (CLNS) end systems may apply appropriate standard or proprietary protocols in the InterWorking Units (IWUs). For applications that use core LAPD protocol in the IWUs, two modes of operations are available:

- Unacknowledged Information (UI) transfer: This mode provides unacknowledged data transfer services.

- Multiple Frame Acknowledged Information transfer: This mode provides connection-oriented data transfer services.

Frame relay is an attractive interconnection method for exchanging of CLNS Packet Data Units (PDUs). It is especially appropriate for interconnecting LANs, since frame relay can provide capabilities similar to the Media Access Control (MAC) service.

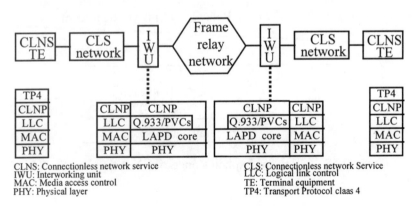

Figure 9-66   Frame Relay Interworking.

9.8.4.6 Frame Relay Data Link Core Protocol

Figure 9-67 shows the frame relay data link core protocol format. It consists of a start flag, address, information (payload), frame check sequence, and an end flag. This frame relay protocol, defined in ITU-T Rec. Q.922, supports frame relay services. The core functions of this protocol are: (1) frame delimiting, alignment and transparency; (2) frame multiplexing and demulitplexing; (3) transmission error detection; (4) congestion control; and (5) verification of frame size and integrity.

The address field is expanded in Figure 9-67. The minimum and default length of the address field is 2 octets. However, the address filed can be extended to 3 or 4 octets to support a larger address range, or to support optional data link core control functions, but this requires bilateral agreement at the user-network interface. This field includes the Data Link Connection Identifier (DLCI; upper and lower bits) the Address Extension bits (EA), a reserved Command/Response (C/R) bit for use by the end-user equipment to support a command/response indication, the Discard Eligibility indication (DE), the Forward Explicit Congestion Notification (FECN), and the Backward Explicit Congestion Control Notification (BECN).

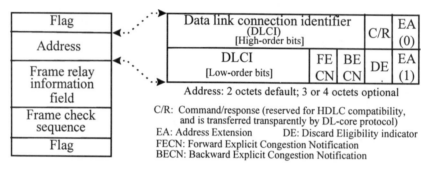

Figure 9-67   Frame Relay Data Link Core Protocol.

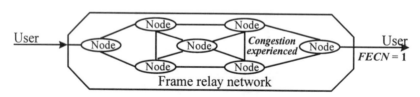

Figure 9-68   Forward Explicit Congestion Notification (FECN).

The functions of the FECN, BECN, DE, and DLCI bits are briefly described as follows:

- Forward Explicit Congestion Notification (FECN): This bit is sent by a congested frame relay network to notify the end user that congestion avoidance procedures should be initiated for traffic being sent in the direction of the frame carrying the FECN indication (Figure 9-68). The frame relay network also sends this bit as logical "1" to the receiver, indicating the network carrying the frame relay signal is experiencing congestion. This indication can be used by the user to control the traffic rate entering the network, thereby relieving the network load. This bit can be set (i.e., set to "1") by the network or the user, but, the network shall never clear (i.e., set to "0") this bit. Networks which do not support FECN shall pass this bit unchanged.

- Backward Explicit Congestion Notification (BECN): This bit can be set by a congested network to notify the user that congestion avoidance procedures should be initiated for traffic being sent in the opposite direction of the frame carrying the BECN indicator. BECN is set to "1" as a positive congestion indication for the receiver (i.e., the traffic it sends may encounter congested resources). This bit can also be used for "source controlled" transmitter rate adjustments.

- Discard Eligibility indicator (DEI): This bit is set to logical "1" to indicate a particular frame may be discarded in a congestion situation. That is, a frame containing a DE bit set to logical "1" has lower priority relative to other frames with DE set to logical "0".

- Data Link Connection Identifier (DLCI):These bits are used to identify the virtual connection (i.e., address) for a bearer channel, at the user-to-network or network-to-network interface.

9.8.4.7 Frame Relay Applications, Service Characteristics, and Congestion Control

Frame relay has advantages over other technologies (e.g., X.25; Table 9-9) used by data customers. The primary advantages of frame relay are listed as follows:

- Block-interactive data applications: Short delay characteristics are normally desired for this application. Because there is less processing in the data transfer phase and higher bit rates are used, the performance of interactive applications is improved.

- File transfer: Users that routinely transfer large files will experience faster throughput and better economic efficiency.

- PC-to-LAN interconnection and groupware office solutions: LAN connectivity for "groupware" (e.g., e-mail) or user-to-user applications perform better, utilize bit rates up to 2.048 Mbps, and exhibit reduced nodal processing delay.

- Multimedia applications: Advanced services (e.g., video, graphics, sound/music, etc.) are supported by frame relay.

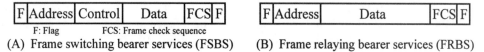

F: Flag   FCS: Frame check sequence

(A) Frame switching bearer services (FSBS)   (B) Frame relaying bearer services (FRBS)

Figure 9-69   Frame Mode Bearer Services.

The ISDN network, in "frame mode" (Figure 9-69), provides basic bearer service by preserving the order of frames that are transferred between users. The frames are routed through the network based on the value of the data link connection identifier (DCLI) which is an attached label for each frame. This label is a "logical identifier" That has local significant. That is, the label may be and usually is changed at each network node.

The user-to-network interface structure allows the establishment of multiple virtual calls, permanent virtual circuits, or both, to many destinations via a single access channel. This service may possess the following characteristics:

- The service supports bidirectional transfer of frames.

- The service preserves the frame orders (as given at the originating user-network interface) when the frames are delivered to their destinations.

- The service provides error detection for several functions: transmission, format, and operational errors.

- The service provides transparent user data transport (at the frame level). Note that the frame address and frame check sequence fields may be modified by the network, but user data remains unchanged.

- The service does not acknowledge frames, and erroneous frames are discarded by the network.

See ITU-T Rec. Q.922 for further details, and Q.921 for description of congestion control functions. The service congestion control is defined by several parameters. When end users do not meet the committed rates negotiated at call set-up, the network enters into congestion state. The congestion associated parameters are briefly described as follows:

Definition 9-7: Congestion is a state of network elements (e.g., switches, transmission facilities, or transmission terminals) in which the network can no longer meet the negotiated performance objectives for the established connections of the end users.

- Access rate: The access rate is the data rate of the user access channel [D, B, H (see Tables 9-10 & 9-11) or other non-ISDN channels]. The speed of the access channel determines how much data (maximum rate) the user can input to the network.

- Committed burst size (B_c): This is the "maximum committed" amount of data that an end user may offer to the network during a specific time period as defined by parameter T_c. The committed burst size (B_c) is negotiated at call set-up; and is set by network administration of the Permanent Virtual Circuit (PVC).

- Excess burst size (B_e): The excess burst size is the "maximum allowed" amount of data (exceeding B_c) that a user can transmit during the time interval specified by parameter T_c. The excess burst size (B_e) generally has a much lower probability of occurrence than B_c, and is negotiated at call set-up.

- Committed rate measurement interval (T_c): The time interval during which the end user is allowed to input the B_c and the B_e is specified by parameter T_c.

- Committed Information Rate (*CIR*): The committed information rate is the transfer rate that the network is committed to support under normal conditions. This rate is negotiated at call set-up, and is set by the network administration of PVC. The CIR is averaged over a minimum increment of the time specified by parameter T_c, and is as given by the following equation:

$$CIR = \frac{B_c}{T_c} \qquad (9\text{-}4)$$

9.8.4.8 User-Network Interface

Figure 9-70 shows the frame relay User-to-Network Interface (UNI) protocol architecture. The UNI provides the interface for both Switched Virtual Circuits (SVCs) and Permanent Virtual Circuits (PVCs; see Chapter 5 for SVC and PVC descriptions).

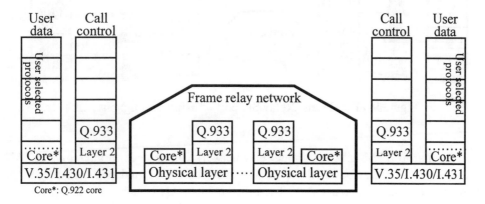

Figure 9-70   Frame Relay User-Network Interface Protocol Architecture.

Call control processing is performed by using the standards defined in ITU-T Recs. Q.933 and Q.921/Q.922 as layer 3 and layer 2 protocols, respectively. However, for PVC, no real time call-by-call establishment is necessary, and all parameters are agreed upon during the initial PVC establishment. Once the channel is established, the value of the logical identifier and other associated parameters is negotiated during call setup as part of the call-control procedures. The network may accept or reject the call depending on the parameters requested. Data transfer service can be provided on several physical layers. The network terminates layer 2 (Q.222 core) protocol is shown in Figure 9-70. In the Data Transfer Phase (DTP) of the OSI connection-oriented network layer, service can be provided by using: (1) X.25 DTP, (2) an appropriate ISO layer 3 protocol, or (3) by a convergence protocol residing above Q.922. Due to the prevalent use of X.25 networks, the combination of Q.922 with X.25 DTP is a preferred choice. ISDN service can be offered on any channel (i.e., ISDN , D, B or H). Some restrictions may apply; for example, the frame size, because in an end-to-end connection at least one of the access channels is the D channel (operating at either 16 or 64 kbps).

Example 9-17: Briefly describe the applications: (1) frame relay support of high throughput X.25, and (2) LAN interconnection using frame relay.

Two requirements, and subsequently features, of frame relay have been compatibility with X.25 networks and throughput improvement (from a maximum throughput of 56 kbps to an improved throughput of 2 Mbps). Frame relay, with a faster bit rate compared to X.25 technology and reduced protocol overhead has accomplished these goals. A small processing overhead is needed for X.25 to frame relay Packet Data Unit (PDU) encapsulation (and the reverse) process, but it does not diminish the advantages of this configuration. Figure 9-70 illustrates X.25 protocol carried over a frame relay network.

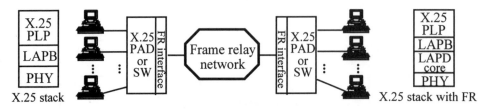

Figure 9-71   Frame Relay Support of High Throughput X.25.

Similar to ATM network, frame relay network can be used to interconnect LANs. Figure 9-72 illustrates four LANs (two Ethernet bus LANs, and two toke-ring LANs) interconnected via a frame network. The Ethernet bus LAN is connected to a frame relay node of the frame network using a bridge or router. In contrast, a token-ring LAN is connected directly to a frame relay node. The core network of the frame network is an ATM network, that contains several ATM switch nodes.

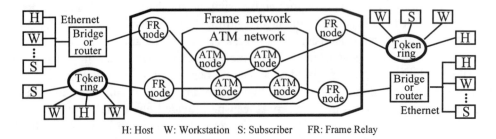

H: Host   W: Workstation   S: Subscriber   FR: Frame Relay

Figure 9-72   LAN Interconnection Using Frame.

Review Questions II for Chapter 9:

(13) (True, False) EIA-232-D protocol is sufficient to implement reliable transmission for data communications.

(14) (True, False) In a Automatic Repeat/reQuest (ARQ) data systems, the receiver typically indicates the "acceptance" or "rejection" of a block of user information.

(15) Two approaches an ARQ (error detection only) systems uses are: _____ ARQ, and _____ ARQ, which can either be _____ ARQ or _____ ARQ.

(16) Data link protocols can be classified into three general groups: _____, _____, and _____ protocol, which has many commonly used protocols such as _____ (HDLC), _____ (LAPB), _____ (LAPD), _____ (MAC), and _____.

(17) HDLC is a _____-oriented _____ continuous "go-back-N" data link protocol, which is the current ISO data link protocol standard. HDLC frame contains five field: two flags, _____, _____, _____ and _____.

(18) _____ and _____ are techniques used to share communication resources in a _____ network, which implies that every device in the network can "_____" every transmission sent by every other device.

(19) A commonly used contention scheme is _____ (_____) with collision detection. That is, stations utilize "_____" (LWT), in order words, stations are transmitting continue to monitor the link.

(20) ITU-T Rec. X.25 was defined in 1976 to standardize the interface between a _____ and a _____ (PSPDN). Worldwide known X.25 networks are: _____, _____, _____, _____ and AT&T's _____.

(21) Several ISDN rate interfaces have been defined by ISDN standards: H0, H11, H12, H21, H22, H31, H32, H4, etc. These rates consists of two basic channels: the __-channel (which is used for all forms of telecommunications services, such as _____, _____, _____, _____ and _____), and the __-channel (which is operates at _____ or _____ kbps, and is primarily used for _____).

(22) Frame relay is a technology that is based on "_____", and is used to interconnect _____. Frame relay is a method, considered to be one of the several "fast" packet switching technologies, to get a higher _____ from an existing data network. Frame relay can support a multiplicity of "_____-_____" and "_____" protocols at the network and higher layers. Frame relay network uses _____ and _____ to notify the end users (at both ends) that congestion avoidance procedures should be initiated for traffic being sent.

Appendix 9-1

American Standard Code for Information Interchange (ASCII Code)

Figure A9-1 shows the ASCII codes for both alphanumeric and special characters. The ASCII code also contains several control codes. They are described here.

- **Format control**: There are six code used for format control.

  (1) **BS** (BackSpace): The BS is used to request movement of the printer or display cursor backward one position from its current position.

  (2) **CR** (Carriage Return): The CR is used to request movement of the printer or display cursor to the starting point of a line.

  (3) **FF** (Form Feed): The FF is used to request movement of the printer or display cursor forward to the starting position of the next page, form, or screen.

  (4) **HT** (Horizontal Tab): The HT is used to request movement of the printer or display cursor forward to the next pre-assigned "tab" or stopping position.

  (5) **LF** (Line Feed): The LF is used to request movement of the printer or display cursor to the starting point of the next line.

  (6) **VT** (Vertical Tab): The VT is used to request movement of the printer or display cursor forward to the next of a series pre-assigned printing lines.

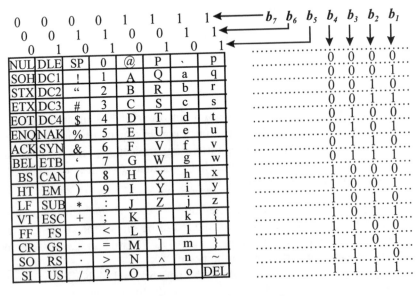

Figure 9A-1   ASCII Code.

- **Transmission control**: There are nine codes used for transmission control.

  (1) **ACK** (Acknowledge): The ACK is used by the receiving device as an affirmation response (i.e., a positive response) to polling messages.

  (2) **ENQ** (Enquiry): The ENQ is used to request a response from a remote station, or may also used as a "WHO ARE YOU" request for a station to identify itself.

  (3) **EOT** (End Of Transmission): The EOT is used to indicate the end of a transmission interval, which may have included one or more "texts" with headings.

  (4) **ETB** (End of Transmission Block): The ETB is used to indicate the end of a block of data for communications purposes. If the format of the processed data is not "blocks", the "ETB" can be used to delineate blocks of data.

  (5) **ETX** (End of TeXt): The ETX is used to terminate a text "grouping" that was started with "STX".

  (6) **NAK** (Negative AcKnowledgment): The NAK is used t a negative response to polling messages.

  (7) **SOH** (Start Of Heading): The SOH is used to indicate the start of a heading, which may contain address or routing information.

  (8) **STX** (Start of TeXt): The STX is used to indicate the start of a text "grouping", and also indicates the end of heading.

  (9) **SYN** (SYNchronous/Idle): The SYN is used in a synchronous transmission system to achieve timing synchronization. When there is no data to be transmitted, the system will send "SYN" characters continuously.

- **Information separator**: Four codes are used for information separation: (1) the hierarchical structure is **FS** (File Separator; the most inclusive), (2) **GS** (Group Separator), (3) **RS** (Record Separator), and (4) **US** (United Separator; the least inclusive). The information separators may be used in an optional manner.

- **Miscellaneous characters**: There are fifteen miscellaneous characters available for various types of usage:

  (1) **BEL** (BELl): The BEL is used to alert a human operator. It may control an alarm bell or attention device.

  (2) **CAN** (CANcel): The CAN is used to indicate that a message or a block preceded by "CAN" should be disregarded (e.g., dropped). The disregard indication is usually the result of detecting an error.

  (3) ~ (6) **DC1, DC1, DC3** and **DC4** (device controls): They are used for the control of ancillary devices or special terminal features.

(7) **DEL** (DELete): The DEL is used to obliterate unwanted characters, for example, by overwriting the current characters.

(8) **DLE** (Data Link Escape): The DLE is used to change the meaning of one or more contiguously characters, and can provide supplementary controls or permit sending data characters having any bit combination.

(9) **EM** (End of Medium): The EM is used to indicate the "physical" end of a magnetic tape or other medium, or the end of the "usable" portion of the medium.

(10) **ESC** (ESCape): The ESC is used to provide code extension by giving a specific number of contiguous characters an alternate meaning.

(11) **NUL** (NULl; no character): The NUL is used for filling in time or space on magnetic tape when data is not being supplied.

(12) **SI** (Shift In): The SI is used to indicate specific code combinations shall be interpreted according to the standard character set.

(13) **SO** (Shift Out): The SO is used to indicate specific combinations shall be interpreted as an non- standard character set, until an "SI" character is received.

(14) **SP** (SPace): The SP is used to separate words, move the printing mechanism, or advance the display cursor forward by one position. Note that the "SP" is a non-printing character.

(15) **SUB** (SUBstitute): The SUB is used to substitute a character for another character, which is erroneous or invalid.

Example A9-1: Determine from Figure A9-1 the corresponding codewords for: "NULL", "2", and the "C" characters.

- The codeword $(b_7, b_6, b_5, b_4, b_3, b_2, b_1) = (\underline{0\ 0\ 0}\ \underline{0\ 0\ 0\ 0})$ represents the character "NUL". The first set (000) comes from the top "NUL" character of Figure A9-1, and the second set (0000) comes from the end of the first row starting with the character "NUL" in Figure A9-1.

- The codeword $(b_7, b_6, b_5, b_4, b_3, b_2, b_1) = (\underline{0\ 1\ 1}\ \underline{0\ 0\ 1\ 0})$ represents the character "2". The first set (011) comes from the top "2" character of Figure A9-1, and the second set (0010) comes from the end of the row containing the character "2" in Figure A9-1.

- The codeword $(b_7, b_6, b_5, b_4, b_3, b_2, b_1) = (\underline{1\ 0\ 0}\ \underline{0\ 0\ 1\ 1})$ represents the character "C". The first set (100) comes from the top "C" character of Figure A9-1, and the second set (0011) comes from the end of the row containing the character "C" in Figure A9-1.

CHAPTER 10

Network Architectures: LANs and WANs

Chapter Objectives

Upon the completion of this chapter, you should be able to

- Define a Local Area Network (LAN), describe the evolution (including the comparison between a LAN and a PBX), the characteristics, the applications, and the transmission medium used for LANs.

- Describe LAN topology (star, radial, bus and ring), LAN access control and logical link control, LAN communications architecture, LAN standards [e.g., IEEE 802.3: Carrier Sense Multiple Access/Collision Detection (CSMA/CD); Ethernet; and IEEE 802.5 token ring].

- Discuss high-speed local area networks [e.g., Fiber Distributed Data Interface (FDDI), FDDI and OSI, FDDI frame structure, FDDI basic operations, FDDI dual-ring architecture, and FDDI fault recovery/reconfiguration], and Distributed Queue Dual Bus (DQDB) standards.

- Discuss LAN-to-LAN internetworking devices: bridges, routers, gateways, and hybrid devices.

- Describe LAN network operations and management: Network Operating Systems (NOS), LAN servers, server operating systems, network management goals, domains, architectures, and implementation. Discuss future LAN development trends and issues.

10.1 INTRODUCTION

Computer interconnections (networks) can be implemented by Wide Area Networks (WANs), Metropolitan Area Networks (MANs), Local Area Networks (LANs), or any combination of these techniques.

- Wide Area Network (WAN): In a WAN, network bandwidth is a precious resource. The entire network design philosophy is focused on the efficient use of the available bandwidth. For data communications, store and forward techniques using relatively expensive packet-switching nodes are used to ensure the bandwidth of the communication links are used to their fullest. Various "shorthand" methods are employed to keep the number of overhead bits in a packet to a minimum. For example, virtual circuits make it unnecessary to include a destination address in data packets. As a result, some of these techniques put an extra burden on the host processors and network nodes (to save the bandwidth).

- Metropolitan Area Network (MAN): A MAN is intended to provide public access for interconnecting local area networks at a moderately high bandwidth. MAN standards are specified by IEEE 802.6.

- Local Area Network (LAN): Compared to a WAN, the cost of LAN bandwidth for this relatively short distances is less expensive. LAN architecture does not require sharing communication facilities with other users. Hence, there is no reason to place restrictions on the amount of bandwidth available for data communications. The aim of the LAN designer is to make the network as simple as possible. There is no economic advantage of reducing the bandwidth requirement at the expense of increasing host complexity. Therefore, it is recommended that the full device or processor addresses be included in every packet. The shift toward host simplicity fits well with the equipment that is likely to be found in the LAN architecture.

10.1.1 What is a LAN?

Definition 10-1:   A Local Area Network (LAN) is a communications network that provides interconnection between a variety of data communication devices within a small area. A LAN is a shared communications medium, implemented as a set of interfaces for computers and terminals.

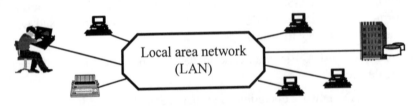

Figure 10-1   Various Data Communications Devices Connecting to a LAN.

It can be seen from Figure 10-1 that many types of devices can be connected to a LAN, assuming the appropriate interface and compatible software is provided. A LAN covers three important aspects:

(1) A LAN is a communications network. It is used to move the data bitstream from once device to another. This requires common application-level software and protocols for every devices that is attached to the LAN to insure compatibility.

(2) A broad variety of communications devices utilize LANs. The devices connected to the transmission medium can be computers, terminals, peripheral devices, PCs, work stations, telephones, facsimiles, sensors (temperature, humidity, security alarms), etc.

(3) The geographical area of a LAN is small. The applications of LANs are typically limited to a college campus, industrial park, high-rise building, and sometimes LANs are, even confined to a single building.

10.1.2 Evolution of Local Area Networks

The evolution of LAN development is clearly divided into three major eras: the 1960s, 1970s, and 1980s. In the 1990s, concentration has been on stabilization of LAN standards.

(1) 1960s: After digital computers were introduced in the late 1950s, it became the designers' goal to improve system speed, memory capacity, and especially "computing capability". The next logical step in developing "never-ending" computer systems was the concept of Local Area Networks. At this point in time, computing needs were handled by a central computer (known as the main frame) that had batch-processing and time-sharing capabilities. A "dumb" terminal was connected, via a low speed transmission facility, to the central computer. Time sharing provided a dramatic improvement over batch system processing, but it had its own set of inherent difficulties. Central processing systems were designed to perform large, computer-bound jobs, hence they were not optimized for small, interactive, computer-based tasks.

(2) 1970s: Computer systems development entered a new era when mini-computers were introduced in the early 1970s. They were commonly used as a means of "off-loading" the central computer. Mini-computers were generally located close to the user groups that required this type of service. This simplified and reduced the costs of installation and connection. In addition, mini-computers offered better price and performance for a variety of applications.

The multiple mini-computer approach to computing is not without its own set of problems. There were tasks that required more power than was available on a single mini-computer. Likewise, some locally generated data bases contained information of value to other individual/organization that were connected to a different system. A logical evolutionary step was to interconnect multiple mini-computers via a "network". The long-haul networking philosophy was applied for this purpose. Individual now had almost immediate access to a wide range of data (information) and a variety of processing capabilities beyond the scope of their "local systems".

(3) 1980s: The explosive growth of intelligent office equipment in the 1980s (such as word processors, facsimile machines, and personal computers) coupled with an increasing number of "intelligent terminals" created a situation where literally hundreds of computers could be found in many business offices.

The requirement for inter-machine communication was greater than ever before. The most cost effective method was to store files/programs on large rotating disk drives. Hence, personal computers were required to "download" needed information (files/programs) onto small independent floppy disk systems.

Applications such as word processing grew rapidly, and were required to communicate directly with typesetting machines for maximum efficiency. Large on-line printers provided better price/performance (quicker printing time and better resolution) compared to the dot matrix devices used by typical personal computer terminals.

It is well-known that Wide Area Network (WAN) technology was commonly used in the early stages of local area networking. This was a result of the availability of appropriate software and hardware products, rather than an effort to create an optimal the local work environment. The long-haul network structure were satisfactory for dealing with a few mini-computers, but it was completely inappropriate when hundreds or even thousands of micro-processor-based systems required communication services. A new communication methodology was needed to deal with the personal computer environment, and the Local Area Network was introduced to satisfy this need.

Example 10-1: Describe how a Private Branch eXchange (PBX) can be considered a LAN.

In modern communications applications, Private Branch eXchanges (PBXs) and Private Automatic Branch eXchanges (PABXs) have been "digitized". A PBX have a lot in common with a local area network.

As shown in Figure 10-2, any device can access another device connected to a network, which includes PBX equipment. Likewise, almost anything (e.g., computers, telephones, printers, hosts, etc.) can be connected to a PBX. A PBX, just like a LAN, functions as a multi-media network, and is also a multi-speed network. However, there are significant differences between a PBX and a LAN. The major difference is the functional channel bandwidth. Most modern PBXs can support 64-kbps clear data channels. For ISDN applications, a PBX can support 384-kbps services (six 64 kbps B-channels) and/or 1.544-Mbps services.

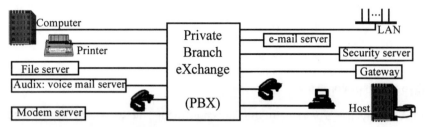

Figure 10-2   A PBX Connection: As a Local Area Network.

10.1.3 LAN Characteristics

Several different types of LANs are offered by various vendors. These LANs differ from one another based on several aspects:

- Technology
- Transmission media
- Topology
- Access methods
- Operations and operating system
- Network management
- Internetworking
- Applications
- Services supported

However, all typical LANs possess the following common characteristics:

- A LAN should allow a number of independent devices (e.g., a combination of terminals, PCs, workstations, facsimiles, printers, storage devices, computers, etc.) to communicate *directly* with each other. Therefore, all devices in a LAN must have same priority so they can communicate with each other as *peers*. That is, no single device can control the network. Network users select only the data addressed to them via the network, and each user should have an equal opportunity for gaining access to the Local Area Network (LAN).

- The communication distance within a LAN is typically an area between 0.5 to 10 km in diameter. LANs are often confined to a single office building.

- The physical channel in a LAN can either be (1) baseband transmission over twisted pair wires (unshielded or shielded), coaxial cable, or multi-mode optical fibers, or (2) broadband transmission over coaxial cables or optical fiber (multi-mode fiber for low speed and single-mode fiber for higher speeds).

- The LAN must have very good transmission performance. A Bit Error Rate (BER) of 10^{-8} is typically expected.

- The physical communication channel of a LAN should support moderate data rates, ranging from 56 kbps to 10 Mbps [for Fiber Distributed Data Interface (FDDI) technology, the speed is up to 100 Mbps].

- A LAN is generally owned and operated by a single entity (i.e., the users) with an organization or company.

- A LAN may use a variety of transmission media, network topologies, and access methods. A LAN differs from WAN in scope and speed.

10.1.4 LAN Applications and Connections

A LAN is typically used to connect a collection of workstations to one or more central processors, and provides a higher-speed communications than a public phone (e.g., PSTN) connection [Figure 10-3(A)]. A LAN also supports communication over greater distances than "hardwired techniques" such as RS449. By using a shared medium (e.g., coaxial cable) wiring costs are significantly lower for LAN architectures than hardwired systems. These combined factors make LANs a favorable choice for data communication applications (e.g., voice, audio, image, video, and data).

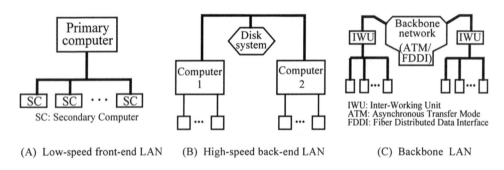

(A) Low-speed front-end LAN   (B) High-speed back-end LAN   (C) Backbone LAN

Figure 10-3   Various LAN Connections.

LANs are used to interconnect the shared resources provided by various components in a computing system [Figure 10-3(B) illustrates a high-speed back-end LAN for this type of applications]. Computing facilities can be spread over a small area, such as a college campus, or an industrial park. LANs can also provide a simple method for connecting "in-house" computers to long-haul networks. With the increased number of available LANs, it is obvious that techniques would be developed to interconnect these separate LANs. Interconnecting devices such as gateways, routers, bridges, and repeaters are applied for accessing a common high-speed network. The high-speed network can also be a LAN that serves as an "information highway", known as a "backbone" network [Figure 10-3(C)]. Presently, the largest single application for LANs is *office automation*. Three service types are found in most office automation systems:

(1) **Electronic mail**: This function generally offers services for preparing text document, storing documents, and distributing messages. Electronic mail systems may interface other applications that can automatically insert messages (data) concerning the status of inventories, accounts payable, etc.

Message delivery is usually confirmed so that the sender is assured the message was received. The ownership of a message may (or may not) be transferred to the recipient. Broadcast distribution is often provided so that messages can be sent to all members of a group as specified by the sender.

Electronic mail systems may include gateways to long-haul networks with features that allows messages to be delayed for delivery to sites in different time zones.

(2) **Electronic filing**: A LAN can offer an effective mechanism for developing a distributed data processing system. A distributed data processing system contains intelligent devices that are placed at multiple sites within an organization. Each device can provide facilities for local storage and processing of data, as well as access to remote (information) resources.

Distributed data processing typically follows the "80/20 rule". That is, 80% of the data gathered at a site is only used at that site. Therefore, it is thus more efficient to store and process local data locally, rather than sending it to a central site for storage and processing.

(3) **Word processing**: In conjunction with personal computers, LANs provides powerful method for employees to perform word processing tasks via a host computer.

LANs have many other applications in the automated office environment, including:

- File and printer sharing
- Factory automation
- Computer Aided Design (CAD)
- Image/graphics processing
- Energy management
- Integrated voice/data communications

The three LAN connections (e.g., front-end, back-end or backbone LANs) illustrated in Figure 10-3 are compared with a Private Branch eXchange (PBX) in Table 10-1. The parameters used for comparison include: network topology (e.g., bus, star, or ring), bit rates, medium used for transporting (unshielded twisted pair wires, shielded twisted pair wires, coaxial cables, or optical fibers), switching technology (circuit-switching or packet switching), number of devices supported, system costs, coverage areas, and implementation examples.

Table 10-1   LANs and PBXs Comparison.

	Front-end LANs	Back-end LAN	Backbone LAN	PBX
Topology	Bus, star, or ring	Bus	Bus, star, or ring	Star
Bit rate	≤ 20 Mbps	≤ Gbps	100~150 Mbps	Up to 2 Mbps
Medium	UTP/STP, Coax, fiber	Coax, fiber	Coax, fiber	UTP, fiber
Switching	Packet VC	Packet VC	Packet VC	Circuit
# of devices	50 ~ 100	Few to 10	Few	100 ~ 1000
Costs	Low ~ moderate	High	High	Low ~ mod.
Scope	1~2 km	~0.1 km	10's km	1~2 km
Example	Ethernet token ring	Hyper channel HiPPI	FDDI	Definity system

UTP: Unshielded Twisted Pair wire;   STP: Shielded Twisted Pair of wire;   Coax: Coaxial cable;
VC: Virtual Circuit   FDDI: Fiber Distribute Data Interface;   HiPPI: High Performance Parallel Interface

10.2 TRANSMISSION MEDIA FOR LAN

The transmission media used for LAN connections are essentially the same as those used in telephone networks [Wide Area Network (WAN)] and Metropolitan Area Network (MAN). Several transmission media will be briefly described in this section with respect to bit rates, configurations, geographical coverage, noise characteristics, and costs.

- Twisted-pair wire characteristics:

    * Diameter approximately 0.016 ~ 0.036 inch [known as 26 AWG ~ 22 AWG; American Wire Gauge (size)].

    * Paired wires are always twisted to reduce cross-talk (interference).

    * Shielded or unshielded twisted pair wire: It can be used for short distances at high bit rates, and longer distances at lower bit rates. It is popular for Ethernet 10 Base-T networks, and is the most economical among various LAN mediums.

    * The bandwidth of a twisted pair can be as high as 250 kHz. Analog applications can span distances up to 5~6 km, while the distance for digital transmission is typically 2~3 km (e.g., a T1 digital carrier system using twisted pair has a speed of 1.544 Mbps up to 6,000 feet without a regenerator).

    * Ethernet 10 Base-T typically uses speeds up between 10 Mbps and 100 Mbps for short distances.

    * Connectivity can be Point-to-Point (P-P) or point-to-multipoint (P-MP; including multicasting to a selected group of receivers, and broadcasting to all receivers) applications, within a single building or between several buildings.

    * Performance is susceptible to external noise, especially Unshielded Twisted Pair (UTP) wire configuration. With proper use of regenerative repeaters (regenerators), the bit error rate can be held in the range of 10^{-7}.

- Coaxial cable characteristics:

    * Diameter approximately 0.4 ~ 1.0 inch; P-P or P-MP applications.

    * Baseband applications up to 10 MHz (10 Mbps for typical digital applications), and broadband applications up to 400 MHz (50 Mbps for digital applications).

    * The number of devices supported for baseband applications is up to 100 per segment, and up to thousands for broadband applications.

    * Geographical coverage is 1~2 km for baseband applications, and <30 km for broadband applications.

    * Performance is insured by shielding. With proper use of regenerative repeaters (regenerators), the bit error rate can be held in the range of 10^{-9}.

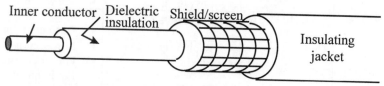

Figure 10-4   Physical Structure of a Coaxial Cable.

- Optical fiber characteristics:

    * Optical fiber has the greatest bandwidth (> 10 GHz) and the best performance (BER < 10^{-9}; practically immune to electrical noise) of all types of the transmission media.

    * The data rate can be up to several Gbps and is increasing constantly.

    * Applications for optical fiber systems are typically point-to-point, up to several hundred miles without using regenerators.

- Airway characteristics:

    * The most important advantage of wireless communications is its quick deployment and low costs (compared to wire and optical fiber installation).

    * With the advent of portable computers (i.e., rising popularity and decreasing prices), the wireless LANs may soon become very popular.

* Airway, as a transmission media, requires "line of sight" transmission.

* Three major frequency spectra for wireless communications are: (1) the infrared range (10^9 to 10^{15} Hz, high security, high environmental susceptibility, and high directivity); (2) the microwave range (16 to 18 GHz, low security, low environmental susceptibility, and low directivity); and (3) the cellular range (800~900 MHz, and 1,800~1,900 MHz, low security, low environmental susceptibility, and low directivity).

Table 10-2 summarizes the characteristics of various transmission media: twisted pair wires, baseband coaxial cables, broadband coaxial cables, airway, and optical fibers.

Table 10-2   Various Media Comparison.

	Bandwidth	Advantages	Disadvantages
Twisted pair	Up to 20 Mbps	• Low costs • Ubiquitous • Easy to install	• Low noise immunity • Un-secure
Baseband coax	Up to 50 Mbps	• Mature technology • Easy to tap	• Low noise immunity • Un-secure
Broadband coax	Up to 400 MHz	• Supporting ISDN	• Higher costs • Difficult to install
Airway	Up to GHz	• Rapid installation • Flexibility	• Low security • Poor performance • Environmental issues
Optical fibers	Up to Gbps	• High capacity • Excellent quality	• Point-to-point connectivity

10.3 LAN TOPOLOGIES

There are several topologies that a LAN network designer can use. The decision for choosing a particular topology is based on physical characteristics and network communications characteristics. The definition of topology is given as follows:

Definition 10-2: Topology is a pattern of interconnections used among various nodes of a network to suit user needs.

The major network topologies used for LANs are listed as follows (and described in the subsequent sections):

1. Star or radial
2. Bus
3. Ring
4. Hybrid

10.3.1 Star or Radial Topology

Figure 10-5 shows a LAN star (radial) connection, which has several distinguishing characteristics. It contains a central node. The network utilizes central routing and switching. The network uses a centralized controller or distributed controlling processors. Typical star LAN examples are: Datakit II, PBXs, and ATM switches.

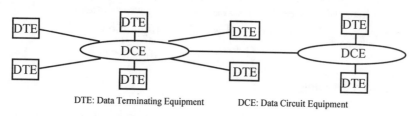

DTE: Data Terminating Equipment   DCE: Data Circuit Equipment

Figure 10-5   Star (Radial) LAN Topology.

- Advantages of a star LAN: The advantages of a star LAN are: ease of service, one device (DTE) per connection, centralized control, centralized failure diagnosis, and simple access protocol.

- Disadvantages of a star LAN: The central node dependency of a star LAN can present problems in controlling network processing. Performance may degrade under loading conditions. In addition, it is expensive to grow beyond the central node's maximum capacity (i.e., the central node has a limited capacity).

10.3.2 Bus LAN Topology

A commonly used bus LAN is known as the Ethernet. The bus LAN utilizes a single length transmission medium, and applies broadcasting methods. Passive taps, which are typically less expensive, are used as connect devices (e.g., workstations to the network). Figure 10-6 illustrates a bus LAN with one termination at each end of the bus. A connector is used to connect two coaxial cables (e.g., one thick and one thin). Each workstation is connected to the LAN via a passive tap. The network can grow by adding bus segments. The controller can be centralized, distributed, or random. Decentralized polling techniques are used to manage network traffic.

- Advantages of a bus LAN: A bus LAN uses a simple cable layout, and is a reliable architecture. It is flexible, allows growth, and supports segment connections. The option of using centralized or decentralized control allows design flexibility. Costs of a bus LAN are typically lower than other LAN (i.e., star, ring) topologies.

- Disadvantages of a bus LAN: Fault diagnosis and fault isolation is difficult to perform in a bus LAN configuration. Regenerators are often required for this type of network. The throughput of bus LAN is relative low compared to other topologies.

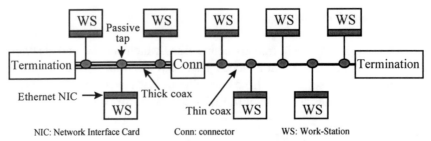

Figure 10-6   Bus LAN Configuration.

10.3.3 Ring LAN Topology

The IBM token ring LAN technique is the most common ring LAN architecture in the data communications industry. The ring network requires active taps, with series of point-to-point connections. Transmission consists of unidirectional data flow on each ring. Rings can be implemented as single, dual slotted, or insertion types. The transmission medium can be twisted pair wires, coaxial cables, or optical fibers.

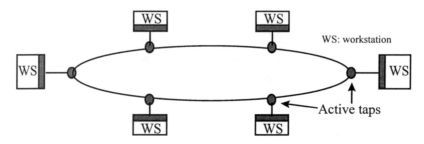

Figure 10-7   Ring LAN Configuration.

- Advantages of a ring LAN: The network architecture can be a single, dual slotted, or an insertion ring. The routing algorithm is simple. The throughput is higher than other LAN configurations. Several types of transmission media have been developed for ring LANs.

- Disadvantages of a ring LAN: Some failures can result in service interruption for many nodes. Data transfer delays may be long for far end nodes because of unidirectional data flow characteristics.

10.3.4 Hybrid Topologies

In addition to traditional bus, star, and ring topologies, LANs can be implemented as a tree or mesh configuration. The network can consist of a simple, complete, or hierarchical (tree) interconnection topologies (Figure 10-8).

The hierarchical (tree) topology is a variation of the bus topology, and is typically used for the broadband applications (coaxial cables). The IBM PC network adopted this topology. Its advantages are: easy to expansion/growth and fault isolation. The entire network is dependent on the "root" (headend).

The simple and the complete interconnection [Figure 10-8(B) and (C)] are easy to implement and easy to maintain. However, both are expensive to implement, and reliability, routing, and flow control present additional issues.

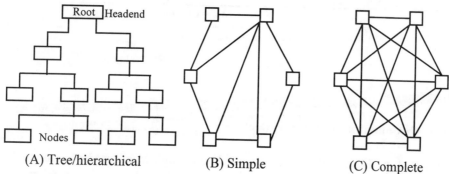

| (A) Tree/hierarchical | (B) Simple | (C) Complete |

Figure 10-8   Tree/hierarchical, Simple and Complete Interconnections.

10.4 LAN ACCESS CONTROL/STANDARDS

Like other aspects of telecommunications, in order to ensure compatibility between LAN equipment produced by different manufacturers, it is important to define standards. The IEEE has been engaged in establishing LAN standards through the 802 Committee (responsible for both LAN and MAN standards). The primary LAN standards established by the IEEE Committee are listed as follows:

- IEEE 802.1 "Network Management and Internetworking (NMI)"
- IEEE 802.2 "Logical Link Control (LLC)"
- IEEE 802.3 "Carrier Sense Multiple Access/Collision Detection (CSMA/CD)"
- IEEE 802.4 "Token Bus"
- IEEE 802.5 "Token Ring"
- IEEE 802.6 "Distributed Queue Dual Bus (DQDB)"
- IEEE 802.7 "Broadband"
- IEEE 802.9 "Integrated Voice Data Terminal Equipment"
- IEEE 802.10 "LAN Security"
- IEEE 802.11 "Wireless LAN"
- IEEE 802.12 "100 VG - Any LAN"

The interrelationship among these standards is illustrated in Figure 10-9. These standards consists of four sections: (1) internetworking; (2) logical link control; (3) medium access control; and, (4) physical layer.

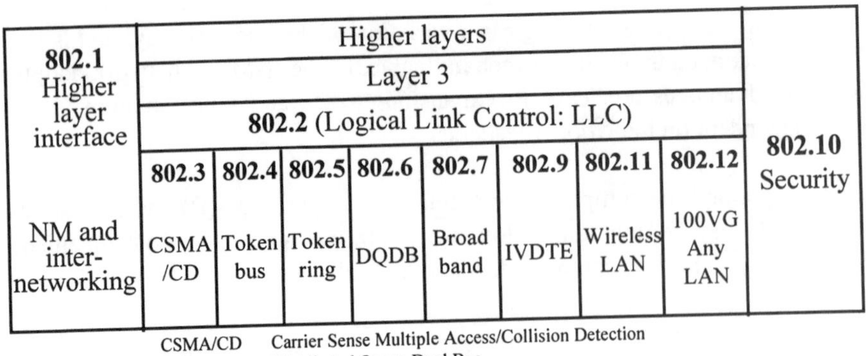

802.1	Higher layers									802.10
Higher layer interface	Layer 3									Security
	802.2 (Logical Link Control: LLC)									
	802.3	802.4	802.5	802.6	802.7	802.9	802.11	802.12		
NM and inter-networking	CSMA /CD	Token bus	Token ring	DQDB	Broad band	IVDTE	Wireless LAN	100VG Any LAN		

CSMA/CD   Carrier Sense Multiple Access/Collision Detection
DQDB   Distributed Queue Dual Bus
IVDTE   Integrated Voice Data Terminal Equipment

Figure 10-9   Interrelationship among IEEE 802 standards.

10.4.1 LAN Communications Architecture

As illustrated in Figure 10-10, LANs (including high-speed LANs such as FDDI applications) generally provides only the first two (or three) layers of the OSI model for Open Systems Interconnection (OSI). This is because many of these networks are broadcast types, and do not require routing functions. In addition, many LANs provide congestion control at the physical layer. Therefore, the routing function and congestion control, which are the principle functions of layer 3 (network layer), are provided by most LANs, but are not a separate layer of protocol.

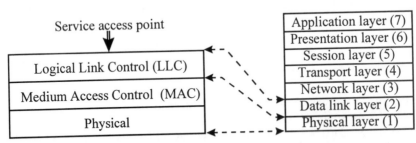

Figure 10-10   LAN Communications Architecture.

In addition to the layers defined in the OSI model, the LAN requires a layer to control access to the medium due to the broadcast nature of a LAN. This is referred to as the Medium Access Control (MAC) layer and is defined in the ANSI X3T9.5 and IEEE documentation. As shown in Figure 10-10, the MAC layer is located within layer 2 of the OSI model. It should be noted that the LAN provides two or three layers of protocol, but it does not provide "end-to-end layers". Therefore, in order to achieve full network functionality, a local network must operate in conjunction with higher layers of protocol. The LAN layer functions (Figure 10-10) are summarized as follows:

- Link layer functions:

  * Logical Link Control (LLC): It provides the service access point function for both connection-oriented and connectionless mode services.

  * Medium Access Control (MAC): It assembles addressing and error fields at the transmitter, disassembles recognized address, and detects error(s) at the receiver. MAC also manages communication over the link.

- Physical layer functions: This layer performs encoding and decoding. It generates and removes preamble. It transmits, receives and restores digital bitstream.

10.4.2 IEEE 802 Standards

A local network must operate in conjunction with higher layers of protocol to achieve the full network function of a LAN. The IEEE has decided to leave the definition of the higher layers to other standard bodies. This section describes the IEEE 802 standards and applications.

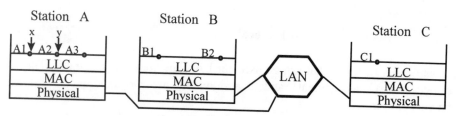

Figure 10-11   Logical Link Control (LLC) of a LAN.

10.4.2.1 Logical Link Control

The Logical Link Control (LLC; Figure 10-11) specifications defined by the IEEE 802.2 consist of three parts, described as follows:

(1) The interface between the LLC sublayer and the MAC sublayer: The IEEE 802.2 LLC standard defines the control information attached to the data units passing between the sublayer of the LLC and the MAC sublayer. It is defined so that the protocol of the control information is independent of the particular type of MAC procedure used.

(2) The LLC sublayer peer-to-peer protocol: The IEE 802.2 LLC standard also specifies interactions that take place between LLC layers in the sending and receiving stations, defined as "peer-to-peer protocol". Using sequence numbers, the protocol provides timing recovery mechanism and retransmission capability (similar to LAPB, LAPD,

and HDLC protocols). The major functions of this peer-to-peer protocol are end-to-end error control/acknowledgment, and end-to-end flow control.

(3) The LLC sublayer services to upper layers: A single station (in a LAN) is capable of supporting simultaneous data exchanges on different logical links with multiple stations in the network. This requires two important functions. First, individual physical devices in the network must be recognized. This is handled by the addressing mechanism of the MAC layer. Second, the links for different data exchanges must be identified. Service Access Points (SAPs) are used to support identification, and can be considered ports (access points) to higher layers.

The Logical Link Control (LLC) layer defined by IEEE 802 provides services, via the SAPs, to the layer above it. This is similar to the services that a data link provides to the network layer. Services are specified by describing the information flow at the interface between two layers or sublayers. However, the LLC layer also performs the functions found in the network layer of the OSI model. For example, the Logical Link Control provides the following services to upper layers: (1) connectionless services; (2) connection-oriented services; and (3) multiplexing data transfer with multiple end points over the single physical link to the network.

10.4.2.2 LAN Medium Access Protocols

There are many methods that can be used for LAN medium access control. They can be classified as fixed assignment, random assignment, demand assignment, and adaptive techniques (Figure 10-12).

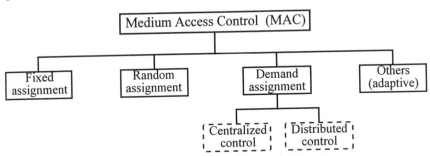

Figure 10-12   LAN Medium Access Control (MAC) Techniques.

- Fixed assignment techniques: These techniques allocate the system bandwidth to the various users in a fixed (static) way that is independent of the users' activities. Examples include: Frequency Division Multiple Access (FDMA) and Time Division Multiple Access (TDMA) techniques.

- Random access techniques: These techniques allocate the entire system bandwidth as a single channel that is accessed randomly by the users. Collision of messages from multiple transmitting stations can occur, hence a methodology for sensing activity on the line prior to transmission is often used. An example of this technique is Carrier Sense Multiple Access (CSMA) and variations thereof (i.e., collision detection or not).

The fixed and random techniques represent extremes in the methods used for allocation of channel bandwidth. Other techniques (Figure 10-12), that are described as follows, fall between these two extremes.

- Demand assignment with centralized control: In this method, an explicit need for transmitting information must be expressed by the transmitting station before channel space is allocated. The procedure used to allocate channel bandwidth is known as "polling". The "polling" is done by a central controller which periodically "asks" the user terminals if they have messages to send. The allocation can also be done using reservation techniques, with requests for channel space being initiated by the user. Both methods require a central controller to allocate bandwidth.

- Demand assignment with distributed control: This technique provides higher reliability and better performance than the centralized control method. Higher reliability results from the fact that in distributed systems the control functions are not contained within a single unit, but are dispersed among several physical elements (either co-located or geographically separated). Better performance results from the direct access that can be provided to small user communities. For example, distributed control can reduce the turnaround time in a batch-processing environment or it can provide faster responses in a real-time applications environment.

  A distributed control algorithm must exchange control information among users either implicitly or explicitly. Because all users can independently execute the same algorithm, coordination of their actions is required.

- Adaptive techniques: For specific applications, the access strategy should be adjusted according to the traffic demand placed on the network. That is, the access method should adapt itself to the varying needs of the network. For example, a network could use a CSMA technique at low traffic loads, but switches to a token-passing scheme when frequent message collisions occur during increased user demand intervals.

10.4.2.3 Logic Link Protocol Data Unit Format

The data sent between Logical Link Control (LLC) sublayers has the format shown in Figure 10-13, and is called an LLC Protocol Data Unit (LLC PDU, or simply data unit). To carry user information from its source to the destination, the LLC PDU is passed from the LLC sublayer to the MAC sublayer below, and then to the physical layer (see Figures 10-10 and 10-11). It is then sent over the network, which serves as the transmission medium. The reverse occurs on reception. That is, at the receiving end, the network delivers the LLC PDU to the physical layer. The physical layer passes PDU to the upper layers (the MAC and LLC sublayers) for processing.

The LLC PDU (Figure 10-13) consists of four sections: the Destination Service Access Point (DSAP), the Source Service Access Point (SSAP), the Control, and the information (payload) fields. Their usage are briefly described as follows:

- DSAP and SSAP field: The upper protocol layers send data to the LLC sublayer via the SSAP. The LLC sublayer then transport the data across the network in the information field of the LLC-PDU. The SAP that receives data from the LLC sublayer is called the DSAP. The SAP is physically associated with a particular user. The "user" can be a process running in the host station, or a terminal port attached to the host station.

The 8-bit DSAP field starts with an Individual/Group (I/G) bit followed by seven Destination (D) bits. When I/G = 0 this indicates individual DSAP bits are processed, and when I/G = 1 this indicates the DSAP bits are processed as a group. The seven D bits identify none, one or more, or all of the SAPs serviced by the LLC. A special DSAP address having I/G = 1 and all the D bits set to "1", is the global DSAP address used for broadcast applications.

The 8-bit SSAP field starts with the Command/Response (C/R) bit followed by seven Source (S) bits. When C/R = 0 this indicates a command, and when C/R = 1 this indicates a response. The SSAP address Source (S) bits identify the specific SAP from which the LLC information field was obtained.

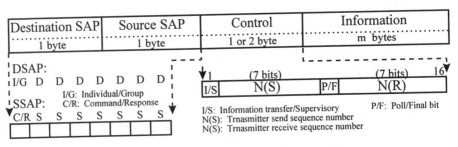

Figure 10-13   LLC Protocol Data Unit (PDU) Format.

- Control field: This field specifies the type of LLC-PDUs used in data communications between SAPs. This field may contain 8 bits or 16 bits, depending on the type of LLC-PDU.

Unnumbered LCC-PDUs use a one byte (8-bit) control field. Other PDUs employ a two-byte (16-bit) control field. These PDUs include the information transfer mode and supervisory mode applications.

In the information transfer mode, the first bit (I/S) of the control field is set to a logical "0", followed by the 7-bit N(S) field which represents the transmitter send sequence number. The 2nd byte of the control field starts with the "Poll/Final" (P/F) bit, followed by the 7-bit N(R) field which represents the transmitter receive sequence number. Upon reception of a command PDU with the P/F bit set to "1", the receiver must reply using a response PDU with the P/F bit set to "0". The "P/F" bit is normally set to "0" when not being used.

If the LLC-PDU contains a supervisory information, the first bit (I/S) of the 1st byte of the control field is "1", and N(S) = "00SS0000", where the "S" bits are the supervisory function bits. The 2nd byte [including P/F bit and N(R) bits] has the same organization as in the information transfer mode.

If the LLC-PDU is unnumbered, the control field contains 8 bits. The first bit is "1", followed by "1MM(P/F)MMM". The "M" bits are the Modifier function, and P/F is the "Poll/Final" function.

- Information field: This field contains the data obtained from higher layers that is to be transferred across the network. This field length is multiples of bytes (8-bit groups) with the upper limit set by the MAC sublayer. For some applications, a LLC-PDU will only contain control information (i.e., it will not have an information field).

Example 10-2:   Describe the similarity and differences between the Logical Link Control Protocol Data Unit (LLC-PDU), the Link Access Protocol-Balanced (LAPB), and the High-level Data Link Control (HDLC).

The LAN Logical Link Control Protocol Data Unit (LLC-PDU) format structure is based directly on HDLC. However, there are several difference between LLC-PDU, LAPB, and HDLC frames:

- Address fields: LLC-PDU extends the address field to allow both the source and destination address to be specified, as well as a group destination address if required. This is necessary because LAN links are multi-source and multi-destination links.

- PDU types: The LLC-PDU consists of additional PDU types for supporting connectionless information transfer (e.g., datagram services) which are not found neither in LAPB nor HDLC applications.

- Exclusion flags, CRC, abort sequences, and bit stuffing: These functions are provided by the Medium Access Control (MAC) sublayer.

10.4.2.4 Logical Link Control Services

According to IEEE 802.2, the LLC's network service specifications provide for three types of data communication operations between Service Access Points (SAPs). The types of data communications are: (1) type 1 operation (unacknowledged connectionless), (2) type 2 operation (connection-oriented; unnumbered Protocol Datagram Unit or supervisory PDU), and (3) type 3 operation (acknowledged connectionless).

- **Unacknowledged connectionless services** (Type I: Figure 10-14): Type 1 operation provides for unacknowledged connectionless (or datagram) service. No data-link connection is logically established for the exchange of PDUs between peer LLC layers. The data units are sent over the logical data links without any correction to previous or subsequent data units. Datagram service is provided via the SAPs to the upper layers, with no guarantee of delivery of data units between Logical Link Controllers (LLCs).

    The type 1 features include the following: no sequence checks, no acknowledgments, no flow control, no error recovery, and data units can be sent to individual address (point-to-point), group address (point-to-multipoint), or broadcast.

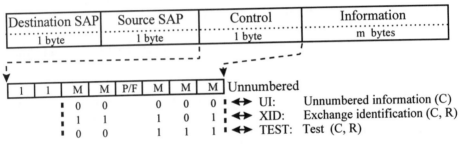

Figure 10-14   LLC-PDU Type 1 Operation: Unacknowledged Connectionless.

As illustrated in Figure 10-14, there are three basic LLC-PDU arrangements for type 1 operation, described here.

(1) Unnumbered information PDU (U-format PDU): In this arrangement the first two bits of the control field are set to "11". A data unit can be sent to individual, group, or global addresses with the "P/F" bit set to "0". It is only used in conjunction with a command PDU [i.e., the Command/Response (C/R) bit in the Source Service Access Point (SSAP) field is "0"; Figure 10-13], and reception of this LLC-PDU is not acknowledged.

(2) EXchange IDentification PDU (XID): This application can be either a command or a response. The "P/F" bit in a command PDU may be set to "1" or "0", with the same value used in the response PDU. The XID use can include (1) conveying the types of LLC services supported by the LLC entity; (2) conveying the receive window size for the LLC entity; (3) conveying the presence of the LLC entity via a broadcast; and (4) requesting the availability of station(s) by use of a group poll command.

(3) Test PDU: This arrangement is used to perform a basic connectivity test for each LLC to LLC transmission path involving both command and response functions. As an option, it can also contain an information field.

- **Connection-mode services** (Type II): Type 2 operation is used for connection-oriented services. The operation involves establishing a logical link connection between a sending sublayer and a receiving sublayer. That is, a virtual circuit connection is established between Service Access Points (SAPs) at the LLC sublayer. In addition, type 2 operation provides transfer of multiple data units, acknowledgment, retransmission (if needed), and termination of the data-link connection. The features of type 2 operation include: sequence checks, acknowledgment, flow control (sliding window mechanism), error recovery, and data units sent to individual addresses only (i.e., limited to point-to-point applications).

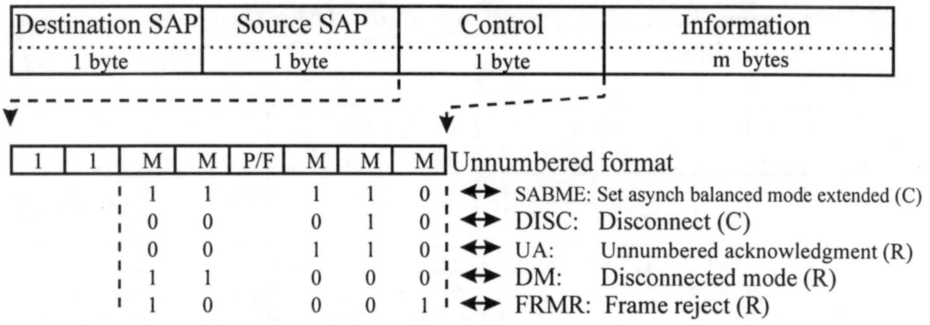

Destination SAP	Source SAP	Control	Information
1 byte	1 byte	1 byte	m bytes

1	1	M	M	P/F	M	M	M	Unnumbered format
1	1			1	1	0	↔	SABME: Set asynch balanced mode extended (C)
0	0			0	1	0	↔	DISC: Disconnect (C)
0	0			1	1	0	↔	UA: Unnumbered acknowledgment (R)
1	1			0	0	0	↔	DM: Disconnected mode (R)
1	0			0	0	1	↔	FRMR: Frame reject (R)

Figure 10-15   LLC-PDU Type 2 Operation: Unnumbered Connection-Oriented.

After establishing a link connection, each LLC sublayer involved in the operation sets a "Sent-counter" [N(S)], which is used to indicate the current send sequence number. Similarly, a "Receive-counter" [N(R)] is used to indicate the sequence number of the next expected PDU to be received. These counters are 7 bits in length (allow sequence numbers from 0 to 127). The "P/F" ("Poll/Final") bit in a command PDU may be set to "1" or "0", with the same value used in the response PDU. The five unnumbered PDU formats for this operation are shown in Figure 10-15, for connection establishment, connection termination, and other control functions. These five formats are briefly described as follows.

(1) Set Asynchronous Balanced Mode Extended (SABME) PDU: The sender sends a SABME PDU to request the LLC link connection establishment.

The receiver responds with a Unnumbered Acknowledgment (UA) if it accepts the connection request. The counters [i.e., the sent and receive counters; N(S) and N(R)] are set to all "0s". If the receiver rejects the request, a disconnect mode (DM) PDU will be returned to the sender.

(2) Disconnect Mode (DM) PDU: A DM PDU is used by a receiver to indicate rejection of a link connection establishment request.

(3) DISConnect (DISC) PDU: A DISC PDU is used to terminate a link connection. This request can be originated by the sender or the receiver. The response returned for a DISC PDU is either a UA or a DM, and will cause disconnection of the Logical Link Control (LLC) link.

(4) Frame Reject (FRMR) PDU: Several conditions can cause a data unit to be interpreted as an invalid PDU. Some examples are: (1) incorrect N(S) and/or N(R); (2) information field does not belong to the frame; (3) an unexpected response is received; or (4) the PDU maximum length is exceeded. Any of these conditions will be interpreted as invalid, and will result in sending a FRMR PDU. A SABME or DISC can also be used to perform the FRMR function.

(5) Unnumbered Acknowledgment (UA): A UA PDU is used in conjunction with a SABME or DISC.

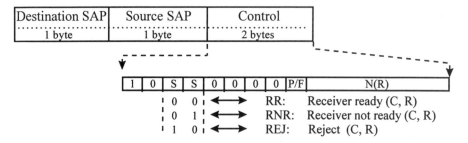

Figure 10-16   LLC-PDU Type 2 Operation: a Supervisory PDU.

In type 2 operation, the PDU can transport a user data bitstream, which is placed in the information field . The control field has a length of two bytes (16 bits; Figure 10-13); with the first bit (I/S) set to "0". This is called Information PDU (I-PDU), which can be used as a command PDU or a response PDU. In this application, the counters [N(S) and N(R)] represent PDU sequence numbers supporting error control and flow control. The "P/F" bit is set to "1" in the last PDU to indicate the end of the data bitstream. When P/F = 1 is detected, the receiver responds with a response PDU (e.g., I-PDU, REJ, etc.), and indicating an acknowledgment. (Note that the usage of the "P/F" ("Poll/Final")'bit has previously described, and briefly reviewed as follows. A sender will transmit a poll command with "P/F" of "1". The receiver must send a response message to this request with a final response of "P/F" = 1.)

In addition to the I-PDU, type 2 operation can be used to send a supervisory PDU, used for acknowledging the reception of I-PDU and flow control. The supervisory PDU does not contain an information field (Figure 10-16). There are three supervisory PDUs in type 2 operation:

(1) Receiver Ready (RR) PDU: The RR-PDU is used if a message is received by a LLC sublayer that has no data to return to the sender, and the receiver wants to acknowledge previously received information transfer PDUs.

(2) Receiver Not Ready (RNR) PDU: When the receiver is "not ready" to receive data transfer PDUs, a RNR message is returned to the sender. A common cause for RNR is the lack of buffer space, which prevents the receiver from accepting new information frames.

(3) REJect (REJ) PDU: The REJ-PDU will cause **retransmission** to occur. In the REJ-PDU, the N(R) field indicates to the sending station which sequence number needs to be retransmitted. All messages sent before this sequence number are assumed (by the sender) to have been accepted without errors.

- **Acknowledged connectionless** (Type III): The LLC sublayer-network interface type 3 operation provides acknowledgement for connectionless services. The protocol consists of a single data unit that is transmitted, and then acknowledged before a subsequent data unit is transmitted. The advantage of this arrangement is that it relieves the acknowledgment burden from the upper protocol layers. The features include: (1) a connection does not need to be established; (2) acknowledgments are generated by the receiver for each data unit delivered; and (3) data units are sent to individual addresses only (i.e., point-to-point services). A typical application of this type of service is real-time environments (e.g., factory LANs).

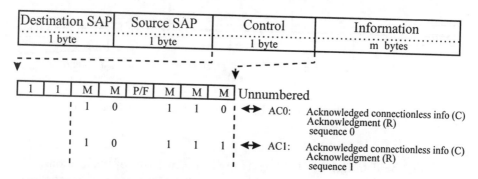

Figure 10-17   LLC-PDU Type 3 Operation: Acknowledged Connectionless.

Assume that a control signal (e.g., an alarm signal) needs to be sent to a certain device. The time spent in setting up the connection, establishing the handshaking exchange, and tearing the connection down involves considerable overhead bit capacity. Therefore, a connectionless acknowledged service is of interest for this application. An acknowledgment is important in this case because the sender must be sure that the alarm signal was received.

As illustrated in Figure 10-17, there are two types of acknowledgments:

(1) Acknowledgment AC0: AC0 represents a command PDU (which indicates an acknowledged connectionless *information* sequence number zero) and a response PDU (which indicates an acknowledged *acknowledgment* sequence number zero).

(2) Acknowledgment AC1: AC1 represents a command PDU (which indicates an acknowledged connectionless *information* sequence number one) and a response PDU (which indicates an acknowledged *acknowledgment* sequence number one).

In order to keep track of lost data units, the sender alternates the use of AC0 and AC1. In the case of lost or damaged data units, a timer for acknowledgment will expire and the data unit will be retransmitted with the original acknowledgment sequence number.

10.4.3 IEEE 802.3 CSMA/CD Description and Architecture

The IEEE 802.3 standard for a Carrier Sense Multiple Access/Collision Detection (CSMA/CD) was first published in 1985, and subsequently re-published in 1988. The CSMA/CD is based upon the Alto implementation. Ethernet was a Xerox Palo Research Center experiment in 1972, and was further enhanced in 1981 by Xerox, DEC and Intel. Ethernet has been primarily used for commercial applications. Ethernet is described in a later section in this chapter.

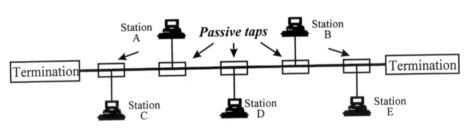

Figure 10-18   The IEEE 802.3 CSMA/CD Bus Operation.

While the data rate of 10 Mbps is used in a majority of applications, the IEEE 802.3 standard allows for operations with a speed of 1 Mbps up to 20 Mbps (typically 1, 2, 5, 10 and 20 Mbps). This standard specifies a structure with every station passively connected to a bus. The stations [Data Terminating Equipment (DTE)] are interconnected using a bus topology (Figure 10-18), that can be expanded into a tree topology. However, the actual wiring of the IEEE 802.3 bus network can be a star configuration (e.g., AT&T's StarLAN implementation).

The IEEE 802.3 standard also specifies a contention bus Medium Access Control (MAC) mechanism that serves as the CSMA/CD access method. In this method, any DTE on a common bus can transmit whenever it detects a quiet period on the medium. If two or more stations attempt to transmit data simultaneously, a collision will occur. If this happens, the stations must stop transmitting, "back-off" and retransmit at a later time. The "back-off" mechanism (implemented after a collision) relies on a random wait time before a retransmission attempt is allowed.

- Advantages of the IEEE 802.3 standard: It is the most widely used LAN standard, and has a huge installed base. It uses a simple algorithm for implementation. The network (local area network) is easy to install and maintain, and has a good performance for low to medium traffic loads.

- Disadvantages of the IEEE 802.3 Standard: It is a probabilistic access method, which is different from the deterministic access method used in a token-passing bus or token-passing ring. The result is a higher collision probability. Therefore, a method for handling collision is required, which results in higher overhead. This access method does not have a priority mechanism to allow transmission of "important" data units. Under heavy load conditions, the performance will degrade as the number of collisions increases.

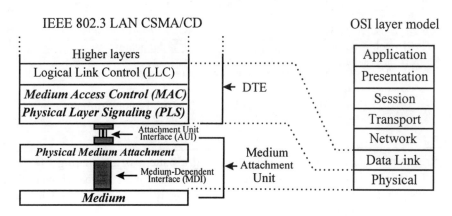

Figure 10-19   The IEEE 802.3 Architecture.

Figure 10-19 illustrates the IEEE 802.3 architecture. The IEEE 802.3 standard specifies the CSMA/CD MAC sublayer, physical signaling layer, and the physical medium. The relationship between the IEEE standard and the OSI reference model is also illustrated in Figure 10-19.

- The Medium Access Control (MAC) sublayer and the IEEE 802.3 Logical Link Control (LLC) sublayer together form the data link layer of the OSI reference model.

- The physical layer of the IEEE 802.3 standard consists of the Physical Layer Signaling (PLS) sublayer and the Medium Attachment Unit (MAU) sublayer. These two sublayers can be interconnected by the Attachment Unit Interface (AUI), or can be integrated without an AUI.

- The Physical Medium Attachment (PMA) sublayer, the Medium Dependent Interface (MDI), and the AUI form the Medium Attachment Unit (MAU). The MAU interconnects the bus trunk cable to the branch cable (which is a part of the AUI) and contains the electronics which send, receive and manage the encoded signals. The MDI ensures mechanical, and electrical compatibility with the physical medium.

10.4.4 IEEE 802.3 Frame Medium Access Control (MAC)

The IEEE 802.3 Medium Access Control (MAC) frame format is shown in Figure 10-20, which consists of eight possible fields. These fields are described as follows:

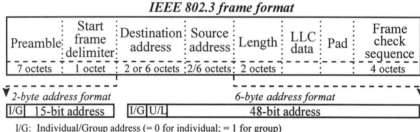

IEEE 802.3 frame format

Figure 10-20   The IEEE 802.3 MAC Frame Format.

(1) Preamble: This is a 7-byte field containing a pattern of alternating "1s" and "0s" "10101010...1010." The preamble is used to allow the Physical (Layer) Signaling (PLS; Figure 10-19) function to establish steady state synchronization with the received frame timing.

(2) Start Frame Delimiter (SFD): This 8-bit field has a pattern of "10101011" [i.e., ABH (AB in Hex)], and immediately follows the Preamble. The SFD frame delimiter is used to indicate the start of a frame.

(3) MAC Source Address (SA): The source address can be either two bytes or six bytes in length. It identifies the station from which the frame was initiated. It is a unique address on the network, and the "I/G" (Individual/Group) bit is set to "0" (Figure 10-20) indicating an "individual" address.

(4) MAC Destination Address (DA): The destination address is either 2 bytes or 6 bytes in length, and identifies the station for which the frame was intended. This destination address field can be an individual or group address (i.e., the "I/G" bit is either "1" or "0"; described as follows); and, can be a locally or globally administered address (described as follows).

* Individual or Group Address: If the "I/G" bit is set to "0", it indicates the address is an individual address (i.e., point-to-point application). If the "I/G" bit is set to "1" (i.e., point-to-multipoint application), it indicates an address that: (1) can be a *multicast* group address associated with a (selective) group of *logically related stations*, or (2) a *broadcast* address denoting a set of *all* the stations on the network.

* Local or Global administered address: A 6-byte address can be a locally (U/L bit is set to "1"; Figure 10-20) or globally (U/L bit is set to "0"; Figure 10-20) administered address. A globally administered address (universal address) is unique in any network conforming to the standard.

It should be noted MAC addresses (DA and SA) can be implemented using either 2 bytes or 6 bytes. However, the most recent implementations of the IEEE 802.3 standard use 6-byte address. It is important that the source and the destination addresses on a particular LAN be the same size for all stations to insure proper operation.

(5) Length: This two-byte (length) field indicates the number of LLC data octets in the Logical Link Control (LLC) data field.

(6) Data field: The data field contains a LLC-PDU (DSAP, SSAP, control, and information; Figure 10-13). This field must byte-aligned. That is, an integer number of octets must be correspond to the value of the "Length" field.

(7) Pad: Whenever the length of the data field is less than the minimum required for proper operation of the protocol, a "Pad" field is added following the "Data" field.

(8) Frame Check Sequence (FCS): The FCS field contains 4 octets, and is a CRC-32 frame check sequence used to verify the destination address, the source address, the length, the LLC data, and the pad fields.

Example 10-3: Describe the collision detection and recovery process used for the IEEE 802.3 Carrier Sense Multiple Access/Collision Detection (CSMA/CD) MAC operation.

In the IEEE CSMA/CD MAC operation, a station that is transmitting will continue to "listen" to the medium for collision detection indication. Whenever multiple stations attempt simultaneous transmission, a collision occurs, and signals interfere with each other. A collision usually occurs only during the initial part of the transmission (known as the **collision window**), before the signal has been propagated to all stations. However, after the collision window has passed, a station is said to have *"acquired the medium"* and no collisions will occur because all the stations sense the active signal and defer attempting transmission until the medium is determined to be idle.

In the event of a collision, the physical layer of the transmitting station turns on the collision detect signal, after it senses interference. The collision-detection signal is received by the MAC sublayer, and the collision handling procedure is activated. The sending station immediately stops its current data transmission, and sends out a "jam" signal (having a length of 32 bits in a 10 Mbps system). Transmission is stopped after the "jam signal" is sent, and the station will delay any further attempt to transmit (back-off) for a random (integer) number of multiple time slots.

In the case of repeated collisions, retransmission is still attempted, but the delay interval is different. For the first 10 transmission attempts, the delay interval is doubled for each attempt. The delay interval remains constant for retransmission attempts 11 through 16. After 16 repeated collisions, the station informs the higher layers of the transmission protocol that a failure has occurred, and completely halts any further attempts to transmit.

10.4.5 IEEE 802.3 MAC Operation/Parameters

The MAC operation of the CSMA/CD standard is illustrated by the state transition diagrams shown in Figure 10-21. There are two concurrent and independent activities in the MAC operation: (A) the receive activity, and (B) the transmit activity.

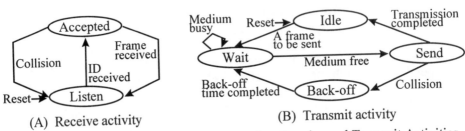

(A) Receive activity   (B) Transmit activity

Figure 10-21   The IEEE 802.3 MAC Operation: Receive and Transmit Activities.

- The receive activity [Figure 10-21(A)]: When the MAC sublayer is first powered up (or reset), it enters the "listen" state . The MAC sublayer is in this state for most of the receive activity. In this state, all frames arriving from the physical layer are analyzed. When the frame's header contains a destination address matching the node's individual address or an acceptable group address, the MAC sublayer enters the "accepted" state, and the frame is accepted.

    After frame acceptance is complete, the LLC sublayer is signaled and the MAC sublayer returns to the "listen" state. During frame acceptance, a collision may occur. In the event of collision, the frame acceptance is aborted, and the MAC sublayer is forced back into the "listen" state.

- Transmit activity [Figure 10-21(B)]: When the MAC sublayer is first powered up (or reset), the MAC sublayer enters the "idle" state. A frame is transmitted over a medium only as a result of a request made by the LLC sublayer.

If a transmit request is made, and the node is not in the process of frame acceptance, the MAC sublayer enters the "wait" state. In this state, the node waits until the medium becomes free (or idle). If the medium is busy, the node will remain in the "wait" state.

When the medium becomes free, the MAC sublayer will delay for a period (known as the interFrameSpace period; discussed later in this section) before entering the "send" state. The MAC sublayer then begins transmitting the frame in a multi-access manner (i.e., other stations can access the medium at the same time). Even when the MAC sublayer is transmitting, it continues to listen to the medium. If the frame transmission is completed without collision, the node will return to its "idle" state. If a collision is detected during frame transmission, a "jam" signal is immediately sent, the frame transmission is aborted. The MAC sublayer will enter the "back-off" state, and will delay for a period of time (delay period discussed later in this section), and then enters into the "wait" state.

There are several parameters and definitions associated with the IEEE 802.3 standard, and briefly described as follows:

- Collision window: The collision window is a period of time that is long enough to cover all possible collisions during transmission. This period starts with the initial bit that is transmitted, and must accommodate the possibility that the most distant station may start transmission at the same time the original signal arrives at that station. That is, the collision window is defined as follows:

$$W_c = 2 \times \tau_d \tag{10-1}$$

where W_c is the collision window, and τ_d is the propagation delay between the two stations that are farthest apart. The time for the original signal to reach the far station and the colliding signal to return, must be less than the collision window. That is,

$$\text{All MAC frame sizes} > \text{collision window} \tag{10-2}$$

It should be noted that a collision is possible only during this time window (W_c).

- jamSize: The "jamSize" is the number of jam bits sent by the transmitting source when a collision is detected so that all other nodes (stations) have knowledge of the collision. Note that the jam signal duration must be long enough to allow all other stations on the network to "hear the collision". The typical length of the jamSize is 32 bits.

- slotTime: The "slotTime" is a network parameter used to determine the dynamics of collision handling. Its value must chosen to exceed the sum of the physical layer round-trip propagation time and the MAC sublayer maximum jam time. The typical slotTime value is 512 bit-intervals.

- interFrameSpacing: The "interFrameSpacing" is the minimum interframe idle time that allows for interframe recovery in other CSMA/CD sublayers and receiving circuits in the physical medium. That is, a time interval must exist between frames on the network so that the receiving nodes can determine that the prior frame has ended, and prepare to receive a new frame. The typical interFrameSpacing value is 96 bit-intervals.

- maxFrameSize: The "maxFrameSize" specifies the maximum value of a MAC frame. This prevents a single station from monopolizing the medium, and transmitting long data streams. In the IEEE 802.3 standard, exclusive of the preamble and start frame delimiter, the "maxFrameSize" is set to be 1,518 octets.

- minFrameSize: The "minFrameSize" is used by the receiver in all stations. It specifies the minimum length of a MAC frame so that a collision can be correctly detected. In the IEEE 802.3 standard, exclusive of the preamble and start frame delimiter, the "minFrameSize" is set to be 64 octets.

10.4.6 IEEE 802.3 Physical Layer Specifications

The IEEE 802.3 physical layer standard defines the physical signaling services, physical signaling, medium and attachment, and repeater specification. There are several Medium Attachment Unit (MAU) physical layer alternatives, and described as follows:

- 10BASE5: It is based on Ethernet, and uses a thick coaxial cable.

- 10BASE2: It uses a "thin" coaxial cable (e.g., Cheapernet used in personal computer networks).

- 10BROAD36: It can use either dual-cable or split-cable.

- 10BASEFP: It is based on optical fiber medium, and the star is passive, power splitting devices are used.

- 10BASEFA: It is based on optical fiber medium, and the star is active.

A comparison of these physical layers is provided in Table 10-3, from medium, transmission speed, and distance viewpoint.

Table 10-3   Physical Layer Alternatives and Comparison.

Standard	Medium	Speed (Mbps)	Distance (meters)
10 BASE 5	*Coaxial cable*	*10*	*500*
10 BASE 2	*Thin coaxial*	*10*	*185*
10 BASE T	*Twisted pair*	*10*	*100*
10 Broad 36	*Carrier system*	*10*	*3,600*

10.4.7 Ethernet/Ethernet Frame Format

Ethernet was officially invented on May 22, 1973. It was described in a memorandum written by R. M. Metcalfe and colleagues at Xerox Corp's Palo Alto Research Center. Its original name was the "Alto Aloha Network", which was used internally. In 1976 it was announced to public as a 3 Mbps local network. Later Intel and Digital Equipment Corp. (DEC) joined Xerox to collaborate on the further development of the Ethernet. In, 1980 DIX (DEC, Intel, Xerox) announced a 10 Mbps Ethernet. DIX proposed the Ethernet definition to the IEEE, and after modification it was adopted as the IEEE 802.3 standard in 1983. It became an ISO (International Organization for Standardization) standard in 1985.

Figure 10-22 illustrates the Ethernet frame format, which consists of the preamble, the destination address, the source address, the type field, the data field, and the frame check sequence. Comparing this frame format and the IEEE 802.3 frame format (Figure 10-20) reveals that they are quite similar. These fields are described as follows:

- Preamble: The preamble is used to provide synchronization and to mark the start of an Ethernet frame. The Ethernet preamble is the combination of the preamble and the starting frame delimiter of the IEEE 802.3 frame. Therefore, the pattern consists of 7 bytes of alternating "1s" and "0s" (101010...1010) and an 8th byte of 10101011. The preamble is actually generated and removed as part of the data encoding/decoding function of the physical layer, and is not always shown as part in the Ethernet frame format. Thus, some illustrations of the Ethernet frame format may only show the address (destination and source), the type field, the data field, and the Frame Check Sequence (FCS) field.

Preamble	Destination address	Source address	Type field	Data field	Frame check sequence
8 octets	6 octets	6 octets	2 octets	(46 ~ 1,500) octets	4 octets

Figure 10-22   Ethernet Frame Format.

- Address fields: Unlike IEEE 802.3, Ethernet specifies both the destination and source addresses, using 48 bits for each.

- Type field: Ethernet does not support the use of the length field and padding (as in IEEE 802.3 standard). Instead, Ethernet uses a two-byte type field, whose value is only meaningful to the higher network layers. It is not defined as part of the Ethernet standard specifications.

- Data field: The data portion of the Ethernet frame is passed to the data link layer. Ethernet defines a minimum frame size of 72 ($\equiv 8 + 6 + 6 + 2 + 46 + 4$) bytes and a maximum frame size of 1,526 ($\equiv 8 + 6 + 6 + 2 + 1,500 + 4$) bytes. It should be noted the data field must be a multiple of 8 bits. If the data to be sent is smaller or larger than these sizes, it is the responsibility of the higher layer protocol to pad the data or frame size (to reduce problems in collision handling).

- Frame Check Sequence (FCS): This field has a length of 4 octets, and is a CRC-32 frame check sequence. It is used to check the destination address, the source address, the type field, and the data field (i.e., the preamble is not checked).

Example 10-4 Describe a typical implementation of the Ethernet functions.

The data link functions and the data encoding/decoding function of the physical layer are parts of the controller, which is installed in a network device such as a personal computer. This implementation is illustrated in Figure 10-23.

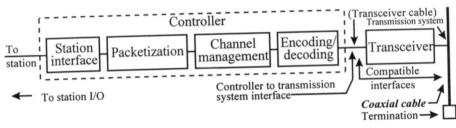

Figure 10-23   The Implementation of the Ethernet Functions.

10.4.8 IEEE 802.5 Token Ring

The IEEE 802.5 standard defines the token ring Medium Access Control (MAC): shown in Figure 10-24. This protocol is intended for a ring topology (Figure 10-7). The IEEE 802.5 standard encompasses both the MAC and the physical layers.

Definition 10-3: The IEEE 802.5 standard defines the token ring MAC protocol, physical layer specification on shielded twisted pair, using differential Manchester signaling.

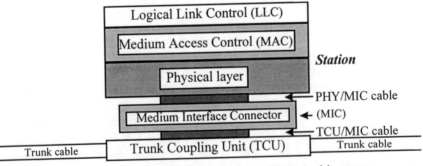

Figure 10-24   The IEEE 802.5 Token-Ring Architecture.

The 802.5 standard can be viewed as having four parts: (1) MAC service specifications; (2) MAC protocol; (3) Physical layer entity specifications; and, (4) Station attachment specifications. These parts are described as follows:

- MAC service specifications: They define (in functional terms) the services provided by the IEEE 802.5 to the Logical Link Control (LLC) or any other high-level user. The interfaces facilitates transmitting and receiving high-level data units, and provides per-operation status information used by higher-layer error recovery functions. The specifications "hide" the details of the MAC and the physical layers from the MAC user. Thus, a variety of transmission media should not be visible (or of concern) to the user unless it affects system performance.

- The MAC protocol: The MAC protocol is the heart of the IEEE 802.5 standard. It is often simply referred to as the "token ring standard". This specification defines the frame structure and the interactions that take place between MAC entities.

- The physical layer specifications: The physical specifications consist of two parts. First, the medium-independent part specifies the service interface between the MAC and the physical layers. This interface includes facilities for passing a pair of bit streams between the two layers, and specifies the details of the signaling method, including symbol encoding and data rate. The second part of the physical layer specification is medium-dependent. It specifies the functional, electrical, and mechanical characteristics of the medium attachment.

- Station attachment: It is assumed that each station is attached to the ring through a Trunk Coupling Unit (TCU). The 802.5 standard specifies the transmission medium and interface for connecting the station to the TCU.

10.4.8.1 IEEE 802.5 Token Ring Operation

A token (passing) ring consists of a set of stations connected sequentially by a medium that forms a continuous closed loop (i.e., a ring). The choice of the transmission medium for connecting any two adjacent stations is independent of the media that connects other stations to the ring. The physical connectivity of the medium establishes the logical connectivity of active stations to the ring.

Definition 10-4: **A station**, as defined in the IEEE 802.5 standard, is an entity that serves as a means for attaching one or more devices (e.g., terminal or workstation) to a ring for the purpose of communicating with other devices on the network (ring).

A station can be either in active mode or in bypass mode. If a station is in the bypass mode (station D in Figure 10-25), the station is essentially disconnected from the ring although it remains physically connected to it. If a station is in its active mode, the information is sequentially transmitted (bit by bit) from one active station to the next in a single direction (unidirectional transmission). Note that each active station functions as a repeater with 1 bit buffer.

In this token passing ring, a station gains its right to transmit information onto the medium, after it has detected a token on the medium and has "captured" it. A token is a symbol of authority that is passed from "station to station", after each end of transmission of an information frame (using a token access method). The station that "holds the token" also has the access control of the medium. Physically, the token is a control signal consisting of a unique signal sequence, and can be though of as a special MAC frame that circulates on the medium.

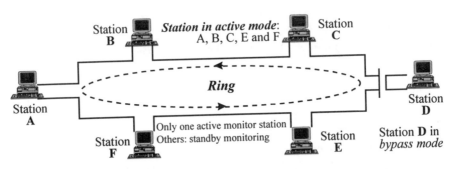

Figure 10-25   A Token Passing Ring Station Interconnection.

A source station, after receiving the token, begins to transfer information (in place of the token) onto the ring. The information circulates from one station to the next. When the information reaches the addressed destination, the destination station(s) copy the , and then pass it to the next station. After the information has circulated back to the source station (i.e., traversed), the ring it is removed. Finally, the source station transfers access control of the ring by transmitting a new token onto the ring, which is then passed to the next station.

The active stations on the ring determine which a station will actively monitor and oversee the health of the ring to insure the ring operates properly. This "active monitor" uses various timers to check that the network is functioning properly, and provides the synchronization timing for the entire network. Another active station acts as a "standby monitor" station, and these timers should be in sync with the active monitor station. Note that the token ring applies a "deterministic" MAC method that allows multiple stations on a LAN to share network resources.

Definition 10-5: The term **"deterministic"** Medium Access Control (MAC) method implies that the user can predict and control the maximum length of time a station waits before gaining access to the network.

10.4.8.2 IEEE 802.5 Token Ring MAC Layer

The IEEE 802.5 Medium Access Control (MAC) layer provides for the operation of the token ring, helps administer the system, and performs maintenance functions when needed. Station additions, deletions, ring initialization, failure monitoring, failure detection, and failure recovery functions are all provided through the MAC layer. For multiple ring connections, the MAC layer routes the MAC frame to the appropriate LAN.

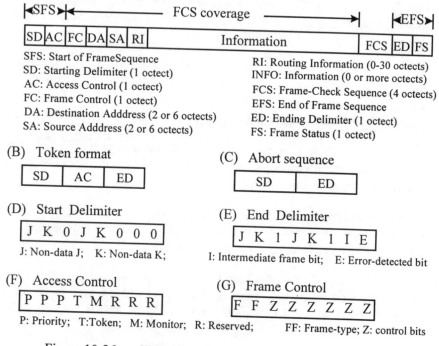

SFS: Start of FrameSequence
SD: Starting Delimiter (1 octect)
AC: Access Control (1 octect)
FC: Frame Control (1 octect)
DA: Destination Adddress (2 or 6 octects)
SA: Source Adddress (2 or 6 octects)

RI: Routing Information (0-30 octects)
INFO: Information (0 or more octects)
FCS: Frame-Check Sequence (4 octects)
EFS: End of Frame Sequence
ED: Ending Delimiter (1 octect)
FS: Frame Status (1 octect)

(B) Token format

| SD | AC | ED |

(C) Abort sequence

| SD | ED |

(D) Start Delimiter

| J | K | 0 | J | K | 0 | 0 | 0 |

J: Non-data J;   K: Non-data K;

(E) End Delimiter

| J | K | 1 | J | K | 1 | I | E |

I: Intermediate frame bit;   E: Error-detected bit

(F) Access Control

| P | P | P | T | M | R | R |

P: Priority;   T:Token;   M: Monitor;   R: Reserved;

(G) Frame Control

| F | F | Z | Z | Z | Z | Z | Z |

FF: Frame-type; Z: control bits

Figure 10-26   IEEE 802.5 Token Ring MAC Frame Format.

- MAC frame format: There are three types of MAC frame formats, as described:

  (1) The token frame: This format contains the Starting Delimiter (SD), the Access Control (AC) field, and the End Delimiter (ED).

  (2) The abort frame: This format contains the abort sequence, used to prematurely terminate the transmission of an information frame, in cases when the sender decides not to continue sending a frame (i.e., eliminate wasting bandwidth on the ring).

  (3) The information frame: Two types of information can be transmitted y using the information frame. The first type is a Protocol Data Unit (PDU) passed from the Logical Link Control (LLC). The second type is control information generated by the MAC sublayer or Station Management (SMT) functions.

Figure 10-26(A) shows an IEEE 802.5 token ring MAC frame format. As illustrated, this frame contains 10 fields, described as follows.

(1) Start Delimiter (SD): This octet contains a unique pattern of "JK0JK000" to indicate start of a MAC frame. The (J, K) bits are "non-data" MAC symbols, which are typically code violations when represented as actual signals on the physical medium. However, the (J, K) bits always occur with the Start Delimiter.

(2) End Delimiter (ED): This octet is similar to the starting delimiter and is used to indicate (flag) the end of a MAC frame. It has a unique pattern of "JK1JK1IE", where the "E" bit is used to indicate whether error has been detected.

(3) Access Control (AC): This octet is used to control the access of the station to the ring. It consists of three Priority bits (PPP), one Token bit (T), a Monitoring bit (M) and three Reserved bits (R). The priority bits are used to indicate the priority of a token, and determine which stations are allowed to use the token to access the ring.

(4) Frame Control (FC): This octet specifies the frame type (i.e., token frame, abort frame, or information frame) using two F bits, and also specifies certain MAC and information frame functions using six Z bits.

(5) Destination Address (DA): This field can be 2 or 6 octets in length; the choice is an implementation decision. It specifies the MAC address(es) of the destination station(s) which can be unique, multicast, or broadcast.

(6) Source Address (SA): This field can be 2 or 6 octets, and specifies the address of the MAC source station. In multi-ring configurations, the Most Significant Bit (MSB) of the SA is used as the Routing Information Indicator (RII), which indicates the presence or absence of the Routing Information (RI) field.

(7) Routing Information (RI): This field is only used in multi-ring networks that implement source routing enhancements. Note that this field exists in the MAC frame if the RII bit in the SA field is set to "1".

(8) Information field: This field can contain Logical Link Control (LLC) data (i.e., a LLC data frame) or information related to a control operation (i.e., MAC control frames).

(9) Frame Check Sequence (FCS): This field contains a CRC-32 code computed over the FC, DA, SA, RI and information fields (highlighted as FCS coverage in Figure 10-26).

(10) Frame Status (FS): The details of the FS applications are described as follows.

- Frame Status field (FS): The frame status field is *not* used in the IEEE 802.3 or IEEE 802.4 frame format. As shown in Figure 10-27, the frame status octet in the IEEE 802.5 format contains two nibbles (4 bits each). Each nibble has one Address Recognized bit (A), one Frame-Copied bit (C), and two Reserved bits (r r, which are currently set to 0 0. When a frame arrives at the interface of a station with the associated destination address, the interface sets the "A" bit to "1" as it passes through. When the interface copies the frame to the station, the interface sets the "C" bit to "1" as well.

As the transmitting station "drains" the frame, the station examines both "A" and "C" bits to determine the status of the frame. If (A, C) = (00), the destination address is not present or the station is not powered up. If (A, C) = (10), the destination address is present, but the frame has not been accepted (e.g., a station might fail to copy a frame due to the lack of buffer space, congestion, or similar reasons). If (A, C) = (11), the destination address is present and the frame has been copied by the station. If (A, C) = (01), it is an invalid condition, and will be ignored by the station. This procedure provides an automatic acknowledgment for each MAC frame. Note that the (A, C) bits are presented twice in the frame status octet for reliability purposes.

An IEEE 802.5 MAC information frame:

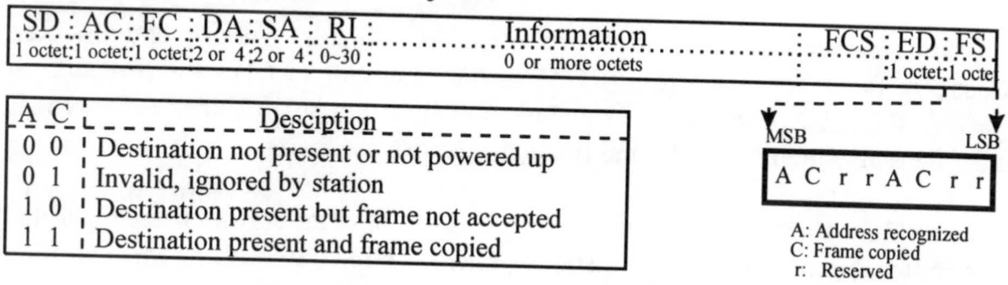

A C	Desciption
0 0	Destination not present or not powered up
0 1	Invalid, ignored by station
1 0	Destination present but frame not accepted
1 1	Destination present and frame copied

Figure 10-27 Frame Status Field of IEEE 802.5 MAC Information Frame.

Definition 10-6: A "***valid frame***" is bounded by a valid Starting Delimiter (SD) and Ending Delimiter (ED); has the "E" bit in the ED field equal to "0"; is an integral number of octets in length; contains only "0" and "1" bits between the SD and ED; has the "FF" bits of the FC field equal to "00" or "01"; has a valid FCS; has a minimum of 10 octets for 2-octet addressing, or 18 octets for 6-octet addressing between SD and ED; and does **not** contain another valid SD or ED delimiter between the bounding SD and ED delimiters.

- Control frames: Figure 10-28 illustrates the structure of an IEEE 802.5 MAC control frame. If the Frame Control (FC) octet indicates that the frame is a MAC control frame (i.e., the "FF" bits in the FC field are equal to "00"), the associated "information" field of the frame specifies the MAC control frame type.

Definition 10-7: The term "***vector***" denotes a fundamental unit of MAC and Station Management (SMT) information. A vector contains the Vector Length (VL), Vector Identifier (VI) of its functions, and zero or more "**subvectors**". A subvector is defined by its Sub-Vector Length (SVL), its Sub-Vector Identifier (SVI), and its Sub-Vector Value (SVV). The "VI" field contains the value that specifies the control frame type. **Note that only one vector is permitted per MAC frame**.

There are many possible MAC frame types (i.e., $2^8 = 256$ maximum frame types that can be specified by the 8-bit "VI" field) have been described by the IEEE 802.5 standard. The most common MAC frame types are shown in Figure 10-28 and described as follows:

* Beacon (BCN; VI = 2): A "beacon" frame is sent when a serious ring failure has occurred, such as a broken cable or "jabbering" station. This frame type is used for localizing (i.e., identifying and analyzing) the fault condition.

* Claim Token (CL_TK; VI = 3): This frame type is used by a standby monitor station to determine if there is an active monitor station on the ring. It sends CL_TK frames, and inspects the Source Address (SA) of the CL_TK MAC frames it receives.

    If the received SA matches its own "My Address (MA)", and the Received Upstream (neighbor's) Address (RUA) in the subvector matches the Stored Upstream (neighbor's) Address (SUA), the standby monitor station has "claimed the token", it will enter the active monitor mode, and finally generate a new token.

* Purge (PRG; VI = 4): This frame type is used to clear traffic from the ring. It is transmitted, by the active monitor station, after claiming the token or when performing a re-initialization of the ring.

An IEEE 802.5 MAC information frame as control frame:

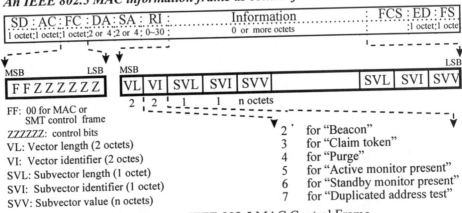

Figure 10-28   An IEEE 802.5 MAC Control Frame.

* Active Monitor Present (AMP; VI = 5): This frame type serves as the "heartbeat" for the active monitor station, and is transmitted by the active monitor station. It is queued for transmission either following the successful purging of the ring or

following the expiration of the Active Monitor Timer (AMT). Any station in standby monitor mode which receives this frame type will reset its Standby Monitor Timer (SMT) for synchronization purposes.

* Standby Monitor Present (SMP; VI = 6): This frame type serves as the "heartbeat" for the standby monitor station, and is transmitted by the standby monitor station. After the standby monitor station receives an AMP or an SMP frame type [with "A" and "C" bits in the Frame Status (FS) field equal to (00); Figure 10-27], the Queue PDU Timer (QPT) is reset. When the QPT expires, an SMP PDU (protocol data unit) will be queued for transmission.

* Duplicated Address Test (DAT; VI = 7): The duplicated address test is a part of the ring initialization process. The DAT field is transmitted with the Destination Address (DA) equal to My Address (MA). If the frame returns with the "A" bits (Figure 10-27) set to "11", this indicates that another station on the ring has same address. In this situation, the station's network manager is notified and the station returns to "bypass" mode. Any station that copies a DAT frame will ignore it.

10.4.8.3 IEEE 802.5 Priority Mechanism

The IEEE 802.5 standard defines multiple levels of priority for independent or dynamic assignment, depending on the relative class of service required for any given message. For example, a service can be a synchronous real-time service, an asynchronous inter-active service, an immediate network recovery service, etc. The priority scheme uses the Priority ("PPP") bits and the Reservation ("RRR") bits in the Access Control (AC) field of a MAC frame (Figure 10-26).

To illustrate the priority mechanism, the following notation is used:

P_T = The priority of frame to be transmitted
P_R = The received priority (in frames or tokens)
R_R = The received reservation (in frames or tokens)

The following illustrates the priority operation, using the above notations.

- A station that is waiting to transmit of a frame must wait for a token with

$$P_T \geq P_R \tag{10-3}$$

- While waiting, a station may reserve a future token at its priority level, P_T.

  * When a data frame goes by, the station sets its Reservation ("RRR") field to its priority level (i.e., RRR = P_T). The reservation field can also have a value that is less than its priority level (i.e., RRR < P_T).

* When a free token goes by, the station sets its Reservation ("RRR") field to its priority level (i.e., RRR = P_T). If $R_R < P_T$, and $P_T < P_R$, this will preempt any lower priority reservations.

- When a station seizes a token, the station sets the token bit to "1", the reservation field to "0", and keeps the priority field set to its original value. Following transmission, the station issues a new token with: (1) its priority set to the maximum of P_T, P_R, and R_R, and (2) its reservation set to the maximum values for P_T and R_R.

- Stations of lower priority along the ring cannot seize the token as it passes by their interfaces. The token is "passed to" and "captured by" the requesting station (or an intermediate station) sending equal or higher-priority data.

Example 10-5: Describe the IEEE 802.5 priority methodology.

Figure 10-29 illustrates the IEEE 802.5 priority mechanism. Follow the sequence by referring to the numbers 1 through 6 in the large rectangles.

First, station "A" is transmitting data to station "D", and station "C" makes a higher-priority reservation (to enter the LAN). "A" generates a token containing the higher-priority level requested by "C", and preempts the lower-priority activity (i.e., transmitting to "D"). Sooner, "C" detects the matching priority, and uses the token to send its data to station "B". The operation is continued as shown in Figure 10-29.

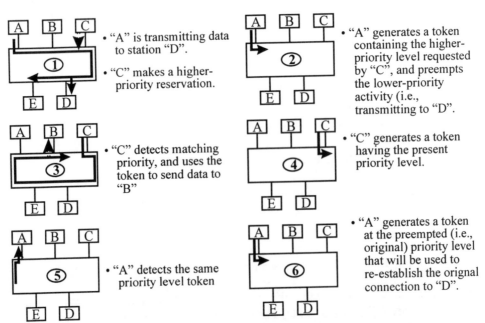

Figure 10-29   IEEE 802.5 Priority Mechanism Operation.

10.4.8.4 IEEE 802.5 Token Ring Physical Layer

The IEEE 802.5 token ring physical layer provides for ring synchronization and bit transmission on specific types of physical media (e.g., shielded twisted pair and unshielded twisted pair for 1 to 4 Mbps; coaxial cable for up to 16 Mbps). The physical layer performs many functions including:

- Encoding method converting PHY-symbols to the line signals: The differential Manchester encoding method is adopted for converting he four possible MAC symbols ("0", "1", "J" and "K") into signals for transmission on the medium.

  * MAC symbol "0": During one-bit intervals, the transition in the middle of the interval remains the same as that of the previous bit interval.

  * MAC symbol "1": During one-bit intervals, the transition in the middle of the interval is the opposite of the previous bit interval.

  * MAC symbol "J": This symbol is used for a non-data bit interval, and does not have a transition in the middle of a bit interval. It has the **same polarity** with respect to the "trailing" element of the preceding symbol.

  * MAC symbol "K": It is used for non-data bit interval and does not have a transition in the middle of a bit time. It has the opposite polarity to the "trailing" element of the preceding symbol.

    To avoid accumulating a "DC" component (i.e., voltage offset), non-data symbols are typically transmitted as a paired (J, K) symbols.

MAC bit (symbol) stream:

- A NRZ polar binary code:

- A differential Manchester code:

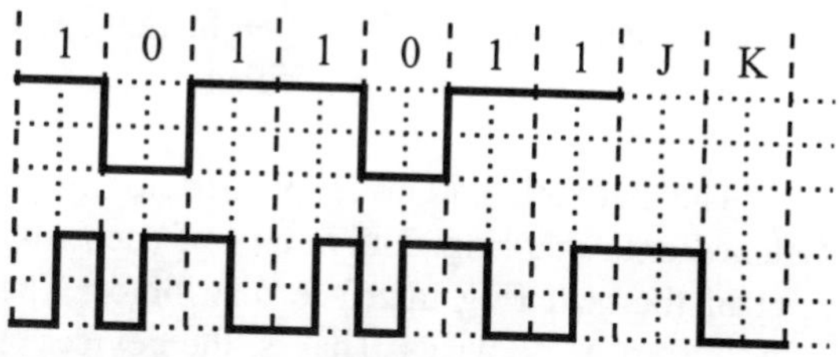

Figure 10-30   Differential Manchester Code for MAC symbol Coding.

- Data rates and symbol timing: The IEEE 802.5 standard supports various data rates. The most common rates used are 4 and 16 Mbps. The physical layer depends upon the ones density of the received bit stream (provided by the differential Manchester code; see Figure 10-30) to recover the timing at the receiver. In normal operations, the active monitor station provides the master clock for the entire ring, and all other stations are phase-locked to the active monitor station. The Phase-Locked Loop (PLL) must be able to support at least 250 stations (including repeaters) on the ring. All stations, when entering the ring, must achieve phase-lock within 1.5 ms.

10.4.8.5 IBM Token Ring

The IBM token ring operation is similar to the IEEE 802.5 ring. The ring can use a variety of transmission media [e.g., Shielded Twisted-Pair wires (STP) or Unshielded Twisted-Pair wires (UTP), coaxial cables, or fibers]. This type of ring can support up to 72 devices using unshielded twisted pair media, and up to 260 devices using shielded twisted pair media. The IBM ring can support both 4 and 16 Mbps data rates. A star network topology with baseband transmission scheme is typically used, and functions as a deterministic network (defined in Section 10.4.8.1; Definition 10-5).

- Hardware components: The IBM token ring network is a star shaped ring. That is., a logical ring network formed from a series of ring-shaped, linked stars that provides integrity, error tolerance, and redundancy characteristics.

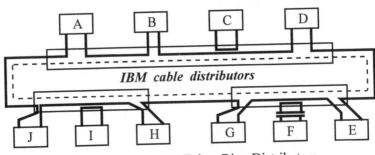

Figure 10-31   IBM Token Ring Distributors.

Devices are attached to the token ring via the IBM 8228 ring interface distributor. This has connections for up to eight devices that form an internal ring. The attached devices manage the overall ring functions.

The network can be expanded to up to 33 ring interface distributors that are switched onto one ring. The output of each ring interface distributor is connected to the input of the next ring interface distributor. These connections are different in function from those of the devices. That is, the devices attached to the multi-station unit could be repeaters, bridges, etc.

- Software: The basic IBM LAN software is called the LAN support program. The NETBIOS™ and LLC interfaces are implemented in accordance with IEEE 802.2 and ISO 8802/2 standards.

Applications (Figure 10-32) reside (without being altered) on top of the NETNIOS™, APPC/PC interface (which requires LLC 8802/2 underneath it), or the new 3270 emulation (which also requires LLC 8802/2). Two important systems that extend LAN functionality are based on the DOS (Disk Operating System) and OS/2 (Operating system/2). These systems are: (1) the IBM LAN server, and (2) Novell Netware, which is largely hardware independent. Each server can undertake specific network management functions, such as resource allocation, name, password, priority handling, and error reporting. A dedicated central PC can act as the network manager. The IBM Asynchronous Communications Server Program (ACSP) will allow an indefinite number of PC systems (connected to the LAN) to access remote computers via two switchable ports.

The PC3270 emulation/LAN management program passes network management data to the NetView application on the host. Therefore, it is possible to monitor work in progress on various PCs from the host, and react quickly in case of errors. In addition to the token ring manager program's view of the system, the LAN network manager program views all stations on the broadband PC network (as well as token rings with several bridges) as being connected together (via bridges).

The Remote Initial Program Load (RIPL) is an important function in these systems. The RIPL allows diskless PC or PS/2 machines that reside in the network to load programs and data remotely.

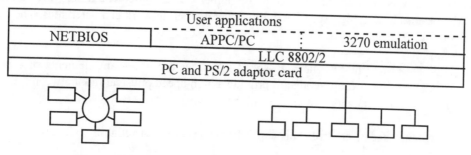

Figure 10-32   IBM Token Ring Software Architecture.

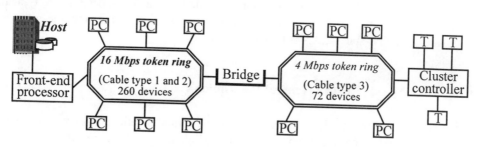

Figure 10-33   Interconnection of two IBM Token Rings.

Example 10-6: Describe the architecture and properties of interconnected IBM token rings.

Figure 10-33 shows a IBM 16 Mbps token ring, which was introduced in late 1988. Associated with this product are PC interfaces that support either 16 Mbps or 4 Mbps, and network interfaces (e.g., the cluster controller 3174, and front-end processor 3745). Adapters were also announced for IBM 9370 and Series 1 mini-computers. As illustrated in Figure 10-33, a bridge program permits users to link a 16 Mbps ring to a 4 Mbps ring either locally or remotely.

The 16 Mbps token ring uses Shielded Twisted Pair (STP) and can support up to 260 active stations. Microcomputer interfaces include the token-ring network 16/4 adapter for the IBM PC and the 16/4 adapter/A for Micro Channel-based models of the PS/2 line. Both adapters support 16/4 Mbps networks and are physically smaller because they use CMOS technology. Larger data frames can support up to 18,000 bytes.

10.5 HIGH-SPEED LAN NETWORKS AND NETWORK PERFORMANCE

The speed of local area networks is constantly increasing. The term "high-speed" can not be explicitly defined. A LAN with a speed of 100 Mbps seemed impossible in the 1980's. Today, a LANs with speed of 2 Gbps or higher can definitely be attained. A modern LAN, besides having high speed, exhibits several other network characteristics. The most important LAN characteristics are:

- High-speed interfaces: The high-speed interfaces are important elements of a high-speed LAN. They are intended to provide a high-speed physical link between a station (e.g., a computer), its peripherals, and the network.

- Distributed access control: This capability is desirable for reliability and efficiency.

- Limited distance: High-speed LANs are typically used for limited distance applications.

- Limited devices: In addition to distance limitations, a high-speed LAN typically serves fewer devices. For example, the number of mainframe and mass storage devices in a high-speed LAN is typically 10 to 20.

10.5.1 High-Speed Network General Description

A high-speed LAN is intended to meet a variety of communications requirements, and is typically specified when higher cost is justified. High-speed LANs are often used in the following applications:

- Office networks: A traditional office includes a variety of devices with low to medium speed data transfer requirements. These requirements can often be satisfied by IEEE 802 type LANs. However, with new applications in the modern office environment, such as document image processing (with 1024 x 1024 pixels or greater image-size), can only be supported by high-speed devices. An image is typically represented by many scattered pixels. With a higher pixel number, imagine resolution is improved. Because pixels are transmitted as digital signals, each one requires a certain bandwidth to be carried over the network. Therefore, an image with more pixels requires a higher speed network. Note that a pixel is also known as a picture element (pel).

- Backbone local networks: A high-speed LAN can support premises-wide data communications that interconnects equipment in a single large building or a cluster of smaller buildings. Rather than connecting multiple buildings using one network over which all devices communicate, a better alternative is to employ several small (economical) LANs and use a high-speed network (with higher costs) to interconnect the smaller LANs. The high-speed LAN is referred to as a "backbone network".

- Backend networks: A high-speed LAN can be used to interconnect large "mainframe" computers and mass storage devices. The purpose of a high-speed LAN in this application is to transfer bulk data among a limited number of devices in a small area (e.g., a computer center, college campus, or corporate computer support area).

Many data communications users derive benefits from high-speed LANs. Most high-speed LAN are found in bulk data transfer and data processing intensive applications. Many new applications are visual (graphic) analysis and display oriented. The following is a list of typical high-speed LAN applications:

- Large digital libraries
- Weather analysis
- Computer Aided analysis and Design (CAD)
- Satellite photograph analysis
- High-speed medical graphics
- Multi-media applications
- Video images

10.5.2 Physical Media for High-Speed LANs

Traditional low to medium-speed LANs typically use twisted-pair wires (unshielded or shielded) and coaxial cables. However, coaxial cables and optical fibers will be the dominate physical media for high-speed LANs. In the future high-speed optical fiber LANs may be the only suitable physical media, as data rates reach multiple Gbps rates.

- Coaxial cables: Three applications for coaxial-based high-speed LANs are: single-channel broadband buses, baseband buses, and passive star networks.

  (1) Single-channel broadband bus applications: This type of high-speed LAN shares several characteristics with bus-based LANs (e.g., packet broadcasting). The Local Distributed Data Interface (LDDI) is an example of a coaxial cable-based

high-speed LAN. LDDI utilizes a single-channel broadband bus topology using a "passive star" physical connection.

(2) Baseband bus applications: The main components of these LANs are coaxial cable, terminators, controllers, and taps. A commercial high-speed baseband LAN is known as HYPER channel. It has a data rate of 50 Mbps, and uses Manchester code for timing recovery. It can support a distance of 1.2 km with a maximum of 30 device connections.

(3) Passive star applications: The DEC™' VAX cluster uses a physical passive star arrangement, but operates as a logical bus architecture. Each station is attached to the central node via two links. A typical data rate is 70 Mbps using Manchester code, which supports a maximum of 16 nodes within a radius of 45 meters.

- Optical Fibers: Optical fibers can be used for high-speed bus, star, and ring LANs. However, a high-speed bus LAN using optical fibers is not practical because of coupling loss. Therefore, the most popular applications are ring arrangements.

  * Star arrangement: Network Systems' DATApipe high-speed LAN uses a star topology. It consists of one passive fiber-optic star coupler, DATApipe adapters, and network terminal adapters. It has a speed at 275 Mbps, and supports a radius up to 30 km.

  * Ring arrangement: This is one of the most popular high-speed optic fiber-based LAN architectures. The Fiber Distributed Data Interface (FDDI) is commonly used in these applications. Practical examples are Gigabit Optical Loop (GOL) and Cambridge Fast Ring networks.

10.5.3 Fiber Distributed Data Interface (FDDI) Networks

The Fiber Distributed Data Interface(FDDI) has been defined in a number of documents developed by *ANSI X3T9.5*, which is responsible for high-speed LAN standards. FDDI is a token-ring network operating at 100 Mbps, and it can support up to 1,000 nodes over a maximum distance of approximately 200 km.

10.5.3.1 FDDI and OSI Model

Figure 10-34 illustrates the relationship between the FDDI and OSI model. The lowest OSI layer (the physical layer) corresponds to the FDDI Physical Medium Dependent (PMD) sublayer and FDDI physical (protocol) sublayer. The second OSI layer (the data link layer) corresponds to FDDI Medium Access Control (MAC) sublayer. The FDDI Station Management (SMT) covers both the OSI physical and data link layers. The FDDI specifications care covered by four American National Standards Institute (ANSI) standards, and are briefly described as follows:

(1) Physical (layer) Medium Dependent (PMD) layer: It corresponds to the lower sublayer of the OSI physical layer. The standard includes specifications for power levels, characteristics of the optical transceiver (transmitter and receiver), permissible bit error rates, and timing jitter requirements.

(2) Physical (layer) protocol (PHY) layer: It corresponds to the upper sublayer of the OSI physical layer. The standard deals with the encoding scheme, clock synchronization, and data framing.

(3) Medium Access Control (MAC) layer: MAC protocol corresponds to the lower sublayer of the OSI data link layer. The standard defines rules for medium access, addressing, frame format, error checking, and token management. The Logical Link Control (LLC), on the hand, corresponds to the upper sublayer. However, LLC is not part of the FDDI standard.

(4) Station Management (SMT) layer: It specifies system management applications for each of the FDDI protocol layers. In particular, SMT concerns itself with the control required for correct operation of a station on a FDDI network.

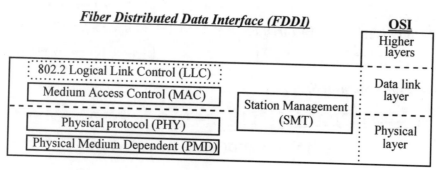

Figure 10-34   FDDI Relationship to OSI Model.

10.5.3.2 FDDI Frame Structure

The FDDI standard is similar to the IEEE 802.5 token ring standard. In a FDDI ring, the FDDI token circulates on the ring when all stations are in an idle state. If a station becomes active and is ready to transmit, the station seizes the token and immediately transmits a FDDI frame. During this time there are no available tokens on the ring and stations (other than the one that captured the token) must wait until the token becomes available again. After the sending station has finished its transmission, it generates a new token and places it on the ring indicating the ring is available. However, there are differences between the FDDI and the IEEE 802.5 token ring that are described as follows.

In the FDDI there is "no flipping of a bit" on a token to signal that the ring is busy. This is considered impractical because of the high speed (100 Mbps) of the FDDI ring.

Similarly, a station releases (generates) the token as soon as its frame(s) has been transmitted. Because of speed constraints, it does not wait until the frame circulates around the ring and returns to the original sender before releasing the token, even though the frame will eventually return to the sender and be removed from the ring.

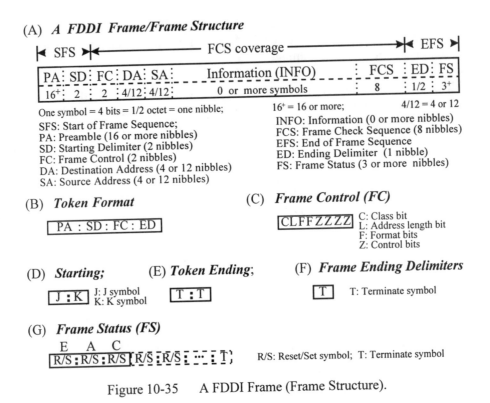

Figure 10-35   A FDDI Frame (Frame Structure).

Figure 10-35 shows the FDDI frame structure. The field lengths of various fields are expressed in the units called symbols (or nibbles), which are 4 bit in length (i.e., half of an octet). The description of the various fields in a FDDI is given as follows:

- Preamble (PA): This field has a minimum length of 16 symbols (64 bits). It is used for frame synchronization. The content of this field depends upon the particular encoding method used in the network.

- Starting Delimiter (SD): This field has a length two non-data symbols known as J and K. The definition of the J and K symbols was given for IEEE 802.5 token rings (see Section 10.4.8.4).

- Frame Control (FC): This two-symbol field contains the pattern "CLFFZZZZ" (8 bits). The "C" bit specifies whether the transmission is synchronous or asynchronous; the "L" bit specifies the use of 16 or 48 bit-addressing; the "F" bit indicates whether it is a MAC control frame or Logical Link Control (LLC) frame; and, the four "Z" bits are used as the control bits.

- Destination Address (DA): This field can be 4 or 12 symbols (16 or 48 bits) in length, depending upon the implementation. If the first bit is set to "0", this indicates the destination address is an individual address. If the first bit is set to "1", it indicates the destination is a group address, a group address of all "1s" indicate s a broadcast address.

- Source Address (SA): This field can be 4 or 12 symbols in length, and indicates the sender's address. The first bit is always "1" in the SA field.

- Information (INFO): This field contains either LLC data or control data.

- Frame Check Sequence (FCS): This is an 8 symbol (32 bits) field containing CRC-32 code that covers the FC, DA, SA and INFO fields.

- Ending Delimiter (ED): There are two types of Ending Delimiter fields: a token ending delimiter and a frame ending delimiter. Their lengths are one and two T symbols (4 or 8 bits), respectively.

- Frame Status (FS): This field contains specific indicator symbols: the "E" symbol for error detected use, the "A" symbol for address recognized use, and the "C" symbol for frame copied use. Field length is a minimum of 3 symbols (12 bits).

The FDDI ring standard is similar to the IEEE 802.5 token ring standard. Refer to Section 10.4.8.2 and Figures 10-26 through 10-28 for additional information.

10.5.3.3 FDDI Basic Operation

The operation of the FDDI token ring is similar to the IEEE 802.5 token ring. Figure 10-36 illustrates an example with six stations (A, B, C, D, E and F) in a FDDI ring. The numbers 1 through 6 shown in Figure 10-36 corresponds to the following numbered descriptions:

1. Initially it is assumed no traffic (data) is in the ring, and the Token (T) is circulating. Station "A" is waiting for the token to reach its port because "A" has two frames of data (F_1 and F_2) to be transmitted.

2. Station "A" seizes the Token (T) and begins to transmit two frames (F_1 and F_2) of data. After transmitting the two frames of data, station "A" appends a new token to indicate the end of transmission. This new Token (T) is ready for another active station to seize.

3. Assuming the data (F_1 and F_2) destination address is station "D", F_1 and F_2 will be copied by station "D". Simultaneously, it is assumed that station "F" is ready to transmit data, will seize the token, and begin to transmit its data (F_3).

4. The data (F_3) is followed by a new Token (T) indicating that station "F" has finished its transmission. Assuming the data (F_3) destination address is intended for station "C", station "C" will copy F_3. At this time, the data (F_1 and F_2) has circulated back to station "A". Since the F_1 and F_2 frames were originated by station "A", they will then be absorbed by station "A".

5. However, station "A" allows data frame F_3 to pass, since it was not sent by "A". Hence, F_3 and the Token (T) will pass station "A", will reach station "F", and is absorbed by "F".

6. Station "F" will let the Token (T) pass, indicating that the ring is now ready for any active station to seize the Token (T) for transmission.

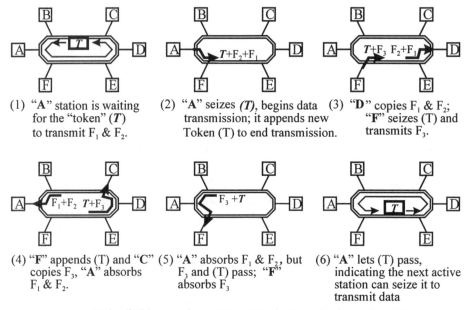

(1) "A" station is waiting for the "token" (*T*) to transmit F_1 & F_2.

(2) "A" seizes (*T*), begins data transmission; it appends new Token (T) to end transmission.

(3) "**D**" copies F_1 & F_2; "**F**" seizes (T) and transmits F_3.

(4) "**F**" appends (T) and "**C**" copies F_3, "**A**" absorbs F_1 & F_2.

(5) "**A**" absorbs F_1 & F_2, but F_3 and (T) pass; "**F**" absorbs F_3

(6) "**A**" lets (T) pass, indicating the next active station can seize it to transmit data

- Station "A" has two frames (F_1 & F_2) to be transmitted to station "D".
- Station "F" has one frame (F_3) to be transmitted to station "C".

Figure 10-36   Basic Operation Example of a FDDI Token Ring.

10.5.3.4 FDDI Dual-Ring Architecture

A FDDI token ring provides considerable flexibility for configuring different topologies, and can also provide protocols suitable for a variety of applications. The FDDI application does not place any lower limits on the number of nodes or the distance between nodes. Likewise, there are no absolute upper limits either. For example, assuming the ring latency needs to be kept to a few milliseconds, a FDDI can include up to 1,000 nodes on the ring, up to 2 *km* between two adjacent nodes, and up to 200 km of total fiber length. However, these parameters can be adjusted to produce the optimum configuration for a specific application. For example, if more nodes need to be added on a ring, the distance between nodes must be reduced.

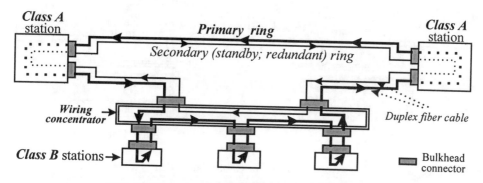

Figure 10-37   FDDI Dual-Ring Architecture.

A FDDI token ring is a combination of two independent "counter-rotating" rings, each having a speed of 100 Mbps. If both rings operate simultaneously, the effective throughput of a FDDI ring is 200 Mbps. A prominent advantage of having two rings is reliability. If one fails, the network can reconfigure using the other ring and service is maintained.

In some practical applications one ring is connected to all stations, while the second ring is connected to only a few selected stations. Figure 10-37 shows the primary ring connected to all the stations.

Definition 10-8: Nodes connected to both rings in a FDDI network are referred to as *class A* station, while *class B* stations are connected to only one ring. Typically, the stations that require greater fault tolerance are configured as class A. Less critical stations (e.g., lower priority) can be configured as class B stations.

A wiring concentrator, which serves as a hub for connecting several stations to the ring, should be connected as a class A station. Note that both class A and class B stations can be connected to the ring via a wiring concentrator (see Figure 10-37).

10.5.3.5 FDDI Fault Recovery/Ring Reconfiguration

Several levels of fault tolerance are possible in a FDDI ring. For a certain types of cable faults (e.g., cable cuts), the fault condition will cause the ring to reconfigure. Other types of cable faults may only cause the ring to send an alarm to the maintenance center. Similarly, loss of power on certain nodes may switch an optical relay that maintains the ring connection. Several fault conditions and faulty recovery schemes are as follows:

- Ring reconfiguration: Faults in any network are caused by either failed components or broken (cut) cables. Even if a connection in not fully broken there may be a substantial performance degradation, which results in an unacceptable Bit Error Rate (BER).

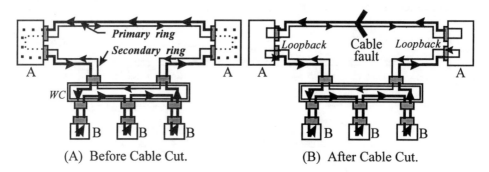

(A) Before Cable Cut.   (B) After Cable Cut.

Figure 10-38   Before and After Cable Fault: Ring Reconfiguration.

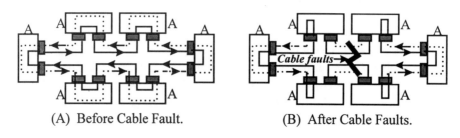

(A) Before Cable Fault.   (B) After Cable Faults.

Figure 10-39   Before and After Cable Faults: Isolated Networks.

The FDDI token ring illustrated in Figure 10-37 has been redrawn in Figure 10-38(A). In this ring there are two class A stations, three class B stations connected to the primary ring via a Wiring Concentrator (WC), one primary ring, and one secondary ring. As shown in Figure 10-38(A), before the cable fault, the primary ring can be used for communication between the two class A stations. After detecting a cable fault, the stations use the appropriate paths on the secondary ring. As shown in Figure 10-38(B), a loopback scheme is used to keep the network operational. Typically a FDDI ring reconfiguration happens automatically within a few milliseconds. FDDI standards define a station management interface for this possible condition. After the fault has been cleared (i.e., the broken ring has been restored), the station management handshake will allow the ring to be returned to the original configuration.

Figure 10-39 illustrates the case when two separate cable faults are detected. As shown in Figure 10-38(B) the network has been reconfigured into two separate and smaller (independent) networks. Each of the independent two networks still operates properly internally, although full connectivity is not possible. It should be understood that if a cable fault occurs in the cable connected to a class B station, this station will be "cut off" from the network, because the wiring concentrator will provide a bypass (loopback) for nodes associated with class B stations.

- Optical bypass: If the stations connected to the FDDI ring lose power (e.g., the power is turned off), the network maintains service by applying optical bypasses. An optical bypass provides a path for light to pass around a node by using an electrically operated relay. When power is lost, a mirror re-directs the light through an alternate path so the network remains operational.

10.5.4 Distributed Queue Dual Bus (DQDB) Network

A Distributed Queue Dual Bus (DQDB) high-speed LAN is a multi-access network capable of supporting integrated communications for voice, data, and video traffic. In 1991, the IEEE 802.6 released a standard for DQDB.

DQDB uses a shared medium to transfer information at speeds greater than 40 Mbps in two directions. DQDB was initially standardized for the DS3 rate, and the IEEE 802.6 committee is interested in also supporting DQDB at SDH rates (see Chapter 6). The 802.6 standard has been designed from the perspective that DQDB is suitable for Metropolitan Area Network (MAN) applications using DQDB to LAN interconnectivity.

In addition to using shared-medium, a dual bus structure and high speed, the DQDB has fixed length (53 octets) entities called DQDB slots. DQDB supports both "connectionless" and "connection-oriented" services (previously described in Chapter 5). As shown in Figure 10-40, a DQDB has two buses that support data transfer in opposite directions. Each station (node) is attached to both buses. The stations at the end of the DQDB bus are called head ends (head end stations).

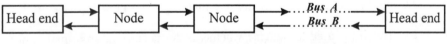

Figure 10-40   Distributed Queue Dual Bus (DQDB) LAN.

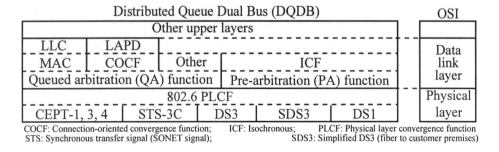

COCF: Connection-oriented convergence function;   ICF: Isochronous;   PLCF: Physical layer convergence function
STS: Synchronous transfer signal (SONET signal);   SDS3: Simplified DS3 (fiber to customer premises)

Figure 10-40   IEEE 802.6 (DQDB) Protocol Model versus OSI Model.

The IEEE 802.6 protocol model for DQDB is illustrated in Figure 10-41, along with the corresponding ISO OSI reference model. Initially, DQDB supported only the 44.736 Mbps DS3 physical layer used in μ-law digital networking. It has been modified to support simplified DS3 signals for fiber to customer premises (known as SDS3), DS1 signals, 2.048 Mbps, 34.368 Mbps, and 139.264 Mbps CEPT signals in A-law networking applications. Eventually, it will support the SONET STS-3C signal rate (see Chapter 6 for the description of STS-3C signals).

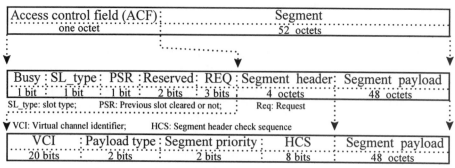

Figure 10-42   IEEE 802.6 (DQDB) Slot Format.

Queue Arbitration (QA) function supports asynchronous connection-oriented service, and the Pre-Arbitrary (PA) function supports isochronous services.

As shown in Figure 10-42, the IEEE 802.6 (DQDB) slot format consists of 53 octets. Five octets are assigned as the slot header [one octet of Access Control Field (ACF) and 4 octets of segment header], and 48 octets are segment payload. The slot format has two parts: the ACF (a length of one octet) and the Segment (consisting of a 4 octets segment header and a 48 octet segment payload). The functions of these fields are described next.

- Access Control Field (ACF): There are five functional "bit groups" in the ACF octet:

  * Busy: This bit is used to indicate whether a slot is carrying information or not. It is set to "1" when the slot carries information; and "0" if not.

  * SL_type: If the slot is Pre-arbitrated Access (PA), this bit is set to "1". Likewise, if it is a Queued-arbitrated Access (QA), this bit is set to "0". These two modes of access control are described as follows:

    ♦ Queued arbitrated Access (QA): When the dual bus is used to carry non-isochronous services, such as the transfer of data packets, the dual bus is said to be in the QA mode. This mode is controlled by distributed queuing known as the QA protocol.

    ♦ Pre-arbitrated Access (PA): This mode is used for isochronous services and is controlled by a pre-arbitrated query (different from distributed queuing) known as PA protocol.

(3) PSR: This bit is set to "1" if the segment in the previous slot should be "cleared". If the segment of the previous slot should be retained (not cleared), it is set to "0".

(4) Reserved: Two bits are reserved for future applications, and have not been defined by the standards.

(5) REQ contains 3 bits with each bit of the "request" corresponding to a separate priority level. There are three priority levels: level 0, 1 and 2 (level 2 is the highest priority). The appropriate REQ priority bit is set to "1" by a node, thereby requesting access (at that priority) to a QA slot on the dual bus.

- Segment: This field has a fixed size of 52 octets that contain segment header and segment payload information.

  * Segment header: 4 octets (32 bits) that perform the four following functions.

  (1) Virtual Channel Identifier (VCI): It contains 20 bits that are used to uniquely identify the virtual channel to which the QA segment or the PA segment belongs. A connectionless MAC service sets the VCI field to all "1s". All the other VCI bit patterns represent connection-oriented services. Note that the VCI is assigned by the node at the head end of the bus.

  (2) Payload type: It contains 2 bits that are used to identify the payload type. Presently, the only defined value is "00", which indicates the payload is user data.

  (3) Segment priority: It contains 2 bits that are presently undefined.

  (4) Segment Header Check Sequence (HCS): This CRC-8 error control field is calculated over VCI, payload type, and segment priority bits. The generator polynomial is $g(x) = 1 + x + x^2 + x^8$.

  * Segment payload: It contains 48 octets (384 bits; fixed length) of user data.

Example 10-7: Describe the basic distributed queue algorithm used for a single priority level application.

The operation of the distributed queuing algorithm for a single priority level is illustrated in Figure 10-42. Assume that bus "A" is the forward bus, bus "B" is the reverse bus, an Access Unit (AU) has a QA segment to send on bus "A".

This AU enters the queue for access, by initiating a single REQuest (REQ) that is sent on the reverse bus "B". The REQ bit is set = 1 in the next available slot (see Figure 10-42) on the reverse bus (B). After the REQ has been written on the reverse bus (B), it is passed to all the AUs located upstream (relative to the data flow on the forward bus "A"). As shown in Figure 10-43(A), the REQ bit indicates to all upstream AUs that a "new" QA segment is queued for access on the forward bus "A". This algorithm does not allow an AU to queue more than one QA segment (per priority level) for access on the bus.

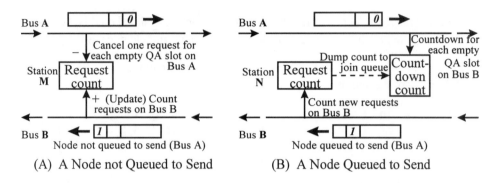

(A) A Node not Queued to Send   (B) A Node Queued to Send

Figure 10-43   The Basic DQ Algorithm for Single Priority Level.

Each AU keeps track of the number of QA segments that are queued downstream from it by counting the "REQ" bits as they pass on the reverse bus, and incrementing the "request counter (RQ)" [see Figure 10-43(A)]. There are two cases of interest that should be recognized: (1) a node not queued to send, and (2) a node that is queued to send.

- Station **M** (node **M**) is not queued for QA access on the forward "A" bus: Station M decrements its request counter (RQ) by 1 (if RQ > 1) whenever it reads an empty QA slot. An empty QA slot has bit "BUSY = 0" (see Figure 10-42). This permits the empty slot to be used by an AU downstream from node **M** (that has a QA slot to send). Through decrementing, the value of the RQ counter at **M** always represents the number of QA slots queued downstream from **M**.

- Station **N** (node **N**) is queued for QA access on forward bus "A": If node **N** is queuing for QA access, it will send out its REQ on the reverse bus "B". In addition, the node N will perform two actions:

  (1) Transfer the present contents of its request counter (RR) to another counter called countdown counter [Figure 10-43(B)].

  (2) Reset the ReQuest counter (RQ) to zero.

The countdown counter is decremented by one for every empty slot detected on the forward bus. The first empty QA slot after countdown counter reaches the value zero will be used by station **N** to transmit its QA slot. For any REQ received by node **N** on the reverse bus "B", **N** will increment the request counter by one. This scheme ensures that after the transmission of its QA slot, the request counter will correctly track the number of QA segments queued upstream to **N**, so that the next QA access is correctly identified. The proper usage of the request counter and countdown counter can effectively implement a "first-come-first served" [i.e., First-In-First-Out (FIFO)] queue for QA access on the forward bus "A". Note that the same implementation is required for the reverse bus "B".

Example 10-8: Describe the Pre-arbitrated Access (PA) DQDB protocol.

The Pre-arbitrated Access (PA) slot is typically used for isochronous transmission (previously mentioned). The major difference between a QA access and a PA access is that PA slots are designated by the node at the head of the bus. Therefore, access to a PA slot may be shared by more than one Access Unit (AU).

The payload of a PA segment contains several octets that are written by an AU. An AU may write "0", "1" (or more) isochronous service octets in designated positions of the PA segment. Each AU examines the Virtual Channel Identifier (VCI) field of the PA slot to determine: (1) if the VCI is not in use by the AU, the PA slot is ignored by the AU; and (2) if the VCI is in use by the AU, the AU will provide a table indicating the octet offsets within the slot that the AU must read and write. The AU will read the positions that are marked to be read, and will write positions that are designated to be written as isochronous service octets.

The major functions of the node at the head of the bus are to control the designation of PA slots; assign the PA octets to different AUs; generate the PA segment header; and assign the VCI.

10.5.5 ATM Networks

ATM technologies including packet switching, cell structure, and applications have been previously described in Chapter 5. Therefore, only ATM network applications are briefly discussed in this section. From a high level viewpoint, an ATM network can serve as a local area network that is referred to as an ATM LAN. Figure 10-44 shows an ATM LAN network architecture that interconnects various processors (IBM, HP, etc.), imaging equipment, Unix server, DOS server, graphics equipment, Ethernet network, Computer-Aided Design (CAD), Computer Aided Manufacturing (CAM), and similar services. Thus, an ATM LAN is both a "server network" and a "distributed processing network".

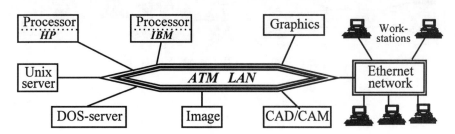

Figure 10-44   ATM LAN Server and a Distributed Processing Network.

Figure 10-45 illustrates an ATM network that interconnects with several ATM public switches to form a Metropolitan Area Network (MAN). In this example, the ATM switches communicate using packetized signals (OC-3C and OC-12C), at speeds of

155.52 Mbps and 622.08 Mbps. The interconnecting links are usually optical fibers, but electrical signals (STS-3C and STS-12C) can also be used.

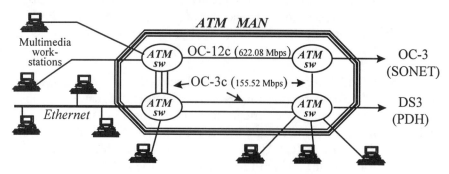

Figure 10-45   ATM MAN Network.

ATM technology can be used to serve as a Wide Area Network (WAN). As shown in Figure 10-46, several types of customer premises can be interconnected by a WAN. For example customer premises based on Ethernet LAN (IEEE 802.3) standards, token ring standards in addition to Ethernet LAN, or FDDI ring LAN standards are common applications for ATM WANs.

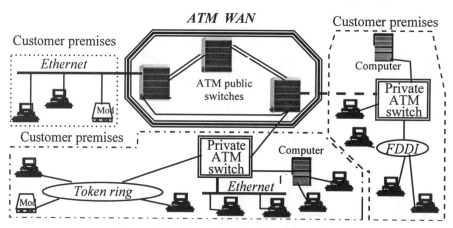

Figure 10-46   ATM WAN Network.

10.5.6 LAN and High-Speed LAN Performance

The factors that effect the performance of a LAN are classified in three areas: (1) Network characteristics, including channel bandwidth or capacity, packet length, cable length and propagation delay; (2) protocols, including LAN protocols (e.g., MAC protocol) and higher level protocols; and (3) traffic density on the network, including number of stations and loading characteristics.

Many parameters can be used to measure the performance of a LAN or high-speed LAN. Three measures that are commonly used include:.

(1) Delay (D): There are several types of delay in LAN data transmission. However, among various types of delay the delay that occurs between the time a packet (frame) is ready for transmission from a node to the time that successful transmission completes is the most important delay measurement.

(2) Throughput (S): Throughput is the overall rate of the data being transmitted between nodes in a LAN. However, throughput can be used in other applications. For example, a modern ATM switch can accept several 155.52 Mbps signals at its input. If the switch is designed to accept sixteen 155.52 Mbps signals per port, and there are 8 ports, this switch has a throughput of 20 Gbps derived as:

$$16 \times 8 \times 155.52 \text{ Mbps} = 20 \text{ Gbps}$$

(3) Utilization (U): The utilization of a LAN indicates the fraction of total capacity that is being used.

The relationship among these three parameters is given as follows

$$D = \text{Propagation time} = \frac{d}{V} \tag{10-4}$$

$$S = \text{Throughput} = \frac{L}{D + \textit{Transmission time}} \tag{10-5}$$

$$U = \text{Utilization} = \frac{S}{R} = \frac{1}{1+a} \tag{10-6}$$

$$a = \frac{\textit{Pr opagation time}}{\textit{Transimission time}} = \frac{Rd}{VL} \tag{10-7}$$

$$\text{Transmission time} = \frac{L}{R} \tag{10-8}$$

where

L = Length of a frame
R = Data rate of the LAN
d = Distance of the common path
V = electron velocity on the medium
a = Propagation time/Transmission time
D = Propagation delay (time)

Review Questions I for Chapter 10:

(1) A LAN is a communication network the provides interconnection between a variety of data communication devices within a _____ area. A LAN is a shared communication _____, implemented as a set of _____ for _____ and _____.

(2) A LAN allows a number of independent devices (e.g., _____, _____, _____, _____, _____, _____ etc.) to communicate directly to each other.

(3) (True, False) The transmission media used for LAN connections must be different from those used for WANs and MANs.

(4) Topology is a pattern of _____ used among various nodes of a network to suit user needs. The major network topologies used for LANs are ____, _____ (or _____), _____ and _____.

(5) Since the IEEE 802 Committee has been responsible for LAN and WAN standards, several well established LAN standards are: the IEEE _____ (Network Management and Internetworking), IEEE _____ (Logical Link Control), IEEE _____ (CSMA/CD), IEEE _____ (Toke ring), IEEE _____ (DQDB).

(6) Among three LAN layers, LAN's _____ corresponds to OSI data link layer, LAN's _____ and _____ corresponds to OSI physical layer.

(7) The four fields of a LAN Logical Link Control (LLC) Protocol Data Unit (PDU) are: _____ (_____), _____ (_____), _____, and _____ (_____).

(8) According to IEEE 802.2, the LLC's network service specifications provide for three types of data communication operations between SAPs: Type 1 operation is _____, Type 2 is _____ (_____ or _____ PDU), and Type 3 is _____.

(9) The IEEE _____ on [_____(CSMA/CD)] is the most widely used LAN standard, and has a huge installed base, and its MAC frame contains the following fields: _____, _____ _____, _____, _____, _____, _____, _____ and _____.

(10) Ethernet frame contains the following fields: _____, _____, _____, _____, _____ and _____.

(11) The IEEE 802.5 standard defines the _____ MAC protocol, physical layer specification on _____, using _____ signal (code). The IBM token ring operation is similar to the _____ token ring.

10.6 INTERNETWORKING

To provide internetworking requires extension of a LAN, interconnecting a LAN to another LAN, or interconnecting a LAN to a WAN. Many organizations must support more users on their LAN, and accomplish this by adding another segment to an Ethernet or another token ring LAN to the existing token ring. In some situations, several LANs may have a need to pass information to each other, and LAN-to-LAN interconnectivity (internetworking) becomes necessary. In other applications there is a need to transfer information from a LAN to another device which is connected to (or part of) a WAN. Hence, LAN-to-WAN internetworking is required, which needs special devices (e.g., repeaters, bridges, routers, and gateways) The functions of these devices are also described in this chapter.

Definition 10-9: (**interoperability** and **internetworking**): The ability of a system to transfer an application running on one station to another, via a connected network, is referred to interoperability. Internetworking refers to the capability to move information from one station on one network, to another station on another network.

However, the telecommunications industry often refers to *internetworking as: internetworking plus interoperability.*

Definition 10-10 (**internet**): A large network that consists of two or more networks the interface via internetworking protocol is commonly referred to an internet. The constituent networks in this configuration are called subnetworks (or subnets).

Definition 10-11 (**relay**): When two systems are not directly connected together, and connectivity is made through an intermediary, the intermediary is called a relay [in accordance with the International Organization for Standardization (ISO)].

Definition 10-12 (**layer *n* relay**): When a relay shares common layer *n* protocol with other systems, but does not participate in a layer (*n+1*) protocol when relaying information, this relay is called a "layer *n* relay".

10.6.1 LAN-to-LAN Internetworking Devices

For interconnecting LANs, and LANs to WANs, four types of devices are usually required. They are: repeaters, bridges, routers, and gateways. A repeater is a layer 1 relay device. That is, a repeater operates at the physical layer, and cannot perform other layers' functions (e.g., control or route information). A bridge operates at the data link layer (i.e., layer 2), and can determine if a packet address is destined for another subnetwork (subnet). A router operates at the network layer (i.e., layer 3), and has intelligence to handle several levels of addressing. A gateway operates at layer 4 (or above) and can interconnect networks or media with different architectures and protocols. Figure 10-47 provides a high level view of a bridge, router, and gateway.

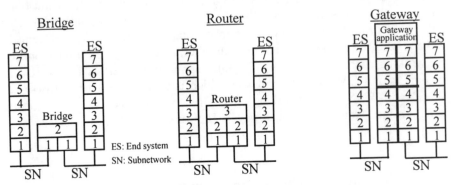

Figure 10-47   Some Basic Devices for Internetworking.

It should be understood that not every product fits exactly into these basic device types. Some products are hybrid in nature. For example, a "brouter" performs the functions of a bridge and some functions of a router. Likewise, a "trouter" performs the function of a router and a terminal server. Some of these internetworking devices are described in detail in the following sections. Note that the terminologies of bridges, routers, and gateways are sometimes used differently:

- Front-end processors and simple controllers are often referred to as "bridges or gateways".

- In public networks, Digital Cross-connect Systems (DCSs) are referred to as "gateways".

- When connecting public and private networks, some vendors refer to multiplexers as "bridges".

- In the TCP/IP terminology, a gateway is referred to as a "router" (using OSI standards).

10.6.1.1 Bridges

As shown in Figures 10-47 and 10-48, a bridge operates at the data link layer, and relays frames or packets between two LANs. A bridge has several physical ports and, at most one subnetwork of an internet is connected to each port on the bridge.

A bridge can operate on networks having similar architectures, such as Ethernet to Ethernet, or token ring to token ring. However, a bridge can also operate between LANs with dissimilar MAC sublayer protocols, provided they follow the same Logical Link Control (LLC) protocol. For example, a bridge can connect an Ethernet LAN with a token ring LAN since they share a common IEEE 802.2 LLC format. This dissimilar interconnection often requires a higher-level protocol conversion than is provided by bridges, and may result in reliability problems for internetworking.

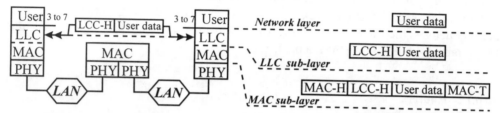

Figure 10-48   Bridge Operation: Relay Frames (Packets) between LANs.

A bridge can connect two or more LAN segments that may differ in their physical and Medium Access Control (MAC) layers, but still have the same LLC layer. LLC and higher-layer protocol information is passed through the bridge transparently. A bridge is said to be "protocol independent" in this sense, even though no device can ever be entirely protocol independent.

A bridge does not provide flow control, and there can be congestion within a bridge. Bridges must have the ability to buffer frames. Protocols at higher layers have the responsibility for recovering frames that are either lost or discarded by a bridge when its buffer is full (overflow).

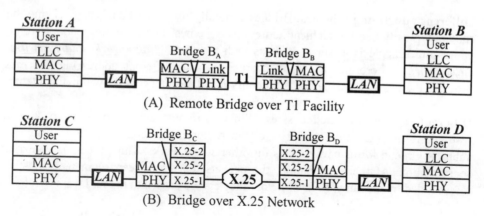

Figure 10-49   Remote Bridge Operation.

Interconnecting two LANs is not limited to the use of a single bridge. When LANs are far apart (i.e., not adjacent), they can be connected by two bridges that are connected by a communications facility. Figure 10-49(A) shows a T1 digital carrier system connecting two bridges (*B_A* and *B_B*). Bridge *B_A* gets the MAC frame from station **A**, "wraps" it in its link layer frame (with header and trailer), and sends it via T1 to bridge *B_B*. Bridge *B_B* decodes the link layer frame, and sends the original MAC frame to its destination station **B**, via a LAN.

Figure 10-49(B) illustrates another example of remote bridge operation. The T1 facility [Figure 10-49(A)] is replaced by a X.25 network, and stations **C** and **D** are users of two LANs that are located far apart. Bridge B_C receives the MAC frame from station **C** and generates an X.25 frame in packet format, and sends it to the X.25 network. The X.25 network delivers the frame to bridge B_D, which "unwraps" the X.25 packet, and sends the MAC frame to station **D** via the remote LAN.

10.6.1.2 Routers

In addition to bridges, a router is often required for interconnecting networks. Bridges are applicable to configurations involving LANs of the same type (i.e., use protocols that agree at the LLC and higher layers).

A router is a general-purpose device that operates at the network layer, and can be used to provide internetworking among dissimilar networks. For some applications, there may be a need to access devices on a WAN via a public or a private switched network (e.g., to access a public database).

Since a router is often used to interconnect both dissimilar and similar networks, it must accommodate several different characteristics inherent to the networks it interconnects. Some examples of router applications are given as follows:

- **Different addressing schemes**: Bridges generally use a flat addressing scheme, but routers typically use hierarchical addressing schemes. For example, a simple router addressing scheme is a pair of address with the form [*subnetwork*, *address within subnetwork*]. Therefore, the subnetworks can use different addressing schemes, provided there is a global method for identifying all the subnetworks within the internet.

- **Different maximum packet sizes**: Since different subnetworks have various restrictions on maximum packet size, the router must separate packets from one subnetwork, and forms new packets for other subnetworks. This process is known as segmentation. At their destination, the packets that have been segmented must be reassembled by the network layer before they can be passed to higher layers.

A router must share a common network layer protocol with all stations. The stations must also share the same protocols at the network layer (and alone) to allow successful communication between end stations. As shown in Figure 10-50, a router can be a "local router" or a "remote router". Local routers are typically simpler than remote routers, which may have to support a variety of interfaces to connect MANs or WANs, over which they route LAN traffic.

To support routing between different LANs, routers must not require modifications to the architecture of any of the attached networks. Instead, the router must accommodate the differences inherent to these networks. The most important issues are listed as follows:

- **Addressing schemes**: The networks to be interconnected may use different end-point names, addresses, and directory maintenance schemes. Therefore, global network addressing must be provided in addition to the directory service.

- **Maximum packet size**: Packet sizes of the networks to be interconnected may be different. Therefore, the packet from one network may have to be modified into a different packet size for transport to another network.

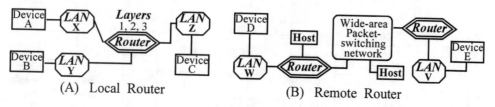

(A) Local Router   (B) Remote Router

Figure 10-50   Local and Remote Routers.

- **Error recovery**: Interconnecting various networks (i.e., internetworking) and systems within a network (i.e., intra-networking) often require different error recovery schemes. For intra-networking, the scheme may range from "no error recovery" to a highly reliable "end-to-end service". For internetworking, the service should not be dependent on the nature of the individual network's error recovery capability. That is, the internet must set its own error recovery criterion.

- **Different time-outs**: A LAN may adopt different time-out schemes for retransmission. For example, a connection-oriented transport service may wait for acknowledgment until a time-out expires, at which time the system re-sends its segment of data. Therefore, a longer time is required for successful transmission, but avoids unnecessary retransmission of segments of data.

- **Routing techniques**: In general, intra-network routing may dependent on fault detection and congestion control techniques peculiar to each network. The internetworking facility must be able to coordinate these to adaptively route data between data terminating equipment (DTEs) on different networks. Routing protocols are used between routers to set up routing tables.

10.6.1.3 Gateways

As shown in Figures 10-47 and 10-51, a gateway must operate at all seven layers (PHY$_1$, DL$_1$, NL$_1$, TCP/IP, and higher layers) of the OSI model. A gateway may be responsible for connecting incompatible proprietary networks, administering electronic mail systems, converting and transferring files from one system to another, or enabling interoperability between dissimilar operating systems or database management systems. Examples of typical gateway products are described in this section. A gateway can be used to interconnect dissimilar networks such as SNA and DECnet , or TCP/IP and SNA (Figure 10-51). Another common example is the e-mail systems used by LANs in different organizations (or within the same organization), which may be a combination of cc:Mail, IBM PROFS, MHS, SNADS, uucp or EasyLink. These e-mail systems have different formats, addressing schemes, routing, etc. To provide transparent connectivity between dissimilar e-mail systems, special gateway products (e.g., SoftSwitch Central) have been deployed, and protocol standards (e.g., X.400 help) have been established.

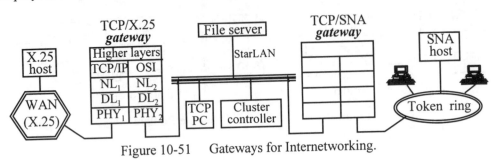

Figure 10-51   Gateways for Internetworking.

10.6.1.4 Hybrid Devices

Two hybrid devices, "brouters" and "trouters" (Figure 10-52), used for internetworking described in this section. A "brouter" is routing bridge that provides the functionality of both a router and a bridge concurrently. Brouters are typically used in networks with mixed network layer protocol traffic.

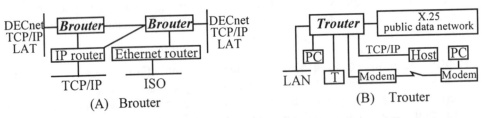

Figure 10-52   Internetworking Hybrid Devices: Brouters and Trouters.

As shown in Figure 10-52(A), a brouter operates at protocol layer two and three (i.e., the data link and network layers). A brouter combines the protocol transparency of a bridge with the ability to route traffic to several subnetworks, based on the network layer protocol. A brouter can forward frames within the internet, and handles many different types of layer three protocols. It examines the layer three header, decides which protocol the packet is using, and then routes the packet on that basis. If the brouter cannot recognize the protocol or senses a non-routable protocol (e.g., DEC's LAT), the brouter will act as a transparent bridge for that packet. A brouter can also provide custom filtering features, which allow a brouter to forward or to filter frames based on predefined conditions. These conditions include parameters such as destination address, protocol type, frame size, and the address type. Custom filtering can provide greater management and control over network operations.

Another important feature that some brouters provide is the ability of "source explicit forwarding". This capability is used in conjunction with routing tables to authorize certain stations to forward specific frames through the brouters. For example, the local administrator can authorize the forwarding of address-specific frames through particular ports of a brouter. This feature helps in fault isolation and in improving network security.

Figure 10-52(B) illustrates a trouter, which combines the capabilities of a multi-protocol router and a terminal server. A well-known trouter, developed by Cisco System Inc., simultaneously performs routing and terminal server functions. This trouter contains two ports, that can be connected to two IEEE 802.3 networks, to two synchronous serial links, or to one of each. The serial ports can support T1 facilities, or transmission using X.25, HDLC, and LAPB protocols at speeds up to 4 Mbps. The router can support many protocols including TCP/IP, DECnet, XNS, NetWare/IPX, and AppleTalk. The terminal server can support up to 16 asynchronous devices (e.g., PCs, printers, terminals, and modems) at speeds up to 33.4 kbps. The trouter multiplexes the traffic from all the devices onto either T1 or IEEE 802.3 interfaces. The router portion provides unique remote access capabilities for connecting several asynchronous devices to a LAN or a WAN.

10.6.2 Other LAN-to-LAN Internetworking Issues

LAN-to-LAN internetworking can be performed using FDDI or DQDB (previously described in Sections 10.5.3 and 10.5.4). A FDDI can be used for interconnecting other LANs by using InterWorking Units (IWUs), as shown in Figure 10-53(A), where an IEEE 802.5 token ring LAN is connected to an IEEE 802.3 LAN. Similarly, IEEE 802.3 LANs and IEEE 802.5 token rings can be interconnected by DQDB (IEEE 802.6) as shown in Figure 10-53(B).

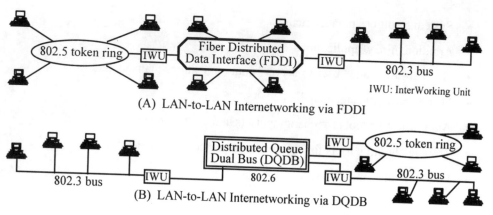

(A) LAN-to-LAN Internetworking via FDDI

(B) LAN-to-LAN Internetworking via DQDB

Figure 10-53   LAN-to-LAN Internetworking via FDDI or DQDB.

10.7 NETWORK OPERATING AND MANAGEMENT SYSTEMS

A computer always requires an Operating System (OS) that allows the hardware elements (and peripherals) to perform its functions. If two or more computers are properly connected together, they can share information by applying communications software (i.e., networking software). A Network Operating System (NOS) is the software that gives the network its multi-user, and multi-tasking capabilities (see Figure 10-54). It is the "brain" of a LAN, determines the type of devices that can be deployed in the network, and arbitrates service requests from users. The selection of a NOS provides the framework for the entire LAN. A NOS consists of software that is added to each device on the network, and usually "sits on top" of the internal operating systems of the computer devices. One device, attached to the network, is designated as the "server", and contains more complex NOS software than the other devices (e.g., user PCs).

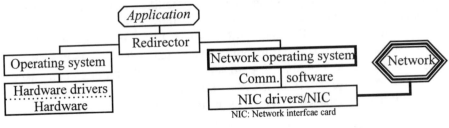

Figure 10-53   Network Operating System (NOS).

10.7.1 Network Operating System (NOS) Functions

A NOS performs many functions. These functions are provided by software and supported by hardware, but may differ depending on the LAN environment. The following is a list of functions provided by the NOS.

- System resources management

- Addition of new applications

- "User-to-user" and "user-to-server" communications management

- Data security management

- Administrative tools for changing users and/or resources

- Trouble-shooting tools for system maintenance management

- Fault tolerance management

- Multi-tasking environment management

- User to user file transfer

10.7.2 NOS Philosophy, Basic Concepts and Evaluation Criteria

The computer era started with centralized computer systems without networks. This architecture is referred to as a centralized resource, Figure 10-55(A), and the computer hardware has a local operating system with applications that "sit on top" of it. With the advent of local area network technology, the need for software to control communications between "local hosts" became an important part of the system design. The early stages of development required simple software for handling the transfer and the reception of data, such as mail and file transfers [Figure 10-55(B)]. This data needed to be translated by the receiving nodes before it could be interpreted by the end users.

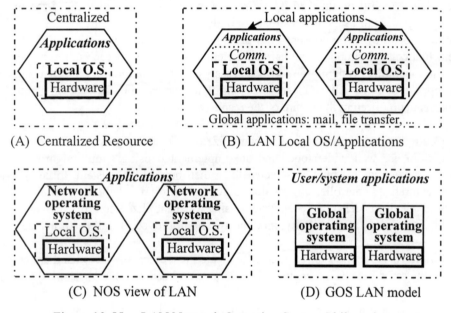

(A) Centralized Resource

(B) LAN Local OS/Applications

(C) NOS view of LAN

(D) GOS LAN model

Figure 10-55   LAN Network Operating System Philosophy.

The LAN operating and management environment became increasingly complex as LAN technology advanced. When users became accustomed to LANs with the communications management layers, they soon requested new features. The LANs and extended resources (e.g., distributed data management) were enhanced to provide each user station with access to the entire system's data bank (versus just a fraction of it in earlier systems). To provide better services to these users, new applications required the addition of features in the communications management software. These improvements resulted in the next class of LAN system management software called Network Operating System [NOS: Figure 10-55(C)].

A NOS provides transparent use of the system's resources, and extends beyond mere communications management. It allows users to request services (as in older systems) that are oblivious to whether it is a "local" or "remote" request. The NOS invokes the control process or data accesses as requested, without the user knowing the details of the network interaction that occurred.

The next development was the Global Operating System (GOS) model. The GOS principle eliminated local and network components, and then constructed a new operating system based on network and user applications. The key feature of this approach (compared to previous schemes) is one single (global) operating system built on the hardware, with user and system applications "on top" of the GOS [Figure 10-55(D)].

The basic function of a network operating system, including the GOS, is to **serve** the users/devices via their attached LAN. A LAN often has several distributed resources. To provide services to users/devices that are both probabilistic and fair, a NOS must have a "policy" to follow. The concept is to provide a *collection of servers*, which implement the actual control of underlying hardware elements. That is, for each job to be performed by the operating system, the NOS possesses one or more servers that implement appropriate actions. All NOS servers control resources, and the type of control used depends upon different the nature of the resources.

- Centralized versus distributed (decentralized) control: The mechanisms of centralized control are well understood, and are implemented using simple algorithms. Thus, centralized control may be selected for a distributed LAN system. In comparison, a decentralized controller utilizes distributed assets to provide better overall services to users/devices. Hence, a LAN system using a decentralized control NOS will achieve higher availability, flexibility, modularity, and improved overall performance.

- Single versus replicated resources: Replicated resources operate on and are controlled by the same processing engine. Thus, in a centralized computer system, the notion of replicated resources is not an issue. In a distributed computer system, replicated resources are a source of both problems and major gains. Because the replicated resources must be controlled and acted on by a variety of processing engines, methods must be used to keep their status consistent with one another.

- Autonomous versus cooperating resources: An autonomous server or resource can provide its service without interaction with other servers or resources. However, a cooperating server or resource must interact with companion servers or resources. It must also interact with peer elements to effect the operation that it's designed for. For example, in a distributed database case, whenever an item in the database must be updated, the server must converse with every site that has a copy. It must also inform them of its intent to update, and then get a consensus agreement before actually performing the update.

Each NOS supports both basic and special features, in addition to its computer operating system. The following list provides the criteria used for selecting a NOS:

- Network administration
- Connectivity to clients
- Routing capabilities
- Disk caching
- Built-in facility for data backup
- Multi-protocol support at the transport layer
- Security facilities
- Multi-processing
- Ease of use (e.g., add/delete users, change a user's password, on-line help, etc.)

10.7.3 LAN Servers and Server Operating System

A server is a LAN node that is dedicated to a particular type of service(s). Figure 10-56 illustrates several types of LAN servers (e.g., file servers, terminal servers, terminal concentrators, disk servers, printer servers, etc.). In a LAN there may be several servers, some of which may provide the same or similar services. The devices on the network that request services are designated as "clients".

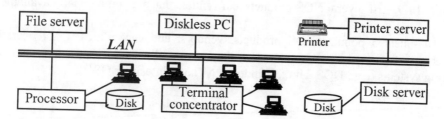

Figure 10-56   Various LAN Servers.

Typically the server portion of the network operating system can be divided into five subsystems as shown in Figure 10-57, and described as follows:

(1) Control (system) kernel: The kernel is the "heart" of a NOS. It coordinates the various processes in the other subsystems. The kernel design contains processors that optimize access to services for user activities. The synchronization and multi-tasking support services may be supplied by a host operating system, that resides on top of the NOS functions.

(2) Network interface: The network interface supports functions that are in the actual network media implementation. It also handles low-level subnet protocols and provides basic translation functions between these protocols when bridging services are required.

(3) File system: File systems are the mechanisms used to organize, store, and retrieve data from storage subsystems available to the NOS.

(4) System services: Network system services cover (handle) all services that do not fit easily into any of the other categories of the model. They may be system-level store-and-forward services (e.g., queuing protocols) or resource accounting subsystems.

(5) System extensions: System extensions define the "openness" of the system. Third-party developers use these extensions to develop "add-on products". The system extensions commonly offered by vendors are high-level protocol handlers that perform operations (e.g., translations between file-access protocols) required by different client operating systems.

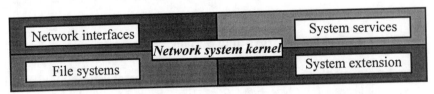

Figure 10-56   Basic Subsystems of the Server of a NOS.

Example 10-9: List several NOS products and vendors that are commercially available.

Table 10-4 lists 5 popular NOS products, vendors, and capabilities. LAN operating systems vary from vendor to vendor, but, they are usually based on popular computer operating systems (e.g., DOS, Unix, Windows, NT, Macintosh, or OS/2).

Table 10-4   Major Operating Systems.

NOS	Vendor	Capabilities
NetWare	Novell	*Clients supported: DOS, Windows, Unix, OS/2, NT, Macintosh*
Vines	Banyan	*Clients supported: DOS, Windows, Unix, OS/2, NT, Macintosh*
Windows NT	Microsoft	*Clients supported: DOS, Windows, Unix, OS/2, NT, Macintosh*
LAN Server	IBM	*Clients supported: DOS, Windows, Unix, OS/2, NT, Macintosh*
LANtastic	Artisoft	*Server based: supports DOS & Windows clients* *For OS/2 peer-to-peer: supports OS/2 clients*

A NOS must support a number of services to justify installation of the LAN. These services include e-mail, file transfer, security, central database maintenance, and a variety office automation applications. Typical office automation applications are word processing, personal schedule managers, and similar processes that run "on top" of the NOS.

Example 10-10: List several common NOS vendor protocols and applications.

Figure 10-58 shows the LAN NOS protocols, and OSI representation for products by IBM, Novel, and Banyan.

OSI	MAP	IBM OS/2	IBM DOS[1]	Novell	Banyan[2]	
7	ASCE, FTAM, MMS, Directory services	Application / LAN server core services	Application	Application	Vines application	OSI application
6	ISO 8822/8823	Requester (SMBs) OS/2 — NET-BIOS	NET-BIOS / APPC	Netware APPC NETBIOS Transport Layer Interfaces	Vines socket or UNIX TLI	ISO presentation
5	ISO 8826/8827	NET-BIOS / APPC		(TLI) pipes		ISO session
4	ISO 8072/8073			OSI TCP/IP IPX/SPX	ISO 8072/8073	
3	ISO 8348/8473	NETBIOS and APPC interface directly to 802.2 LLC		IBM SNA NETBEUI ATP	ISO 8473 9542	X.25
2	IEEE 802.2 LLC / IEEE 802.4 MAC	802.2 LLC; 802.5 MAC; 802.3 MAC; PC network		Open data link interface	802.2 802.3 802.5	LAPB
1	IEEE 802.4 Broadband or Carrierband	802.3; 802.5 Broadband Other		Physical	802.3 802.5	X.21

1. IBM also provides TCP/IP services under DOS;   2. Banyan also provides TCP/IP and MAC through AppleTalk

ACSE	Association Control Service Element	ISO
AFP	Apple File Protocol	Apple
API	Application Programmer Interface	
APPC	Advanced Program-to-Program Communications	IBM
ATP	AppleTalk Protocol	Apple
CMIS	Common Management Information System	OSI
CMIP	Common Management Information Protocol	OSI
FTAM	File Transfer Access and Management	ISO
GOSIP	Government Open Systems Interconnection Profile	US Govt.
NETBIOS	NETwork Basic Input Output System	IBM
SMB	Server Message Block	IBM

Figure 10-58   IBM, Novell, and Banyan NOS Protocols.

10.7.4 LAN Network Management (NM)

Network management as a general topic for telecommunications networks is discussed in Chapter 12. However, a simplified definition of network management is also provided in this section. Up to this point, the focus of Chapter 10 has been centered on what constitutes a network operating system [i.e., the essential parts of all machines (nodes) connected to the LAN. LAN network management are the functions used to maintain a LAN so that the subscribers can use the services effectively.

Definition (**network management**): This concept encompasses the tasks (human and automated) that support the creation, operation, administration, maintenance, and evolution of a network.

The activities associated with LAN network management are described as follows:

- Operations management: These functions include reporting status and managing of LAN traffic, performance, and accounting.

- Administration management: This function deals with managing the use of the network.

- Maintenance management: These functions include detecting, reporting, troubleshooting, and fixing network problems.

- Configuration management: This function supports managing the network's life cycle, and evolving new configurations for future needs.

- Security management: The security management function detects and prevents unauthorized network access.

- Planning: Planning is often considered a subset of configuration management because it involves planning new network configurations to meet the constant growth of network use.

- Database management: The database associated with the network may be centralized and/or distributed over various individual nodes. This function allows the data bases to be shared among different nodes, and regularly updated to support efficient use of network resources.

- Documentation and training: Accurate documentation and well-trained network support personnel are essential to successful network resource utilization.

10.7.5 LAN NM Goals and Domains

LAN network management has one basic goal: "To support continuous and efficient operation of LAN communication systems." This goal is often divided into five areas:

(1) Configuration management: This function provides the capability to accurately initialize, reset, and "shot-down" an entire LAN system, or single entities within a LAN.

(2) Fault management: This function provides the capabilities of error detection, problem diagnosis, and fault correction.

(3) Performance management: This function provides the capability for a system to measure various performance parameters such as the response time (delay) of the network, quality of service, congestion, availability, etc.

(4) Access control management: The function provides the capability for system control of user access to the network. It also checks for security breaches, and records/reports suspected incidents.

(5) Accounting management: This function provides the capabilities for the LAN system to implement proper distribution of the system cost to is users.

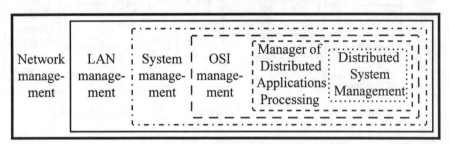

Figure 10-59   Network Management Domains.

Network Management (NM) for LANs is an important issue in modern data communications. A LAN typically consists of a moderate to large number of autonomous, multi-vendor interconnected devices, therefore networks may not be 100% interoperable. With the arrival of MANs, WANs, and global networks, the partitioning of network management into separate domains is somewhat nebulous. However, the management domains shown in Figure 10-59 have been clearly identified, and are well defined.

10.7.6 LAN NM Architecture and Implementation

In this section LAN NM architecture will be defined starting with the IEEE architecture model, which is based on the OSI layer model. This description is continued to the integrated model, which was contributed from the European community. Figure 10-60 illustrates the IEEE LAN management architecture (model). It can be seen that the model is divided into two parts: (1) layer management, and (2) system management.

The layer management (shown as dashed boxes in Figure 10-60) is implemented by processes within the individual layers [i.e., the physical layer the data link layer with Logical Link Control (LLC) and Medium Access Control (MAC) sublayers] that are responsible for collecting management information. These processes are called Layer Management Entities (LMEs).

The individual layer management functions are unified by a System Management Applications Process (SMAP). SMAPs provide management of the overall LAN system. SMAPs communicate with LMEs via Layer Management Interface (LMIs). The SMAPs and LMEs communicate with each other to determine status and obtain information from other. SMAPs communicate with each other via a System Management Data Service Interface (SMDSI).

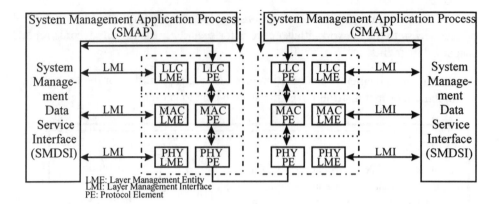

Figure 10-60   IEEE LAN Management Architecture Model.

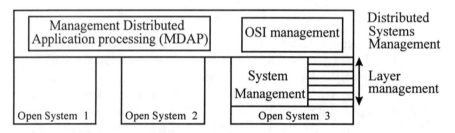

Figure 10-61   LAN Management Architecture Integrated Model.

In European applications there are two related management groups: (1) Management of Distributed Application Processing (MDAP), and (2) Special Interest Group on Distributed System Management (SIGDSM).

A distributed system is a group of systems that are interconnected by a LAN, WAN, or internetwork. A "system" is generally a node with processing capabilities. Management Distributed Applications Processing (MDAP) is a process to process function, concerned with end system resource management. It can be build on, or interact with, information and services specified by network and other management standards. In contrast, OSI LAN management is an operating system to operating system function, and Distributed System Management (DSM) is a completely system to system function. Thus, one can view DSM as "the sum" of MDAP and OSI LAN management. The integrated LAN management architecture model is illustrated in Figure 10-61, where three open systems are depicted. One of these open systems (open system 3) is illustrated in detail, and contains a system management and layer management functions. The individual open systems are connected together by OSI management, which works in conjunction with Management of Distributed Applications Processing (MDAP). The entire (whole) system resides in the domain of Distributed System Management (DSM).

The implementation of LAN network management is briefly described in this section. A LAN network management system is supported by hardware and attached software. This type of system is referred to as Network Control Center (NCC), which is typically attached to a LAN through a Network Interface Unit (NIU), consisting of a micro- or mini-computer, keyboard, and screen interface.

The functions performed by an NCC involve observation and/or active control. These functions can be grouped into three categories: (1) configuration management (e.g., directory management); (2) monitoring functions (e.g., token monitoring, packet parameter monitoring, collision monitoring); and (3) fault isolation functions (e.g., handling a failed station on a ring).

In addition to Network Operating System (NOS) and Network Management System (NMS) software, there are several software packages that enhance LAN management and operations. Examples of software that supports LAN management are:

- Help desk: This software supports trouble ticketing, problem routing, error reporting features, suggested solution, etc.

- Inventory and asset management: It creates a database of system components.

- Storage management: This software is used to backup client and server disk drives, if requested by the user.

- Server management: This software is responsible for server utilization, disconnection of users, remote command execution, etc.

- Security: This software performs access control, data encryption, modem call-back, fire-wall implementation, etc.

- Remote monitoring (RMON) capability: This software enables remote system monitoring from several remote sites.

Example 10-11: Provide examples of commercial Local Area Network (LAN) Network Management Systems (NMSs).

Commercial LAN network management systems available in the market are:

- OpenView: This NMS was developed by HP, and is considered to be the market leader. OpenView is described in detail in Chapter 12. It is a LAN network manager for Datakit II Virtual Circuit Service (VCS) networks that runs under the Unix environment. The OpenView Network Management Server (NMS) supports the HP OpenView architecture on Unix workstations, and is based on an X-windows and Motif graphical user interface.

- LAN network manager™: This NMS was developed by IBM, and is a LAN management program that supports IBM token rings. It provides a set of functions to manage a station using the IEEE 802.2 Logical Link Control (LLC) protocol. The system runs on a dedicated PC under PC-DOS or OS/2, and can also run under NetView/PC.

- NetWare: This is a generic NMS, and was developed by Novell. NetWare can run on many different commercial LANs.

- Communications System Management (CSM): This LANNMS is based on the Network Control Center (NCC) implementation.

- There are many other NMSs developed, but are not as well-known as the above NMSs. They are: (1) the System management server by Microsoft; (2) Spectrum by Cabletron; (3) Polycenter by DEC; and (4) LAN term by Novell.

10.8 LAN SELECTION/DESIGN AND FUTURE TRENDS

In selecting or designing a Local Area Network (LAN), there is no specific process to follow or equations in which substituting the required input or parameters will yield "a perfect LAN" for a particular application. A LAN designer, after being given an assignment, can never develop a final solution without several iterations of design and analysis (see Figure 10-62). The solution often depends on the designer's experience with LANs, the available technology, economical and political influences, and personal preferences, combined with the performance expectations specified by the end users. Because of non-technical factors, and the effect of numerous engineering "trade-offs", LAN design/selection is often considered more of an "art" than a "technique".

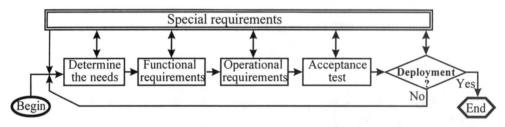

Figure 10-62   LAN Selection Method.

10.8.1 Initial LAN Selection Steps

No LAN design/selection solutions are typically unique, but they are never "perfect". That is, the procedures followed by every LAN designer may be completely different from those used by another. However, several initial steps are commonly adopted when selecting/designing a LAN. They are briefly described as follows:

- Determining the needs: The computer needs for various business organizations can be vastly different. If the primary activity of a business is data entry and retrieval combined with occasionally printing records, then a time-shared host computer may be the best solution. However, if the host computer's processing power is insufficient, the company may need to network several mini-, micro- and personal-computers with file-sharing, and printer sharing capabilities. In addition, if the users require e-mail and similar office automation functions, then a LAN will definitely be a better choice. Once the user needs are established, the designer will then proceed to determine:

  * User profile: This is a description of the type of tasks that users perform, the users application needs, their level of computer sophistication, the typical information exchange modes (e.g., fax, paper documents, or data management/distribution), and the hardware that they presently possesses/use. This profile varies based upon job categories and employment classifications.

  * Organization profile: Information about the organization will influence the LAN design/selection. Factors such as the size of the organization, the geographical distribution of the users, the nature of the business, special groups that require unique computer needs, and future growth projections must all be considered as part of the LAN design.

  * Environmental profile: The environmental conditions that influence LAN design/selection are: the existing transmission facility cable types (e.g., twisted-pair wires, coaxial cables), the existing equipment (e.g., PBXs, imbedded LANs), the equipment types/locations, and future expansion plans (e.g., addition of fiber optics, remote locations, new staffs, etc.).

- LAN functional requirements: LAN functional requirements can be divided into the three following categories:

  (1) Functions the LAN is intended to support: Functional definitions determine precisely what the system (LAN) is required to do. This includes the definition of the all the functions the system must perform, and inter-relationships. Typical inter-relationships are: data flow, control flow, communications, transformations (e.g., routers and gateways), precedence, and priority. The functional definition should also describe the major applications that are planned, and any future/special applications that are anticipated.

  (2) Performance requirements: Performance requirements include the rate or timing for functions to execute, the system's data processing capacity, responsiveness to changes in operating conditions, precision, and acceptable accuracy limits.

  (3) Environmental and physical constraints: These aspects of the functional requirements deal with the issue of what components are required. For example, special purpose processors and peripherals that the LAN must be used. Other parameters that are considered include size, weight, and power.

Once the functional requirements have been defined, a correlation and combination of various parameters can be used to derive the performance and environmental requirements for the LAN. For example, based on the previously established data, aggregate dataflows can be determined. These dataflows, along with an allocation of functions to devices, can be used to calculate the maximum LAN throughput requirements. Likewise, the control flow transformations and communications patterns exhibited by these functions provides the information needed to specify a class of protocols (e.g., closed loop, broadcast, or point-to-point). The type of calling routines will be selected based on response requirements and environmental factors. These considerations will also yield requirements for speed and the cable quality needed to survive the environmental conditions.

The service needs obtained from users, in terms of the average volume of transfers and timing requirements, determines the switching methods required. For example, when there is no need for highly reliable large transfers, a datagram service is probably sufficient. However, if devices need to "lock onto" each other for long periods of time or communicate with short delays, a circuit switching method may be more appropriate.

Environmental information combined with the geographical dispersion of devices and their interaction requirements, can be used to derive the network topology. If one device (location) is required to process data and then distribute it to serve points, a star configuration might be a better choice than a ring or a bus. In contrast, a bus is typically suited for "demand-based" communications in which access to the media based on user need outweighs other criteria. Rings are typically suited for general-purpose low-level information flow between a limited number of users.

- LAN operational requirements: To finalize the design/selection of a LAN before building it, an organization must develop a set of operational requirements. These requests are typically divided into two categories:

  (1) Life-cycle goals: These goals reflect long-term system qualities and attributes that must be achieved during the life of the system. These goals usually drive the actual requirements for the LAN, along with the functional requirements. (Note that the parameters used are reliability, fault tolerance, survivability, availability, maintainability, and growth/flexibility. To achieve these requirements typically results in the addition of: excess capacity, redundant paths, power supplies, communications hardware, control protocols, monitoring devices, excess address capability, ports, and inter- and intra-LAN communications devices.)

  (2) Allocated goals: These goals tend to be abstract measures that deal with overall system effectiveness criteria. For example, an allocated goal is that a new LAN must provide the capability to monitor and control all sensorized components in both the factory and offices of a company. Often this capability can only be verified after deployment of the device in the customer's environment.

- Acceptance test: Acceptance testing is the final step in LAN selection/design process. During these tests, user profiles, the network profile, and other factors are examined. The details of these profiles are dependent upon several sets of isolated performance parameters that the LAN must meet. These performance measures typically include the following items:

  * The ability of users to perform tasks via an application

  * The ability of management tools to make LAN performance measurements

  * The throughput of the LAN under specific "worst-case" load conditions

  * The ability to provide "LAN to LAN" interconnectivity with a specific level of throughput

  * The ability to meet ElectroMagnetic Interference (EMI) requirements under both typical and heavy load conditions

The number and level of acceptance tests often depends upon the nature and needs of the user organizations.

10.8.2 LAN Future Development Trends

There are many factors that influence future LAN development trends. Customers are demanding that LANs become: cheaper, more reliable, error free, more flexible, easily growable, interworkable, more accessible, and more secure. Vendors that satisfy these demands will lead the industry by implementing enhancements in the following technologies:

- Transmission medium
- Interworking capabilities
- Application support
- NOS and LAN network management

User applications have a significant influence on LAN development trends. Potential applications include enhanced video, voice and data integration, improved LAN security, "groupware", and multimedia.

10.8.2.1 LAN Standards

An important factor that influences LAN development is the evolution of industry standards. As illustrated in Figure 1-63, IEEE 802.9 defines a unified access method that offers Integrated Voice/Data (IVD) services for a variety of public or private "backbone network" applications. The IVD is further described in Example 10-12.

Example 10-12: Describe the Integrated Voice/Data (IVD) LAN interface configuration used for IVD service.

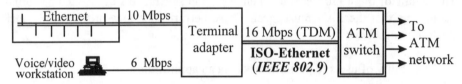

Figure 10-63   The IEEE 802.9 (ISO-Ethernet) Access Method.

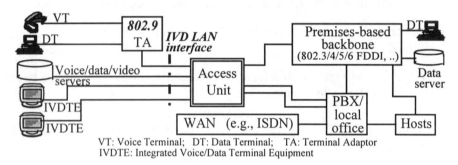

VT: Voice Terminal;   DT: Data Terminal;   TA: Terminal Adaptor
IVDTE: Integrated Voice/Data Terminal Equipment

Figure 10-64   IEEE 802.9 IVD LAN Interface Configuration.

Figure 10-64 illustrates an Integrate Voice/Data (IVD) LAN interface configuration for a typical customer premises that uses an Access Unit (AU) in conjunction with Integrated Voice/Data Terminal Equipment (IVDTEs).

The IVD LAN interface consists of a multiplexed digital data bitstream that contains various channel types over which a variety of services can be offered. The IVDTEs may contend for access to IVD services offered by the AU, or by external equipment connected to the AU via networks that support IVD services. Thus, the AU may be connected to an existing IEEE802 LAN, FDDI network, ISDN switch, or an IEEE 802.6 IVD network (see Figure 10-64).

Several IEEE standards apply to LANs, and are briefly described as follows:

- IEEE 802.11: The IEEE 802.11 establishes the architecture for a wireless Medium Access Control (MAC) based on MAC alternatives, channel characteristics, and market requirements. The standard also takes IEEE 802.10 and 802.9 into consideration.

- IEEE 802.10: The IEEE802.10 specifies the standard for interoperable LAN security. Its objectives are to (1) utilize a security architecture as defined in ISO 7498 Part 2; (2) define a standard that it is appropriate for the international community; (3) allow various "key management" architectures; (4) define the data exchange method that is independent of "key management"; and (5) allow interoperability among LAN products in an Open System Interconnection (OSI) architecture.

- IEEE 802.8: This committee is the Fiber Optic Technical Advisory Group (FOTAG), which investigates different architectures and topologies for fiber-optic media and related components. This group works in close collaboration with IEEE 802.3, 802.5 and 802.6.

- IEEE 802.3 (100 Base T/F): It specifies "fast Ethernet". This technology has three topologies, which are briefly described as follows:

   (1) 100 Base-Tx: Its speed is 100 Mbps over category 5 Unshielded Twisted Pair (UTP) wires. It applies 2-pair UTP for half-duplex operations, and 4-pair UTP for full-duplex operations. The line code used is 4B/5B, for timing recovery (synchronization) purpose.

   (2) 100 Base-Fx: It has the same characteristics as 100 Base-Tx except that it uses fibers to eliminate ElectroMagnetic Interference (EMI) problems.

   (3) 100 Base-T4: Its speed is 100 Mbps over category 3, 4 or 5 UTP wires. It has a symbol rate of 25 megabaud. It applies 4-pair UTP for half-duplex operations, three pairs for data exchange, and one pair for collision detection. The line code used for timing recovery (synchronization) is 8B/6T.

- IEEE 802.12 (100VG-AnyLAN) : Its speed is 100 Mbps over category 3, 4 or 5 UTP wires. It uses the Ethernet frame format, but **not** Carrier Sense Multiple Access/Collision Detection (CSMACD). Star topology is the typical network architecture, which has no collisions and applies MAC for demand priority protocol. The line code used is 5B/6B.

10.8.2.2 Transmission Medium

For general communications applications, four types of transmission media are used throughout the world. They are: Unshielded Twisted-Pair (UTP) wires, coaxial cables, fibers, and airway (airlink; wireless, radio, and satellite applications). It should be understood that a fifth type of medium, known as "waveguide", has also been used. However, they are not as popular as the four other media. Of these four media, UTP has the largest installed base in customer premises wiring, and is the most economical "per user" connection. It is believed that UTP will continue to be the "medium of choice" for the foreseeable future in the areas of local networks.

- Unshielded Twisted-Pair (UTP) wires: UTP was first deployed in Plain Old Telephone Service (POTS) and Plain-Old-LAN (POL) networks. The POL era began with a 1 Mbps StarLAN service over UTP. Since then, UTP has remained competitive with coaxial cables and fibers as a "medium of choice" for LANs. The IEEE approved the 10 Base T standard using UTP in 1990, and the UTP market has been expanding ever since. However, prior to 10 Base T, many analysts expected the number of token ring connections to surpass Ethernet. This has not happened. Wireless LANs may eventually impact UTP and cable LANs sales, but the "rule of thumb" is that UTP will dominate small to medium BWD (BandWidth × Distance) LANs while fiber will be deployed in high BWD applications.

- Coaxial cables: One advantage of coaxial cables over UTP is its low noise characteristic. However, with the rapid development of fiber (costs reduction and speed improvement), the role of coaxial cables in LAN applications is becoming less important. Quite a few cable systems have been deployed for long-haul LAN systems. The most noteworthy coaxial cable application is the T3 digital carrier systems. It carries 672 digitized voice signals, and used in the North American networks.

- Optical fibers: From a material viewpoint, there are three types of optical fibers. The lowest speed and least expensive is plastic fiber, which consists of a plastic fiber core (for carrying the light) and plastic fiber cladding (for guiding the light within the core). This type of fiber has **not** been used for telecommunications. The second type is Plastic Cladded Silica fiber [PCS, or Plastic Optical Fiber (POF)] which has a glass core surrounded by plastic cladding, and has been used in low to medium speed LANs. The IEEE 802.3 and 802.8 standards recommend POF as a low cost addition to the IEEE 802.3 Ethernet family. The third type of fibers is called glass fiber (uses glass for both the core and the cladding), which is typically deployed in high-speed and/or long distance systems.

- Airlink: The airway as transmission medium for LAN has been studied as a substitute for UTP, coaxial cable, and fiber in certain environments. The primary advantages of a wireless LAN are: (1) elimination of installed medium, and (2) the portability of terminals. Two wireless technologies have been proven acceptable for wireless LAN applications: (1) traditional radio-frequency (specifically, microwave frequency) transceivers, and (2) infrared electromagnetic spectrum transceivers. Additional information about wireless LAN technology is provided in Appendix 10-1.

10.8.2.3 LAN Security

Since LANs are privately owned and limited to small areas (e.g., a separate building, or campus), they are not as susceptible to malicious attack as Wide Area Networks (WANs). However, LANs have unique problems of their own. The ISO Reference Model 7498-2 standards suggest several security mechanisms for protecting communications over public/private networks. Technologies such as *encryption*, *digital signature*, *key management*, *access control* and *audit trail* can be used, depending upon the application and LAN environment. For typical LAN applications *encryption*, *access control,* and *audit trail* offer sufficient protection. Figure 10-65 illustrates an example of the LAN Security Data Exchange (SDE) frame format.

Because of the local nature of a LAN, physical security (e.g., wire-tapping) is a less important threat than direct access. The security manager must be confident that access control mechanisms (e.g., logins, passwords, group security ,and file access security) are commensurate with potential security threats. No type of access control` measure is effective if legitimate users do not protect their means of access. Although access control begins with the system, its ultimate success depends upon the users. To monitor the system for intrusion, errors, or failures, it is necessary to have an audit-trail mechanism as part of network security management. Similarly, any time data leaves the "local" LAN, data encryption should be considered (especially for wireless LANs).

Since data is openly broadcasted, it makes LANs more vulnerable from a security viewpoint. Computer viruses are multiplying in epidemic proportions. In addition, user must recognize the need for protection against viruses, and then implement security measures to safeguard their networks. Organizations must install virus protection software and network security systems to protect LANs, with the virus protection focus being shifted from a "search-and-destroy" strategy to "preventing introduction" into the network.

MAC header	LLC or security indicator	Security*	LLC Protocol Data Unit (PDU)	Security trailer*	MAC trailer

* This field exists only if the security field exists.

Figure 10-65   LAN Security Data Exchange (SDE) Frame Structure.

10.8.2.4 Technology Advances, Multimedia and High-speed LANs

There will always be advances in technology that affect future LAN development. Several advances are briefly discussed as follows:

- Distributed processing: A LAN is a natural environment for a company to utilize distributed computer power. Distributed computing, rather than a centralized computer, offers many benefits: high performance, high throughput, increased reliability, and improved access to data for all LAN users. The emphasis on corporate downsizing, and improved performance of mini-computers, both favor applications such as distributed database systems, automated manufacturing, remote sensing, and coordinated decision making.

- Multiple processors and super servers: Servers are fast-growing products in the LAN market. A super server is a specialized "high-end sever" designed to eliminate the shortcomings of PC based servers. Super servers achieve high performance through multiple processors, large cache memory, high bus speeds, and additional I/O channels. Multiple processor architectures allow separate processors to be dedicated to performing different tasks (e.g., disk I/O, and CPU processing, etc.).

- LAN-based e-mail: The migration to LAN-based e-mail is accelerating rapidly, and is driven by the evolution of network computing, coupled with established corporate infrastructures. Host-based mail systems have been replaced by distributed, "enterprise-wide" messaging systems that facilitate ubiquitous, seamless communications between organizations, their customers, suppliers, and partners. A modern message system must be compatible with various messaging platforms that are already in use. In addition, the system should allow users access to the same features and capabilities they are accustomed to, regardless of the operational environment.

With the fast growth of data communications (speeds and technology), and the processing power of PCs, telecommunications users have indicated a strong need for integrated voice, data, image, and/or graphic video services. This will eventually lead to full integration of services on the office desktop PC, and corresponding growth in multimedia LANs. Commercial multimedia LANs have already made an entrance into the market place.

Several standards have been developed to define and specify multimedia LAN interfaces. ANSI FDDI-II (Fiber Distributed Data Interface-II), with a high-speed long distance networking capability, satisfies the requirement of multimedia networks, concurrent transmission, and mutual synchronization of data streams (e.g., voice, audio, image, and data) on the same medium with conventional packet traffic. IEEE 802.9, which was briefly described in Section 10.8.2.1 and Example 10-12, defines the Integrated Voice/Data Terminating Equipment (IVDTE) interfaces to an IEEE 802.9 multimedia LAN. This standard enables IVDTEs to be connected to an IEEE 802.9 LAN, and allows them to communicate with other Integrated Voce/Data (IVD) stations as "data-only stations", "voice-only stations", or via premises-based networks offering ISDN services. With the rapid development of multimedia LANs, there is a corresponding increased need for gateways and Terminal Adapters (TAs). A TA permits direct coupling of terminal devices (e.g., data modules, voice modules, and ISDN terminals) to an IEEE 802.9 LAN interface.

The need to transport image and bulk data has led to the development of large bandwidth and high-speed local area networks. Real-time interactive visualization, and techniques for presenting simulation and modeling results are two examples of high bandwidth graphical LAN applications. LAN applications with low latency requirements and relatively low transaction processing may still benefit from higher bandwidth and lower access latency characteristics.

In the next generation of high-speed LANs, a number of factors will influence the selection of data rate. First, and foremost, is the requirement of data rates in excess of FDDI's 100 Mbps speed, to serve high-speed graphic applications. A potential speed limit may be less than 2.5 Gbps, since the current SONET/SDH networks have been implemented at 2.5 Gbps (OC-48 or STS-48 for SONET and STM-16 for SDH networking). However, it is likely that a speed of 155.52 Mbps may be the very first high-speed LAN since it is equivalent to the SONET STS-3c (OC-3c) or SDH STM1 signal, which is most popular digital signal rate.

The links in the next generation LAN will be duplex, for compatibility with FDDI and to provide a backup-channel for link failure recovery. The LAN will allow a physical topology based on a dual-ring of trees, and thus allows the use of existing FDDI cable plants, including star wired cables routed to individual offices. These high-speed LANs will need high performance protocols, such as the Xpress Transfer Protocol (XTP) which was designed for high-speed performance, and to minimize errors in LANs.

10.9 WIDE AREA NETWORK (WAN)

An overview of a network (i.e., a public wide area network) was presented in Chapter 2, where a typical end-to-end connection for voice applications was described. The details of the components in this network have been described in Chapters 4 through 7. This section shows several network applications that are based on the technologies previously described. A Wide Area Network (WAN) can be used as a local exchange, a trunk exchange, and a gateway exchange network. From a performance viewpoint, a WAN typically operates at a higher speed than a LAN.

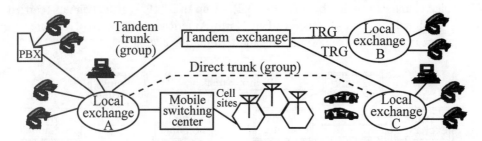

Figure 10-66   A Typical Local Exchange network.

Figure 10-66 shows a WAN used as a typical local exchange network. A local exchange switching office serves voice [including private branch exchange (PBX)], data, and video subscribers. Two local exchange offices can be interconnected via a direct trunk group or a tandem trunk group. The direct trunk group is typically used for high-density routing, while the tandem trunk group provides flexible traffic routing. The local exchange, which accepts the call request, is called the originating exchange and the exchange serving the "called party" is known as the terminating exchange.

The transmission facility used to connect Plain Old Telephone Service (POTS) to the local exchange is called a loop or a line. Loops are typically analog in nature. In addition to voice applications, the loop is often used to serve PC data transfer via modem. The direct trunk and the tandem trunk (group) are typically digital trunks. The transmission facility connecting a PBX to the local exchange office is called a PBX trunk or a "tie trunk". The local exchange office houses switching machines, transmission equipment such as analog-to-digital converters (pulse code modulation), multiplexers, and Digital Cross-connect Systems (DCSs). Another type of transmission equipment, regenerators, are usually deployed along the transmission path.

The local exchange office can also serve a cellular network by connecting to a Mobile Switching Center (MSC), which serves one or more cell sites (base stations). The cell site communicates with mobile stations or handsets via airlinks. In this type of application, a network consisting of local exchanges, tandem exchanges, PBXs, etc. is referred to as a landline or wireline network. In contrast, the network consisting of mobile switching centers is called a cellular or wireless network. The roaming, call delivery, and handoff (handover) functions are performed by the MSC, not the local exchange.

For toll connections, a communications network is configured as trunk exchange network, which consists of at least two (or more) local exchange offices and several trunk exchange offices (Figure 10-67). The trunk connecting the local exchange office to the trunk exchange office is known as the "toll-connecting trunk", or the access trunk group. The trunk connecting two trunk exchanges is called the "exchange trunk" or "inter-toll trunk". The capacity of an exchange trunk is typically larger than that of an access trunk. For example, a commonly used access trunk has a capacity of 24 voice channels in North American digital networks (see Chapter 6). The capacity of an exchange trunk is typically 672 voice channels (carried by a DS3 signal), or up to 24,192 voice channels (carried by an FT-G signal). A long-distance call in North America typically involves three trunk exchanges, in addition to the originating and terminating exchanges.

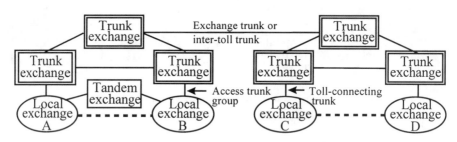

Figure 10-67   Trunk Exchange Offices.

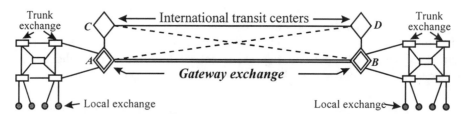

Figure 10-68   The Gateway Exchanges.

Gateway exchanges and an international transit center are used to interconnect networks from two different countries (see Figure 10-68). The most important functions of a gateway exchange is protocol conversion. For example, from the physical layer viewpoint, the gateway must perform (1) traffic concentration, (2) μ-law to A-law conversion (and vice versa), and, (3) 24-imeslot to 32-timeslot conversion (and vice versa).

Typically an international call is served by two gateway exchanges using direct routing. However, if direct routing is not possible, the call must be routed through one or more international centers, known as transit centers. For example, consider a call from Tokyo (Japan) to London (UK) (see Figure 10-69). It requires a gateway exchange in Japan, shown as the originating gateway exchange. The call enters the North American digital network at an exchange in Hawaii, which is the international transit center (i.e., transit gateway exchange) for performing gateway functions. Before the call leaves the North American digital network (e.g., from New York City), the gateway functions must be implemented again before leaving the transit gateway exchange in New York City. Finally, the call reaches London, the terminating gateway exchange.

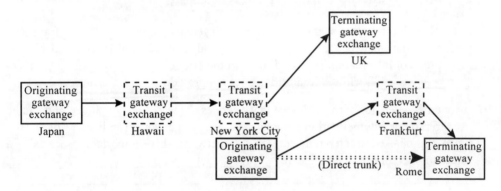

Figure 10-69   Two Examples of International Connections.

Another example is a call to Rome that originated in New York City may be routed via Frankfurt. There is a gateway exchange (originating) in New York City and a gateway exchange (terminating) in Rome, but the exchange in Frankfurt is an international transit center (transit gateway exchange).

The signaling network (e.g., SS7) used to perform call-related functions required for this type of international call was described in Chapter 4. The electronic switching machines used in the gateway exchanges, toll exchanges, and local exchanges were described in Chapter 5. Transport related equipment and facilities were described in Chapter 6.

Review Questions II for Chapter 1:

(12) Many organizations must support more users on their Local Area Network (LAN), and accomplish this by adding another segment to an _____ or another _____ LAN to the existing LAN.

(13) (True, False) Under any circumstance, a LAN has no need to be connected to a Wide Area Network (WAN).

(14) The ability of a system to transfer an application running on one station to another, via a connected network, is referred to _____.

(15) A LAN bridge operates at the _____ layer. It is used to _____ frames or packets of data between two _____. Logical Link Control (LLC) and higher-layer protocol information is passed through the bridge _____ (i.e., "protocol _____"). However, a bridge does not provide _____ control.

(16) A router is a general-purpose device that operates at the _____ layer, and can be used to provide internetworking among _____ networks (unlike a bridge). But, it can also be used to interconnect _____ networks. Five important issues using a router to interconnect networks are: _____, _____, _____, _____ and _____.

(17) A gateway used in LAN interconnection must operate at _____, and may be responsible for connecting _____ _____ networks.

(18) Besides bridges, routers, and gateways there are two types of hybrid devices used for LAN interconnection. A _____ is a combination of a _____ and a _____; and a _____ is a combination of a _____ and a _____.

(19) Network Operating System (NOB) performs several functions: _____, _____, _____, _____, _____, etc. These functions are provided by _____ and supported by _____.

(20) A LAN server is a LAN node that is dedicated to a particular type of _____. The commonly seen servers are: _____, _____, _____, _____, _____ and _____. The five primary subsystems of NOB server are: _____, _____, _____, _____ and _____.

(21) LAN network management has one basic goal: "To support _____ and _____ operation of LAN communication systems". This goal is often divided into five areas: _____, _____, _____, _____, and _____ management.

(22) There are many factors that influence future LAN development trends. Customers are demanding that LANs become: _____, _____, _____, _____, _____, _____, _____ etc.

Appendix 10-1

Wireless LAN and In-Building Networks

The technologies used for wireless Local Area Networks (LANs) and "in-building" wireless LAN applications are described in this appendix. The rational for wireless LANs and the advantages/limitations of wireless LANs are also presented.

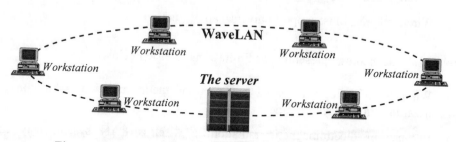

Figure 10A-1   A Wireless LAN: A Server and Workstations.

10A.1 Rational, Requirements, and Limitations of Wireless LANs

Most LAN applications are located in metropolitan business districts and industrial parks. The rapid changes in communication technologies has resulted in constantly changing office environments. Reconfiguration of office buildings has become a routine activity for moderate to large companies. A majority of the wire and/or cable communication systems (including LANs) have been installed in buildings for many years. It is difficult and expensive to change cable configurations. Walls must opened for rewiring, and the physical building often requires extensive changes. Wireless LAN technology clearly has an advantage with respect to flexibility and reconfiguration. For existing "old buildings", especially masonry structures, the expense of reconfiguring communication systems can be prohibitive. In some cases, the expense of re-cabling can be as great as the costs of the new telecommunications/computer hardware and software.

The issue of transmission speed has led the communications industry, specially data processing, to invest in wireless LAN technologies. Optical fibers, and wired LANs presently operate in the range of 20 Mbps. For example, Ethernet can support data speeds up to 10 Mbps, and token-rings can provide speeds up to 16 Mbps. It is expected that wireless LANs will eventually support data speeds up to 100 Mbps.

Corporate employees with notebook computers are the biggest potential users of wireless LANs. Field auditors who pull together LAN workgroups for short-term situations are another category of wireless LAN users. In some applications, robots that communicate with controller(s), or each other, utilize wireless LAN technology. The **requirements** for wireless LAN technologies are listed as follows:

- Wireless LANs must be easy to install, re-locate, and operate.

- Wireless LANs must be able to co-exist with wire, cable, and optical fiber LANs.

- Wireless LANs must provide equivalent (or greater) data speeds with respect to the technology being replaced.

- Wireless LANs must be reliable.

- Wireless LANs must be cost effective.

- Wireless LANs must support universal applications.

Wireless LAN technology presently has **limitations**, as listed below:

- Wireless technology is based on electromagnetic radiation, which may be hazardous in work environments.

- Because of electromagnetic radiation, a wireless LAN system may cause interference in other systems. Similarly, other equipment may introduce interference in wireless LANs. If the external interference is severe enough, it may " blank out" the wireless LAN signals.

- Line of sight limitation: Although wireless LAN transmission is multi-path transmission (see Chapter 8), the direct path is the most important signal. If infrared technology is used, stringent line of sight physical limits are imposed on the wireless LAN system.

- Wireless LAN technology has distance and/or range limitations. These limitations are affected by many factors: line of sight, transmission path barriers, environmental changes, and weather (atmospheric) variations.

- Wireless LANs require special "software drivers" to function properly. The development of proprietary software often leads to proprietary hardware, and higher system costs that may prevent wide acceptance/deployment.

- Wireless LAN technology development is still in its early stages. Present costs are considerable, and users may not accept newly developed technology until field trials have confirmed their expectations.

- A serious limitation is available data speed. If "spread spectrum" or "infrared" technology is applied, present data speeds are not fast enough to support customer applications. It is believed there is a great potential for speed improvement in wireless LANs, especially for Wireless In-building Network (WIN) applications.

10A.2 Wireless LAN Technologies

In additional to the technologies previously described in this book [e.g., radio transmission, modulation, demodulation, and multiplexing for cellular and mobile communications], other technologies are used for wireless LAN applications. These technologies are spread spectrum, narrowband microwave, and infrared techniques. They are described as follows:

- **Spread spectrum technology**: The principle of spread spectrum, which has been employed in Code Division Multiple Access [CDMA; specified in Interim Standard (IS)-95] systems, is described in Chapter 8. The difference for wireless LAN applications is the frequency spectrum that is used. The proposed frequency range for wireless LANs is between 300 MHz and 3 GHz.

  The principle of spread spectrum technology is to "spread" (distribute) the data information that originates from a small frequency range into a much wider frequency range that is used for radio transmission. The result of frequency spectrum spreading is a unique *waveprint*. This waveprint can only be decoded by equipment that "understands" the spreading algorithm implemented by the transmitter. Likewise, the receiver always requires a "special key" to decode the spreading algorithm, and restore the original data bit stream.

  This technology was first developed during World War II for military applications that required high security. Spread spectrum equipment was essential to prevent eavesdropping, and is still used for anti-jamming applications in modern military systems.

  The FCC has selected several frequency bands for spread spectrum and other wireless applications. The commercial frequency bands that are assigned for wireless data communications are:

  * 902 MHz to 928 MHz
  * 2.4 GHz to 2.4835 GHz
  * 5.725 GHz to 5.85 GHz

  In addition to frequency band assignments, the FCC also regulates the *low power requirements* for commercial wireless systems. In particular, for wireless data systems, the power level is limited to 1 watt maximum. This in turn limits the coverage radius to about 800 ft. Besides bandwidth availability and distance limitations, the present spread spectrum technology can only transmit data bit streams up to about 2 Mbps. It is expected that spread spectrum technology will improve coverage distances and transport speeds in the future. An example of a wireless LAN that uses spread spectrum technology is Lucent's WaveLAN (described later in this appendix).

- **Narrowband microwave technology**: This technology utilizes a different frequency spectrum, from 18 GHz to 19 GHz, which the FCC has designated as the Digital Terminal Service (DTS) band. These frequencies are in the low to moderate microwave frequency range (see Figure 8-1 in Chapter 8 for major frequency band assignmenets).

Because of its higher frequency range, this technology can be applied to develop a virtually "interference free" system. In addition, spectrum re-use is less complicated in this frequency range than in lower (more crowded) ranges. The result is that systems can transmit data at much higher rates. Typically rates of 15 Mbps are available, and higher rates (e.g., 100 Mbps) may be achievable in the future.

Narrowband microwave technology has several disadvantages. First, the signal can be easily blocked by high-rise buildings/structures. The result is signal attenuation, which limits the coverage distance. Second, multi-path problems are more severe at higher frequencies. Therefore, sophisticated equalizers must be applied, and this increases equipment costs. Finally, strict regulations must be imposed because of high data rates, and the need to insure efficient frequency re-use. One example of a wireless LAN using narrowband microwave technology is Motorola's WINs (Wireless In-building Networks, described later in this appendix).

- **Infrared technology**: The infrared spectrum has a wavelength higher than 700 nm (0.7 μm; the wavelength of the color "RED"). For wireless infrared LAN applications, the proposed frequency is 3.75×10^{14} Hz (a wavelength of $\lambda = 0.8$ μm; where $\lambda \times f = c \approx 3 \times 10^8$ m/s).

Infrared technology offers many advantages, compared to lower frequency radio, as a medium for wireless LANs. First, infrared equipment designed for this frequency spectrum is practically immune to electrical interference, and is not hazardous to humans or the environment. Second, this high-frequency spectrum is presently not subject to FCC regulations, thus abundant bandwidth is available. Therefore, the technology can use different subcarrier frequencies for uplink and downlink transmissions to avoid interference. Third, because very high frequencies are used, infrared technology allows system to use smaller and less expensive components [e.g., light emitting diodes (LEDs) instead of multi-mode, single-mode, or single frequency lasers] to implement networks and equipment. This also insures low power levels.

Infrared technology has another fundamental characteristic. *The infrared signal can be reflected from a mirror, and will pass through glass*. Therefore, infrared systems can utilize mirrors as relay stations to overcome limited "line of sight" conditions. Some modern buildings use glass walls to divide offices, hence infrared signals can pass through these glass walls. Therefore, the requirement of "line of sight" can be met, in situations when glass walls are part of the physical transmission path.

A disadvantage of infrared technology is that the signals can not penetrate **dense materials**. Thus, transmission of infrared signals require "line of sight", conditions which limit the coverage distance. However, this disadvantage (under certain circumstances) can be used to provide security, and reduce the effect of interference. That is, if solution is implemented to overcome this disadvantage, it then becomes a positive for infrared technology.

Table 10A-1 summarizes and compares three technologies: (1) spread spectrum; (2) narrowband microwave; and, (3) infrared. The parameters used for comparison are frequency spectrum, data rate, coverage distance, line of sight requirement, transmitted power, etc.

Table 10A-1   Wireless LAN Technology Comparison.

Parameter	Spread spectrum	Narrowband microwave	Infrared
Frequency spectrum (GHz)	*0.902~0.928* *2.000~2.483* *5.725~5.825*	*18.825~19.205*	*375,000*
Data rate	*2 Mbps*	*15 Mbps*	*4/16 Mbps*
Typical coverage distance	*100~800 ft* *(≈ 50,00 ft²)*	*40~130 ft* *(≈ 5,00 ft²)*	*30~80 ft* *Linear/reflective*
Line of sight	*Not required*	*Not required*	*Required*
Transmit power	*< 1 watt*	*25 mW*	*Variable*
License required	*No*	*Yes*	*No*
Interbuilding use	*Possible*	*No*	*Possible*
Usage comparison	*Most common*	*Motorola*	*Fairly common*
Wired LAN bridge	*Yes*	*Yes*	*Yes*
(Product) Vendors	** Lucent(1)* ** CA Microwave Inc.(2)* ** O'Neill Comm. Inc.(3)* ** Telesystems SWL(4)*	** Motorola(5)*	** BICC (6)* ** Photonics(7)*

Notes on Table 10A-1:

(1) Lucent's WaveLAN   (2) CA Comm's RadioLink;   (3) O'Neil's LAWN   (4) SWL's ArLAN
(5) Motorola's Altair   (6) BICC's InfraLAN   (7) Photonics Corp.'s Photolink

10A.3 Wireless LAN Systems

The wireless LAN products listed in Table 10A-1 (e.g., Lucent's WaveLAN) are described and compared in this appendix.

Example 10A-1: (Spread spectrum technology) Lucent's WaveLAN (Figure 10A-2).

- The characteristics and features of Lucent's WaveLAN system are given as follows:

   * Spread spectrum technology; frequency band: 902 ~ 928 MHz

   * Optional data encryption; uses Data Encryption Standard (DES)

   * Compatible with MS-DOS and OS/2 operating systems

   * Date rate: 2 Mbps

* Coverage distance:

  ◆ 400 ft radius using an omni-directional antenna
  ◆ (Optional) 5 miles line of sight using a directional antenna

* LAN OS/Manager supported by:

  ◆ Novell NetWare 2.X and 3.X
  ◆ LAN Manager and TCP/IP through Network Driver Interface Specification (NDIS)
  ◆ NetWare Requester for OS/2

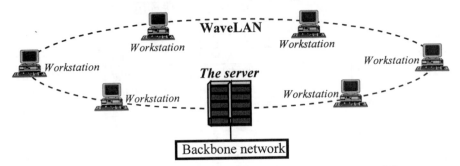

Figure 10A-2   Lucent's WaveLAN Wireless LAN: Using Spread Spectrum.

* The WaveLAN product set consists of the following components:

  * Network Interface Card (NIC) - The NIC includes an RF modem, and host adapter
    with two sockets for optional programmable features [i.e., boot ROM and security
    data encryption standard (DES)]. An NIC functions as the host (PC)
    communication adapter.

  * WaveLAN software - This software comes with the NIC, and includes the LAN
    driver and configuration utility programs. The LAN driver works in conjunction
    with the network operation system, and allows the PC to function as either a
    network server or a workstation. The current network driver interfaces supported
    by WaveLAN are: (1) Network Driver Interface Specification (NDIS), and (2)
    Internetwork Packet eXchange (IPX) protocol.

  * Network utilities - The present set of utilities contain menu-driven diagnostic routines.

  * Antenna system: an omni-directional antenna and cable are provided.

  * Optional features -There are several optional features, listed as follows:

    ◆ Data Encryption Standard (DES; for security).
    ◆ Boot ROM (allows the NIC to be used as a "diskless" PC).
    ◆ Antenna extension cable (improves signal transmission distance).
    ◆ Directional antenna (increases coverage distance to 5 miles).

- WaveLAN security: Security for WaveLAN can be provided at a level that is better than a typical wired LAN. WaveLAN has three levels of security, described as follows:

(1) The first security level spreads data over a frequency spectrum - User information is spread, in a scrambled manner, across the frequency spectrum. The WaveLAN signal is transmitted at low power (< 1 w). Using spectrum spreading and a low power transmission, a signal transmitted on WaveLAN resembles hidden background noise. Intercepting the signal requires very sensitive equipment, a frequency spectrum analyzer, and technical knowledge of frequency spreading. Frequency spreading also makes the WaveLAN signal difficult to jam.

(2) The second security level is network identification - Each WaveLAN has its own network ID, which is not known by outside users.

(3) The third security level is an optional DES - WaveLAN provides the ability to encrypt and decrypt user data in accordance with DES standard.

Table 10A-2   Wireless LAN Product Comparison.

	WaveLAN	**Photolink**	**Lawn**	**Altair**	**ArLAN**
Line of sight	*No*	*Yes*	*No*	*Yes*	*No*
Coverage (ft)	*800*	*70-600*	*100-500*	*130/cell*	*500-1000*
Security	*Yes*	*No*	*Proprietary*	*Yes*	*Proprietary*
Bit rate (kbps)	*2000*	*1000*	*38.4*	*5700*	*1000*
Novell support	*Yes*	*No*	*No*	*Yes*	*Yes*
LAN manager support	*Yes*	*No*	*No*	*Yes*	*No*

- WaveLAN competition: WaveLAN technology competes with both wired LANs and other wireless LANs.

  * Wired LANs - Two common wired LANs are Ethernet and Token-Ring LANs. These technologies stress standardized protocol, lower initial costs, high reliability, and (presently) higher speeds.

  * Wireless LANs - Table 10A-2 (in addition to Table 10A-1) provides a comparison between WaveLAN and other wireless LANs.

Example 10A-2: (Spread spectrum technology) California Communication's microwave radioLINK, is marketing its Radiolink system for applications requiring asynchronous communications up to 38.4 kbps. This system utilizes the spread spectrum technique in the frequency range of 902 MHz to 928 MHz. Main characteristics are:

- Applications: Supports traditional LAN applications.

- Protocol support: RS-232C (async/sync), RS-485, V.35, X.21 bis, 802.3, and AppleTalk.

- Distance coverage:
  * Line of sight - 5 miles
  * Office building - 800 ft
  * Dense building - 500 ft

- Transmit power: 1 watt (peak power).

- Signal rate: 38.4 kbps (planning 64 kbps for future offerings).

- FCC license: Not required.

- Strengths: secure and easy to install.

- Limitations: Speed constraints and interference possibilities.

Example 10A-3: (Spread spectrum technology) O'Neill Communications' Local Area Wireless Network (LAWN). This system utilizes the spread spectrum technique in the frequency range of 902 MHz to 928 MHz. The main characteristics of this system are:

- Applications: It supports file transfer, peripheral sharing, and e-mail.

- Protocol: It supports AX.25 (X.25 for radio).

- Distance coverage:
  * Inside building - 1000 ft
  * Unobstructed in space - 5000 ft

- Transmit power: 20 mw.

- Signal rate: 38.4 kbps.

- FCC license: Not required.

- Strengths: inexpensive.

- Limitations: Not compatible with NetWare and other LANs. Can communicate with only one other network simultaneously.

Example 10A-4: (Spread spectrum technology) Telesystems SLW's ArLAN 440/450. This system utilizes the spread spectrum technique in the frequency range of 902 ~ 928 MHz. The main characteristics of this system are:

- Applications: It supports wireless PC LANs, mixed combinations of wireless and cable LANs, PC-to-host connections, and network-to-network bridges.

- Protocol: It supports Ethernet/IEEE802.3.

- Distance coverage:
  * Line of sight - 6 miles
  * Indoor/office - 500 ft
  * Open factory/warehouse - 3000 ft

- Transmit power: 1 watt (peak power).
- Signal rate: 230 kbps typical (1 Mbps max).
- FCC license: Not required.
- Strengths: supports up to 100 PCs per network.
- Limitations: Speed of network.

Example 10A-5: (Infrared technology: optical wavelength at 0.87 μm) BICC InfraLAN's. The main characteristics of this system are:

- Applications: It supports traditional LAN applications.
- Protocol: It supports ties to token-ring networks.
- Distance coverage: 80 ft between nodes.
- Transmit power: 50 to 100 mw optical power.
- Signal rate: 4 Mbps/16 Mbps.
- FCC license: Not required.
- Strengths: Minimal interference and inexpensive.
- Limitations: Typically requires a line of sight configuration.

Example 10A-6: (Infrared technology: optical wavelength about 0.8 μm) Photonics' Photolink's. The main characteristics of this system are:

- Applications: It supports traditional LAN applications.
- Protocol: It supports a protocol that is compatible with TOPS (Sitka), PhoneNET, LocalTalk, or RS-232 links (4 devices).
- Distance coverage: 7 to 600 ft.
- Transmit power: 25 mw.
- Signal rate: 1 Mbps.
- FCC license: Not required.
- Strengths: Secure, easy to install, and planning future 10 Mbps speed offering.
- Limitations: Supports only LocalTalk, current system is relatively low speed, affected by weather, and requires a line of sight configuration.

10A.4 Wireless In-Building Network (WIN)

The need for wireless in-building local area networks is growing rapidly, and narrowband microwave technology has been proposed/implemented to meet this need. Two other technologies, spread spectrum and infrared, can also be used for WIN applications. The requirements for designing this type of network are listed as follows:

- The network must be compatible with existing network interfaces and equipment (both physically and logically).
- The network must be installed, used and maintained efficiently.
- It must fit inside and be fully compatible with existing PCs.
- It must be transparent to existing operating systems and application software.
- It must conform to network management standards.
- The technology must have a way to compensate for intermittent signal-fading caused by moving obstacles, people, doors, etc.
- The network must provide high performance in all of the following areas -
  * Security
  * Reliability
  * Availability
  * Throughput
  * Short delay

10A-5 WIN Network Architecture

A Wireless In-building Network developed by Motorola, using narrowband microwave technology, divides the coverage area into microcells (Figure 10A-3 shows two microcells). Each microcell is controlled by a Control Module (CM: also called the Central Module), which uses a distinct carrier frequency for its coverage area. The coverage area is typically between 450 and 5000 m². The CM in each microcell controls several User Modules (UMs) which interface the user devices (e.g., PCs).

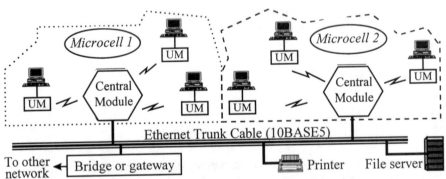

Figure 10A-3   Wireless In-Building Network (WIN) Architecture.

Motorola's WIN system utilizes 18 GHz radio with 10 MHz channels, and provides a data speed of 5.7 Mbps. The system is targeted for office, factory, and warehouse environments. Currently, there is one PC (workstation) per 10 m² in Motorola's typical Wireless In-building Network (WIN) system configuration.

There are other enhancements being developed for the narrowband microwave wireless local area network technology. Some examples are given as follows:

- **Six-sector intelligent antenna**: A 6-sector antenna is used to reduce co-channel interference, and achieve better system performance (this technique has been discussed in Chapter 8). This "intelligent antenna" can automatically select the best signal for individual data customers.

- **Gallium Arsenide Monolithic Microwave Integrated Circuit (GaAs MMIC):** This type of Integrated Circuit (IC) enables narrowband microwave technology to use miniature components for system designs. Presently the transceiver has been reduced to the size of a deck of playing cards, and further reduction is possible.

- **Integrated devices for packet switch and network interfaces**: This device (chip) allows the system to perform three levels of switching functionality including: (1) management, (2) organization, and (3) routing the high-speed data bit stream. It also ensures the integrity of the data stream. One million connections per second can be processed via this chip-based switching function.

- **High performance RF digital signal processor**: Used for data synthesis and data recovery. This signal processor is designed with specialized modulation and demodulation techniques that achieve a bit error rate of 10^{-8}.

10A-6 WIN Microcell, Control Module, and User Module

The narrowband microwave wireless LAN technology for in-building applications is based on the microcell arrangement (Figure 10A-3 shows two microcells). Microcells are the building blocks of the wireless LAN system. There are two components in each microcell: (1) the Control Module (CM), and (2) the User Module (UM). In one microcell, only one CM is required, but with many UMs.

- The main characteristics of a WIN microcell are described below:

  * Coverage area: Each microcell can cover an area between 450 and 5,000 m². The coverage varies with environment. That is, in areas with a large number of obstructions, 450 m² is the expected coverage.

  * Data speed: A traffic rate of 3 Mbps can be expected (i.e., 30 LAN devices can be supported by each microcell).

  * Separation of microcells: In order to minimize co-channel interface so that a specific Carrier-to-Interference (C/I) ratio performance can be achieved, each microcell operates at a different frequency. Frequency re-use is allowed, provided

the system performance criterion is met. Typical microcell separation is between 30 and 50 meters (i.e., between CMs using the same frequency).

It should be understood that a microcell cannot be used to connect two networks together [i.e., bridges, routers, or other gateways cannot be connected directly to a User Module (UM)].

- Control Module (CM): Each CM functions as a relay point (hubbing machine) that connects (1) the User Module (UM) to the CM, and vice versa; (2) the CM to the backbone network, and vice versa; and, (3) the UM to the CM, then to another UM. Note that a UM can not communicate directly with another UM, and all connections must be made via a CM. The CM provides different services such as allocating bandwidth for transmission of packets, filtering and routing packets in the microcell, and providing an interface to the "enterprise" network.

In addition, the CM constantly provides a steady stream of synchronizing signals throughout the microcell for timing coordination purposes.

- User Module (UM): The User Module (UM) is typically located on an office desktop (Note that control modules are normally placed in the ceiling of the building), and is connected to the end-user terminal equipment. A single UM handles up to six LAN devices (e.g. PC workstations, file services or printers; Figure 10A-3).

The control module and user module transmit and receive on the same frequency. That is, Time Division Duplex (TDD) [which is different from Frequency Division Duplex (FDD) technology] is used in WIN systems. The difference is shown in Figure 10A-4. For TDD, half of the time (known as a subframe; two subframes form one frame) is used by the control module to "talk" to the user module. During the other half of the time, the user module "talks" to the control module. Both transmission directions use the same frequency. In a FDD system, the communication from a CM to its UM, and a UM to its CM occurs during the same time interval (frame), however, two different frequencies are used.

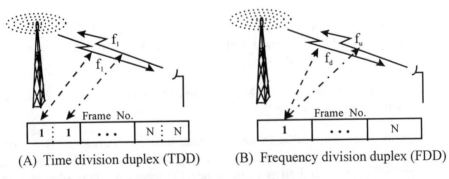

(A) Time division duplex (TDD)   (B) Frequency division duplex (FDD)

Figure 10A-4   Time- and Frequency-Division Duplex (TDD and FDD).

10A-7 Data Communication within a Microcell

Data communication within a microcell (or a control module) has the following major characteristics/features:

- Signal format: Data is packetized.

- Frequency and rate: The RF carrier frequency is 18 GHz, with a 10 MHz bandwidth. The basic data rate is 5.7 Mbps.

- Modulation/demodulation: Binary (basic) Phase Shift Keying (BPSK) techniques are used (see Chapter 6 for detail description).

- Multiplexing/demultiplexing: It applies Time Division Multiple Access [TDMA; discussed in Chapter 8, instead of Frequency Division Multiple Access (FDMA) or Code Division Multiple Access (CDMA)], in conjunction with Time Division Duplex [TDD; Figure 10A-4(A)].

  * Frame: Time is divided into frames. For this system, based on 500 frames per second for this type of system.

  * Subframe: A frame is divided into two equal length subframes. The first subframe is used for communication from the control module to the user module. The second subframe is used for communication from the user module to the control module.

- Procedure for a UM joining a microcell: When a user module wants to join a microcell it "listen" for control packets in order to "learn" the radio propagation environment. It "listens" to each of the six antennas to detect a control packet, and selects the one with the best signal quality (C/I ratio).

- Procedure for accessing a microcell: After the best path between the UM and microcell has been selected, four steps are performed for a UM to access the microcell:

  (1) The UM sends registration request information to the CM using an appropriate request slot.

  (2) The CM checks a restricted access table to insure the UM is permitted to access the system.

  (3) Upon validation, the CM notifies the UM of its permission status. Note that the CM will deny the permission if validation is not granted.

  (4) The registration request also tells the CM which antenna to use when attempting communication with this particular UM.

A request/grant protocol is used to assign time slots to all of the user modules within the microcell. Each UM will request transmission time from the CM when the UM receives packets sourced by one of the devices connected to its local LAN segment that are destined for a device located across the microcell. The data is then transferred from the UM to the CM by using the appropriate time slots.

10A-8 WIN Protocol Architecture

Wireless In-building Networks (WINs) utilize a two stack protocol (stack A and B), related to the OSI layers as shown in Figure 10A-5.

- Stack A protocol: The stack A protocol is used to manage and coordinate the interaction between a control module and its user modules within a microcell. This protocol is related to the aspects of system synchronization and control, along with the algorithms and protocols used for antenna selection and module registration. The stack A protocols are necessary and used in the radio environment, and radio protocols are inter-related.

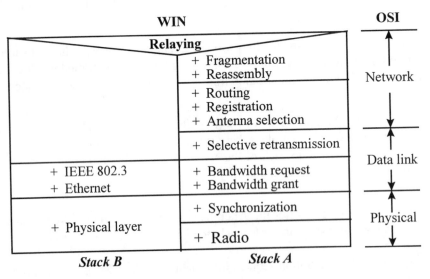

Figure 10A-5   WIN Protocol Architecture.

- Stack B protocol: The stack B protocol is used to transfer data within the microcell. This protocol handles Medium Access Control (MAC) and internetworking functions.

Example 10A-7: (Narrowband Microwave Technology) Motorola Altair Plus II uses a carrier frequency of 18 GHz with a bandwidth of 10 MHz, with major characteristics of:

- Applications: Wireless networking of PCs, printers, and terminals.

- Protocol: It supports the IEEE 802.3 and Ethernet.

- Distance coverage: 5,000 to 50,000 ft^2.

- Transmit power: 25 mw.

- Signal rate: 5.7 Mbps throughput.

- FCC license: Required.

- Strengths: It has a potential speed of 100 Mbps, implements (insures) security via data encoding, utilizes higher frequency (lower interference), and supports Simple Network Management Protocol (SNMP).

- Limitations: Uses proprietary technology that is not compatible with some network management system, directional antennas are required.

10A-9 Wireless LAN Standardization Effort

Presently there are no fully approved standards applicable to wireless local area network technology. However, there are many standardization activities progressing in different regions of the world. The three most active regions working on standards for wireless local area network technology are North America, Europe, and Japan. Their activities are briefly described as follows:

- North America: Two organizations are presently involved in these activities.

  * IEEE established a standards working group for wireless LANs in July, 1990. This working group is specifying IEEE 802.11 (see Example 10A-8).

  * ANSI T1P1 (October, 1990): The T1P1 subcommittee (a branch of T1 committee) is chartered with responsibilities for system engineering, standards planning, and program management of wireless networks (primarily for voice applications). Its first project is Universal Personal Telecommunications (UPT), which enables a user to access network services from any terminal (fixed or mobile).

- Europe [European Telecommunications Standard Institute (ETSI) and European Computer Manufactures Association (ECMA) joint committee]: This joint committee has established a charter for supplying the IEEE working group with European requirements for wireless LANs. The committee also coordinates European radio spectrum harmonization, and provides technical contributions toward the aim of implementing a worldwide standard for wireless LANs.

- Japan: Wireless technologies are one of the primary research in wireless fields in Japan, and four groups in Japan are particularly interested in wireless LAN technology:

* TTC of MPT: This council is responsible for frequency allocation, and has recommended the following -

  ♦ Frequency range 1,250 to 3,400 MHz for radio LAN systems.
  ♦ Frequency range 17.7 to 21.20 GHz for other services.

* RCR within MPT: This center is responsible for preparing the Japanese wireless standards.

* IEICE and MITI: These two institutions are the primary research organizations in Japanese wireless communications.

Example 10A-8: The IEEE 802.11 (Wireless LAN MAC layer standard) generated by the IEEE working group, is an open forum with international participation and broad interests.

The voting members are representatives for major computer vendors and user groups. The objectives of this working group are as follows:

* To study radio channel characterization.

* To encourage allocation of frequency bands to achieve global harmony (i.e., compatibility), elimination of end-user license requirements, and preferably (below 3 GHz) in accordance with the following recommended frequency allocations:

  *   902 to   928 MHz

  * 2,400 to 2,500 MHz

  * 5,725 to 5,875 MHz

* To establish appropriate standards for developing a single MAC that will work with a variety of physical media (including infrared technology).

* To introduce the standard to ISO.

* To develop conformance standards/requirements.

CHAPTER 11
TCP/IP: Voice & Fax over IP (VoIP & FoIP)

Chapter Objectives

Upon the completion of this chapter, you should be able to:

- Describe Internet Protocol (IP) historic milestones, (Transmission Control Protocol) TCP/IP standards organizations, and the Request For Comments process (RFCs; web site-http://www.isi.edu/rfc-editor).

- Describe TCP/IP architectures and services including: components of a TCP/IP network, TCP/IP protocol organization, TCP connection setup and release, Internet layer protocols, IP address, IP datagram structures, Internet Control Message Protocol (ICMP), and Address Resolution Protocol (ARP).

- Discuss TCP and User Datagram Protocol (UDP) including: UDP services, TCP services, TCP logical connections, TCP segment format, and TCP options.

- Discuss application layer protocols including: Domain Name System (DNS), Telnet, File Transfer Protocol (FTP), Trivial File Transfer Protocol (TFTP), Simple Mail Transfer Protocol (SMTP), Multipurpose Internet Mail Extension (MIME), Simple Network Management Protocol (SNMP), HyperText Transfer Protocol (HTTP), and Dynamic Host Configuration Protocol (DHCP).

- Discuss network interfaces including: Serial Line IP (SLIP), Point-to-Point Protocol (PPP), IP over SONET, IP over DIX Ethernet and IEEE 802 LANs, and IP over X.25 (frame relay). Describe "voice over IP (VoIP)", "fax over IP (FoIP)", Internet Telephone Service Provider (ITSP), internet integrated services, and associated ITU-T standards and standard documentation.

11.1 INTRODUCTION

The term Transmission Control Protocol/Internet Protocol (TCP/IP) refers to an entire networking technology based on a rich suite of communications protocols (i.e., in addition to TCP and IP protocols, dozens of other important protocols are involved). TCP/IP includes the following (widely/commonly used) applications protocols:

- File Transfer Protocol (FTP): This protocol is used by remote computers to transfer data files between each other.

- Telnet: This protocol is used to run interactive sessions in a remote computer system.

- Simple Mail Transfer Protocol (SMTP): This protocol is used to administer e-mail (electronic mail) services.

- Simple Network Management Protocol (SNMP): This is a network management protocol (detail description is provided in Chapter 12).

- HyperText Transfer Protocol (HTTP): This is a protocol used to access information via the World Wide Web (www).

TCP/IP is a dominant internetworking technology that allows multiple component networks (e.g., LANs and WANs) using diverse technologies (e.g., Ethernet, token ring, X.25, frame relay, and ATM) to be "*connected together*" via an *internet* (i.e., an interconnected network).

Applications processes, by appropriate use of the TCP/IP suite of protocols, can share files, exchange e-mail, carry out network management tasks, and support other communications facilities, with a high degree of transparency among computers that communicate via a TCP/IP-based internet connection.

The flexibility of the TCP/IP protocol allows it to be used in the global Internets, and many independent applications. The TCP/IP protocols are supported on several different hardware platforms and operating systems (e.g., most versions of Unix, DOS, Windows3.1, Windows95, Apple, Windows NT, IBM OS/2, and many other platforms). These protocols are specifically developed and refined to serve needs of the internet.

11.1.1 Historic Milestones

The first experimental packet switching network, known as "**ARPARNET**", began operation in 1969, and can be considered to be the start of TCP/IP technology. This project was funded by the Advanced Research Project Agency (ARPA or DARPA) of the U.S. Department of Defense (DoD). Initially the network had only four nodes, but later it developed into a network interconnecting research centers, military bases, and government sites. This experimental technology used the 56 kbps leased line services connecting switching nodes, and was designed for collaboration through e-mail and similar applications. These packet switching protocols eventually evolved into the "Internet" by using the TCP/IP protocols.

Later, DARPA contracted the engineering firm Bolt, Beranek, and Newman (BBN) to implement TCP/IP protocols for Berkeley Unix software and to provide the code with Berkeley System Distribution (BSD) of the Unix operating system. This seeded TCP/IP technology among universities and research centers by promoting Unix connectivity.

The introduction of the Ethernet Local Area Network (LNA) in the 1980s further encouraged the expansion of TCP/IP in both U.S.A. and Europe. The Wide Area Networks (WANs) in the U.S.A. and other countries were later connected to ARPARNET, which formed an international network known as "*The Internet*".

The TCP/IP protocol became an Internet standard in 1973. Although ARPARNET was dismantled in 1990, TCP/IP has continued to expand outside Internet applications. TCP/IP is still evolving to support new needs of the Internet and other applications. TCP/IP has experienced an explosive growth, with the number of hosts doubling every year since 1989 (the estimated number of hosts was over 200 million, and the estimated number of domain names was 32 million as of 1998). The number of web servers has also doubled about every 6 months since 1993 (the estimated number of web sites was 300 millions as of 1998).

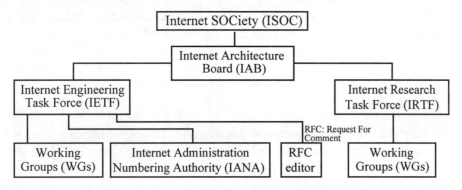

Figure 11-1   TCP/IP Standard Organizations.

11.1.2 TCP/IP Standards Organizations

The fact that there is no single point of control or promulgator of policy for the entire Internet has actually encouraged the success of the Internet. Each individual network within the Internet is free to tailor its policies to suit its own needs, as long as it cooperates to the extent needed to ensure network interoperability. With this approach, it is clear that only a minimal standards organization structure is required (see Figure 11-1).

This structure is provided by the Internet SOCiety (ISOC) and the Internet Architecture Board (IAB). The Internet Engineering Task Force (IETF) and the Internet Research Task Force (IRTF), both report to the IAB, and function as standard bodies working on Internet technologies. The IETF's responsibility is to coordinate the technical aspects of the Internet and its protocols, and ensure these protocols function effectively. In addition, the IRTF supports research on new and emerging technologies that have potential value to the Internet. It is the IAB that issues TCP/IP protocol standards and other documents which are widely disseminated to the vendor community. These documents are referred to as Request For Comments (RFCs), and this material is accessible (at no cost) via an Internet website.

The Internet Administrative Numbering Authority (IANA) is an organization under the IETF (Internet Engineering Task Force) that is responsible for setting and documenting various parameters, protocols identifications, and addresses (e.g., the port number) required for effective operation of TCP/IP protocols. The IP address (which is required for a network to be connected to the Internet) assignment is handled by the Internet Register (IR), which consists of the Internetwork Network Information Center (InterNIC) and its designated regional NICs. The NICs also deal with registering the names of the appropriate level domains of the Internet.

As previously mentioned, the official documentation pertaining to TCP/IP technology is primarily available in the form of Request For Comments (RFCs), even though not every RFC is a "**standard**". A RFC, which may be any topic relating to computer communications, is a working set of notes based on Internet research. Any document submitted to the appropriate task force for technical review can become a RFC, but it must be reviewed by the rules stated in "RFC 153". Once the document becomes an official RFC, a RFC number is assigned to the document. Revised/updated RFCs are assigned new numbers.

RFC are classified into two groups: "Standard track" and "Off track". Only RFCs that have the potential to become standards are placed under the Standard Track, and they must pass three states before becoming standard protocols: (1) proposed standard, which must be stable and well-understood by the Internet community, (2) draft standard, which must have at least two independent and interoperable implementations with sufficient operational experience, and (3) official standard. Once a RFC becomes an official standard, it can be accessed on many Internet web sites, such as

http://www.isi.edu/rfc-editor

A RFC in the "standard track" can be designed as: "required", "recommended", "elective", "limited use", or "not recommended".

11.2 TCP/IP ARCHITECTURE AND SERVICES

The logical components, and network configurations of an internet implementation are in the following sections. It is recommended that this material be reviewed first to form a foundation for understanding the TCP/IP protocol architecture.

11.2.1 TCP/IP Internet Components

The three major components (Figure 11-2) of a TCP/IP internet are the hosts, networks, and routers. The point-to-point link between the router and the host is also a network with devices connected to it. The frame relay switches do not have TCP/IP modules, and therefore have no role in IP level internetworking. The three components are briefly described as follows:

(1) Host: The hosts are computing systems, equipped with appropriate operating system software and other software, that either directly incorporate or can invoke TCP/IP modules. They are used by human operators to run network applications (e.g., connecting remote computers, sending/receiving e-mail, exchanging files, visiting web sites, etc.).

Since a host is connected to networks (e.g., LANs or WANs), or connected by point-to-point TCP/IP links, it requires suitable hardware or software interfaces using proper network-specific technologies. For example, a host on an Ethernet LAN is equipped with an Ethernet network interface card that applies the Ethernet CSMA/CD (Carrier Sense Multiple Access/Collision Detection; Chapter 10) protocol to send/receive Ethernet frames via the LAN. That is, using an IP module, allows hosts to send/receive packets via their network interfaces.
In general, a host is attached to a single network and has a single interface. However, there are cases when a host may need multiple interfaces. This type of host is called a "multi-homed host". A file server is a multi-homed host. Note that multi-homed hosts are not routers, because they do not forward datagrams. It only sends datagrams of its own, or receives datagrams for which it is the destination.

(2) Networks: The networks connected in an internet must be able to carry IP packets, but the details of how they operate internally are transparent to the IP software, hosts, and routers that exchange the IP packets. For example, assume the host "A" in an Ethernet is sending an IP packet to another host "B" on a different type of network (e.g., FDDI). The network interface card of host "A" on the Ethernet will send the IP packet "enveloped" in an Ethernet frame. Upon its arrival, the network interface card of host "B" receives this packet "enveloped" in an FDDI frame, and delivers the packet to the IP module in host "B". Thus, the IP module does not "worry" about the details of the individual network technologies (e.g., CSMA/CD, token passing, frame relay, X.25 or ATM). The networks connected to an internet can be any combinations of the following network types:

* LANs [e.g., Ethernet, token ring, and FDDI (Fiber Distributed Data Interface)].
* MANs [e.g., FDDI and DQDB (Distributed Queue Dual Bus)].
* WANs [e.g., X.25, ISDN, frame relay and ATM (Asynchronous Transfer Mode)].

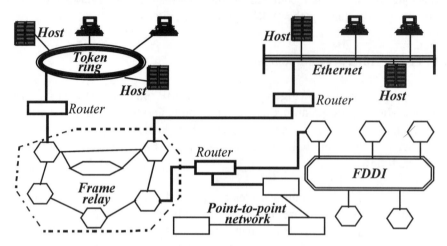

Figure 11-2   Components of a TCP/IP Internet.

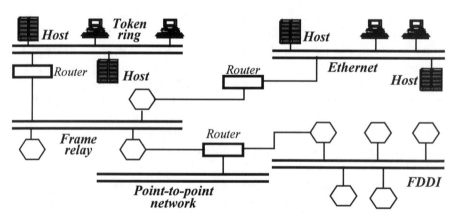

Figure 11-3   Logical View of a TCP/IP Internet (Figure 11-2).

(3) Routers: A TCP/IP router is a special computing system that is equipped with IP and related modules. A router can be equipped with multiple interfaces so it can be connected to two or more networks. The networks and their associated interfaces can use different technologies. A router is optimized to perform routing and forwarding functions (e.g., receiving IP packets via an interface, or using the address information in a packet to determine where it should be sent). That is, a router is a device that operates at the network layer, and can be used to provide internetworking among dissimilar networks.

Figure 11-3 illustrates a logical view of the internet shown in Figure 11-2. Each network operates like a "pipe" which accepts datagrams at one and delivers them to the other end. The systems, which perform IP processing activities (e.g., routers or hosts), are connected via these pipes. Two IP modules that are on the same pipe can exchange packets by using the pipe. The exact mechanism by which the datagrams move through the pipe is transparent to the IP modules. It is the network interface that is concerned with the details of this mechanism.

11.2.2 Internet Network Configurations

The networks interconnected by an internet can virtually be of any kind provided two characteristics are met: (1) the ability to carry datagrams, and (2) operating at a reasonable speed (9.6 kbps or higher). That is, point-to-point links, such as LANs, MANs, or WANs can be used transport media for the TCP/IP internet.

- Point-to-point links: Point-to-point links over leased lines, dial-up telephone lines, or ISDN telephone lines are popular methods by which internet access is made available to homes. Protocols such as Serial Line IP (SLIP) or Point-to-Point Protocol (PPP) are commonly used over these relatively low-speed lines. The High Performance Parallel Interface (HPPI) can also be used. For the higher-end of the speed spectrum, SONET/SDH facilities with a speed of 51.84 Mbps, 155.52 Mbps, or 622.08 Mbps, can be used to carry datagrams.

- LANs: TCP/IP transported over LANs are ubiquitous in the business world. That is, IP operating over LAN protocols are fairly common. For example, in a host/router attached to an Ethernet LAN (e.g., token ring, ATM, or FDDI), IP operates over the LAN driver which implements CSMA/CD or token passing protocols. These protocols, in turn, interface to the LAN media-specific physical layer protocols (e.g., 10BaseT, 100BaseT, etc.).

- MANs/WANs: IP hosts and routers may be connected to MANs (e.g., FDDI, DQDB, or SMDS). The networks can be X.25, ISDN packet-switched mode X.31, frame relay, or B-ISDB/ATM networks.

Definition 11-1 (Internet): A collection of networks that apply the TCP/IP suite of protocols to achieve internetworking and interoperability for the host components is called an internet, or a TCP/IP internet. However, "***the Internet***" is a specific internet that is a loosely-organized international collaboration of autonomous, independently managed, interconnected networks. The communication between the hosts of each individual network in the "Internet" is supported by voluntary adherence to the open protocols and procedures of the TCP/IP protocol suite. Most component networks of "the Internet" are TCP/IP internets, while the other networks may be internets that apply different internetworking protocols (e.g., the OSI suite of protocols).

11.2.3 TCP/IP Protocol Architecture

Figure 11-4 is a summary of TCP/IP protocol architecture. Since this protocol predates the seven-layer OSI reference model by about a decade, it doesn't coincide with the OSI model. The four-layer TCP/IP protocol architecture is briefly presented here, additional details are described in the following sections. *It should be understood that each layer makes use of the services provided by the immediate lower layer.*

Internet		OSI
Architecture	Protocols	
Application/Process Layer	DNS, FTP, HTTP, SMTP SNMP, Telnet	Layers 5, 6, and 7
Host-to-Host Layer	User Datagram Protocol (UDP), TCP	Layer 4
Internet Layer	IP, Internet Control Messsage Protocol (ICMP)	Layer 3
Network Interface Layer	PPP, 802.x, HIPPI, X.25, ATM Frame relay, SONET/SDH	Layers 1, 2, (and 3)

Figure 11-4   TCP/IP Protocol Architecture.

- Network interface layer: This layer (the lowest TCP/IP protocol layer) is responsible for communications between two devices in the same network. It uses network-specific technologies (e.g., PPP, 802.x, X.25, frame relay, HIPPI, SONET/SDH, or ATM). The protocols of this layer are not specified in the TCP/IP standards.

- Internet layer: This layer is concerned with the connectionless exchange of packets between hosts, via intermediate routers. It provides a "best-effort" datagram service without assurance of delivery or error control. The protocols associated with this layer are IP and Internet Control Message Protocol (ICMP).

- Host-to-host layer: This layer handles information exchange between hosts connected to the internet. It offers a choice for the higher layer to use either a reliable connection-oriented, end-to-end transport service using TCP, or a connectionless, "best-effort" delivery, end-to-end transport service using User Datagram Protocol (UDP).

- Application/process layer: This is an application or process layer, and the highest TCP/IP protocol layer. It allows different processes on separate host systems connected to an internet to support special applications (e.g., e-mail, file transfer, remote login and network management, etc.). The protocols used by this layer are Domain Name System (DNS), File Transfer Protocol (FTP), HyperText Transfer Protocol (HTTP), Simple Mail Transfer Protocol (SMTP), Simple Network Management Protocol (SNMP), and Telnet.

It can be seen, from Figure 11-4, that the internet Network Interface Layer corresponds to the OSI physical and data link layers (OSI layers 1 and 2). In some network technologies, the Network Interface Layer extends up to the OSI network layer (i.e., layer 3). The Internet Layer is equivalent to the OSI network layer (i.e., layer 3). The Host-to-Host Layer covers the OSI transport layer (i.e., layer 4), and a portion of the OSI session layer functionality (i.e., layer 5). The Application/Process Layer covers the OSI session layer, presentation layer, and application layer (i.e., layers 5, 6, and 7).

11.2.4 Transmission Control Protocol (TCP) Connection Setup and Release

Figure 11-5 illustrates the TCP connection setup process. As shown, two devices establish a logical connection to support the data stream exchange of information they received from their higher layer processes. During the connection setup phase, TCP applies a "connection-oriented" approach to build state tables (some "hand-shaking" occurs between two TCP processors) and exchange messages before exchanging actual application layer information. This setup phase typically involves two events and "hand-shaking" processes as follows:

(1)   The server "listens" for connection: The server process (assuming a service is running on host A) indicates its willingness to accept information from either a specific or unspecific client process.

(2)   The client is "opens" a connection: A client process (running on Host B) requests service (provided by the server of host A) from the server.

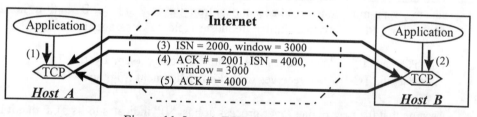

Figure 11-5   A TCP Connection Setup.

(3)   [Steps (3), (4) and (5)] During the "hand-shaking" setup process, the two TCPs exchange several state parameters:

•   A "window", each side informs the other about the number of bytes it is willing to accept. Typically, this number depends on the buffer capacity available at the host.

•   Each side determines where it will start numbering the bytes received from the higher layer process, and delivers this Initial Sequence Number (ISN) as part of the hand-shaking procedure.

•   Each side finally acknowledges the ISN received from other side.

These initial exchanges of TCP messages require three steps as shown by (3), (4) and (5) in Figure 11-5(A). After the connection setup phase being successfully completed, higher layer data can flow in messages with variable size bytes.

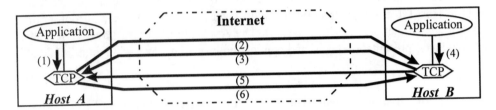

Figure 11-6   A TCP Connection Release.

Figure 11-6 [Note that steps shown in () in the figure corresponds to the following steps] is used to illustrate a connection release between two TCP modules. The sequence of events is described as follows:

(1)   The release is triggered by the higher layer process at one of the hosts (in this example, host A). It indicates to the TCP at "A" that it has finished sending all its data stream information, and requests to release the connection.

(2)   The TCP at "A" waits to ensure that all the data from its end, which is already in the pipeline, has been acknowledged. When the acknowledgement is received, it sends an appropriate control message indicating its desire to release the connection, to its peer TCP at host "B". Although the TCP at "A" no longer sends any more higher layer data to "B", it must continue to accept data from the TCP at host "B" until it (i.e., the TCP at host "A") receives a similar "request to release" message from host "B".

(3)   The TCP at "B" acknowledges the control message (sent by the TCP at "A"). Likewise, the TCP at "A" receives the acknowledgement from host "B".

(4)   Assume that the peer higher layer process at host "B" indicates to its TCP that it has also finished all its data transmission. After ensuring there are no pending acknowledgements to data that has already been sent, the TCP at host "B" sends a release connection control message to its peer TCP at host "A".

(5)   The TCP at "A" receives this message from host "B" and releases all its state tables and other information relating to this connection. The TCP at "B" waits to receive an acknowledgement to release its connection to host "A". Even if it does not receive the acknowledgement, it will still release the connection because it must purge all the information relating to this connection.

(6)   The release request is acknowledged by host "A", and received by host "B". Thus the connection between hosts "A" and "B" is completely disconnected..

Example 11-1 Describe the support for TCP/IP protocols that is offered in several popular implementations.

(1)   Since the beginning of TCP/IP, there has been a close coupling between TCP/IP and the Unix operating system. Therefore, it is natural that most support for the TCP/IP stack is available in Unix-based implementations. For example, Berkeley System Distribution (BSD) version 4.x of Unix, HP's HP-UX, IBM's AIX, DEC's Ultrix, Novell's UnixWare, SunSoft' SunOS & Solaris, and Santa Cruz Operation's (SCO) XENIX, all contain implementations of the Unix operating system support for TCP, IP, SMTP, and ARP.

(2)   IBM has developed products to support TCP/IP for mainframes using VM (Virtual Machine) and MVS (Multiple Virtual System) operating systems. They are known as TCP/IP for VM and TCP/IP for MVS.

(3)   Due to the popularity of PCs and LANs (i.e., the connection medium for PCs), many vendors have developed TCP/IP connectivity software for DOS, Windows, OS/2 and Macintosh devices. For example, FTP Corporation's PC/TCP, and Apple Corporation's MacTCP are examples of this type of software.

(4)   Network Operating System [NOS; a NOS is the software that gives the network its multi-user, and multi-tasking capabilities (see Figure 10-54; Chapter 10). It can be viewed that NOS is the "brain" of a LAN for determining the type of devices that can be deployed in the network, and arbitrates service requests from users]. It is clear that NOSs also support TCP/IP. Examples are Novell's NetWare, Bayan's VINES, and Microsoft's Windows NT.

11.3 INTERNET LAYER PROTOCOLS

The Internet Layer is the 2nd layer of the IP protocol (see Figure 11-4) which corresponds to the OSI reference model layer 3. The protocols of this layer is Internet Protocol (IP) and Internet Control Message Protocol (ICMP). The details of the Internet Protocol version 4 (IPv4) are described in this section (a newer version IPv6 is described later in this chapter). IN ADDITION, companion protocols of IP are also described, including Internet Control Message Protocol (ICMP), Address Resolution Protocol (ARP), Reverse Address Resolution Protocol (RARP), and Inverse Address Resolution Protocol (InARP). The problems these protocols are designed to address, the services they provide, their message formats, and their operations are all covered in this section.

11.3.1 IP Version 4 (IPv4)

The description of IPv4 includes: (1) the services provided by IP to higher layer protocols; (2) the interfaces between IP and the protocols that operate at the higher layer and at the lower layer; (3) The concepts of IP subnetting, subnet masking, and their applications; (4) the structure of the IPv4 address, and its use by routers and host to move the packets from a source device to destination devices; and (5) the IP packet format, including the header and the payload field.

11.3.1.1 Services Provided by IP

The "best-effort delivery" datagram (i.e., the basic information unit exchanged between IP entities is a *datagram*) is the basic service provided by the IP protocol entity to its higher layer entities. It is a "connectionless" packet-switching service. A datagram carries the full addresses of the sender (source) and the intended recipient (destination). Each datagram can be independently routed, by an intermediate device (e.g., a router), using the specified destination address information. When a source sends a sequence of datagrams to a specific destination, it possible that the path (i.e., router) followed by one datagram in the sequence is different than that of another datagram in the same sequence. That is, datagram may follow different paths through a network to reach the same destination.

IP does not provide mechanisms for dealing with lost packets, packets delivered out of sequence, or misinserted packets:

- If a datagram is corrupted by channel noise during transmission, it may contain an un-recognizable destination address, and an intermediate device may simply discard the datagram. This results in lost packet.

- Similarly, when a datagram is queued for processing by an intermediate device, if the buffer overflows, datagrams can be lost.

- Likewise, the destination address may be correct, but certain datagrams can arrive out of sequence because the transmission is "connectionless".

- If the destination address contains errors, it may be delivered to the wrong receiver (i.e., destination). This results in misinserted packets.

"It is the responsibility of the higher layer protocol
to deal with the problems described above."

Another service provided by the IP is multiplexing and demultiplexing IP packets onto different network layer interfaces. A device (e.g., a router) may be connected to more than one subnet, and can have a multiple network interfaces. An IP entity may be sending packets over several network interfaces, and may also be receiving IP packets from several interfaces. The routing tables and the destination addresses are used to determine which network interface packets are passed by the IP entity.

Multiple higher layers typically use the services of IP. For example, the TCP or UDP entity may be sending messages to the IP with a request to send. The IP uses a protocol identifier field to distinguish the IP packets that should be received by TCP,

UDP, or another higher layer protocol entity. The protocol ID enables the receiving IP to pass the "correct packet information" to the "appropriate higher layer process". This is a protocol level multiplexing/demultiplexing feature that is related to higher layer processing.

IP forward packets (datagrams) "hop" based on the routing tables, which are only locally significant. That is, between two adjacent network nodes, a unique routing table is used. The IP software performs error checking on the packet header, but not on the higher-layer information. If errors are detected, the datagram will be discarded. The IP software does not generate acknowledgements for datagrams that are successfully delivered, nor does it trigger requests for retransmission in the case of undelivered datagrams.

The IP service has the ability to fragment (segment) a packet into multiple independent packets so that it can be later reassembled to form "new packets".

Example 11-2 (TCP/IP): Describe the relationship between datagrams, byte organization, and transmission sequence.

A unique way of representing the items that make up a unit of information, which is transmitted between peer entities of that protocol, has been adopted by each protocol in the TCP/IP suite. Note that the unit of information is the same as the Protocol Data Unit (PDU) in OSI terminology.

The transmission sequence is organized so that the fields comprising the unit of information is always interpreted "from left to right", and "from top to bottom" with respect to the datagram. The transmission sequence of a byte, which represents the value of the field, is Most Significant Bit (MSB) first and Least Significant Bit (LSB) last. The value can be represented by decimal, binary, or hexadecimal code (symbol). For example, if a field has a value of 185 in decimal it can be represented as "10111001" in binary, or B9 in hex. The transmission sequence is "1", "0", "1", "1", "1", "0", "0", and "1". The practice of transmitting MSB first is often referred to as the "Big endian order"

11.3.1.2 IP Interacting with Higher Layer Protocols

"Higher level" processes, such as TCP and UDP, make use of the services of IP software to communicate with peer processes running on the other devices. The interaction between IP and the "higher-level" processes are defined by two service primitives: (1) the "send" service primitive, and (2) the "receive" service primitive.

When the Higher Layer Protocol (HLP) requests that IP send a "message" , the HLP uses the "SEND" service primitive. Likewise, the IP delivers the "message" to the appropriate HLP by using the "RECV (receive)" service primitive. Both primitives have several parameters as shown in Figure 11-7. These parameters are described in a later section of this chapter.

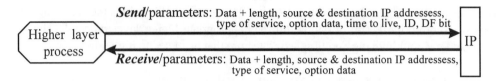

Figure 11-7   Interaction between IP and Higher Layer Protocols (HLPs).

11.3.1.3 IP Address

The IP address for IPv4 is a field of 32 bits, which identify the interface of a device to a subnet. An IP address does not identify the device itself (i.e., it is different from an Ethernet MAC address which identifies the device itself). Therefore, if the device is connected to two subnets, it requires two IP addresses (one associated with each interface). If a device is moved from one subnet to another, the IP address used to access the device must be changed accordingly. There are four parts in the 32-bit IP address: (1) the class bits (there are four different classes of IP address), (2) network identification bits (net-id), (3) subnet identification bits, and (4) host identification (host-id) bits. The network id and the host id are briefly described as follows:

- Network id (net-id): It identifies a network component of the internet. For those networks connected to the global Internet, the network id is uniquely assigned and administered by a centralized authority (organization). In any internet (even those not connected to the global Internet), the net-id value must be unique for all the subnetworks (subnets).

- Host id: (host-id) It identifies the network interface of the IP to the associated network. It is typically assigned and administered by the local administrator of the network. The host-id value must be unique within a subnet, but the same host-id values may be used repeatedly in different subnets. The concept of "subnetting" allows a single network id to be used for several subnets by dividing the host-id into:

  * A subnet id: The most significant bits of the host-id are assigned (as the subnet id), to identify the subnet.

  * A host id: The remaining bits are used to identify the host that belongs to the subnet (i.e., identified by the subnet id).

To accommodate subnets of various sizes, the IP address structure defines five classes of address for IP4v protocols (four of them are shown in Figure 11-7), described as follows:

(1) Class A: This class of addresses are used in large network. One bit, "0" is assigned to indicate the class type. Seven bits are used for net-id, and the host-id has a length of 24 bits as shown in Figure 11-8(A).

(2) Class B: This class of addresses are used in medium size networks. The class is indicated by two bits "10". The net-id requires 14 bits, and the host-id occupies 16 bits (a total of 32 bits for the address field) as shown in Figure 11-8(B).

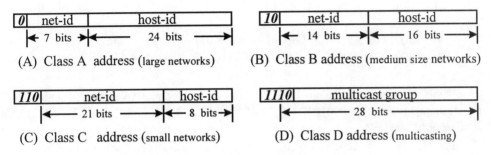

Figure 11-8   Four Classes of IP Address.

(3) Class C: This class of addresses are used in small size networks. The address field consists of a 3-bit class value "110", a 21-bit net-id, and an 8-bit host-id.

(4) Class D: This class of addresses are used for multicasting. The class is indicated by four bits "1110". There are 28 bits used to identify the multicast group. Note that there is no distinction between network id and host id for this class.

(5) Class E: This class of addresses are reserved for future use, however, the class bits are assigned as "1111".

For most applications, the addresses fall into class categories A, B and C. The value of all "1s" and all "0s" are reserved, hence the number of possible valid network id's and host id's for each of the three classes are shown in Table 11-1 reflect this condition. For example, class B address have 14 bits assigned for the net-id. Therefore, the total possible net-ids is obtained as $2^{14} - 1$ (all "1s") $- 1$ (all "0s") = 16,382. Likewise, each net-id has 16 bits assigned for the host-id, thus, the total possible host-ids is obtained as $2^{16} - 1$ (all "1s") $- 1$ (all "0s") = 65,534. Finally, the total possible class B IP address is 16,382 × 65,534 = 1,073,577,988.

Table 11-1   Possible Valid Network-id's and Host id's.

Class	No. of Net-id's	No. of host-id/net	No. of addresses*
A	126	1,677,214	2,113,928,964
B	16,382	65,534	1,073,577,988
C	2,097,150	254	532,676,100
Total	2,113,658		3,720,183,052

* Some addresses are reserved for certain types of broadcasting when subnets are involved, but this calculation does not exclude the special broadcast addresses involving subnets.

Example 11-3: Explain the traditional IP address notation.

The 32-bit IP address field is divided into four bytes (one byte = one octet = 8 bits), and each byte is expressed as a decimal number in the range of (0 ~ 255). In this notation, the values of the four bytes are separated by dots. Two examples are shown as follows:

- 00001011 00000011 00000101 00100011 =   ***11.3.5.35***
- 10000011 00011000 00000100 00110011 = ***131.24.4.51***

Note that the relationship between binary and decimal values are: "00001011" = 11; "00000011" = 3; "00000101" = 5; "00100011" = 35; "10000011" = 131; "00011000" = 24; "00000100" = 4; and "00110011" = 51. Therefore, the first four bytes are "11", "3", "5", and "35. They are represented by using a "." (dot) between them as: 11.3.5.35.

11.3.1.4 IP Subnetting and Subnet Mask

There are several occasions when subnetting is essential. For example, when an organization decides to segment an existing LAN or add a new LAN to meet expanding needs (e.g., improving performance on an Ethernet), it does not have to go through the expense or delay involved with getting a new network-id assigned by the Internet Administration Numbering Authority (IANA). IP allows a network planner (administrator) to create and implement a flexible addressing structure that may have further levels of hierarchy within each of the three address classes (i.e., class A, B and C). To achieve this objective, the host id (as previously described) is divided into two parts: (1) the subnet id, and (2) the host id. The subnet id is used to identify multiple subnets within the subnet identified by the net-id value. An example of applying the subnet id is given in Example 11-3.

Class B net: 131.31.0.129

(1) Subnet id: ***0001***; IP: 131.31.16.129   (2) Subnet id: ***0010***; IP: 131.31.32.129

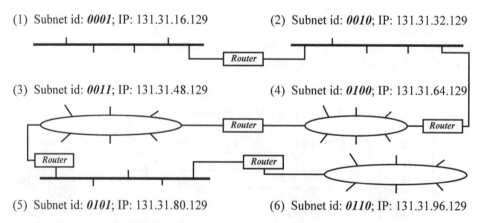

(3) Subnet id: ***0011***; IP: 131.31.48.129   (4) Subnet id: ***0100***; IP: 131.31.64.129

(5) Subnet id: ***0101***; IP: 131.31.80.129   (6) Subnet id: ***0110***; IP: 131.31.96.129

Figure 11-9   Class B Net: Net-id, Host-id.

Example 11-4: Illustrate the principle of IP subnetting, and subnet ids.

Assume the following: (1) an organization has a network connected to the global Internet, that has a class B address with a net id of 131.31 (i.e., **10**000011 00011111; where "10" identifies address class B, and "000011 00011111" for net-id) for its network; and (2) this organization has its own intranet (six in total). The subnet id assignment is administered as follows:

The network administrator may decide to allocate 4 bits of the 16-bit host id field of the IP address to identify the six intranets (even though 3 bits are enough for six intranet, one extra bit is allocated for future growth). The six subnet id are assigned as: "0001", "0010", "0011", "0100", "0101" and "0110". The remaining 12 bits (in this example, they are assumed to be "0000 10000001") of the host id are used to identify the interface of the hosts to each of these six subnets. The routers outside the intranet can regard the entire intranet as "one network" identified by the net-id 131.31. However, internal to this intranet, one or more routers that are connected to the global Internet separate the IP packets that are delivered to the single net-id, and send them to the appropriate subnets based on the first four bits of the host id. The subnets have the subnet ids shown in Table 11-2, and illustrated in Figure 11-9.

Table 11-2   IP Address (with subnet-ids) Example.

Subnet id	*IP address*			
(6 intranets)	Class	Net-id	Host -id	Decimal
0001	10	000011 00011111	*0001*0000 10000001	131.31.16.129
0010	10	000011 00011111	*0010*0000 10000001	131.31.32.129
0011	10	000011 00011111	*0011*0000 10000001	131.31.48.129
0100	10	000011 00011111	*0100*0000 10000001	131.31.64.129
0101	10	000011 00011111	*0101*0000 10000001	131.31.80.129
0110	10	000011 00011111	*0110*0000 10000001	131.31.96.129

Class B net** is assumed: **131.31.0.129

Definition 11-2: An subnet mask (associated with an IP address) is a mechanism used to isolate the portion of an IP address devoted to the identification of a network and subnet. A subnet mask consists of 32-bit field.

Hosts and routers apply the subnet mask to determine whether a destination IP address is on their subnet or not. The concept of a subnet mask is similar to the function of filtering. A host that does not know its subnet mask obtain it via an ICMP (Internet Control Message Protocol) broadcast message. The subnet mask is assigned as follows:

- The bit of subnet mask is set (= 1) for each bit position in the IP address that is part of the class, net-id, or subnet-id.

- The bit of the subnet mask is not set (= 0) for each bit in the IP address that is part of the "real" host id.

Example 11-5: Describe the IP addresses have been reserved for special purposes.

Several special (reserved) IP addresses are:

- **Net-id = 0 and host-id = 0**: If all the bits of the net-id and the host-id are set to "0s" [net-id = 0 and host-id = 0], the IP address is interpreted as "***this*** network", "***this*** subnet", and "***this*** host". That is, the IP address is interpreted as "This host (on this subnet) of this network". An IP address with an all "0s" can only appear as a source address, and never as a destination address in an IP packet. However, it may be applied by a host to send an IP packet when it does not know its own IP address (e.g., a diskless workstation that is being powered up and initialized).

- **Net-id = 0 and host-id = x**: It is interpreted as "Host x on this network". This application is only used for source addresses.

- **Host-id = –1 (i.e., host-id have all "1" bits)**: It is used for limited broadcast to either a specific network or subnet, depending on the net-id and subnet field. It can only be used as a destination address, not a source address. There are several applications available for this type of special address, described as follows:

  * Net-id = –1 and host-id = –1: The IP packet is limited broadcasted on this subnet.

  * Net-id = n and host-id = –1: The IP packet is directed broadcast to network "n".

  * Net-id = n, subnet-id = s and host-id = –1: The IP packet is directed broadcast to subnet "s" of network "n".

  * Net-id = n, subnet-id = –1 and host-id = –1: The IP packet is directed broadcast to all hosts on all subnets of network "n".

- Net-id = 127: It is used to perform a loopback test on a host to check the IP software. This address (which uses a net-id of 127 and any value in the remaining field) should never appear in an IP packet on any network or subnetwork.

11.3.1.5 IP Datagram Structure

Figure 11-10 illustrates the IP datagram structure, which consists of two parts: (1) the header, and (2) the higher layer data (payload). The header of the datagram is required to have a length $32n$ (n = an integer). The data (information) can be a variable number of bytes or octets. It does not require a multiple of 4 bytes as in the header, but must end at a byte boundary. The transmission sequence of the datagram is "from left to right", and "from top to bottom" with the MSB first and the LSB last. The header contains:

- **Version**: This 4-bit field represents the version of IP software that is being used. For example, the description given in this chapter is version 4 (IPv4), hence this "version" field contains the value "0100".

- **Header Length Indicator** (IHL): This 4-bit field is used to indicate the length of the header in multiples of 32 bits (4 bytes). The minimum and maximum values of IHL are 5, and 15 respectively, which correspond to a (20-byte minimum/60-byte maximum) header lengths ($4 \times 5 = 20$, and $4 \times 15 = 60$).

Header: 4n bytes	*Higher layer data: m bytes*			

32-bit wide

Version	IHL	Service type		Total length	
Identification			Flags	Fragment offset	
Time to live		Protocol ID		Header checksum	
Source IP address					
Destination IP address					
Options (0 to 40 bytes)				Padding	

Figure 11-10   IP Datagram Structure.

- **Service type**: This 8-bit field is divided into two subfields. The first 3 bits is called the "precedence" which is used to indicate the "priority" of the packet. The "priority" determine the queuing time for the packet. The remaining 5 bits are used to indicate the service type.

- **Total length**: This 16-bit field is used to indicate the total length (in bytes) of the IP datagram (header + data). Since it has a length of 16 bits, the maximum datagram size is 65,535 (= $2^{16} - 1$) bytes. However, most current/traditional networks can not handle this size. The standard requires that all hosts and routers support a datagram with a minimum packet size of 576 bytes.

- **Identification, flags and fragment offset**: These fields are used together to handle packet fragmentation and reassembly (described later in this chapter).

- **Time To Live** (TTL): This 8-bit field is used to indicate the maximum lifetime of the packet (expressed in seconds) in the internet. RFC-791 specifies that each router should decrement this TTL value by one (second) whenever the time spent in a queue at the router and the transit delay to the next "hop" is less than one second. Since the delay is relatively short and difficult to estimate, it has been recommended to no longer include delay in the standards. If the TTL value reaches zero, the packet should no longer be relayed, and is dropped. This condition typically occurs when a packet is looping, or incorrectly wandering in the internet.

- **Protocol ID**: This 8-bit field is used to indicate the type of higher layer protocol information being carried in the packet. The receiving IP (at the destination) uses this ID to pass the information to the proper process. The available (valid) protocol IDs are specified in RFC-1340. Some examples are given as follows:

* Protocol ID = 1 ⇒ ICMP (Internet Control Message Protocol)
* Protocol ID = 4 ⇒ IP in IP (encapsulation)
* Protocol ID = 6 ⇒ TCP
* Protocol ID = 8 ⇒ Exterior Gateway Protocol (EGP)
* Protocol ID = 17 ⇒ UDP

• **Header checksum**: This 16-bit field is used for checking transmission errors in the header. When errors are detected, the packet is dropped. The details of the header error checking process is explained in Example 11-6.

• **Source IP address**: This 32-bit field is the source address of the IP interface sending the packet.

• **Destination address**: This 32-bit field is the destination address of the IP interface which is the intended recipient of the packet.

• **Options**: This is a variable length field (0 to 40 bytes maximum) containing zero or more options (described later in this chapter).

• **Padding**: This field is used as a filler to ensure that the header ends on a 32-bit boundary.

Example 11-6: Describe the IP header error checking algorithm.

The IP checks errors on the datagram header only (i.e., not on the higher layer data). The mechanism used for the header checksum is adequate, but not as effective as CRC-32, which is typically used for LANs. Datagrams with detected errors are discarded.

One's complement (review): The 1's complement of a "bit string" is the same length, but the original value of each bit is inverted:

$$10101010\ 10101010 \xleftarrow{\text{1's complement}} 01010101\ 01010101$$

One's complement addition (review): Adding two bit strings using 1's complement arithmetic is performed by adding bit-by-bit (including the carry bit). Note that in the following example a "−" represents no carry bit. Finally, add the MSB carry bit is added to the sum, as shown below:

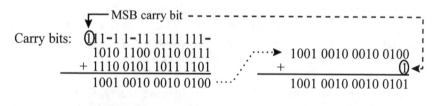

Therefore, one can obtain the 1's complement sum of "1010110001100111" and "1110010110111101" as "1001001000100101".

The header checksum is computed as "a 16-bit 1's complement of the 1's complement sum of all the 16-bit field in the header, after the checksum field itself has been zeroed". That is, the IP checksum computation adds up all the 16-bit fields of the IP header using the 1's complement, after "zeroing out" the header checksum field. If a receiving IP calculates a header checksum value that is different from the checksum in the datagram, this indicates an error has been detected.

11.3.1.6 IP Datagram Forwarding, Fragmentation and Reassembly

IP datagrams can be forwarded directly or indirectly. The network components of a network can transport information using different formats and sizes. Therefore, a device must be able to fragment an information unit (or packet) into another form that can be reassembled for transport to another network.

- Direct or local forwarding (of a datagram) by a system: An IP process checks the destination to determine if it is one of the subnets that it is directly attached to. This process requires that the subnet be identified for each IP interface. This can be established by performing a logical "AND" operation of the IP address of the interface with the subnet mask for that interface. The same logical "AND" of the subnet mask with the destination IP address will give the subnet associated with the destination. If the results of these two "AND" operations are equal for a certain interface, then the destination is the respective subnet. This is referred to as "*direct, or local forwarding*". That is, the network or subnet of the destination agrees with network of an interface of the system.

- Indirect forwarding: If the subnet of the destination IP address is different from the subnet associated with all the interfaces of the host or the router, then an indirect forwarding action must be used. That is, the IP must send the datagram to a neighboring router to reach the destination subnet. The routing is based on a table, which is required to permit a datagram to be connected to the next hop router.

Each network interface places restrictions on the maximum size of an IP datagram (or maximum packet size) that can be transmitted over the network. This size is called the Maximum Transmission Unit (MTU). The MTU value depends on the specific protocol and implementation. For example, the maximum frame size for a 100 Mbps FDDI can be up to 4,096 bytes, while for a 10 Mbps Ethernet the maximum frame size is up to 1,536 bytes.

The MTU for the interfaces of a router can be different. For example, a router might receive a packet size of 3,000 bytes, but the interface at the router output transmits a packet size of 1,000 bytes. Instead of discarding the incoming packet, the router splits the 3,000 bytes into multiple packets of appropriate size, and sends these newly-formed packets as separate datagrams to the output interface. This function is known as **fragmentation** or **segmentation**. It should be understood that these packets must be reformatted into a large packet before the information is passed to the higher layer. This function is called **reassembly**.

Three fields in the IP datagram header (Figure 11-10) facilitate the segmentation and reassembly process. They are: (1) **ID**; each packet is assigned an identification number by the source IP entity. When a packet is fragmented, each fragment carries the same ID number. The destination recognizes all the fragments carrying the same ID as a single packet. (2) **Offset**; this value indicates the position where a fragment's data starts (in increments of 6 bytes) with respect to the data content (byte position) of the original packet. (3) **MF** (More Fragment); if there are additional fragments to be received the MF bit is set to "1". If the fragment is the last one, the MF bit is set to "0". The structure of a fragment is the same as the original packet.

Example 11-7: Describe IP datagram fragmentation and reassembly process (Figure 11-11). Assume the datagram arriving at the router has a MTU of 3,000 bytes, the output interface of the MTU is 1,000 bytes, and the higher layer data has a length of 2,400 bytes.

In this example, the arriving datagram contains a higher layer data field of 2,400 bytes, a 20-byte header field, and has an ID = 2,005. Since the departing packet has a MTU of 1,000 bytes, it requires a three-segment fragmentation. All three fragments have the same ID of 2,005. The first two fragments have an MF = 1 while the last fragment has an MF = 0.

The first fragment carries data bytes 0 through 975 of the original 2,400 byte data. The header is 20 bytes in length. The total fragment length is 996 bytes, which is under 1,000 bytes. The MF (More Fragments) field = "1", and this first fragment has an offset = "0". Note that the offset is expressed in multiples of 8 bytes, thus a length of 976 bytes is the maximum data size fragment.

The second fragment is similar to the first, except the "offset" is 122 because 976 = 122 × 8 bytes. The second fragment carries bytes No. 976 through No. 1951, and MF = "1".

The third (last) fragment has an "offset" of 244 (because 1952 = 244 × 8) and carries byte No. 1952 through No. 2399. Note that the MF = "0" to indicate this is the last fragment of the data transport.

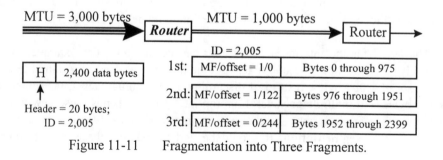

Figure 11-11   Fragmentation into Three Fragments.

The fragment reassembly is performed at the destination. As a connectionless protocol, different fragments may follow different paths to reach the destination. Therefore, intermediate routers do not attempt reassembly. A reassembly timer is associated with the overall process. When the first fragment arrives at the destination, the timer is started. If all the related fragments arrive at this destination before the timer expires, they are reassembled and a complete large packet of information is passed to a higher layer. However, if the timer expires before all the fragments are received, then reassembly is abandoned and buffers associated with the reassembly of the datagram with this ID are cleared. An ICMP (Internet Control Message Protocol) message is sent to the source, and the source is responsible for taking the appropriate action (i.e., re-send, ignore, etc.).

The fragmentation procedure is not always favored by network architects because of the potential problems it can cause. The most serious problem is that any one fragment that is lost may cause a higher layer to retransmit all the fragments. This is considered a waste of system bandwidth resources.

A second problem is that the host can not reuse the ID numbers during the "Time To Live (TTL)" period because the ID is used during fragment reassembly. There are 16 bits assigned for each ID, hence 65,536 distinct packets can be identified. If the TTL is assumed to be 2 minutes, then $65,536/120 \approx 546$. That is, the packet rate is 546 packets/s. Assume the packet size is 1000 bytes, then the speed of the system will be 4.368 Mbps (546 packets/second × 100 bytes/packet × 8 bits/byte = 4.368 Mbps), which is inadequate for many applications.

Finally, the host may encounter the problem of "buffer starvation". If a host is performing parallel reassembly from several interfaces, the buffers may be fully utilized for these reassembly activities. Therefore, the host may not have enough buffer space to perform any other activities.

The best solution for these problems is to minimize or eliminate fragmentation. A special algorithm is called path MTU discovery. A higher layer requires a strategy to "disallow" segmentation to be performed by using a "don't fragment" option that appears as a flag in the IP datagram header field.

11.3.1.7 IP Options

As shown in Figure 11-10, up to 40 bytes of the IP datagram (i.e., 0 to 40 bytes) are reserved for optional use. They were initially allocated primarily for network testing and debugging. All hosts and routers must process these options. The specifications for common options are described as follows:

- **Security and handling restrictions**: This option is used to carry - security, user group, compartmentation, and handling restriction codes. This is a fixed-length option.

- **Loose Source Route and Record** (LSRR): This option is used for routing IP datagrams, based on information supplied by the source IP about *some* intermediate routers in the path between the source and destination. This option has a variable length. Further details are provided in Example 11-9.

- **Strict Source Route and Record** (SSRR): This option is used for routing IP datagrams, based on information supplied by the source IP about *all* the intermediate routers in the path between the source and destination. This option has a variable length. Further details are provided in Example 11-9.

- **Record route**: This option is used to trace all the routers that a datagram has traversed from the source to the destination. This option has a variable length. Further details are provided in Example 11-10.

- **Timestamp**: This option is used to record the time at which each intermediate router along the path processed the datagram. This option has a variable length. Further details are provided in Example 11-11.

- **No operation**: This is a dummy option (one byte with the value "00000001") that is used between options to align the starting point of a new option on a 4-byte boundary.

- **End of option list**: This option is used to indicate the end of all options. If the end of the options is not coincide with the end of the IP header, padding is applied. This option has a fixed length.

Example 11-8: Describe the IP generic option format.

Figure 11-12 illustrates the generic format of an IP option field. There are three fields in the option field, and are described as follows.

(1) Code: This field is one-byte in length. The code field consists of three subfields.

      * Copy (C; 1 bit): When a datagram has not been fragmented the option must be copied into each fragment, and bit C = "1". If the datagram is already fragmented, the option is only copied into the first fragment, and bit C = 0.

      * Option Class (OC; 2 bits): If OC = 00 (a value of 0), this indicates the option is related to datagram or network control functions. If OC = 10 (a value of 2), this indicates the option is related to debugging and measurement functions. The codes CO = 01 and 11 are reserved for future use.

      * Option Number (ON; 5 bits): If ON = 00000, this indicates an "end of option list" option. If ON = 00001, it is a "no operation" option. If ON = 00010, it is a "security" option. If ON = 00011, it is a "Loose Source Route (LSR)" option. If ON = 00100, it is a "timestamp" option. If ON = 00111, it is a "record route"

option. If ON = 01001, it is a "Strict Source Route (SSR)" option. The codes ON = 00101, 00110, 01000, 01010, 01011, etc. are reserved for future use.

The "end of options" and the "no operation" option do not have the "length" and "option data" fields as shown in Figure 11-12. The options with variable lengths have the following two additional fields:

(2)   Length: This field is one-byte in length and is used to indicate the number of bytes for a specific option (including the option class), the length, and the option data field.

(3)   Option data field: This field may have a length of 1 to 18 bytes, and is specified by the particular option. For example, if it is a "record route", a "loose route", or a "strict route" option, the option data field contains a pointer and route data.

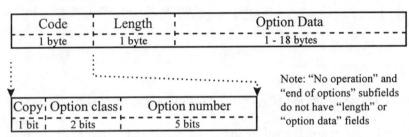

Figure 11-12   The IP Option Generic Format.

Example 11-9:   Describe the *Loose Source Route Record (LSRR) and Strict Source Route Record (SSRR) IP option*s.

The Strict Source Route and Record (SSRR) and the Loose Source Route and Record (LSRR) options are used by the higher layer process in the source host IP to control the route followed by the datagram to reach its destination. These options include a list of IP addresses called the source route. In the SSRR option, the source route describes the exact path of all the intermediate routers traversed to reach the destination. In the LSRR option, the source route includes some of the intermediate routers that must be traversed in sequential order, but the actual path taken by the datagram may also include other routers. The option format [Figure 11-13(B)] for the SSRR or LSRR option consists of:

• Option type (8 bits; shown as Code in Figure 11-13): For SSRR, this field is set to "10001001 (137)". For LSRR, this field is set to "10000011 (131)". In the case of fragmentation, the "option type" field is copied on all fragments.

• Length (8 bits): This field indicates the number of bytes in the option.

• Pointer (8 bits):This field identifies the byte number within the option where the next IP address that must be processed begins.

- Route data (variable length): This field has a maximum length of 36 bytes, and can contains up to nine IP addresses.

(A) A generic IP option format:

Code*	Length	Option data
1 byte	1 byte	1 - 18 bytes

* Also called option type

(B) An IP "record route" option format:

Code*	Length	Pointer	Route data
00000111	1 byte	1 byte	Varaible

(C) An IP "timestamp" option format:

Code*	Length	Pointer	Overflow	Flags
01000100	1 byte	1 byte	4 bits	4 bits

Figure 11-13   IP Option Formats: "Record Route" & "Timestamp".

Example 11-10: Describe the *IP record route option* [Figure 11-13(B)].

The IP record route option is used by the source to generate a record of all routers in the path that the IP datagram follows. When a datagram containing the record route option is processed by a router, it checks whether the pointer value is less than or equal to the IP address length: (1) if it is, the router records the IP address of its outgoing interface (starting at the byte position indicated by the pointer) and increments the pointer value by 4; or, (2) if not, the route data field is full and the router does not record the IP address. In either case, the datagram is routed in the usual manner. The option length does not change as the datagram is routed through the internet. The fields of the IP record route option [Figure 11-13(B)] are described as follows:

- Option type: This field is assigned as "00000111" (7). The MBS = "0" implies that if the datagram is to be fragmented, the option will appear in the 1st fragment only and will not be copied in the other fragments.

- Length: This 8-bit field indicates the number of bytes, including the length byte itself, that are in the option.

- Pointer: This 8-bit field identifies the byte within the option where the next IP address should be recorded. The minimum pointer value is 4.

- Route data: This is a variable length field, which consists of an area to record IP addresses. Initially, the source fills the area with zeros.

Example 11-11: Describe the *IP timestamp option* [Figure 11-13(C)].

The timestamp option is used to obtain information about delays in the path that a datagram traverses from the source to its destination. The fields of the IP timestamp option [Figure 11-13(C)] are described as follows:

- Option type (8 bits): The 8-bit field is assigned as "0 10 00100" (68). The MSB = "0" indicates that the option will not be copied on fragmentation. The next two bits of "10" (2) indicates that it is a class 2 option used for debugging and measurement. The last five bits of "00100" (4) indicates that the option is the timestamp function.

- Length (8 bits): This 8-bit field indicates the number of bytes in the option.

- Pointer (8 bits): The pointer indicates the location of next timestamp value to be recorded. It is the number of bytes from the beginning of the option to the end of the currently recorded timestamp plus 1 byte. The minimum pointer value is five. The timestamp area is "full" if the pointer value exceeds the option length value.

- Overflow (4 bits): This field indicates the number of IP modules (routers) that could not record timestamp information because the option field did not have enough space.

- Flags (4 bits): As shown in Figure 11-12(C), the timestamp area consists of 32 bits. The flag field is used to indicate the type of data that the timestamp area contains:

  * Flag = "0000" (4) ⇒ Timestamp values only are recorded in consecutive 32 bit increments.

  * Flag = "0001" (1) ⇒ Each timestamp value is preceded by an IP address of the registering IP entity.

  * Flag = "0011" (3) ⇒ IP addresses are pre-specified. Only the IP module whose address matches the next specified address (identified by the pointer) will record timestamp information.

Of the IP options described in this section, presently only the "Strict Source Route" (SSR) and the "Loose Source Route" (LSR) options are used. Another way to achieve source routing, without using options, is to apply "IP within IP". The "record route" and the "timestamp" options are now performed under applications such as "traceroute", which is an alternate application layer software developed to provide similar features. This approach is sued because IP router vendors have two concerns about router performance: (1) router operations can be optimized to process datagrams that do not have options; and (2) routers incur performance penalties when using datagrams that contain options.

11.3.2 Internet Control Message Protocol (ICMP)

The Internal Control Message Protocol (ICMP) was designed as a mechanism to provide feedback about problems in the delivery of IP datagrams. An ICMP message will be sent if any one of the following conditions occurs during datagram transport:

- An IP datagram can not be delivered to a destination because the destination subnet or host is unreachable.

- An intermediate IP router is unable to forward the datagram because buffer capacity is insufficient.

- A request to report errors in IP processing is sent.

- A request to test the path to a distant host is sent.

- A request for an address mask is sent.

ICMP is not designed to "make IP reliable", and cannot insure all problems occurring in IP will be reported. That is, an IP datagram may not arrive at its intended destination. Likewise, there are no guarantees that IP datagrams that are not delivered will trigger an ICMP message to be sent to the source host to report the loss. If greater reliability is required, additional procedures must be implemented by higher level protocols.

ICMP messages are sent as part of IP datagrams. Thus, the entity performing ICMP functions operates as if it is a higher layer process to IP. Because the ICMP message is considered an integral part of an IP datagram, each IP module in a host and router must implement the ICMP function.

Recursive ICMP messages are not allowed. This is enforced by not allowing an ICMP message to be sent for reporting an ICMP condition. In addition, when processing IP datagram fragments, ICMP messages are only sent for errors that occur when processing the first fragment.

There are several different types of ICMP messages, but they have common fields. Each message carries a message type field (to identify the message types) and a code which identifies the specific condition relating to the message. Six common ICMP messages are described in the following sections, and listed as follows:

(1) Destination unreachable ICMP message
(2) Time exceeded ICMP message
(3) Parameter problem ICMP message
(4) Source quench ICMP message
(5) Redirect ICMP message
(6) Echo request/reply ICMP messages

11.3.2.1 Destination Unreachable ICMP Message

The "destination unreachable" ICMP message occupies the first 8 bytes of the IP data field in the IP datagram as shown in Figure 11-14. This 8-byte field consists of four subfields: type, code, checksum, and zero.

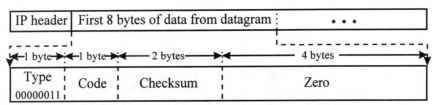

Figure 11-14   Destination Unreachable ICMP Message.

The value of the "type" field for the destination unreachable ICMP message is "00000011" (3). Six different conditions associated with this type of message are represented by the 8-bit "code" field as follows:

(1)   Net unreachable (code = 00000000): This message can be sent by an intermediate router which determines, from its routing table, that the distance to the destination network is infinite (i.e., cannot be reached).

(2)   Host unreachable (code = 00000001): When a host is down, absent, or otherwise unreachable, the router sends this message.

(3)   Protocol unreachable (code = 00000010): When the indicated protocol module is inactive, the destination host sends this message.

(4)   Port unreachable (code = 00000011): This message can be sent by the destination host when the indicated port is inactive.

(5)   Fragmentation needed but DF set (code = 00000100): This message can be sent by an intermediate router that is forced to discard a datagram when it is larger than the MTU (of the associated interface) and fragmentation is not allowed. This action (i.e., discarding the datagram) is taken because the "Don't Fragment" (DF) condition is set in the datagram.

(6)   Source route failed (code = 00000101): This message can be sent by an intermediate router that discards the datagram containing the source route option because it could not forward the datagram along the specified route. This condition is more likely to occur in the case of Strict Source Route and Record (SSRR) than for the Loose Source Route and Record (LSRR) option.

11.3.2.2 Time Exceeded ICMP Message

The "time exceeded" ICMP message has the same format as the "destination unreachable" message shown in Figure 11-14. The message type field contains the value "000001011" (11). Two conditions can trigger the time exceeded message:

(1)   Time To Live (TTL) exceeded in transit (code = 00000000): If an intermediate router determines that the TTL value of the datagram is zero and the datagram must be discarded, the router may send this message.

(2) Reassembly time exceeded (code = 00000001): This message may be sent by a destination host that cannot complete reassembly of a datagram because all the fragments did not arrive before the reassembly timer expired.

Under both these conditions the datagram is discarded.

11.3.2.3 Parameter Problem ICMP Message

This message has a format similar to the "destination unreachable" message, except the 4-byte "zero" field (Figure 11-14) is replaced by a "4-byte pointer". The message "type" field contains the value "00001100" (12), and two conditions can trigger this message.

When a router or a destination host encounters a problem in processing IP header parameters and the datagram must be discarded, the router and destination host will send this message. The code has a value of "00000000" (0), and the pointer value indicates the byte number in the header where the problem occurred. If a parameter is missing, the code has a value = 00000001, and the pointer value is not used.

11.3.2.4 Source Quench ICMP Message

The "source quench" ICMP message is used to indicate to the source that it should reduce the rate at which it is sending datagrams to the destination. This message has a type value of "00000100" (4). There are three conditions that can trigger the source quench ICMP message:

(1) When a destination host receives datagrams so rapidly that they cannot be processed, it sends this message as a flow control request.

(2) When a router does not have enough buffer space to queue up a datagram for subsequent forwarding, the router must discard the datagram. The router will also send the source quench ICMP message.

(3) A router may send a source quench ICMP message when its buffer is nearing the capacity, rather than waiting until the buffer capacity is exceeded. In this case, the datagram may be successfully delivered even though a source quench message was issued by the router (i.e., the datagram might not be discarded).

11.3.2.5 Redirect ICMP Message

A "redirect" ICMP message is sent by a router to the source host in the following situation. The router "A" receives a datagram from the source host [(1) in Figure 11-15] via the network to which it is attached. Using its routing table, router "A" finds the address of the next hop, which is router "C" [(2) in Figure 11-15], on the path to reach the final destination address of the datagram. Router "A" sends the datagram to router "C"

[(3) in Figure 11-15]. Router "A" determines that router "C" and the host are on the same network [(4) in Figure 11-15]. Router "A" sends a redirect ICMP message [(5) in Figure 11-15] to the host advising it to send future datagrams intended for this destination directly to router "C" because this is a shorter path to the destination [(6) in Figure 11-15]. If router "A" does not send the redirect ICMP message, it will continue to forward datagrams to router "C".

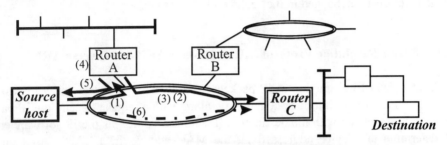

Figure 11-15   Redirect ICMP Message.

As shown in Figure 11-14, when sending a redirect ICMP message, the "type" field value is set to "00000101" (5). There are four different code values associated with this "redirect" ICMP message type:

(1)   Code = "00000000" (0): This code is used to redirect a datagram to the network associated with the destination IP address.

(2)   Code = "00000001" (1): This code is used to redirect a datagram for the destination host.

(3)   Code = "00000010" (2): This code is used to redirect a datagram based on the combination of the type of service indicated in the datagram and the network of the destination address.

(4)   Code = "00000100" (4): This code is used to redirect a datagram based on the combination of the type of service and the destination host.

11.3.2.6 Echo Request and Echo Reply ICMP Messages

The IP "echo request" and "echo reply" ICMP messages provide a method (known as PING) that can help a user determine whether or not a specific network interface is can be reached from the user's interface. It can also help a network administrator troubleshoot and resolve problems encountered in network operations.

The format of these two ICMP messages are similar to the illustration as in Figure 11-14, but the "zero" field contains two bytes of "identifier" information. The type values for the "echo request" message and the "echo reply" message are "00001000" (8) and

"00000000" (0), respectively. The "identifier" value in the "echo request" message is specified by the sender, and the associated "echo reply" message must carry the same value. The reason for this is the sender may be simultaneously involved in processing multiple echo messages, and the identifier allows the "echo reply" to be correlated with its associated "echo request" message. In this application, the inclusive of a data field is optional (if included the default length is 56 bytes). The data field in an "echo request" message is returned unchanged in the "echo reply" message.

11.3.3 Address Resolution Protocol (ARP), Reverse ARP and Inverse ARP

The **direct forwarding** function of IP packets requires the IP software entity to pass the IP packet to the network interface layer entity, along with a request to send the IP packet to the device associated with the destination IP address. To do this the IP software entity must determine the device address (e.g., the MAC address in a LAN) based on the destination's IP address.

For the **indirect forwarding**, the IP software entity uses a routing table to find the IP address of the next hop router, and passes the IP packet to the network interface layer entity along with a request to send the IP packet to the device address that corresponds to the router's IP address. To do this the IP software entity must determine the device address (e.g., the MAC address in a LAN) based on the destination's IP address.

- Address Resolution Protocol (ARP):

    "Knowing the IP address of a target device's network connection" is essentially of determining a hardware element's address and is an ***address resolution*** problem. The Address Resolution Protocol (ARP) was developed to solve this problem, particularly for those networks with simple broadcast capabilities (e.g., Ethernet and token ring LANs). The basic principle behind ARP is: (1) The source that needs to resolve the IP address "abc" sends a broadcast ARP message asking "Who, out there, has the IP address abc?", (2) Every device in the subnet receives this broadcast message, and (3) The device that recognizes the IP address "abc" as its own responds to the broadcast (i.e., it informs the source of its hardware address and the frame is deleted and ignored by all other devices in the subnet). The message format for address resolution, reverse address resolution, and inverse address resolution protocols (ARP, RARP and InARP) is shown in Figure 11-16.

    The ARP message includes an operation code (query or response) and four additional fields: (1) sender hardware address (a variable length field), (2) sender IP address, (3) target hardware address (a variable length field), and (4) target IP address. The target hardware address length depends on the hardware type (e.g., Ethernet uses 48-bit hardware addresses). Both ARP query and the response messages have the same format. However, the target hardware address field is blank in an ARP query message. The target hardware that responds to an ARP query message typically responds by filling in the four fields, and interchanging the target and the sender values. The Htype (Hlength) field contains two bytes for identifying the type of hardware address. The Ptype (Plength) field also contains two bytes for identifying the type of internet address.

32 bits	
Hardware type	Protocol type
Hlength	Plength	Operation code
Sender hardware address (variable length)	
Sender IP address	
Target hardware address (variable length)	
Target IP address	

Figure 11-16 Format for ARP, RARP, and InARP Messages.

The ARP operational details can be found in the standard RFC 826, and is briefly described as follows. Assume that an IP entity wants to send an IP datagram to a specific IP address via a specific network interface, and finds there is no entry in the local ARP cache memory associated with that IP address. An ARP query message is broadcasted over the network interface. The ARP query message includes the sender's Hardware Address (HA), sender's IP address, and the "target" IP address. The device that recognizes the "target" IP address will respond via a directed reply ARP message that includes its HA.

Definition 11-3 **A proxy ARP**: A device "X" can be configured to answer ARP requests from one subnet on behalf of hosts in another subnet (refer to the standard RFC 925), and this is known as a "proxy ARP".

- Reverse Address Resolution Protocol (RARP)

A RARP message has the same format as an ARP message (Figure 11-16). A host fills in its HA as the "target" hardware address and sends a broadcast message over the subnet. The designated server will then send a reply to the "target" hardware address that contains the host's IP address. A RARP is typically used by a diskless workstation that knows its HA, but cannot identify its own IP address.

- Inverse Address Resolution Protocol (InARP)

The description of an InARP message is given in the standard RFC 1293. As described in Chapter 5, frame relay and ATM networks apply Virtual Channel Identifiers (VCIs) for routing functions. A router knows the VCI, but may not know the associated IP address of the "target" hardware element. Thus, a router uses a variation of ARP, by sending an In ARP message using the VCI as the HA of a virtual channel. The reply to an InARP message will include IP address of the "target" hardware element associated with the VCI.

11.3.4 IPv4 and IPv6

The need for a new (enhanced) version of Internet Protocol (IPv6; IP version 6) is evident. First, there are an insufficient number of addresses available for new and growing networks. Second, many new service features require expanded addressing and routing capabilities. Likewise, maintaining the Quality of Service (QoS) is a highly desirable feature, and service security (via encryption and authentication) has become a necessity for modern telecommunications systems.

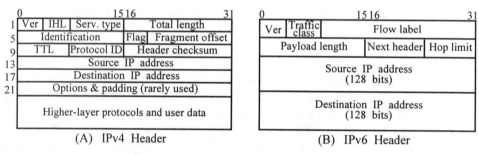

(A) IPv4 Header   (B) IPv6 Header

Figure 11-17   IPv4 Header versus IPv6 Header.

Figure 11-17 shows the difference between the existing IPv4 header and the enhanced IPv6 header formats. In the IPv6 header, the traffic class allows setting the priority of packets at the source. The flow label is used by higher level applications to define QoS. The payload length is used to indicate the size of the remainder of the packet. The "next header" field is used to indicate the header type that follows the IPv6 header.

The Simple Internet Transition mechanism (SIT) is protocol used to upgrade hosts and routers to operate with IPv6. Encapsulation is implemented by generating "IPv4 packets with IPv6 headers", and likewise "IPv6 packets with IPv4 headers".

11.4 TCP & USER DATAGRAM PROTOCOL (UDP; HOST-TO-HOST LAYER)

This section describes two protocols: the Transmission Control Protocol (TCP) and the User Datagram Protocol (UDP), of the TCP/IP host-to-host layer (see Figure 11-4). These protocols correspond to the transport layer (layer 4) of the OSI model. The simple (unreliable) datagram services of UDP (standard RFC 768) is described first, then the connection-oriented (reliable) comprehensive services of TCP (standard RFC 793) is presented

11.4.1 UDP Services

UDP can extend the (connectionless) datagram delivery service provided by IP to the application layer processes. UDP enables an application process running on a host to exchange messages with another process (running UDP) on another host. In addition, the two hosts running UDP do not have to establish a prior "logical connection".

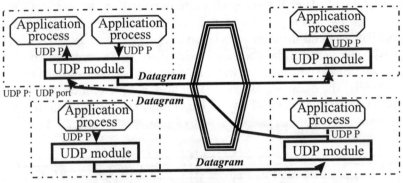

Figure 11-18   UDP Datagram Delivery.

Because UDP does not perform any reliability functions, the application layer programs that use UDP must accept full responsibility for dealing with problems such as packet loss, misinserted packet, duplication of messages, packet delay, delay jitter, and out-of-order packet delivery.

The primary feature provided by UDP is the ability for multiple higher layer processors to concurrently use UDP. To facilitate this type of multiplexing, UDP applies the concept of a "logical port" which is effectively the identification of the communicating application layer process. The application layer function is based on a "client-server interaction" model. A "client" is an application process that contacts a "server" application process running on another machine. The Internet Assigned Numbers Authority (IANA) maintains a list of (published) important port numbers assigned to UDP services.

Figure 11-19 illustrates the UDP message format. It contains an 8-byte UDP header (four 2-byte fields) and a variable length field for carrying application layer user data. The functions of the four header fields are briefly described as follows:

(1)   UDP source port (two bytes): This field carries the port number that identifies an abstract access point where an application process is accessing the sending UDP module, and identifies where the reply message should be sent. When this field is not used, it contains the value "00000000 00000000".

(2)   UDP destination port (two bytes): This field is required, and identifies where a destination application process is accessing the intended destination UDP module.

(3)   UDP message length (two bytes): This field contains the total number of bytes in the UDP message, including the UDP header and the user data.

(4)   UDP checksum (two bytes): This field is optional. If is not used, it contains the value "00000000 00000000". The use of the UDP checksum field is described as follows:

As an option, UDP can be configured to perform error detection on the user data. The source UDP calculates the parity-check information on the user data stream, and includes the results in the checksum field of the transmitted UDP datagram. The destination UDP performs the same calculation over the received datagram, and compares the result with the value in the checksum field of the received datagram. A mismatch between the two checksum values indicates an error has been detected. In this case, UDP "silently discards" the datagram. Because UDP does not perform reliability functions, it is the application layer's responsibility to handle this erroneous packet condition (e.g., request a retransmission of this packet).

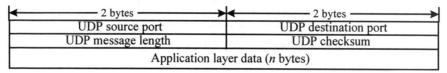

Figure 11-19   UDP Message Format.

Example 11-12 (UDP checksum): Describe the "one's complement of the one's complement sum" algorithm used to calculate the UDP checksum.

The UDP calculates the checksum using a method similar to the IP datagram (described in Example 11-6), but has the following differences:

•   The UDP checksum is calculated on an end-to-end basis, while the IP header checksum is calculated between two adjacent network nodes. That is, the IP checksum must be recalculated at each intermediate router as the value of certain fields [e.g. TTL (Time To Live)] change.

•   The IP header checksum parity calculation is limited to only the fields in the IP header. The UDP checksum parity calculation is over the entire content of the datagram, and five other fields that are not part of the datagram. These fields are referred to as the "pseudoheader", and consist of: a 4-byte source IP address, a 4-byte destination IP address, a dummy "zero" byte (00000000), a one-byte protocol identifier [for UDP, the value is "00010001" (17)], and a two-byte UDP datagram length indication.

If the UDP datagram contains an odd number of bytes, one-byte of padding is added so that the length is an even multiple of 16 bits (i.e., the total number of bits can be evenly divided by 16). As previously mentioned, the checksum is optional, and it is set to zero if not used. If it is used, but has a value of zero it is necessary to distinguish between these two cases. Because the one's complement of "all zero bits" or "all one bits" both result in a "zero" checksum value, a valid "zero checksum" is represented by a string of 16 "1s".

11.4.2 TCP Services

The Transmission Control Protocol (TCP) is specified in standard RFC 793, and the related standard RFC1323 specifies "TCP extensions for high performance". Compared to UDP, TCP is a complex, reliable, connection-oriented, and feature-rich protocol.

The service that TCP provides to higher layer applications is the ability to send a data stream from an application process running on a host to an application process running on another host, via an internet. To support this service, a logical connection is established for the interval that data is exchanged over the connection. The data stream has the following characteristics: (1) The data bytes are usually delivered in the same order as they were sent by the peer application; (2) Each data byte is delivered only once; and (3) Data bytes are checked for transmission errors, and no data bytes are delivered with detected errors.

The higher layer process places the data bytes into a "transmit buffer". The TCP process takes an appropriate number of bytes from this buffer, and creates a *TCP segment* that is sent to the IP layer for delivery to the peer TCP application. Since both TCP modules involved in a connection can concurrently send and receive data segments, TCP operations are referred to as *"full duplex"*.

TCP data segments that are sent by a TCP module carry contiguously numbered data bytes, and include an indication of the starting data byte number in each segment. The data segments also carry an acknowledgement for the contiguous data bytes received from a peer TCP module. This is achieved by a field in the header that shows the next expected data byte number. Therefore, a receiving TCP can handle (identify) a lost data byte and/or a duplicated data byte by monitoring the received segment's data byte number. Likewise, the source TCP can purge acknowledged data bytes and can use timers to trigger retransmission of unacknowledged data bytes by monitoring the acknowledgments it receives.

A TCP module can support multiple logical connections simultaneously on behalf of different application processes running on a host. Each data segment relating to a connection is identified within the TCP header by the source TCP. This allows the destination TCP to deliver the data associated with a data particular segment to the proper application process in the network. As previously mentioned, data bytes sent by an application process are stored in a transmit buffer (Figure 11-20).

Under normal conditions, if the buffer has enough bytes for segmentation and/or sufficient time, the source TCP will send out a segment. However, there are situations that require the buffer storage to be cleared without waiting. A segment can be sent by using a "***push*** bit mechanism". In this case a "push bit request" must be conveyed as part of the TCP header within the segment so that the peer TCP can deliver the data byte to the destination application at the other end with minimum delay.

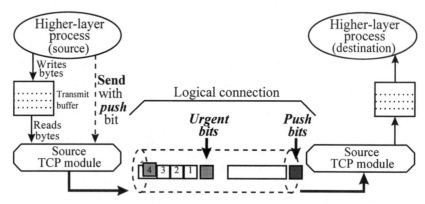

Figure 11-20   TCP Logical Connection: Push/Urgent Bits.

Another situation, known as an "urgent bit" is also illustrated in Figure 11-20. Normally, bytes are delivered in the same order as they are sent by the application. However, an application may need to deliver high priority information to its peer entity immediately. The "urgent bit mechanism" can be applied in this case. An "urgent bit" request must be conveyed as part of the TCP header within the segment so that the peer TCP can deliver the data byte to the application at the other end using priority treatment.

11.4.2.1 A TCP Logical Connection

Establishing a logical connection can be viewed as three different stages: (1) call (connection) setup to establish the connection; (2) conversation (data transfer) starts when the connection is established; and (3) call (connection) release "frees" the connection for the next user/activity.

(1)   Connection set up: Establishing a logical connection between two peer TCP modules requires an exchange of control messages between them. These control messages set-up state tables and parameters for the exchange of higher layer data. For example, each TCP must inform the other TCP about the initial sequence number it will use to identify the data bytes that will be sent. Likewise, the destination TCP must inform the source TCP of the maximum data segment size it can handle.

(2)   Data transfer: After the connection has been established (set-up), data bytes are sent "segment by segment". The header of each data segment carries an indication of data byte numbers included in the segment as well as acknowledgments and

"window advertisements" announcing how many more bytes the sending TCP can accept beyond the last acknowledged byte. By using the information in these segment headers, each TCP module can keep track of what data bytes it can send and receive, as the connection session progresses. During the data transfer period, there are procedures used by the TCP associated with error control, flow control, and congestion control.

(3) Connection release: There are two types of connection releases: (1) an orderly and graceful termination, and (2) an abrupt termination. In an orderly release, one TCP module is informed by its application process that there is no more data to send, and the TCP initiates an exchange of control messages to terminate the connection that results in a "half-close" of the connection. When the other TCP receives and acknowledges this request, it may still continue to send data until informed by its own application process that there is no more data to be sent. Following the exchange of control messages between the two TCP modules, there is a "full-close" of the connection. In the case of an abrupt termination, the other TCP will no longer send data even if its application has more data to send. A full-close of connection in an abrupt termination is also concluded after the two TCP modules have exchanged control messages about the termination.

Detailed description of the connection setup, data transfer, and connection release processes are provided in the following examples:

Example 11-13: Describe the concept of TCP sockets and connections.

A TCP connection is identified by two end-points of the connection, called sockets. Each socket is specified by two parameters:

- The IP address of the interface on the host.
- The port number for the application process that uses the TCP connection.

TCP user port numbers identify applications in exactly the same manner as the UDP function (Section 11.4.1). Important server processes use (published) well-known port numbers, and wait for client processes to contact them. In comparison, client processes apply locally selected port numbers, referred to as "ephemeral ports", to initiate connections to the server. Server processes that use either UDP or TCP usually have the same well-known (published) port number assignments, but they are completely independent functions.

Example 11-14: Describe a typical TCP connection setup process.

The TCP connection setup involves application processes A and B (App-A and App-B). It is assumed that process B (a server; Figure 11-21) is running on a specific port on host

B, and is ready to accept data from either a specific client or from any client. This is indicated by sending a "passive open" call to the TCP at host B (see Figure 11-21). Subsequently, client process App-A, running on host A, issues an "active open" call to its TCP thereby indicating it has data to send to the server at host B. (This example is the most common connection. However, it is possible that both application processes at both ends can simultaneously issue an "active open" to their respective TCPs, thereby triggering both TCPs to send data segments to each other).

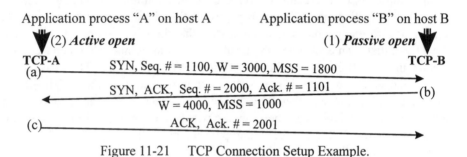

Figure 11-21   TCP Connection Setup Example.

After the "passive open" and "active open" calls have been issued, a "three-way handshake" procedure will take place. This is a three-step exchange of TCP segments between TCP-A and TCP-B to set up a logical connection for supporting data exchange between the App-A and App-B processes [steps are identified by (a), (b) and (c) in Figure 11-21].

(a)   TCP-A sends out a segment indicating that it needs to setup a connection and synchronize (SYN) on the initial sequence number (Seq. # = 1100) that will be used to send data bytes over the connection. The segment header includes a "window advertisement" of 3,000. This indicates TCP-A can accept a maximum of 3,000 data bytes from TCP-B at this time. This limitation is related to the size of the receive buffer allocated for this particular connection. The Maximum Segment Size (MSS) is 1,800 bytes, which is based on the Maximum Transmission Unit (MTU) of the network interface.

(b)   TCP-B, on host B, acknowledges the initial sequence number (1100) by sending a message indicating it expects the next data byte to be #1101. TCP-B informs TCP-A that its initial Sequence Number (Seq. #) for the data bytes that it will send is #2,000. It also informs TCP-A that it can accept a window of 4,000 data bytes (to be numbered from #1101 to #5100), and has a MSS of 1,000 bytes.

(c)   TCP-A, after receiving the initial sequence number (#20000 sent by TCP-B, acknowledges this reception by indicating that the next data byte number it expects to receive from TCP-B is #2001.

Example 11-15: Describe the state diagram for the TCP connection setup process.

Figure 11-21 illustrates a state diagram for TCP connection set-up. Assume that when TCP "ends" are **not** connected together, they are in a fictitious state called "Closed". The "Closed" state can be considered the "start" state for connection process. If an application layer (typically a server) issues a "passive open" message, the TCP will enter the "Listen" state. In the "Listen" state the server receives a TCP segment (R:RST, addressed to the server's port number) from a client with an indication of the local port number of the client. This will cause the server's TCP to send an ACK (ACKnowledgement) for the R:SYN segment it received, along with the S:SYN from the local TCP. The state then changes to the "Syn_rcvd" state. When an R: ACK is received from the peer TCP to its own SYN, the TCP state will enter the "Established" state, which is the state in which data transfer begins.

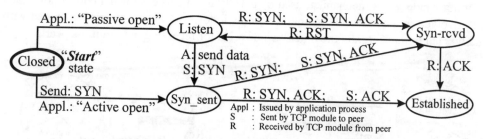

Figure 11-22   State Diagram For TCP Connection Setup.

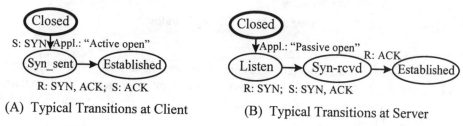

(A) Typical Transitions at Client   (B) Typical Transitions at Server

Figure 11-22   Typical Transitions at Client and at Server.

As an alternative, if the application layer issues an "active open" message from the "Closed" state (that is, client attempts to contact the server), then TCP sends out a TCP segment carrying the SYN bit with the appropriate source TCP port and destination port provided in the parameters of the open service primitive. The TCP then enters the "Syn_sent" state. When the client TCP receives an ACK and R:SYN from its peer, it will send out an S:ACK for the SYN received from the peer. The TCP enters the "Established" state, and data transfer begins.

In unusual situations, a TCP that is in a "Listen" state may receive a "send data" message from its higher layer application process. This will cause the local TCP to act like an "Active Open" has been issued, and it will cause a SYN segment to be sent. The local TCP will change from the "Listen" state into the "Syn_sent" state. If the TCP receives a S:SYN (e.g., in the case of a server in the "Listen" state that receives a "send data" message from its local application), it will repeat its old SYN and send out an ACK for the SYN it receives. The TCP will change from the "Syn_sent" state to the "Syn_rcvd" state.

If a TCP is in the in a "Syn_rcvd" state and receives a RST from its peer, it will return to the "Listen" state. Figure 11-23(A) summarizes the typical transitions at the client TCP, and Figure 11-22(B) shows the typical transitions at the server TCP.

Example 11-16: Describe the concept of a "sliding window for TCP modules.

A sliding window is a mechanism used by a TCP module to establish a connection. Each TCP involved in a connection maintains two "windows". One window is associated with sending data to its peer, and the other "window" is for receiving data from its peer.

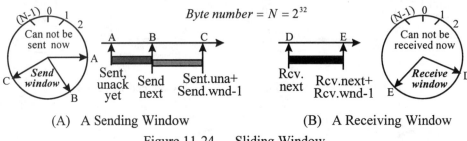

(A) A Sending Window   (B) A Receiving Window

Figure 11-24   Sliding Window.

Figure 11-24 illustrates a static example of the sending and receiving windows at a given instance in time (i.e., a "snapshot" view). Each window references a "dial" containing all the possible byte numbers that can be used $[0 \sim (2^{32} - 1)$; since the sequence number has a length of 32 bits].

The sending window's dial divides the byte numbers into three ranges:

- (Between A and B) Byte numbers associated with this range of data bytes have been sent, but valid acknowledgements have not been received from the TCP modules peer. These "yet to be unacknowledged' data bytes must be held in a buffer, because the TCP may be required to retransmit them.

- (Between B and C) Byte numbers associated with this range of data bytes have not been sent yet, but are ready to be sent now. Based on the window advertised by the peer TCP and other congestion/flow control policies, this range is referred as the "usable send window" (or "send window").

- (Between C and A) Byte number associated with the range of data bytes can not be sent at this time.

Example 11-17: Describe the TCP retransmission function.

To achieve good throughput in a network, it is important to properly set a time-out period for triggering retransmission.

- If the timer's time-out value is too short, then it causes unnecessary retransmission.
- If the timer's time-out value is too long, it causes excessive delay and wastes bandwidth in network.

There are two approaches that can be used to implement a retransmission timer: (1) static and (2) dynamic. If the connection between the two end points is a fixed path, a static retransmission time-out is based on the average time required for a round trip propagation plus the average processing times of all the devices along the connection path (including two end points). However, the path taken by different IP packets associated with a connection may be quite different. Therefore, standard RFC 793 recommends a dynamic time-out approach. The "smoothed average measured round-trip time" (T_{srt}) for each new sample is given as a function of the "initial smoothed round-trip time" (T_{isrt}) and the "round-trip time" (T_{rt}) as shown in the following equation:

$$T_{srt} = a \times T_{isrt} + (1 - a) \times T_{rt} \qquad (11\text{-}1)$$

Where a = a smoothing factor (0.8~0.9; recommended value = 0.9). The round-trip time (T_{rt}) is the time that has elapsed between the instant a segment containing data bytes has been successfully transmitted by a TCP, and the instant when an acknowledgment for the data bytes contained in that segment has been successfully received from the peer TCP. The "retransmission time-out" (T_{rto}) is given by:

$$T_{rto} = \text{Max} [L, \min (U, b \times T_{srt})] \qquad (11\text{-}2)$$

where

        b = A delay variance factor (1.3 ~ 2.0, recommended value = 2)
        L = Lower bound on time-out (1 second, recommended)
        U = Upper bound on time-out (1 minute, recommended)

Assume the round-trip time T_{rt} = 0.5 sec, the initial smoothed round-trip time T_{isrt} = 0.4 sec, "a" = 0.9, and "b" = 2; then using Eqs. (11-1) and (11-2) obtain T_{rto} = 1 sec. From this, the following conclusion can be drawn:

$$T_{rto} = L \qquad\qquad \text{if } b \times T_{srt} < L \qquad (11\text{-}3)$$

$$T_{rto} = U \qquad\qquad \text{if } b \times T_{srt} > U \qquad (11\text{-}4)$$

$$T_{rto} = b \times T_{srt} \qquad\qquad \text{if } L \leq b \times T_{srt} \leq U \qquad (11\text{-}5)$$

In summary, Eq.(11-2) can be represented by three separated eqs. (11-3) to (11-5).

The procedure described in Example 11-17 is simple, provided the round-trip time (T_{rt}) can be easily measured. However, a problem may exist in the ambiguity of the round-trip time. As a result, several methods have been developed; specifically the "Karn and Partidge" and the "Jacobson" algorithms. They will not be discussed in this book, but recommendation can be found in standard RFC 793.

11.4.2.2 TCP Segment Format

Figure 11-25 illustrates the format of a TCP segment, which consists of a TCP header followed by application layer data. The header ends on a 32-byte boundary, but the data field can be a variable number of bytes (including zero bytes).

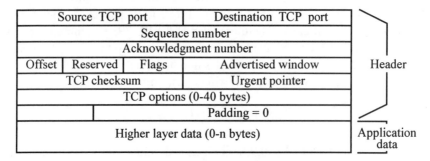

Figure 11-25   TCP Segment Format.

The TCP header consists of the following fields:

- Source TCP port (2 bytes): Identifies the sending application process.

- Destination TCP port (2 bytes): Identifies the intended receiving application process.

- Sequence number (4 bytes): Identifies the first byte number of the data represented in the TCP segment.

- Acknowledgement number (4 bytes): Identifies the next byte number of data expected from the peer TCP. It also serves as an acknowledgment of all the bytes sent by this TCP, whose byte numbers are less than this acknowledgment number.

- Offset (4 bits): Indicates the length of the header (in 32-bit increments). The minimum value is "0101" (5) for a 20-byte header without any options used, and the maximum value is "1111" (15) for a 20-byte header plus 40-byte options.

- Reserved (6 bits): Unused (default value is "000000").

- Flags (6 bits): Each of the 6 bits is assigned as follows:

* The MSB is the URGent bit (URG: _xxxxx).
* The next MSB is the ACKnowledgment bit (ACK: x_xxxx).
* The next bit is the PuSH bit (PSH: xx_xxx).
* The next bit is the ReSeT bit (RST; xxx_xx)
* The next bit is the SYNchronization bit (SYN: xxxx_x).
* The LSB is the FINish bit (FIN: xxxxx_).

* Advertised window (2 bytes): Identifies the number of additional bytes, beyond the first unacknowledged byte from the peer TCP, that the TCP is willing to accept at this time. This number depends on the available buffer space at the TCP.

* TCP checksum (2 bytes): This field is computed using the UDP method, including the pseudoheader (see Example 11-12). Note that the UDP checksum is optional, but the TCP checksum is mandatory.

* Urgent pointer (2 bytes): This field is used points to the byte position where the urgent data bytes start (within a TCP segment) if urgent data exists in the segment. The presence of urgent data bytes is indicated by the URG bit (i.e., the MSB of the "flag" field set to "1").

* TCP options (0 to 40 bye variable length): This field is optional. It can contain no option, one, or several specific options. Available options are discussed later.

* Padding (0 to 3 bytes): This field is used to ensure a TCP header has an integer number of 32-bits, that is, a TCP header must end at a 32-bit boundary.

11.4.2.3 TCP Options

Three TCP options are presently available, and described (Figure 11-26) as follows:

(1) Maximum Segment Size option (MSS, 2 bytes): This TCP option is only used in the initial TCP connection setup (i.e., in the segments where the "SYN" bit in the "flag" field is set to "1"; see Figures 11-25 and 11-26). When this option is used, it indicates the number of bytes that the TCP can accept in a single segment. Associated with the MSS field, a one-byte "kind" field and a one-byte "length" field are required. The "kind" field has a value of 2 (00000010), and the "length" field has a value of 4 (00000100). If the MSS option is not used, a default maximum segment size of 536 bytes will be applied. ($536 = 576 - 20 - 20$; where 576 is the default IP packet size, 20 is the IP header size without options, and 20 is the TCP header size without options.)

(2) Window scale option: This option may sent in two situations: (1) in an initial "SYN" segment with "ACK" off, and (2) in a segment with "SYN" and "ACK" present (provided the window scale option was received in an earlier "SYN" segment). This

option contains three one-byte fields: a "kind" field with a value of 3, a "length" field with a value of 3, and a "shift.cnt" field with a value R (a scaling factor). This is an offer by the TCP to "scale the window value" received in each segment window (other than "SYN" segment or a segment with "SYN" and "ACK") by a factor of 2^R. The value or "R" is between 0 and 14 (a value of 0 implies no scaling).

(3)   Timestamp option: This option is used to obtain an accurate round trip time estimate. The "kind" field of this option is set to 8 and the "length" field is set to 10. The third field is a 4-byte timestamp value (TSval) which contains the current value of the timestamp clock. The fourth field is a 4-byte timestamp echo reply field.

- Maximum segment size option

Kind = 2	Length = 4	Maximum segment size
1 byte	1 byte	2 bytes

- Timestamp option

Kind = 8	Length = 10
TS value (4 bytes)	
TS echo reply (4 bytes)	

- Window scale option

Kind = 3	Length = 3	Shift.cnt
1 byte	1 byte	1 byte

Flag

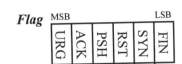

Figure 1-26   TCP Options.

11.5 APPLICATION LAYER PROTOCOLS

There are many TCP application/process layer protocols. Several commonly used and important protocols are discussed in this book. The services and operations of the protocols listed below are described in this section: Domain Name System (DNS); Telnet; File Transfer Protocol (FTP); Trivial FTP; Simple Mail Transfer Protocol (SMTP); Multipurpose Internet Mail Extension (MIME); Simple Network Management Protocol (SNMP: see Chapter 12); HyperText Transfer Protocol (HTTP); and Dynamic Host Configuration Protocol (DHCP).

11.5.1 Domain Name System (DNS)

The Domain Name System (DNS) provides a powerful facility for human users and TCP applications to communicate across the internet. Names are hierarchically organized without the need to deal with IP addresses and other details. In many cases, DNS takes care of the necessary translations in the background (in a transparent manner from the user's perspective). The following are three RFC standards pertain to DNS:

(1) RFC 1034: "Domain Names - Concepts and Facilities"
(2) RFC 1035: "Domain Names - Implementation and Specification"
(3) RFC 1591: "Domain Name Structure and Delegation"

11.5.1.1 DNS Components

The IP address structure provides a unique way of identifying the individual network interface of each system in an internet. However, a 32-bit string of "1s" and "0s" is not suitable for human operators to remember and/or to use. Humans prefer "easy to remember" names. In the early internet era, a flat name space was used to identify different computing systems in the network, and the responsibility for ensuring that systems were given distinct names was a centralized responsibility of the Network Information Center (NIC). The names and IP addresses were maintained in a file (host.txt), and a copy of the file was distributed to all the systems connected to the internet.

As the size of the internet grew, centralized naming was replaced by a distributed approach. This applies a hierarchical name space, where top level names are maintained by the central internet authority. Any organization/entity (e.g., a corporation or a university) registers its name under a domain that is delegated the authority to name subentities under its own administrative process. Thus, the naming procedure can be extended to as many levels as needed.

The "name" associated with a domain is a string of characters having a maximum length of 63 characters, composed of "lower-case/upper-case" letters, digits, and dashes (-). The string of zero length is reserved for the root. Each "non-null name" must begin and end with a letter or a digit. Since both lower and upper case letters are allowed, the two names: "DNS" and "dns" would be considered the "same name". The entity that administers a domain is responsible for ensuring that names shared by the same parent are "unique" within its domain, and should also maintain at least two *authoritative name servers* to provide name-to-address mapping and other information for the domain. The resulting structure is essentially a decentralized database.

A DNS application typically uses the names associated with destinations to send e-mail, login to a remote host, or browse information at a web site. These names must be mapped into suitable IP addresses to allow IP software to perform the necessary routing. The DNS depends on interaction between the client software (called a "name resolver") and one or more name servers to achieve the required mapping. That is, an individual application uses a local name resolver that contacts one or more name servers to obtain the appropriate domain information. This interaction applies DNS query and response messages. The DNS client-server interaction may be based on either TCP or UDP, and uses port number 53 (i.e., UDP port 53 or TCP port 53).

Note: *A domain is an administrative concept with no relation to the actual physical internet's subnetworks*. A complete domain name for a node is a list of names that exist in the path from the node to the root, which are separated by "dots" (e.g., xxx.yyy.zzz.com).

11.5.1.2 Naming Hierarchy: Top-Level Domains

Figure 11-27 illustrates the naming hierarchy for the "top-level" domains, starting from an unnamed root. Under the root (null name) is a set of names called the "Top-Level Domain (TLD)" names. There are seven defined generic TLDs: com, edu, net, org, int, gov, and mil (the last are used in the US only; they are exclusive for US government and military organizations). The two-letter country codes are based on the ISO-3166 recommendation. The seven generic TLDs are briefly described as follows:

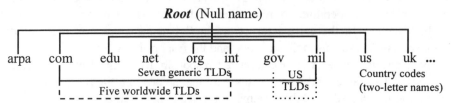

Figure 11-27   Naming Hierarchy: Top-level Domains.

(1) Com: The "com" domain is intended to identify commercial entities and companies. However, this domain has grown very large. The administrative load and system performance have been an increasing concerns to both service providers and users. Eventually this domain will needed to be subdivided, and future registrations may allow companies to register in appropriate subdomains.

(2) Edu: The "edu" domain was originally intended to identify educational organizations. Recently, a decision was made to restrict it to universities and four-year colleges. Other schools and two-year colleges will be registered under their respective country domain instead of the "edu" domain.

(3) Net: The "net" domain is intended to identify "computers" of network providers, administrative "computers", and network node "computers".

(4) Org: The "org" domain is intended to identify organizations that do not fit into the general TLD categories. These organizations may be non-profit and other non-governmental organizations.

(5) Int: The "int" domain is intended to identify international databases or organizations established under international agreements.

(6) Gov: The "gov" domain was original intended to identify all US non-military governmental organizations. Recently, a decision was made to register only agencies of the US federal government. State and local government agencies will be registered under the "us" country domain.

(7) Mil: The "mil" domain is intended for the exclusive use of the US military.

Example 11-19: Describe the operation of name servers and name resolvers.

As illustrated in Figure 11-28, a user program interacts with the domain name space through a name resolver by using queries and responses which are specific to the operating system of the host machines. The name resolvers perform a "lookup" of their cache memory to find the information needed to answer the user queries. Sometimes the information can not be found in the cache, the name resolver will trigger one or more queries of other (foreign) name servers that are on the internet in an attempt to obtain the information. This information may be temporarily cached for the duration of this activity.

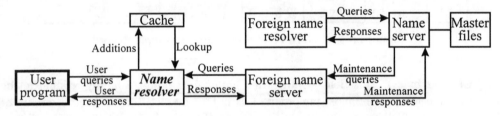

Figure 11-28   Name Servers and Name Resolvers.

A name server can be a stand-alone program on a dedicated machine, or a process on a large time-shared host. A name server may acquire information regarding one or more zones from "master files" residing in its file system, and can provide answers to queries about these zones from "foreign name resolvers". A DNS requires that all zones be supported by more than one name server in order to provide redundancy and increase the reliability of service. Designated secondary (or standby) name servers for a zone must acquire information from a primary server and check for updates by using the "zone transfer protocol" of DNS.

Example 11-20: Describe the function, content, and format of Resource Records.

Each DNS name server maintains a collection of information regarding a part of the domain name tree. The information that the DNS name server keeps about a domain is called a **Resource Record** (RR). Figure 11-29 shows the typical format of a Resource Record, which consists of the following fields:

• Name: This is a variable-length field which consists of the domain name of the node to which this resource record pertains.

• Type (2 bytes): This field indicates the resource record type. Some common types and their assigned values are listed as follows -

  * A [a value of "00000000 00000001" (1)]: the host Address
  * NS [a value of "00000000 00000010" (2)]: the authoritative Name Server

* CNAME (a value of 3): the Canonical NAME of an alias
* SOA (a value of 6): the Start Of a zone of Authority
* WKS (a value of 11): a Well-Known Service description
* PTR (a value of 12): a Pointer to point to another domain name
* HINFO (a value of 13): the Host INFOrmation
* MINFO (a value of 14): Mailbox or Mail list INFOrmation
* MX (a value of 15): Mail eXchange
* TXT (a value of 16): a Text string

Name	Type (2 bytes)	Class (2 bytes)	TTL (2 bytes)	RDLength (2 bytes)	Rdata

Figure 11-29   The Field Format of a Resource Record.

- Class (2 bytes): This field identifies the protocol or protocol family relating to the resource record. The most important class is IN (internet) for the internet family of protocols which has a value of 1. For example: if (type, class) = (A, IN), this indicates the resource record is the IP address of the host.

- TTL (2 bytes; Time-To-Live): This field specifies the maximum time interval that the resource record may be cached before the source of the information must be consulted again. If TTL has a value of zero, it implies that the information should not be cached. For example, the "Start Of a zone of Authority (SOA)" should never be cached, therefore its TTL is set to zero.

- RDLength (2 bytes; Record Data Length): This field indicates the number of bytes contained in the Rdata (Resource Record Data) field.

- Rdata (Record data): This is a variable-length field that is used to describe the resource record. The content of this field is a function of the "type" and the "class".

11.5.1.3 DNS Message Format

Figure 11-30 shows the DNS message format containing five different fields, and described as follows:

(1) Header (12 bytes): This header is a fixed-length field that contains six subfields [i.e., ID containing 2 bytes, (QR, Opcode, AA, TC, RD, RA, Zero, and Rcode) containing 2 bytes, QDCount containing 2 bytes, ANCount containing 2 bytes, NSCount and ARCount containing 2 bytes]. They are briefly described as follows.

* ID (2 bytes): This field contains an unsigned integer placed by the original sender of a query. This same ID value must be repeated in the response so that the sender

can correlate the response with the appropriate query when there are several outstanding queries.

* Query/Response (Q/R: 1 bit): This bit designates whether a message is a query or a response. This bit is set to "0" if the message is a query; and it is set to "1" if the message is a response.

* Opcode (4 bits): This field indicates the type of query that a message relates to. For a standard query, the Opcode is set to "0000". For an inverse query, the Opcode is set to "0001". For a server status request, the Opcode is set to "0010". The value is set by the sender, and the same value must be copied in the response.

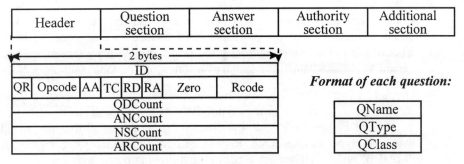

Figure 11-30   DNS Message Format/Header Format.

* Authoritative Answer (AA, 1 bit): This bit is only valid in responses. It is set to "1" to indicate that the responding name server is an authoritative server for the domain name in the question section.

* Truncation (TC, 1 bit): If a message has been truncated because of a restriction on the transmission channel, this bit is set to "1".

* Recursive Desired (RD, 1 bit): If the sender of the query desires that the name server *pursue the query recursively*, this bit is set to "1". It must also be copied in the response as "ID" and "Opcode". It is optional for a name server to support the "RD" function.

* Recursive Available (RA, 1 bit): If the responding name server supports recursive queries, the "RA' bit is set to "1" in its response.

* Zero (3 bits): This field is reserved for future use. The default value is "000".

* Response Code (Rcode 4 bits): This field is used in responses to indicate if a response is error free (Rcode = 0000), or contains format error, server failure, name error, etc.

* QDCount (2 bytes): This field provides a count of the number of questions included in the "question section" field of a DNS message. The count can be 0.

* ANCount (2 bytes): This field provides a count of the number of Resource Records (RRs) included in the "Answer section" of the message. The count can be 0.

* NSCount (2 bytes): This field provides a count of the number of name server Resource Records (RR that point to authoritative name servers, and are included in the authorities section of the message. The count can be 0.

* ADCount (2 bytes): This field provides a count of the number of Resource Records (RRs) that provide additional information, and are included in the additional section of the message. The count can be 0.

(2) Question section: This field can contains as many question parts as indicated in the QDCount of the message header. This section is composed of three subfields:

* Qname: This is a variable-length field used to identify the domain name that the question relates to. The domain name is represented by a sequence of labels. Each label consists of an octet indicating the length, followed by that many octets. The Qname terminates with a zero length byte corresponding to the null name of the root.

* Qtype (2 bytes): This field specifies the type of query. The possible query types include those described in the "type" field of a Resource Record (RR; Example 11-20, and Figure 11-29), and additional "general codes" that can match more than one type of Resource Record. Three additional Qtypes are "AXFR", "MAILB" and "*". They are used for the following purposes:

  ♦ AXFR: This code has a value of 252 (00000000 11111100). This query is used to request the transfer of an entire zone.

  ♦ MAILB: This code has a value of 253 (00000000 11111101). This query is used to request mailbox-related records.

  ♦ *: This code has a value of 255 (00000000 11111111). This query is used to request all records.

* Qclass (2 bytes): This field specifies the protocol family. The possible protocols include those described in the "class" field of the Resource Record (RR; Example 11-20 and Figure 11-29). In addition to those classes, a Qclass with a value of 255 indicates any class.

(3) Answer, Authority and Additional sections: These sections have the same format as the Question Section. Each section consists of a variable number of Resource Records. The number of Resource Records in each section is indicated by the ANCount, NSCount and ADCount in the DNS message header.

11.5.2 Telnet

Telnet is one of the earliest application protocols of the TCP/IP suite. It was developed for supporting remote terminal sessions over an internet. Several RFC standards were designed for Telnet. One group of RFCs are associated with individual options, and another provides general descriptions of Telnet protocol procedures. Some examples are listed as follows:

RFC 854 "Telnet Protocol Specifications"   RFC 855 "Telnet Option Specification"
RFC 856 "Telnet Binary Transmission"   RFC 857 "Telnet Echo Option"
RFC 858 "Telnet Suppress Go Ahead Option"   RFC 860 "Telnet Timing Mark Option"
RFC 861 "Telnet Extended Option-List Option" RFC 1079 "Telnet Terminal Speed Option"
RFC 1091 "Telnet Terminal Type Option"   RFC 1172 "Telnet Remote Flow Control Option"
RFC 1184 "Telnet Linemode Option"

11.5.2.1 Telnet Model

The main advantage of the Telnet protocol is that it allows a user of a PC, workstation ,or a dumb terminal that is connected to a subnetwork of an internet, to set up and engage in a computing session with a remote computer that resides on a different network located many miles away. This process involves three interactions:

(1) The interface between a user entering key strokes at a terminal, and a Telnet client (software) function running on the user device.

(2) The interface between a Telnet client running on a user device and a Telnet server (software) at a remote host that exchanges byte streams over a TCP connection.

(3) The interface between the Telnet server and the remote system.

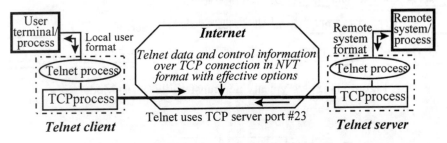

Figure 11-30   Telnet Model.

Telnet provides the underlying reliable TCP connection between the client and the server (Figure 11-31). The Telnet server uses TCP port number 23. An important goal of Telnet is to allow a device with one set of characteristics to transparently exchange information with another device that may have a different set of characteristics. Two typical examples of this condition are:

• For Unix-based systems, a user may enter a "Ctrl-D" sequence to indicate (to the operating system) that the process which is currently executing should be terminated.

- A user may enter a "the carriage return" on a keyboard to indicate the start of a new text line in a local device, whereas a remote system may use a different key stroke (e.g., line feed) to indicate the same function. Thus, the operation of a remote login will not be served if the TCP connection simply transports key strokes generated on one side of the connection to the other side. Instead, the key strokes must have the same effect on both machines. Therefore, Telnet defines an intermediate canonical representation called the Network Virtual Terminal (NVT) format. The interaction between the user's terminal (process) and the Telnet client uses the "local format". This information is converted into the NVT format, and is sent to the Telnet server via an Internet connection. The Telnet server converts it into the format of the remote system and sends it to the process that is interacting with the local user (Figure 11-31).

11.5.3 File Transfer Protocol (FTP)

The most common FTP application involves a user (person) that wants to access a file. In some cases it is a person directly interacting with the server FTP process. Figure 11-32 illustrates the FTP model. The user interacts with the sever FTP via a user interface which facilitates the "command" and "reply" dialogue (in a local language) between the user and a user Protocol Interpreter (PI). The user-PI establishes a control connection with the server-PI which is listening for this type of connection. Standard FTP "commands" and "replies" are exchanged over this control connection (shown by the dashed line in Figure 11-32).

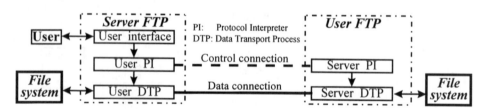

Figure 11-32   Typical File Transfer File (FTP) Model.

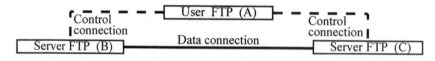

Figure 11-33 Two Host File Transfer Protocol (FTP) Model.

A separate connection, known as the Data connection, is established between the server FTP and the user FTP, which is used for the actual file transfer. That is, the file transfer is not carried over the Control connection. For the data connection, the FTP commands must specify several parameters (e.g., data port, transfer mode, data representation type and structure), and the nature of file system operations (e.g., store, retrieve, append, etc.). After establishing the control connection and exchanging "command" and "reply" messages, the User Data Transport Process (DTP) should "listen" to the specified data port. The Server DTP will then initiate a separate Data connection to allow data transfer to take place according to the parameters specified. The Data connection can be used for sending and receiving data simultaneously.

Figure 11-32 illustrates the most common file transfer scenario, it is also possible to transfer files between two hosts, neither of which is the local host (Figure 11-33). The user (A) may setup control connections with each of the two servers [(B) and (C)] and then arrange for a Data connection between them. The control information is passed to the user-PI, while the actual file data is transferred between the two servers via the Data Transfer Processes.

The FTP data transfer commands include: MODE, STRU(cture) and TYPE. The TYPE command specifies the data format. FTP can only provide a limited set of data type representations and transformations. Transformations desired beyond the FTP capability must be performed directly by the user processes.

11.5.3.1 (FTP) Data Type and File Structure

Four types of data can be specified by the user. They are briefly described as follows:

(1) ASCII (American Standard Code for Information Interchange): This is the default data type, thus it must be supported by all FTP implementations. The sender converts the data from an internal character representation to the standard 8-bit NVT-ASCII form (Network Virtual Terminal). The receiver performs the inverse function to convert the data into its own internal form. The ASCII form (see Appendix 9A-1 in Chapter 9) is the most common type of text files.

(2) EBCDIC (Extended Binary Coded Decimal Information Code): This format is intended for efficient transfer between hosts (e.g., in an IBM environment) that use EBCDIC for their internal character representation.

Both the ASCII and EBCDIC types have an optional parameter that indicates the kind of vertical format control associated with the file. Doing this helps in dealing with printing, storage, and processing functions that a file transfer may need to perform. There are three different formats defined:

* Non-print format: This is the default format when the optional parameter is not used.

* Telnet format: This indicates that the file contains ASCII/EBCDIC control characters (e.g., CR, LF, NL, VT and FF) which the printer process will interpret accordingly.

* Carriage control format: This indicates that the file contains ASA (Fortran) vertical format control characters. In a line or record formatted according to the ASA standards, the first character should not be printed. This character is used to determine the vertical movement of the paper before the text of the record is printed. Several control characters are defined as follows: (1) "blank" means move the paper up one line; (2) "0" means move the paper up two lines; (3) "1" means move the paper to top of the next page; and, (4) "+" means overprint with no movement of the paper.

(3) Image: This data type is intended for binary data, and is used for the efficient storage and retrieval of large files. The data stream is sent as contiguous bits which may be packed into 8-bit transfer bytes. The receiver must store the data stream as contiguous bits. Any required padding for storage or transmission must be all zeros, and they must be "stripped off" before the file is retrieved.

(4) Local: This data type will allow the data stream to be transferred in logical bytes with a user-specified byte size.

The FTP structure command specifies the structures of the data file being sent or received. They are:

* File structure: This is the default structure that is used if the STRU (STRUcture) command is not specified. In this default structure, the file is treated as a continuous sequence of data bytes (i.e., a stream) without any internal structure.

* Record structure: If this structure is specified, the file must be organized as sequential records. For text file transfers using ASCII or EBCDIC data types, all FTP implementations must apply the "record" structure.

* Page structure: Files with this structure are "discontinuous", and sometimes referred to as "random access files". The file may contain a "file descriptor" which is associated with the entire file or particular sections of a file. A section of a file is called a page, which is sent with a page header. A page header has the following fields:

    * Header length: It indicates the number of logical bytes in the header, including the header length field.

    * Page index: It provides an index that is used to identify the specific pages of the file.

    * Data length: It indicates the number of logical bytes of data in a page.

    * Page type: There are four page types used for FTP-

        (1) Last page (value = 0): It indicates the end of the page structure transmission.

        (2) Simple page (value = 1): It indicates a simple paged file that does not have page level associated control information.

(3) Descriptor page (value = 2): It indicates that the data is transmitted as a whole. That is, the file is transmitted as descriptive information.

(4) Access controlled page (value = 3): It indicates that an additional header field is included for paged files with page level access control information.

11.5.3.2 Transmission Modes

A "mode" command specifies how the data bit stream is to be transmitted. FTP provides three different transmission modes:

(1) Stream mode: If the data file is transmitted in this mode, the data is treated as a stream of bytes. There is no restriction on the type of representation used.

* If file structure is used, then "EOF (End Of File)" is applied to indicate the sending host is closing the data connection.

* If record structure is used, then "EOR (End Of Record)" and "EOF" are indicated by a two-byte control character. The first control byte is the escape sequence of all "1s". The second control byte has three different applications: (1) A value of 1 indicates EOR occurring alone; (2) A value of 2 indicates EOF occurring alone; and (3) A value of 3 indicates "EOR" and "EOF" occurring at the same time. Note that if the escape sequence occurs in the data stream, the sequence must be repeated.

(2) Block mode: In this mode, the data file is transmitted as a sequence of blocks [see Figure 11-34(A)], which consist of a header field and a data stream field. The header field contains two parts:

* Descriptor (1 byte): There are several applications assigned for this byte as indicated in Table 11-4:

Table 11-4   The Descriptor Assignments.

Application	Byte assignment	Value
End of record (EOR)	1 0 0 0 0 0 0 0	128
End of file (EOF)	0 1 0 0 0 0 0 0	64
Suspected error in data block	0 0 1 0 0 0 0 0	32
Data block is restart marker	0 0 0 1 0 0 0 0	16
Both EOR and EOF	1 1 0 0 0 0 0 0	192

* Byte count (2 bytes): This field indicates the number of data bytes in the block.

(3) Compressed mode: This mode can be used to send three different information types, as described as follows:

* Regular data sent as a string of bytes: This data type is used to transmit a string of *n* (note that $0 < n < 128$) bytes [i.e., d(1), d(2), ..., d(*n*) as shown in Figure 11-34(B)]. These data bytes are preceded by one byte "*0nnnnnnn*", where the value of "*nnnnnnn*" represents the number of data bytes. Note that the first bit is always a "0". For example, if there are 127 data bytes, then the first (preceding) byte will be assigned = "01111111". Similarly, a first byte = "00000001" represents a data string of one byte.

* Compressed data: This data type is used to transmit a string of *n* ($0 < n < 64$) repetitions of the same data byte *d*. The preceding byte has a leading two-bit (10) followed by the value of *n* ("*10nnnnnn*"), as shown in Figure 11-34(B).

* Filler string: A string of *n* ($0 < n < 64$) filler bytes can be compressed into one single byte. The filler is a SP (space) for ASCII or EBCDIC, and is a "0" for image type data. The preceding byte has a leading two-bit (11) followed by the value of *n*, "*11nnnnnn*", as shown in Figure 11-34(B).

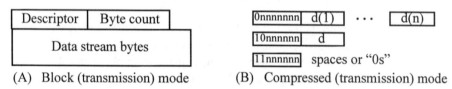

(A) Block (transmission) mode   (B) Compressed (transmission) mode

Figure 11-34   Block and Compressed (Transmission) Modes.

11.5.4 Trivial File Transfer Protocol (TFTP)

The Trivial File Transfer Protocol (TFTP) standard is specified in standard RFC 1350, and is a simple protocol used to move files between two remote systems via an internet. It is "simple" in the sense that a file is sent in fixed size blocks, with 512 bytes in each block. Note that the last block can be 0 to 511 bytes, and the block containing fewer than 512 bytes signifies the end of the data transfer. The sender must wait for an acknowledgment from the receiver for each block sent, before it sends the next block. This is called a "stop-and-wait" approach. The TFTP is commonly implemented on top of UDP. That is, all TFTP packets are encapsulated in UDP datagrams.

11.5.4.1 TFTP Packet Formats

There are five packet formats used in TFTP data exchanges. They are Read Request (RRQ), Write Request (WRQ), data, Acknowledgement (ACK), and ERROR (Figure 11-35).

The different packet formats shown in Figure 11-35 contains several different fields: Operation Code (OpCode), File Name, Mode, Block Number, Data field, Error Code (ErrCode), and Error Message (ErrMsg). These fields are described as follows:

- OpCode (2 bytes): This field is used to identify the packet type. There are five values assigned in accordance with the current standard. OpCode = 1, 2, 3, 4 and 5 indicate a Read Request (RRQ), a Write Request (WRQ), a data packet, an ACKnowledgment (ACK) packet, and a error (ERROR) packet, respectively.

- File name (variable length): This field contains the US-ASCII (known as **netascii**), string that terminates with a byte = "00000000", and only appears in the RRQ and WRQ packets. It is used to identify the file name to be read or written.

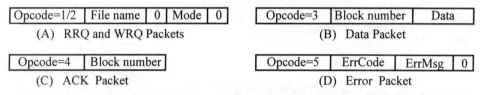

    (A) RRQ and WRQ Packets   (B) Data Packet

    (C) ACK Packet   (D) Error Packet

Figure 11-35   TFTP Packet Formats.

- Mode (variable length): This field also contains the **netascii** string that terminates with a byte = "00000000", and only appears in the RRQ and WRQ packets. The value can be the string "**netascii**" or an "octet" using any combination of upper and lower case characters. A host that receives a **netascii** file can store the file in its "native form".

- Block number (2 bytes): This field only applies to a data or an acknowledgment packet. The functions are described as follows:

  * In a data packet: This field indicates the number of blocks contained in the data packet being sent.

  * In an acknowledgment packet: This field indicates the number of blocks in the data packet whose correct reception is being acknowledged by an ACK packet. If the ACK packet acknowledges a correct WRQ, this filed contains a value of "0". A correct RRQ packet is acknowledged by sending the first block of the file requested.

- Data: The data field contains 512 bytes per block, except for the last block which may contain 0 to 511 bytes.

- ErrCode (2 bytes): This field t only appears in an error packet, and is used to identify the type of error being reported. The following values have be assigned as shown in Table 11-5. For example

  * If ErrCode = "00000000 00000000" (0) indicates that this field is not defined.

  * If ErrCode = "00000000 00000001" (1) indicates the specified file can not be found.

  * If ErrCode = "00000000 00000010" (2) indicates that there is an access violation.

Table 11-5   Error codes and Corresponding Functions.

ErrCode	Function
0	Not defined; explained in error message
1	File not found
2	Access violation
3	Disk full or allocation exceeded
4	Illegal TFTP operation
5	Unknown transfer ID
6	File already exists
7	No such user

- ErrMsg (variable length): This field contains a *netascii* string, and is terminated with a "00000000" byte that provides an explanation of the error that can be interpreted by a human user.

11.5.4.2 Sample TFTP Scenario

Initially, the TFTP entity in one system sends a packet indicating that it wants to write into a "foreign file system", or that it wants to read from such a system. Figure 11-36 illustrates a sample TFTP scenario. The request can be either a RRQ or a WRQ packet. A positive reply to the request consists of an ACKnowledgment (ACK) packet in the case of WRQ, and the first block of data in case of a RRQ. The exchange of RRQ or WRQ packets results in the establishment of the TFTP connection after which data packets (DATA1, DATA2, DATA3, …) can flow between the hosts.

A TFTP connection may be terminated if errors received. This is performed by using an ERROR packet. Unlike the FTP applications, TFTP applications do not provide commands for listing directories, changing directories, or for user authentication. The operation of TFTP is illustrated in Figure 11-36. In this example, it is assumed that host A wants to write a file (e.g., a stockquote) to the file system of host B, using TFTP. The numerical steps [(1) through (12)] shown in Figure 11-36 are described as follows:

(1) TFTP at host A chooses a local Transaction IDentifier (TID) which corresponds to a UDP port, and has a value between "0" and "65,535". For this example, assume that TID = 1988, and the TFTP server is at port 78. The TFTP sends a WRQ packet with the file name "stockquote", and mode "ASCII" to the UDP at host A as a send request; along with source TID = 1024 and destination TID = 78. The UDP at host A sends this packet to the UDP at Host B, encapsulated in a UDP datagram.

(2) The UDP delivers this packet to the server at Host B, which is listening on port 78.

(3)   The server at Host B accepts this WRQ (Write Request), and decides to use local port TID = 2005 for this file transfer connection. An ACK packet with block number 0 is passed to the UDP at Host B with a request to send using the source TID 2005 and destination TID 1988.

(4)   A TFTP connection is established between Hosts A and B. The UDP port 1988 at Host A, and UDP port 2005 at Host B identify the connection.

(5)   The TFTP at Host A sends its first data packet (DATA block 1, indicating a length of 512 bytes).

(6)   The TFTP at Host B sends back an acknowledgment packet (ACK1) after DATA1 is correctly received at Host B.

(7)   Host A sends out the second data packet (DATA2), which in this example is assumed to be lost. Thus, DATA2 will never be acknowledged by Host B.

(8)   At Host B, after a time-out period, the TFTP will retransmit its earlier ACK packet (ACK1). This will cause Host A to retransmit its block 2 data (DATA2).

(9)   The TFTP at Host A retransmits its second data packet (DATA2).

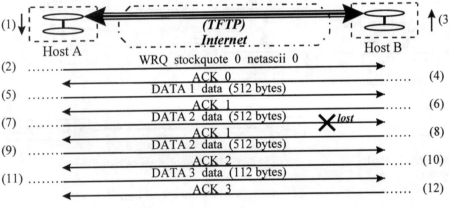

Figure 11-36   An Typical TFTP Scenario.

(10) The TFTP at Host B will send an acknowledgment packet (ACK2), provided DATA2 is correctly received at Host B.

(11) Assume the TFTP at Host A is sending the last data packet (DATA3) with a length of 112 bytes.

(12) The DATA3 packet is acknowledged by Host B after it is correctly received. Host B may close the connection at this time, but usually it will wait for a while because if

the ACK packet is not received by Host A, it may decide to retransmit the same data packet (DATA3). It is possible that Host B may close the connection before receiving the retransmission from Host A. Likewise, after receiving ACK3, Host A can close the TFTP connection.

11.5.5 Simple Mail Transfer Protocol (SMTP)

The Simple Mail Transfer Protocol (SMTP) is one of the earliest protocols of the TCP/IP suite, and is specified in standard RFC 821.

Figure 11-37(A) illustrates the SMTP model. When a user sends a mail request, a Sending SMTP establishes a TCP connection to a Receiving SMTP. The Receiving SMTP may be the ultimate destination for the mail, or an intermediate reply point. SMTP commands are generated by the Sending SMTP, and responses to these commands are sent from the Receiving SMTP in the form of SMTP replies.

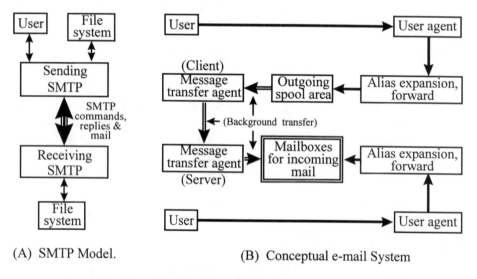

(A) SMTP Model.   (B) Conceptual e-mail System

Figure 11-37   SMTP Model and a Conceptual e-mail System.

After a TCP connection has been established, the Sending SMTP generates a "MAIL FROM" command indicating who the mail is from in the <reverse path>. If the Receiving SMTP is able to accept this mail, it responds with a "250 OK" reply. If it cannot, a reply indicating rejection is sent.

Next, the Sending SMTP generates a "RCPT TO" indicating who the recipient of the mail is in the <forward path>. If the Receiving SMTP is able to accept mail for that recipient, it responds with a "250 OK" reply. If it cannot, a reply indicating rejection is sent. The Sending and Receiving SMTPs will negotiate several recipients. After the negotiation has been completed, the Sending SMTP sends a "DATA" command indicating that it is "ready to send mail". The Receiving SMTP responds with an intermediate reply labeled "354", and actual mail can be sent.

The mail will be terminated by an escape sequence such as "<CRLF><CRLF>". If the receiving SMTP has successfully processed the mail data, it responds with a "250 OK". Note that the dialogue proceeds in a "lock-step" sequence.

Figure 11-37(B) illustrates a conceptual view of an e-mail system. A user, typically a human sitting at a terminal, interacts with the user agent. A user agent is a mail program (software) that provides a user interface for entering and retrieving mail, and also allows the use of aliases and mailing lists. The mail program consults a database of valid aliases that are used as replacement for the recipients names/addresses. Recipients that do not appear in the alias database remain unchanged.

In an e-mail exchange, the remote machine may or may not be active (or connected) at the time the e-mail is sent by the Sending SMTP. If the remote machine is active (or connected), the Sending SMTP does not wait or abort the mail. Therefore, the mail transfer takes place as a background process. In order to deal with this type of delayed mail delivery, a typical mail system places the mail in a queue (private storage) called a "*spooling area*". The system then initiates a transfer of the mail over a connection, with the mail server as the destination. If the transfer is successful, the mail is stored in a mailbox associated with the destination. The mail is subsequently retrieved by the "destination human user" who interacts with the user agent (mail program) to access and read the mail. Several typical mail commands are listed below:

- Mail transaction commands: "MAIL", "RCPT", and "DATA".
- Verifying and expanding commands: "VRFY", and "EXPN".
- Sending and mailing commands: "SEND", "SOML", and "SAML".
- Opening and closing commands: "HELO", and "QUIT".
- Other commands: "HELP", "TURN" , and "NOOP".

Example 11-21: Describe a typical e-mail format.

An e-mail that uses the NVT ASCII (Network Virtual Terminal-ASCII) format for the entire e-mail transaction has three components, described as follows:

- Envelope: This is the information used by the Message Transfer Agents (MTAs) to deliver the e-mail. In SMTP, it is based on the "MAIL" or "RCPT" commands. The contents and use of the envelope are given in standard RFC 821.

- Header: Standard RFC 822 defines the format and functions of several header fields. Each field adopts a generic form of "a name followed by a colon and a value".

Included in the header are the following fields: "From", "To", "Date", "Subject", "Cc", "Message-Id", "Received", etc.

- Body: This is the actual user information exchanged between the "sending user" and the "receiving user".

11.5.6 Multipurpose Internet Mail Extension (MIME)

SMTP is a widely used e-mail protocol. However, it has limitations that include 7-bit ASCII text, and a maximum length of 1,000 characters. These limitations make it difficult to transmit executable files and other large binary objects. The Multipurpose Internet Mail Extensions (MIME) is designed to overcome some of these limitations, and is compatible with standard RFC 822. MIME is specified in three RFC standards:

- RFC 2045: It specifies the various headers used to describe the structure of a MIME message.

- RFC 2046: It defines the general structure of the MIME media typing system, and the initial set of media types.

- RFC 2047: It describes extensions to standard RFC 822, to allow non-ASCII text data in the message header fields.

The characteristics of MIME can be summarized as providing a re-definition of the RFC 822 message format so that it can be used to support several applications:

- Text message bodies and header information in character sets other than ASCII.
- Extended formats for non-text message bodies.
- Multi-part message bodies.

The goal of MIME is to retain as much compatibility with RFC 822 as possible, while also providing an extension to other types of content and headers besides ASCII format (e.g., binary, audio, video, and other media types).

11.5.7 Simple Network Management Protocol (SNMP)

The Simple Network Management Protocol (SNMP) provides one of the most widely used network management frameworks and protocol for LANs and internetworks. SNMP has evolved as two versions:

(1) The first version of SNMP was developed as an interim protocol until OSI management protocols became available. SNMPv1 was documented during 1990-91 in the following four RFC standards:

* RFC 1155: It specifies the structure and identification of management information for TCP/IP-based internets.

* RFC 1157: It specifies SNMP.

* RFC 1212: It specifies concise Management Information Base (MIB) definitions.

* RFC 1213: It specifies MIB for network management of TCP/IP-based internet using MIB II.

(2) Attempts were made for several years to keep SNMP compatible with the Common Management Information Protocol (CMIP) of OSI, with the objective of eventually migrating from SNMP to CMIP. However, this plan never matured, and subsequently the 1996 enhancements made to SNMPv1 were designed to correct deficiencies in the areas of security and manager-to-manger communications. Thus, SNMPv2 was developed and is specified in the following RFC standards:

* RFC 1901: It specifies the introduction of community-based SNMPv2.

* RFC 1902: It specifies the structure of management information for SNMPv2.

* RFC 1906: It specifies transport mappings for SNMPv2.

A more detailed description of SNMP is provided in Chapter 12.

11.5.8 Hypertext Transfer Protocol (HTTP)

The HyperText Transfer Protocol (HTTP) is used for distributed, collaborative hypermedia systems. For example, it has been used in the World-Wide Web (www) global information initiative since 1990. The HTTP/1.1 is specified in standard RFC 2068.

HTTP is a generic, stateless, object-oriented protocol for communications between user agents and servers, proxies, or gateways. It is a request-response protocol: a client sends a request to a server in the form of a request method, Uniform Resource Identifier (URI), and protocol version, followed by a MIME-like message. That is, messages are passed using a format similar to MIME. The server responds with a status-line that includes the protocol version and a "MIME-like" message containing user information.

Most HTTP communication is initiated by a User-Agent (UA) and consists of a request to be applied to a resource located on an "origin-server". User Agents are typically browsers, editors, spiders, web-traversing robots, or similar end-user tools. An "origin-server" is a server where a given resource resides or can be created. A resource is a network data object or service that is identified by a URI. A URI is a formatted string that identifies a resource via a name (e.g., Uniform Resource Name: URN), location (e.g., Uniform Resource Locator: URL), or any other characteristics. HTTP messages can be:

• Request messages having components described as follows:

* Request line [e.g., GET http://www.w3.org/pub/www/proj.HTML].

* General header(s): They apply to both request and response messages, but not to the entity being transferred (e.g., date or transfer-encoding).

* Request header(s): They pass additional information about request or client to the server, e.g., if-modified-since, if-match, or user-agent.

* Entity header(s): They are optional "metainformation" about the entity-body or resource (e.g., last-modified, or content-MD5).

* Message body: It is the actual user content of a message.

- Response messages having components described as follows:

    * Status line [e.g., HTTP/1.1 202 (accepted)].

    * Response header(s) (e.g., Allow, GET, HEAD, or PUT).

    * General header(s): Same as Request message.

    * Entity headers: Same as Request message.

    * Message body: Same as Request message.

- Method using several techniques described as follows:

    * "GET" retrieves information identified by a request Uniform Resource Identifier (URI).

    * "HEAD" retrieves only "metainformation" (POST) for posting messages to bulletin boards and/or newsgroups. "HEAD" also retrieves "metainformation" (POST) for providing block data forms, or appending to databases.

    * "PUT" requests that the enclosed entity be stored in the request URI.

    * "OPTIONS" requests information about communication options.

    * DELETE requests message to be deleted.

11.5.9 Dynamic Host Configuration Protocol (DHCP)

The Dynamic Host Configuration Protocol (DHCP) is used to provide configuration parameters to internet hosts. DHCP is built on a client-server model in which a DHCP server allocates network addresses and delivers configuration parameters to "dynamically configured" internet hosts. The DHCP parameters include the subnet mask, Maximum Transmission Unit (MTU), IP address, default Time To Live (TTL), list of default routers with a preference level for each router, and link-layer parameters [e.g., Address Resolution Protocol (ARP) cache time-out per interface]. Besides delivering configuration parameters, DHCP has a second component that provides a mechanism for allocating IP addresses to hosts. Any network can apply one or more of the three IP address allocation mechanisms described as follows:

- Automatic allocation: The DHCP server assigns a permanent IP address to the client when using this mechanism.

- Dynamic allocation: The server assigns a temporary IP address to a client for a specific time interval. This time interval may be extended if the client requests an extension. It can also be relinquished explicitly by the client. Therefore, thiis mechanism allows an IP address to be reused, and it permits a pool of addresses to be shared by several internet hosts.

- Manual allocation: The network administrator assigns the address, and the DHCP merely conveys this assigned address to the client when using this mechanism.

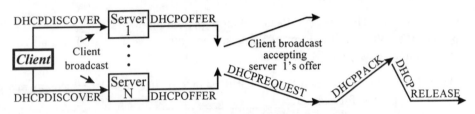

Figure 11-38   DHCP Message Example.

Example 11-22: Describe how DHCP messages are utilized.

Figure 11-37 illustrates the utilization of several typical DHCP messages. The client sends a broadcast message called "DHCPDISCOVER" to locate available DHCP servers in a network. It is possible that one or more servers will respond to this broadcast message with a unicast "DHCPOFFER" message, which offers configuration parameters to the client.

Next, the client may send out a "DHCPREQUEST" broadcast message, accepting the offer made by one of the servers (e.g., server 1) and implicitly declining the offers from all other servers. The chosen server (server 1) sends an acknowledgment of the configuration parameters (including the committed network address) to the client. At the end of the data transfer, the client sends a "DHCPRELEASE" message to relinquish the network address, and thereby cancel the remaining lease on the IP address.

Besides the five messages shown in Figure 11-38, there are four other DHCP messages available. They are briefly described as follows:

- "DHCPNAK": This message may be used by a server to indicate that the client's notion of a network address is invalid, or that the client's lease has expired for an address.

- "DHCPDECLINE": This message may be used by a client to inform the server that a particular network address is already in use.

- "DHCPINFORM": This message may be used by a client to ask the server to provide only the configuration parameters since the client already "owns" an address, or it may be externally configured.

- "DHCPREQUEST": This message, in addition to the application described earlier, may also be used by a client to confirm a previously allocated network address, or to extend the lease on a particular address.

Review Questions I for Chapter 11:

(1) TCP/IP includes the following commonly used applications protocols: _____, _____, _____, _____ and _____. The first experimental packet switching network, _____ (began operation in 1969) is considered to be the start of TCP/IP technology.

(2) (True, False) The official documentation pertaining to TCP/IP technology is primarily available in the form of Request For Comments (RFCs). Thus, all RFCs must be treated as TCP/IP standards.

(3) Once a RFC becomes an official TCP/IP standard, it can be accessed on many Internet web sites, for example: _____.

(4) List three primary components of a TCP/IP Internet: _____, _____ and _____.

(5) The four TCP/IP protocol layers and their corresponding OSI layers are: _____/_____ layer (OSI layers _____), _____ layer (OSI layer __), _____ layer (OSI layer __), and _____ layer (OSI layers _____).

(6) The setup phase of a TCP/IP connection involves two events: the server _____ for connection, and the client _____ a connection, and _____ processes.

(7) The software that gives the network its multi-user, and multi-tasking capabilities is called _____, which can be viewed as the _____ of a LAN for determining the type of _____ that can be deployed in the network.

(8) The enhanced Internet layer protocol is known as _____, which is adopted to improve the present _____.

(9) IP does not provide mechanisms for dealing with lost packets, _____ or _____. It is the responsibility of the _____ protocol to deal with these problems.

(10) The four parts in the IP address are: _____ (____), _____ (____), _____, and _____. The traditional IP address notation for the address of "10001000 01010101 00110011 00010001" is _____.

(11) A domain is an administrative concept with no relation to the physical internet's subnetworks. A complete domain name for a node is _____ that exist in the _____ from the node to the _____, and are separated by _____. There are seven defined generic Top-Level Domain (TLD) names: ____, ____, ____, ____, ____, ____, and ____. The ISO-3166 Rec. suggests a _____ country code, for example, ___ for the USA, and ___ for Great Britain.

11.6 NETWORK INTERFACES

This section describes how TCP/IP operates over several typical subnets, including Serial Line IP (SLIP, RFC 1055), Point-to-Point Protocol (PPP, RFC 1661), DIX Ethernet (RFC 894), SONET (RFC 2176), IEEE 802 LAN (RFC 1042), and X.25 and packet mode ISDN (RFC 1356). Other subnets over which TCP/IP can operate, such as High Performance Parallel Interface (HIPPI), fiber channel, Fiber Distributed Data Interface (FDDI) and Switched Multimegabit Data Service (SMDS) are not described in this book.

11.6.1 SLIP

It should be noted that Serial Line IP (SLIP) is widely used for point-to-point serial connections running TCP/IP, even though SLIP is not an internet standard. The RFC 1055 standard merely provides documentation for the "de facto standard SLIP".

SLIP is typically used for dedicated serial links, and sometimes for dial-up links that connect hosts or routers with other hosts or routers operating at line speeds of 2.4 ~ 19.2 kbps. It is a very simple packet framing protocol (Figure 11-39) that allows easy implementation. SLIP does not provide addressing, error detection, compression, or type identification. The packet framing of SLIP is based on four special characters: (1) "END", which is a byte represented by "11000000" (192); (2) "ESC", which is a byte represented by "11011011" (219); (3) An "ESC" byte followed by "11011100" (220); and (4) An "ESC" byte followed by "11010011" (211).

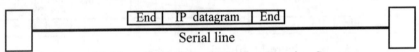

Figure 11-39   Series Line IP Packet Framing Structure.

SLIP simply starts the data transfer by sending IP packets, and when the last data byte has been sent an "END" character is transmitted. It has also been suggested that an "END" character be sent to start the data transmission. Since there is no "standard" SLIP specification, there is no maximum packet size defined for SLIP. The most common maximum size SLIP packet is 1,006 bytes, excluding the framing characters. Note that:

- If the SLIP transmitter encounters an "END" within the data message, it should be replaced by two bytes: "ESC" followed by "11011100".

- If the SLIP transmitter encounters an "ESC" within the data message, it should be replaced by two bytes: "ESC" followed by "11010011".

11.6.2 PPP

Point-to-Point Protocol (PPP) is an internet standard that is designed to provide a common solution for connecting a variety of hosts, bridges and routers using simple links that can transport multi-protocol datagrams between peers. The PPP is designed to overcome the deficiencies (addressing, error detection, ...) of SLIP. The PPP physical links can have different speeds, but the data links will still provide full-duplex operations and deliver data packets in order. Three main components of a PPP are described as follows:

(1) PPP encapsulation: The PPP encapsulation scheme supports multiplexing different network layer protocols concurrently over the same data link. The encapsulated PPP packet contains three fields:

 * Protocol field (one or two bytes): It is used to identify the protocol type of the datagram encapsulated in the information field of the packet.

 * Information field (0 or more bytes): It contains the datagram for the protocol whose type is specified in the "Protocol" field. The maximum length for the information field (excluding the protocol field, but including padding) is called the Maximum Receive Unit (MRU). The MRU has a default value of 1,500 bytes, but PPP implementations may allow negotiation for use of other MRU lengths.

 * Padding field: The information field may be needed to be padded with additional bytes to fill-out the MRU. It is the responsibility of each protocol to distinguish "real information" from "padding bytes".

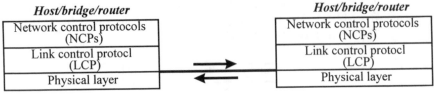

Figure 11-40   Point-to-Point Protocol.

(2) Link Control Protocol (LCP): As shown in Figure 11-40, to establish communications over a PPP link each end (a host, bridge, or router) of the link exchanges packets using the LCP to configure and test the data link. Even after establishing a PPP link, a peer may need to be authenticated using LCP packets.

(3) Network Control Protocol (NCP): After the data link has been established and authentication is complete, one or more network layer protocols can be configured by the use of appropriate NCP packets. Once all the network layer protocols have been configured, datagrams from each protocol can be sent over the link.

11.6.2.1 PPP Link Control Protocol (LCP) Packets

There are three kinds of Link Control Packets (LCPs) used in PPP: (1) link configuration, (2) link termination, and (3) link maintenance packets. They are briefly described as follows:

(1) Link configuration packet: This type of packet is used to establish and configure a PPP data link. Whenever PPP wants to "open a connection", it transmits a "configure-request" packet that contains a list of configuration options. If the options in the "configure-request" packet are recognized and all values are accepted, the receiving PPP will send out a "configure-ack" LCP packet.

It should be understood that the receiving PPP will still send a "configure-nak" if every option is recognized, but some values are not acceptable. Likewise, the receiving PPP will send a "configure-reject" if any option cannot be recognized or accepted for negotiation.

(2) Link termination packet: This type of LCP packet is used to terminate (end) a PPP data link connection. An LCP wishing to close a connection issues a "terminate-request" LCP packet. In response to this packet, the receiving end sends out a "terminate-ack" packet.

(3) Link maintenance packet: There are several link maintenance packets designed to manage and debug a data link. Some of them are:

* "echo-request" and "echo-reply" codes: These codes are used to perform loopback testing, debugging, link quality determination, and performance testing.

* "code-reject": This code is used to indicate that a peer element in the network is operating with a different version.

* "protocol-reject": This code is used to indicate that a peer is using a unsupported protocol.

* "discard-request": This code is used to "ask" a peer to discard specific packets.

11.6.2.2 PPP Link Operations

To establish communications, each end of a PPP link must first send LCP packets to configure and test the data link. As shown in Figure 11-41, after the link has been established the peer can be authenticated. After authentication is complete, the PPP must send NCP packets to choose and configure one or more network layer protocols. Eventually, datagrams from the network layer can be sent over the data link. The link remains configured until explicit LCP or NCP packets are sent to close the link down or an external event occurs (e.g., intervention by a network administrator, or expiration of an inactivity timer).

The PPP link operation can be divided into several phases (Figure 11-41), which are briefly described as follows:

* **Dead phase**: A PPP link begins and ends at this phase. Typically, a link will return to the "Dead" phase after disconnecting from a modem.

- **Link establishment phase**: An exchange of LCP configure packets initiates the link establishment phase. The exchange is complete and the LCP enters the "opened" state when a "configure-ack" LCP packet has been sent and received. During this interval, various configuration options that are independent of the particular network layer protocols can be negotiated.

- **Authentication phase**: This phase is optional. On some links, a peer may be required to authenticate itself before network layer protocol packets are exchanged.

- **Network layer protocol phase**: After the previously described phases have been completed, each network layer protocol must be separately configured by using an appropriate NCP that can be opened or closed at any time.

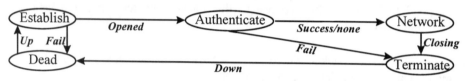

Figure 11-41   Various Operating Phase of a PPP Link Connection.

11.6.3 IP over SONET

SONET/SDH has become a widely deployed physical layer link technology. It is expected that this trend will continue in the future. Therefore, IP over SONET/SDH is a very promising protocol. To transport IP over SONET-SDH, certain minimum data link layer services are required. These services include: framing each IP datagram packet, protocol identification, and addressing. The RFC 2136 standard specifies the services required for PPP. The PPP encapsulation of IP datagrams is shown in Figure 11-42(A).

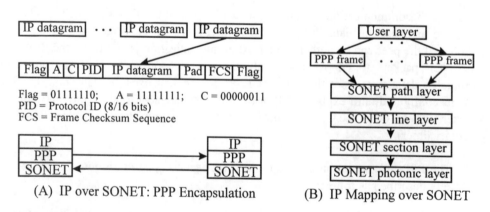

(A) IP over SONET: PPP Encapsulation   (B) IP Mapping over SONET

Figure 11-42   PPP Encapsulation of IP, and IP over SONET.

Mapping PPP frames onto a SONET physical frame is shown in Figure 11-42(B) (SONET/SDH frames described in Chapter 6). First, the PPP frames are mapped into the Synchronous Payload Envelope (SPE) of a SONET frame. The SPE includes the SONET Path OverHead (POH) bytes for path (the end-to-end SONET physical link connection) Operations, Administration and Maintenance (OA&M) functions. After the path layer performs its functions, it gives the SPE to the SONET line layer for implementing the Line OverHead (LOH) bytes' functions. The section layer applies Section OverHead (SOH) bytes to the SONET frame, thereby completing the formation of a SONET frame (containing PPP frames for transmission). The photonic layer is only required if the SONET signal (frames) is to be carried by optical fibers. This layer is required to have the appropriate optical output power, spectral width, operating wavelength (including nominal, minimum, and maximum wavelengths), etc.

11.6.4 IP over DIX Ethernet and IEEE-802 LANs

The Ethernet from Digital, Intel, and Xerox (DIX) was one of the earliest TCP/IP applications, and it has been widely used for data networking.

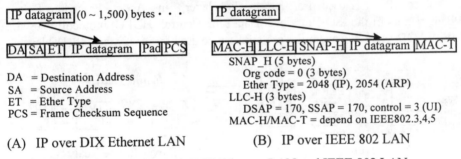

(A) IP over DIX Ethernet LAN   (B) IP over IEEE 802 LAN

Figure 11-43   IP Over DIX Ethernet LAN and IEEE 802 LAN.

The Ethernet frame has a 2-byte Ether Type (ET) field that identifies the protocol information contained in the frame [Figure 11-43(A)]. For IP applications, this field has a value of "00001000 00000000 (0800hex)". The length of the information field is between 46 and 1,500 bytes. Therefore, the IP datagram or ARP message to be transmitted is padded with as many bytes as necessary (up to 46 bytes) to ensure the minimum information field length of 46 bytes. Note that padding is not part of the IP datagram.

The Source Address (SA) and Destination Address (DA) are each 48-bit fields. In the case of unicast transmission, the source and destination addresses refer to the Ethernet Network Interface Cards (NICs). When an IP datagram or ARP message is broadcast to all devices on the Ethernet, the appropriate broadcast address (all 1's) should be used as the Ethernet Destination Address (DA). The resolution (translation) of IP addresses to Ethernet addresses for devices on the same subnet can be done by using static tables stored in all devices, or via ARP request and reply messages.

Figure 11-43(B) shows the frame structure of IP over an IEEE 802 LAN (e.g., IEEE 802.3 CSMA/CD based, 10BaseT, 100BaseT, IEEE802.4 token bus, or token ring).

Figure 11-43(B) illustrates the standard encapsulation of IP and ARP packets in an IEEE 802 LAN. Packets are sent using IEEE 802.2 LLC (Logical Link Control), which is an unacknowledged connectionless operation. Thus, only unnumbered LLC frames are used. That is, frames carrying information are identified as Unnumbered Information (UI) with the control field value being 3. The Destination Service Access Point (DSAP) and the Source Access Unit (SSAP) are set to "10110100" (180). The SubNet Access Protocol (SNAP) uses a 24-bit code, which is set to all zeros for IP or ARP. The Ether Type (ET) is set to 2,048 for IP and 2,054 for ARP.

11.6.5 IP over X.25 or over Frame Relay

IP datagrams and other network layer protocol information can be sent over an X.25 network. Standard RFC 1356 describes the details of this process. X.25 applies a connection-oriented virtual circuit approach that uses a three-layer interface between the user device and an X.25 network switch [Figure 11-44(A)]. For the network layer, Packet Layer Protocol (PLP) is used. For the data link layer, Link Access Procedure Balanced (LAPB) [a variant of the ISO High-level Data Link Control (HDLC) protocol] is used. An X.21, EIA 232D, X.21 bis, or similar protocol can be used for the physical (PHY) layer.

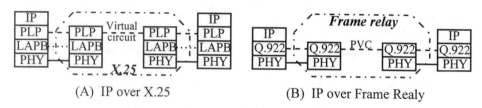

(A) IP over X.25   (B) IP over Frame Realy

Figure 11-44   IP over X.25 and IP over Frame Relay.

Figure 11-44(B) illustrates IP over frame relay. This is considered to be the second generation packet switching protocol. Standard RFC 1490 provides a description of this type of applications.

11.7 TRADITIONAL TELECOMMUNICATIONS SERVICES

Telecommunications networks have been described in Chapters 1 through 10 of this book. A simplified view of a network is shown in Figure 11-45. A telecommunications connection typically consists of two end-offices (Central Offices) that are the originating and terminating switching centers, and a backbone (back-haul) network to provide a high-speed/long-distance transport facility. The facility connecting the Customer Premises

Equipment (CPE) to the originating or terminating central office is known as a loop. A loop is typically implemented using twisted pair wires. Optical fibers and coaxial cables are not typically deployed in the loop for traditional Public Switched Telephone Networks (PSTNs). Recently, wireless loop (fixed wireless or airloop) has been implemented in several areas. This loop is typically an analog facility, therefore modems are required for data transmission in this application.

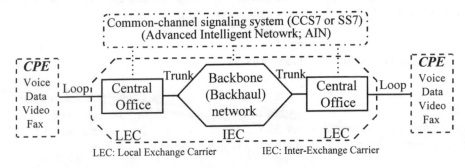

Figure 11-45   A Simplified Telecommunications Network Connection.

A mixture of facilities are used in the backbone (backhaul) network. They can be 4-wire facilities (two twisted-wire pairs), coaxial cables, digital (microwave) radio systems, digital satellite systems, and optical fibers. The connections between the Central Office and the backbone network are known as "trunks". Overall administration of the telecommunications network is accomplished by using a separate Common Channel Signaling system (e.g., CCS7, SS7) to carry control information.

11.7.1 Traditional Voice Communications

A telephone call can be an intra-office call (a local call), for which the switching office serves as both the originating and the terminating Central Office. That is, a local call defined as a call that does not involve with the long-distance (toll) telephone services, and typically involves a fixed flat rate charge. In some cities, in additional to monthly charge, a local call service is charged using call message units. The traditional Local Exchange Carrier (LEC) network contains the following components:

- Loop facilities: both "wire-line" and "wireless" facilities

- Digital switching machines: using stored-program control architecture

- Backbone facilities: wires, coaxial cables, and fibers

- Common Channel Signaling system (e.g., CCS7 or SS7): typically having Advanced Intelligent Network (AIN) capabilities

- Frame relay and/or ATM overlays: used for data customer services

A telephone call can involve one or more Inter-Exchange Carrier (IEC or IXC) networks, which contain components similar to those used in LEC networks (i.e., switching machines, transmission terminals, and transmission facilities). Transmission facilities are known as trunks, which are typically digital radio, coaxial cables, or optical fibers. The IEC switching machines have higher speeds and a larger throughput. Signaling systems are often equipped with proprietary intelligent network capabilities. In addition, for international applications gateway exchange offices are required to perform protocol conversion (e.g., A-law/μ-law conversion, etc.).

11.7.2 Traditional Local Loop Transmission

The traditional loop facilities used to access to a local exchange network are analog twisted-pair wires. The loop facility has a typical bandwidth of 3,000 to 4,000 Hz and a signal-to-noise ratio of about 25 to 30 dB (Figure 11-46). The system was originally designed to carry a human voice which has a typical bandwidth of 4 kHz.

For data signals to be carried by the traditional loop facility, a modem must be applied. The speeds of modems improved rapidly during the late 1980's and early 1990's (from 2.4 kbps to 56 kbps). Higher data speed transmission has been continuously demanded by subscribers.

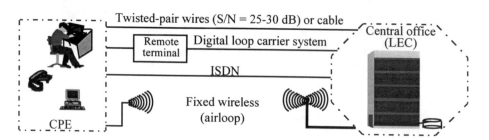

Figure 11-46   Various Access Facilities to Local Exchange Networks.

An Integrated Digital Loop Carrier system (IDLC) has been developed to carry voice, data, and video information over digital facilities such as the T1 carrier system in the US. This type of system provides a substantial improvement in subscriber loop transmission quality, especially for users that are remotely located from the central office. For metropolitan applications, IDLC provides an excellent method for reducing wire duct congestion in the areas where telecommunications networks are heavily deployed. Detailed description of IDLC and its related transmission terminals is provided in Chapter 6.

For quick deployment of services, fixed wireless or airloop access technology has proven to be effective. This approach is especially important in countries with limited existing "wire-line" facilities (description of wireless local loop in Chapter 8).

11.7.3 Integrated Service Digital Network (ISDN) Subscriber Lines

Even though ISDN signal rates and standards have been defined since the early 1970's, this service has not been made generally available to subscribers on a wide-spread basis.

The different ISDN rates that have been defined are H11 (with a facility rate of 1.544 Mbps), H12 (2.048 Mbps), H21 (6.312 Mbps), H22 (8.448 Mbps), H31 (34.368 Mbps), H32 (44.736 Mbps), and H4 (139.264 Mbps). However, in the USA, only two rates have been implemented:

- **Basic ISDN rate**: It contains 2B channels and one D channel (B for information bearing, and D for data link functions), and known as Basic Rate Interface (BRI) ISDN.

  * B channel: A 64 kbps full-duplex channel that can be used to carry (1) circuit-switched voice signals; (2) circuit-switched data services for either downloading or file transfer; and/or (3) packet-switched data services with interactive bursty data applications.

  * D channel: A 16 kbps full-duplex channel used to send signaling messages, and normally applies statistical multiplexing for interactive bursty data.

- **Primary ISDN rate**: It contains 23B channels and one D channel for US applications. The B channels perform the same function as in BRI ISDN applications. The D channel also performs the same functions, however it is increased to a 64 kbps channel for PRI (Primary Rate Interface) ISDN applications.

11.7.4 Digital Subscriber Line (DSL)

Access loop facilities are traditionally analog technology, which has transmission speed limitations. The maximum speeds are not suitable for future subscriber needs. Therefore, several new technologies have been developed to increase the access bandwidth (speed).

- Digital Subscriber Line (DSL): Three technologies have been developed to provide higher speed access than traditional analog loop facilities:

  (1) High-bit rate Digital Subscriber Line (HDSL): Using one twisted-pair wire, it has a speed of 768 kbps symmetric. Three pairs are required for T1.5 services or 2.048 Mbps services.

  (2) Single-line (or symmetric) Digital Subscriber Line (SDSL): It has been proposed to allocate bandwidth at the same speed for bidirectional communications. This line can be used for computer servers or other devices that require symmetric bandwidth.

  (3) Very high bit-rate Digital Subscriber Line (VDSL):This technique provides a very high bit-rate transmission in the downstream direction (from network to user) over limited distances. Its primary application is Switched Digital Video (SDV) services.

- Asymmetric Digital Subscriber Line (ADSL): This type of subscriber line provides services asymmetrically for upstream and downstream communications. The ADSL characteristics are described as follows:

  * The upstream transmission (from user to network) has a speed between 18 kbps and 1 Mbps, depending on distance.

  * The downstream transmission (from network to user) has a speed between 1.5 Mbps and 9 Mbps, depending on distance. These services include www page downloading and one or more broadcast video channels.

  * An ASDL line can also provide a baseband analog voice channel, as in traditional loop facilities.

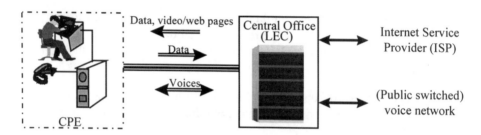

Figure 11-47   Asymmetric Digital Subscriber Line (ADSL).

11.7.5 Voice Digitization

The traditional voice digitization technology is Pulse Code Modulation (PCM), which is described in Chapter 6. To reduce the required bandwidth for carrying speech signals, bit compression schemes have been developed. These methods can be classified into two groups:

(1) Waveform speech encoding: The most commonly used scheme is Pulse Code Modulation (PCM: see Table 11-6 for comparison between PCM and others). It has been implemented in A-law and μ-law digital networks since the early 1960's. An analog voice signal with a bandwidth of 4 kHz is fed to a PCM coder, and the output is a 64 kbps digitized voice signal that is ready for digital networking.

The basic PCM coding method has been modified to form many other schemes: Differential Pulse Code Modulation (DPCM), Adaptive DPCM (ADPCM), Delta Modulation (DM), and Adaptive DM (ADM). Not all of these methods have been adopted for the modern digital networking, but some have been standardized. As shown in Table 11-6, ITU-T G.726 and G.727 have standardized 16, 24, 32, and 40 kbps ADPCM voice digitization methods. These standards have been adopted for ISDN services. ADM technology is widely used in audio Compact Disk (CD) systems.

Hybrid speech encoding: A simplified description this technique is provided in Appendix 11-1 at the end of this chapter. Three commonly used methods are : (1) Code Excited Linear Predictive (CELP) coding, which has been implemented in the North American digital wireless system known as IS-136 [Including Low Data rate CELP (LD-CELP) specified in ITU-T G.728]; (2) Multi-Pulse Linear Predictive (MPLP) coding, including is the Regular Pulse Excited Long Term Predictive (RPE-LTP) coding, which has been implemented in the worldwide digital wireless system known as GSM; (3) Extended Variable-Rate Coding (EVRC); and, (4) Maximum Likelihood Quantization (MLQ). Table 11-6 compares various speech encoding methods that have been used in different telecommunications applications.

Table 11-6   Comparison among Various Speech Encoders.

Encoding method	*Bit rate (kbps)*	*Notes*
Pulse Code Modulation	64	The A- and μ-law system; G.711
Adapted Differential PCM	*16~40*	*ADPCM; G.726, G.727*
LD-CELP	*16*	*G.728*
ACELP	*8*	*Algebraic CELP; G.729*
CDMA-CELP	*13*	*IS-95*
EVRC	*8*	
VSELP	*8*	*IS-54/136*
RPE-LTP	*13*	*GSM*
MLQ	*5.3, 6.4*	*G.923.1*

11.7.6 Voice Services and Feature Group B Voice Service

The voice services provided over the traditional public switched network have been widely accepted for more than a century. Networks involved in voice services have the following characteristics:

- **Fees based on use**: For domestic local connection, service charges may be monthly or charged on the basis of message units. For domestic long-distance and international calls, charges are typically based on the connection time (i.e., length of the call).

- **Service open to competition**: The services known as feature group D are designed for "equal access" in the USA. Prior to divestiture of the US telephone system, customers of different IECs could not access the public switched network equally. For example, AT&T customers could make a long-distance call by dialing 1+nnn+nnn+nnnn. In contrast, other IEC customers were required to dial a special pre-assigned (multi-digits) number before dialing the area code plus the telephone number. Feature group D defines the same number of digits for any IEC customer placing a call: 10xxx + area code + phone number.

- **High quality transmission**: Voice over the traditional Public Switched Telephone Network (PSTN) is known as trunk quality voice services. The service is reliable, and has a minimum delay. These services are typically dedicated full-duplex 64 kbps.

- **Sophisticated Network Infrastructure**: This network is typically implemented using the high-capacity and excellent quality optical fibers (the most popular transport facilities). Modern switches are Stored Program Control (SPC) machines, which provide various customer services. Standardized signaling protocol [SS7 with its associated Advanced Intelligent Network (AIN)] allows fast and reliable connection setup and resource allocation.

11.8 VOICE AND FAX OVER INTERNET PROTOCOL (VoIP AND FoIP)

For many years alternatives have been developed (and will continue to be developed) for carrying voice signals over media other than the traditional Public Switched Telephone Networks (PSTNs). The most promising scheme is the Integrated Service Digital Network (ISDN), with the original intent for carrying various services (voice, data, video, …) over a single network. The motivation for ISDN is to provide less expensive phone service, yet preserve acceptable quality.

The first PC-to-PC voice call was introduced by VocalTec. In this arrangement client **IPhone** was practically "free of charge" since it effectively bypassed the Public Switched Telephone Network (PSTN) tariff. This service requires proprietary directories, and a "third party" must provide access to real telephones. However, voice transmission quality is very low compared to PSTN (e.g., long delays and congestion).

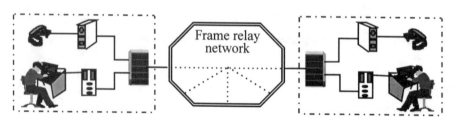

Figure 11-48   Additive Voice Capability to Frame Relay.

Since the mid-1980s frame relay technology has proven to be an effective method for data stream transport. Frame relay is considered a fast "second generation" packet switching technology. The addition of voice capability to frame relay services has made it more attractive. Figure 11-48 illustrates this arrangement in which Frame Relay Access Devices (FRADs) are applied.

11.8.1 Why Voice Over IP?

There are many reasons why the telecommunications industry has shown a strong interest in implementing Voice over IP (VoIP). The fundamental reason is the general trend towards lower costs for services. The initial goal of developing "voice/fax over IP" technology will yield a more efficient network infrastructure so that all traffic (e.g., voice, image, audio, fax, and video) will be carried over packet networks. These networks will also provide simple management functions, thereby encouraging an evolution from "closed" to "open" environments for telecommunications services. This in turn will create additional opportunities for new services and innovation. Four factors are considered triggers for promoting "voice/fax over IP" technology:

(1) **Expected lower costs**: The revenue from customers making US long-distance calls is divided into two parts. One part stays with the IEC (e.g., AT&T, MCI or Sprint) and the other portion goes to the regional operating telephone company (e.g., Bell Atlantic). This latter part is called the access charge. Similarly, for international calls, part of the revenue goes to the called party's PT&T for handling the call. This is called the international settlement charge.

In contrast, an Internet Telephone Service Provider (ITSP) is "presently" classified in the US as an enhanced service provider, and thus is not subject to access or international settlement charges. ITSPs must pay network termination charges in most countries, but they are considerably lower than the access and international settlement charges. This arrangement may be changed by future laws, but less expensive international calls via the internet is still promising.

(2) **Strong competition**: Since the invention of the telephone, subscribers have always wanted the service charges to be reduced. The formation of more telephone service providers has made this expectation real. This phenomenon is by far the most obvious in North America. Deregulation in Europe will eventually lead to the same strong telecommunications competition that is seen in the USA.

(3) **Success of internet technology**: Internet access is practically available in every country. It is particularly popular in North America, the Far East (Japan, South Korea, Taiwan, Singapore, Hong Kong), Europe and the United Kingdom. The internet technology has been using many "de facto" standards that originated in the PC industry. In addition, both international and ANSI standard bodies have been active in establishing internet standards for TCP/IP and the WorldWide Web (www). Therefore, "Voice over IP" (VoIP) proponents believe there is a great opportunity to have a more flexible and feature-rich network at a lower cost.

(4) **Advanced technologies**: Bit compression technologies have been constantly advancing. The bit rate required to carry a voice signal is reducing from the traditional PCM rate by a factor of 8 or more, and speech quality is being improved to the level of the PSTN (known as trunk quality, defined in Appendix 11-1 at the end of this chapter).

Backbone networks have widely developed high-bandwidth optical fiber facilities, that yield excellent quality. The addition of Dense Wavelength Division Multiplexing (DWDM) technology increases the bandwidth by a factor of 30, 40, 80, or even higher.

This will result in extremely low bit rate transmission costs. This, in turn, will make high-bandwidth and low latency transmission (e.g., ATM) become feasible and economical. Voice over IP, IP over ATM, and ATM over SONET/SDH will develop into a global telecommunications trend.

Another important technology required for global voice services is echo control. Previously, echo cancellation was expensive to implement, it is now possible to achieve a 25 ~ 30 dB cancellation at affordable costs.

11.8.2 IP Evolution into Voice Connections

IP was established in 1969 for experimental APARNET applications. It provides a "best effort", connectionless, single priority service. IP was designed for non-real-time applications, and most access fees are flat-rate based on bandwidth. An open environment for IP has encouraged creativity and innovation. The IP explosion in popularity is linked to the availability of browsers and the worldwide web. Figure 11-49 illustrates a relatively new IP concept: several top level IP Service Providers (ISPs) provide services for interconnecting many local and regional ISPs, or connections to other top-level ISPs for wide area IP applications. A local or regional ISP can provide either dial-up IP services or direct access to IP services.

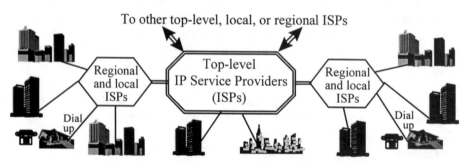

Figure 11-49   Local, Regional and Top-Level ISPs.

For Voice over IP (VoIP) applications, ISPs must provide gateways for "PC-to-phone" or "phone-to-phone" connections via IP networks (see Figure 11-50). The original VoIP application was intended for international calls, which are often expensive compared to domestic calls because of international settlement fees. VoIP savings are typically in the range of 30~70% over PSTN charges. However, service areas are limited to where the gateways have been deployed. One issue that must still be resolved is the transmission delay inherent in packet networks.

Gateways are typically placed in countries where high international tariffs are imposed and high calling volumes are experienced. These gateways must be able to support end users that interface with Public Switched Telephone Networks (PSTNs) via analog, digital (T1.5, T45, 2 Mbps, ...), or ISDN lines. An important consideration is the performance inconsistency among various networks.

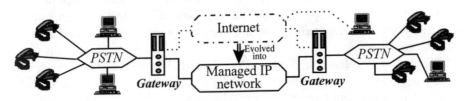

Figure 11-50   Gateways For IP Voice Connections.

As illustrated in Figure 11-50, the Internet has evolved into a managed IP network over time. The objective is to eliminate voice quality dependence on IP network performance. A top priority is providing voice traffic (either strictly , or priority of voice over data) to offer less expensive long-distance voice services. This was the initial plan to position ISPs as enhanced service providers, from a regulatory perspective. How successful or how long this arrangement will exist is unknown, but the basic concept is receiving wide acceptance and support.

Competition and the market growth is expected to be large. Global hardware and software sales of gateway equipment is predicted to be over one billion US$ by the beginning of the year 2000. Voice over IP and fax over IP services will be deployed by about half of the Fortune 1000 companies. Thus, this will cause a predicted revenue loss of billion US$ (or more) during the same time period for international markets, and approximately the amount for the US domestic long distance market one or two years later. These projects have been prepared by several leading research companies (e.g., Forrester, Frost & Sullivan, etc.).

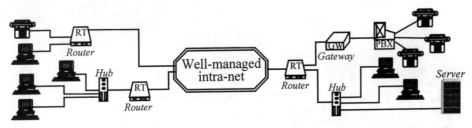

Figure 11-51   Intranet & Gateway for Intra-company and Tail-end Hop-off.

The IP network can be further improved to evolve into a well-managed network for supporting private or dedicated network applications such as an intranet, as shown in Figure 11-51. This arrangement provides the capability of adding voice services to the internet along with intra-company voice services and "tail-end hop-off" applications. In this configuration, which is similar to voice over frame relay, transmission problems are reduced. Figure 2-41 (Chapter 2) illustrates another view of this application.

11.8.3 Internet Telephone Service Provider (ITSP)

Voice over IP and/or fax over IP were first explored by several companies with the primary goal of cost savings. The original experimental setups were implemented as private networks. This arrangement also in more manageable performance control.

The Internet Telephone Service Providers (ITSPs) have started to build their networks extensively. Eventually these ITSPs will consolidate their corporations and networks. The initial objective of ITSPs is "cheap voice service", but this will eventually evolve into enhanced services.

Due to the rapid growth of ITSPs networks, many issues have surfaced that must be addressed and resolved. The following issues are most important, and require immediate attention: (1) IP services require standards for achieving interoperability; (2) The ability to interwork with Public Switched Telephone Networks (PSTNs) must be verified; (3) Regulatory issues must be resolved; (4) Global numbering plans must be generated and deployed; (5) Network management should be defined and standardized; and (6) Billing tariffs are required.

11.8.3.1 A Typical ITSP Call

Figure 11-52 illustrates a typical ITSP call with its required sequences (steps) shown by the number in parenthesis. To make an ITSP call multi-stage dialing may be required. The numbered steps shown in Figure 11-52 are described as follows:

(1)   The first step is to call the gateway using a local access number or a toll-free 800 (888, ...) number. Next, a Personal Identification Number (PIN) must be "keyed in" (may be required only for prepaid minutes). Finally, the destination telephone number is "keyed in".

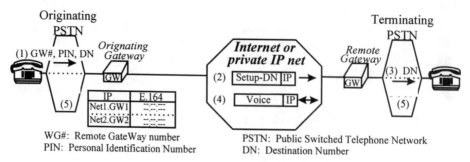

Figure 11-52   Sequence of an ITSP Call.

(2) The originating gateway identifies the remote (called) gateway number (a) by using standard E.164 for IP address resolution, and (b) by sending call setup via IP to the remote gateway.

(3)   The remote gateway calls the destination number and alerts the associated user (e.g., rings the phone).

(4)   Both gateways convert and format speech signals into IP datagrams for transporting bidirectional voice communications.

(5)   After the communication has begun, the originating and the terminating PSTNs process the call involving the end users as two separate local calls.

An ITSP call has unique characteristics that are different from a PTSN call. The following list highlights the characteristics of an ITSP call:

- Less expensive (particularly noticeable for international calls): There are three areas that contribute to savings.

    * IP involves a less expensive infrastructure. The network does not require voice switches, a signaling system, or Advanced Intelligent Network (AIN). Sharing bandwidth via packet switching technology reduces transmission costs. Not having standardized quality or reliability requirements also reduces operating costs.

    * Simpler fee-structure: Pre-paid fees do not require printing or mailing of bills. Most important of all, there is no need to collect unpaid bills.

    * Favorable regulation for enhanced service providers (at least for now): The present regulations require no access charges or international settlement fees for enhanced Internet Telephone Service Providers (ITSPs).

- Potentially more expensive for corporations because there are no negotiations for volume discounts (which is a general practice for the present arrangement).

- An ITSP typically requires longer setup times (as in the case of a credit card call).

- Non-uniform speech quality: The speech quality is not only lower than the PTSN, but it is not uniform because of varying network characteristics. However, voice quality is expected to become better as ITSPs mature.

11.8.3.2 ITSP and Regulation

Since introducing the concept of internet telephone service, many questions have been raised, and the answers are yet to be provided. The following is a summary of the prominent questions that are presently under study:

- Should an ITSP call adopt feature group A, B or D?

    (Definitions of Feature groups are provided as follows.)

Definition 11-4 Feature Group A (FG-A): The call setup involves two-stage dialing. It adopts a non-uniform access code. It doesn't provide Automatic Number Identification (ANI) or answer supervision.

Definition 11-5 Feature Group B (FG-B): The call setup involves two-stage dialing. It adopts a non-uniform access code. It provides ANI if connected directly to the originating switching office, and also provides answer supervision in this configuration.

Definition 11-6 Feature Group D (FG-D): The call setup involves only one-stage dialing. It adopts a uniform access code. It provides both ANI and answer supervision.

- How should (issues on international accounting) rates and settlement fees be set?

  Should there be bilateral agreements, established under auspices of ITU-T, between the dominant carriers? Should rates be based on the cost of providing service with an additive profit margin? Who sets the margin? How big should the margin be? How will over-charging be prevented (due to potential international calls being used to subsidize domestic calls)? Currently, some international settlement fees are equal to half the accounting rate. How much lower should ITSP call rates be reduced? Settlement fees are not equal for two countries involved in an international call. How will an ITSP calls be handled?

- Should an ITSP be considered a "phone company"?

  * "Yes": FCC petition, March 1996: " … it is incumbent upon the (FCC) to examine and adopt rules, policies and regulations governing the users of the internet for the provisioning of telecommunications services."

  * "No": FCC June 1996: "On the internet, voice traffic is just a particular kind of data, and imposing traditional regulatory divisions on that data is both counterproductive and futile" " … we shouldn't be looking for ways to subject new technologies to old rules."

- Should an ITSP be considered an Inter-Exchange Carrier (IEC)?

  If an ITSP positions itself as an IEC it will have equal access options, but it must also pay access charges. Conversely, an ITSP can position itself as an independent technology involving another type of voice service. In either case, an ITSP can claim it is in full compliance with FCC directives.

- Are there applicable regulations outside the USA? Europe? Asia? …

  The European Union (EU) has set its own criteria for regulation of internet telephone. Internet telephone must: (1) be commercially offered; (2) be provided to the public; (3) be positioned between public switched network terminating points on a fixed telephony network; and (4) involve direct transport and switching of speech in real time.

January, 1998 EU: "Calls on the internet are neither sophisticated nor common enough to subject them to regulations which govern phone companies... (the EU) will review the issue by the year 2000."

- What is the Voice On the Net (VON) coalition?

The VON coalition is a volunteer organization of internet telephony pioneers. The organization is trying to forestall/manage internet telephony regulation. It accepts the concept of paying universal service fees. However, it is concerned that regulation will stifle industry innovation and growth of Voice over Internet Protocol (VoIP).

Undoubtedly there will be countless ITSPs domestically as well as internationally, with increased deregulation of the industry. Someday the traditional model of pair-wise relationships between service carriers may break down (i.e., become an obsolete concept).

However, most ITSPs will not achieve a "*global footprint*". In order to expand their reach, they must form partnerships. A broker for interconnecting various ITSPs can be considered a "*clearinghouse ITSP*". A clearinghouse ITSP will provide a single point of contact for global interconnection. It will simplify negotiation and business arrangements for peer ITSPs. It may even provide functions such as authorization, routing, settlement payments, and quality standards. Sometimes, it may even provide transport as well. A clearinghouse ITSP is a carrier's carrier. There are a few "clearinghouse ITSPs" that are functioning now (e.g., Arbinet, ITXC and TransNexus).

The ITSPs will continue to build-out their networks, which should become more reliable. The speech quality and delay problems must be improved to a level approaching PSTN quality. In addition, several valued-added services must be provided. The public network interface capability will also need to be expanded.

11.8.4 Private IP Network for Voice Applications

Like other modern communications technologies (e.g., ISDN, frame relay, LAN, etc.), "Voice over IP" (VoIP) may be implemented first in private networks. This implementation is primarily aimed at saving telecommunications costs. First, it will reduce the number of minutes paid to either LEC or IEC for the intra-company calls. Savings can also be realized by integrating services (i.e., combining voice, fax, and data signals over a common facility). Private VoIP applications can also support "tail-end hop-off" for PSTN calls. Figure 11-53 illustrates a potential architecture for a private VoIP network.

The investment for implementing a Private VoIP network is relatively small. It is expected that the capital costs can be recovered in about one year (may be a little longer depending on usage). The three major expense items are: (1) the installation of gateway equipment (see Example 11-23), (2) the incremental bandwidth in the IP network, and (3) the required router software to implement voice priority over data. A private VoIP network may adopt one of two dialing options. It may use integrated dialing with PBX "least-cost-routing" that it is transparent to users, or it may require a special access code. Speech quality (which may not meet PSTN standards), transmission delay and delay timing jitter must be managed. Likewise, there may eventually be regulatory issues.

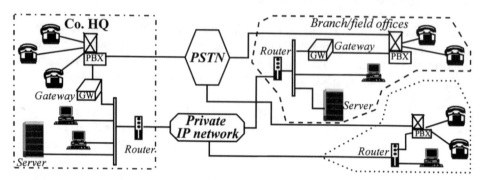

Figure 11-53   Private VoIP Network Applications.

11.8.5 Gateways and Router: IP Equipment

Gateway and router equipment are essential for implementing a "voice over IP" network. Examples 11-23 and 11-24 describe the details of this equipment.

Example 11-23: Describe the characteristics of gateway equipment used for VoIP applications.

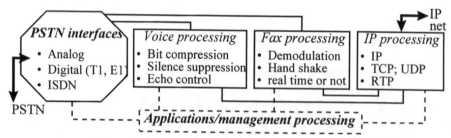

Figure 11-54   Gateway Components/Capabilities.

Gateways are available from several equipment vendors.   They can be stand-alone element, or special circuit packs installed in a PC or router. Gateways should support both voice and data. Router software can also be used to provide voice over data priority capability. Gateway technology is typically implemented with Digital Signal Processor (DSP) based technology. DSPs are primarily used in private networks, but this technology will eventually be extended to public networks. The gateway components and characteristics are summarized in Figure 11-54. ITU-T standards G.723.1 and G.729 define voice bit compression requirements. Voice mail can be added as an enhancement feature. Voice services/call control support can use ISDN, POST signaling, H225, H245, or proprietary system. Data communication interfaces for IP transport (not shown in Figure 11-53) are Ethernet, frame relay, PPP, and ATM. Fax processing can support fax protocol defined in T.4 and T.30. IP processing supports IP, TCP, UDP (previously discussed in this chapter), and Real-time Transport Protocol (RTP; discussed later).

Example 11-24: Describe the characteristics of router equipment used for VoIP applications.

Figure 11-55 illustrates an Autonomous System (AS), which is a network administrated by one organization, that consists of subnets and routers.

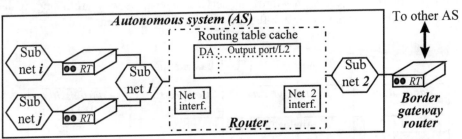

Figure 11-55   Autonomous System and Routers.

IP packets are forwarded on a "hop-to-hop" basis, and a router is used to deliver the packets. Generally, a router "knows the best output port" associated with all the addresses within an Autonomous System. The router chooses the next hop for a packet based on information in a routing table. That is, it identifies the output interfaces based on Destination Address (DA) and knowledge of network. A set of network addresses is associated with each output interface, and the router identifies the physical port associated with the DA. A router must maintain its routing table by exchanging routing protocol messages with neighbor routers. Each routing table entry stipulates the output interface and its data link layer (i.e., Layer 2) protocol. There are typically three different ways a router can obtain the table entries for its routing table. They are:

(1) Default: The default entry of a routing table indicates the output interface to be used if no other table entry is appropriate.

(2) Static method: The routing table context is entered manually by a network administrator whenever updating is required.

(3) Dynamic method: The routing table context is entered automatically based on information provided by a routing protocol.

Two classes of routing protocols have been developed, (1) interior routing protocols [e.g., Open Shortest Path First (OSPF), used within an autonomous system], and (2) exterior routing protocols [e.g., Border Gateway Protocol 4 (BGP-4), which is typically used between autonomous systems].

11.8.6 Fax over IP

Fax services have expanded rapidly since the mid 1980's. It is estimated that there may be more than 100 million fax machines in the world by the end of this millennium. In the USA, almost 10% of the homes have a fax machine. In some parts of the Far East, the percentage is almost three times higher (i.e., 1/3 of the home have fax machines).

A survey conducted in 1997 indicated the following: (1) Telephone bills for fax services was about 25 billion US$ in the USA, and about 90 billions US$ worldwide; (2) Approximately 85% of the faxes originate and about 95% of faxes terminate on stand-alone machines; and, (3) A total of 400 billions fax pages were sent; with 1 million pages carried over IP. The projected growth of fax services over IP is very promising, with an estimate of 4 billion pages in year 2,000 and 250 billion pages by year 2,004.

Table 11-7   ITU-T Fax Standards.

Standard (yr)	Signal type/rate	Compression	Transmission (81/2X11 page)
Group 1 (1972)	Analog (300bps)	None	4~6 minutes
Group 2 (1976)	Analog (1.2 kbps)	Limited	2~3 minutes
Group 3 (1980)	Digital (2.4~14.4kbps)	Complex	< 1 minute
Group 4 (1984)	Digital (56 kbps)	Complex	< 10 seconds

Fax standards have become widely accepted for formatting documents. A fax signal is a modulated digital bit stream, thus it is easy to transmit fax signal over widely spread digital networks. IP network delay is not a serious issue for fax protocols, compared to voice applications. Therefore, it is believed that fax over IP has a much higher near-term potential than voice over IP. There are four primary fax options that can be adopted for fax over IP:

(1) Real time fax services (See Example 11-24, Figure 11-56): The end fax machines are in direct communication via the IP network. A real-time confirmation is provided to the originating machine. Two operational modes have been defined:

   * Fax relay: Implies direct communication between transmitting and receiving machines. This mode can be sensitive to handshaking "time-outs".

   * Fax pad: Implies fax protocol spooling by gateways to avoid handshaking "time-outs".

(2) Store-and-forward fax services: The fax pages are received by a network-based server at the "time of sending", and are delivered a later time. The delivery confirmation is also delayed until the destination gateway has received confirmation from the terminating fax machine. This mode has several advantages:

* It can avoid fax protocol time-out problems.

* It has a low failure rate.

* It is a good match for fax broadcasts or off-peak delivery.

(3) "fax over IP" service bureau: The most important advantage is outsourcing network management and equipment responsibilities/problems. The charge is typically on a "per page" basis. The access method may be similar to ITSP. This approach is good if the main applications are outside the company.

(4) "Build your own" fax service: In this approach the user will purchase/install fax gateways, which are typically part of "voice over IP" gateways. Therefore, savings can be expected through integration of fax, voice, and data. This option is a good match if the main applications are intra-company operations.

Example 11-25: Describe various methods for "real-time" fax applications.

Real-time fax can be implemented using (1) brute force; (2) fax-relay; and (3) fax-pad as illustrated in Figure 11-56.

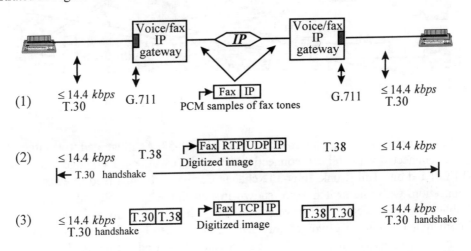

Figure 11-56   Real-Time Fax [(1) Brute-force, (2) Fax-relay and (3) Fax-pad].

(1) Brute force real-time fax: This option does not apply fax protocol; it is simple and basic. The gateway digitizes the fax tones into PCM samples for transport. The ITU-T G.711 standard is applied to meet coding quality requirements. This scheme is very inefficient because a (48 kbps ~ 64 kbps) channel plus overhead bits is used to carry the fax information consisting of 14.4 kbps or less. To resolve the T.30 time out issue the fax delays must be less than (200 ~ 300) ms.

(2)   Fax-relay real-time fax: This option utilizes Wide Area Network (WAN; e.g. PSTN) technology efficiently. The gateway demodulates (using the definition in T.38 which also defines IP transport), fax tones, and sends the original digital fax representation over the network. The fax machines communicate with each other directly, thus no T.30 state-machine is involved in the process. However, this scheme is sensitive to packet loss and the round-trip delays.

(3)   Fax-pad real-time fax: In this approach the gateway also demodulates fax tones and sends the original digital fax representation over the network. The scheme requires fax protocol in gateways for its implementation that uses: (a) T.30 spooling to avoid delay problems (note that the page delivery confirmation should not be spooled); and (b) T.38 for fax modulation standards and IP transport. This option also addresses the problem of protocol timeout.

Example 11-26: Describe ISP methods for transporting fax messages.

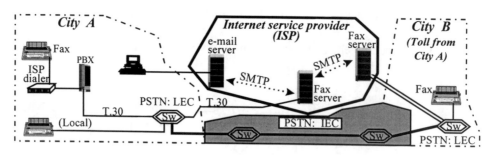

Figure 11-57   ISP-Based Network Fax Option.

ISP-based network fax scheme is shown in Figure 11-57. As illustrated, two cities, A and B, are connected via a toll call connection. There are two Local Exchange Carrier offices (LECs) and one Toll (trunk, Inter-) Exchange Carrier (IEC) involved in establishing this connection. Only the switches are shown in this figure to simplify the inter-exchange Public Switch Telephone Network (PSTN). This is not always the case, in an international call at least two gateway switches must also be involved. In addition, there is an Internet Service Provider (ISP), that provides ISP-based fax service in this example.

Two fax call sequences are illustrated in Figure 11-57: (1) A local fax connection, and (2) A toll fax connection. In addition, an e-mail service is also shown to illustrates that an ISP provides both e-mail and fax services via Simple Mail Transfer Protocol (SMTP). The ISP dialer is the distinction between the local and toll fax calls. The local fax is sent via an IEC PSTN, while the "toll fax" is sent via an ISP. The local ISP fax server receives the fax from a PSTN using T.30 protocol. It then identifies the IP address of the remote fax server (based on the called party's PSTN number), and forward the fax message to the remote fax server using Simple Mail Transfer Protocol (SMTP). The remote ISP fax server receives the fax message via the IP network, and delivers it to the final destination. Note that the dial-up uses T.30 protocol to connect the fax machine.

Example 11-27: Describe the customer Premises Equipment (CPE) method for transporting fax messages.

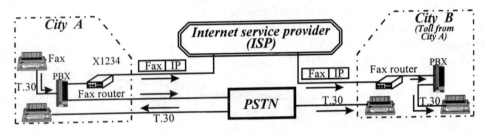

Figure 11-58   CPE-Based Network Fax Option.

A Customer Premises Equipment (CPE) fax scheme is illustrated in Figure 11-58. Three are cases are shown in this figure: (1) A local call using the PSTN; (2) An off-net toll fax call using the PSTN; and (3) An on-net fax toll call using an ISP.

(1) The local fax router serves as the IP gateway. The access is performed by using a standard PBX line or trunk port. A second dial tone is required as a prompt for the destination fax number. New implementations will be based on T.38 (not T.30) protocol.

(2) The fax is sent based on the called party number. The PSTN dial up is established through a PBX for local or off-net destinations. The remote equipment "hops off" to the off-net location (this may not be permissible in some countries).

(3) For the on-net fax call, the fax is sent via the IP network. The fax routers may apply proprietary protocols. The fax information is encapsulated in the IP datagram in real time. Note that a compatible router is required at the destination.

11.8.7 Internet Integrated Services Architecture (ISA)

IP networks were originally designed to handle only "non-real-time "traffic. The Internet integrated Service Architecture (ISA) is intended to enable IP networks to handle "real-time" traffic. Real-time traffic is typically generated by applications that are sensitive to changing network conditions (e.g., timing jitter and bandwidth limitations).

A typical example of jitter-intolerant traffic is packetized video signals. Before delivering a packet video to the end user, the receiving video station has to wait until it has received a sufficient number of picture frames. That is, before the video can be viewed, the receiving station must have sufficient frames stored. The use of ISA can reduce jitter, therefore it will provide improved video performance.

Four IP protocols have been proposed (drafted) for ISA: (1) Resource reSerVation Protocol (RSVP); (2) Real-time Transport Protocol (RTP); (3) RTP Control Protocol (RTCP); and (4) IPv6, which was discussed in Section 11.3.4 of this chapter. A carrier company typically establishes service classes by specifying categories of various traffic flow, delay requirements, quality of services, etc. The service classes are used to determine the service charges. The carrier company can also establish premium access arrangements for higher-priced, higher-quality services (e.g., virtual private network services and carrier business-class ISP services).

Table 11-8 lists the proposed internet Quality of Service (QoS) protocol tools, and the associated functions involving IPv6, IP header bits, RSVP, RTP, and RTCP.

Table 11-8   Proposed IP QoS Tools and Associated Use.

Proposed protocol(tool)	*Proposed use*
IPv6	Each packet specifies priority
IP header bits for "service class"	Used in prioritizing traffic
Resource reservations protocol (RSVP)	Traffic flows with specified delay & throughput
Real-time transport protocol (RTP)	To provide timing and sequence information
RTP control protocol (RTCP)	A mechanism to monitor session quality

- Resource Reservations Protocol (RSVP): RSVP is a signaling protocol used between IP hosts and routers. It is initiated by the host, which requests a specific Quality of Service (QoS). The router can accept or deny the request, since the router can assign priority to traffic with a higher QoS to reserve the best utilization of network resource. There are two methods of QoS operation: (1) Even if the network experiences congestion, it still provides a service level that resembles a lightly-loaded network (known as controlled load QoS operation); and (2) guaranteed QoS. The specific parameters of QoS are negotiated between the hosts and the routers. The following QoS parameters are the most important and commonly used:

  * The intended (planned and negotiated) data rate to be generated
  * The requested throughput (the hosts may request more bandwidth be reserved/agreed than the intended rate)
  * The maximum packet size
  * The data burstiness measure
  * The delay variation bound

Queuing is the responsibility of each intermediate router for RSVP QoS traffic. A packet assigned to a priority queue must be served (i.e., switched through) to maintain the "throughput" and "delay" at the receiver's requested level. It is known that IP provides "better effort" service. A "better effort" approach can only be implemented if other traffic gets "lesser effort". Obviously, this is not feasible if the majority of the traffic is getting "better effort". Therefore, prioritization of traffic is a sophisticated technique that may be implemented differently by various vendors.

- Real-time Transport Protocol (RTP) and RTP Control Protocol (RTCP): RTP is used to provide end-to-end delivery of real-time services (e.g., voice and video traffic). RTP services also include time stamping, sequence numbering, and delivery monitoring. RTP is typically used as an application sublayer riding on top of a User Datagram Protocol (UDP) (not TCP). However, it is not related to real-time network transport or delivery of network-based QoS.

In comparison, RTCP defines a mechanism in which a host (involved in an RTP session) exchanges information regarding the monitor and control of that session. RTCP provides the ability to monitor the quality of an associated RTP session (e.g., packet counts, packet loss ratio, and delay jitter). RTCP carries an identifier of the source RTP traffic. A UDP cannot guarantee packet delivery and ordering since some tasks are common in a "real-time" environment. RTP and RTCP are used to relieve the application software programmer from dealing with these common tasks.

Example 11-28: Describe the function of RTP protocol for a Voice over IP application.

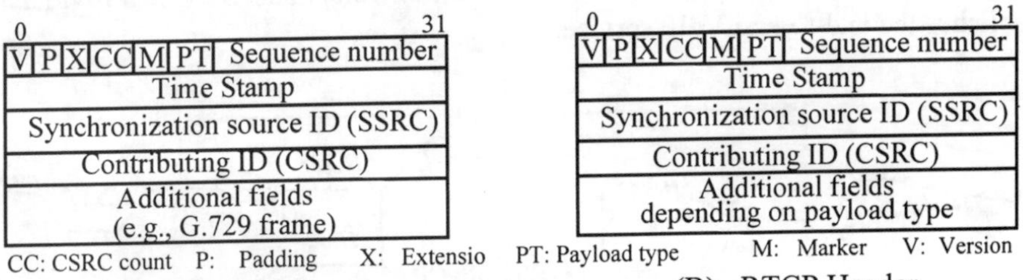

0	31
V P X CC M PT Sequence number	
Time Stamp	
Synchronization source ID (SSRC)	
Contributing ID (CSRC)	
Additional fields (e.g., G.729 frame)	

0	31
V P X CC M PT Sequence number	
Time Stamp	
Synchronization source ID (SSRC)	
Contributing ID (CSRC)	
Additional fields depending on payload type	

CC: CSRC count   P: Padding   X: Extensio   PT: Payload type   M: Marker   V: Version

(A) RTP Header

(B) RTCP Header

Figure 11-59   RTP Header and RTCP Header Structure.

Real-time Transport Protocol (RTP) can be used for "Voice on IP (VoIP)" transport by implementing RTP over UDP. Figure 11-59(A) illustrates the RTP header, and its primary functions are described as follows:

- Sequence number: This field allows the IP message to "playout" in proper order. In addition, it can be used to identify missing packets or misinserted packets.

- Timestamp: This field is used to calculate (determine) packet delay jitter so that the receiver can use the result to adjust buffering. It also allows proper timing of the message "playout" when silence suppression (i.e., elimination of packet generation when there is no speech) is enabled.

- Source identifier: This field is used when multiple calls are multiplexed for transport between gateways.

Example 11-29: Describe the functions of RTCP protocol for VoIP application.

Real-time Transport Control Protocol (RTCP) in a "Voice on IP (VoIP)" network is used to monitor network performance [see Figure 11-59(B)].

- If delay jitter is excessive or many packets are lost, the network will "throttle" non-real-time traffic (i.e., reduce the throughput).

- RTCP is used to adjust voice coding algorithms based on the IP network performance. The voice coding algorithm contains a variable bit rate option so that the voice digitizing rate can be increased or decreased if necessary. It also monitors a quality parameter called the "error control mechanism". Is response to network performance, the voice coding algorithm may request the network to change it error correction mode.

- RTCP can provide a quick connection release by using "Bye" packets (i.e., special packets that cause the network to immediately drop a connection).

11.8.8 IP for Multimedia Communications

Figure 11-60 shows the IP protocols (e.g., IP, TCP, UDP, RTP and RTCP) used for "voice over IP" (VoIP) applications. The Internet Telephone Service Provider (ITSP) establishes the end-to-end VoIP service.

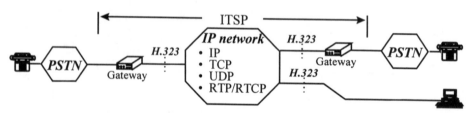

Figure 11-60   Voice over IP Network Protocols.

The ITU-T standard H.323 defines "Packet-based multimedia communications systems", (illustrated in Figure 11-60) for "Voice over IP" applications. Recommendation H.323 is intended for voice, audio, video and data services that are transported over an underlying packet network (TCP/IP layers 3 and 4). The network can be composed of hubs, routers, bridges, and dial-up access. However, the technology should be independent of network topology. The first version of H.323 (version 1) was initially approved in June, 1996, and was revised in February, 1998. Table 11-9 lists the related documentation for multimedia communications: H.323, H225, H245, H.261, H263, G.711, G.722, G.723, G.728, e.g. -

- H.323 "Packet-based Multimedia Communications Systems."
- H.225 "Media Stream Packetization and Synchronization on non-Guaranteed Quality of Service Local Area Networks."

Table 11-9   Recommendations for Multimedia Communications.

Recommendation	*Functions*
H.323 "Packet-based multimedia communications systems"	*System/component description; Call model descriptions*
H.225 "Media stream packetization and synchronization on non-guaranteed quality of service LANs" *Q.931* "Digital subscriber signaling system No.1-ISDN user-network interface layer spec. for basic call control" *H.245* "Control protocol for multimedia communications"	*Packetization, message formats of control stream (H.225/Q.931)* *Channel negotiation and capability exchange (H.245)*
G.711 "PCM of voice frequencies" *G.722* "7 kHz audio-coding within 64 kbps" *G.723.1* "Dual rate speech coder for multimedia comm. Transmitting at 5.3 and 6.3 kbps" *G.728* "Coding of speech at 16 kbps using low-delay code excited linear prediction" *G.729* "Coding of speech at 8 kbps using conjugate-structure algebraic code excited linear prediction" *V.70* "Procedures for simultaneous transmission of data and digitally encoded voice signals over the PSTN, or over 2-wire leased point-to-point telephone type circuits"	*Audio/voice coding and compression: (G.711, G.722, G.723.1, G.728,G.729 and V.70*
H.261 "Information technology-generic coding of moving pictures and associated audio information: video" *H.263* "Video coding for low bit rate communication"	*Video coding & compression: (H.261 and H.263)*
T.120 "Data protocols for multimedia conferencing"	*Data sharing*

11.8.8.1 H.323 Components and Terminal

The major components in a typical H.323 network implementation (Figure 11-61) are terminals, gateways, gatekeepers, and Multipoint Control Units (MCUs). They are briefly described as follows:

- H.323 terminal: These are the "client endpoints" on a network. A H.323 terminal must support audio (voice) specified in G.711 (Table 11-9). It may also support G.723.1 (5.3 and 6.3 kbps) and G.729 (8 kbps) which are recommended for lower quality networks (e.g., the internet). If the option video is used, it must support H.261. For system control functions, the specifications defined in H.245 and H.225 are applicable to H.323 terminals. Real-time Transport Protocol (RTP) is typically used for sequencing media packets.

- H.323 Gateway: Gateways are optional in H.323 networks. Whenever gateways are used, they should support interoperability with other terminal types. A H.323 gateway provides the required translation functions between H.323 and circuit-switched networks including: transmission formats, communication procedures, and audio (voice) and video transcoding. The H.323 gateway supports PSTN, ISDN, and broadband ISDN (B-ISDN) as indicated in Figure 11-61.

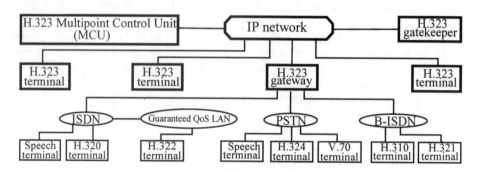

Figure 11-61   H.323 Network Components.

- H.323 gatekeeper: A gatekeeper is optional in a H.323 network. If it is used, it performs the following functions: (1) admission control for the network; (2) bandwidth control and management; (3) address translation; (4) communications using Registration/Admission/Status (RAS) protocol; and (5) management of all terminals, gateways, and MCUs in an given H.323 zone. A gatekeeper can also perform the following optional functions: (1) call control signaling (i.e., it decides whether to process the messages or pass them on), and (2) call management (e.g., call screening, call forwarding, call redirection, and call routing).

- H.323 Multipoint Control Unit (MCU): The MCU supports conferencing between three or more "client endpoints". An MCU has two primary functions:

  (1) Multipoint Controller (MC): The MC performs (A) conference control functions (i.e., determines the destination of all media streams), and (B) capability reconciliation. The MC is function required for all conferences. It may be co-located in a terminal, gateway, or gatekeeper.

  (2) Multipoint Processor (MP): The MP multiplexes, switches, and processes media signal streams.

11.8.8.2 H.323 Call Stage Sequence

The H.323 protocol stack and call stage sequence is described in this section. Figure 11-62 illustrates the H.323 protocol stack along with IP and TCP/UDP functions. As indicated, the Call Control (H.225, Q.931 and H.245) and Data Channels (T.120) require reliable transport services which can be provided by TCP. In comparison, real-time channels such as Audio (G.711, G.722, G.723.1, G.728, G.729 and V.70), Video (H.261

and H.263), Audio/Video Control (RTCP), and Control (RAS) use "best effort" services which are supported by the User Datagram Protocol (UDP).

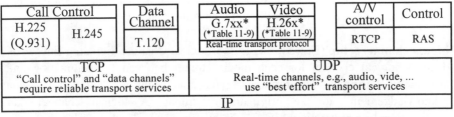

Figure 11-62   H.323 Protocol Stack: IP and TCP/UDP.

There are six stages in the H.323 call sequence. They are described as follows:

(1) **Discovery and registration** [Registration/Admission/Status (RAS)]: The originating H.323 terminal sends out a Gatekeeper ReQuest (GRQ) message to allocate an available gatekeeper. One gatekeeper will send back a Gatekeeper ConFirm/ReJect (GCF/GRJ) message to acknowledge being allocated as the "call's gatekeeper". The originating terminal, after receiving the GCF message, sends out a Registration ReQuest (RRQ) message which can be either confirmed or rejected when a Registration ConFirm/ReJect message (RCF/RRJ) response message is received.

(2) **Call setup** (RAS, H.225, and Q.931): The originating terminal, after receiving the RCF message, sends out Location ReQuest (LRQ) to the gatekeeper for confirmation [the gatekeeper responds with a Location ConFirmation (LCF) message]. The originating terminal then sends an Admission ReQuest (ARQ) to initiate the admission function's call an IP address. The Admission ConFirm/ReJect (ACF/ARJ) message also specifies the maximum data rate to be used for address confirmation. The gatekeeper and the called terminal will exchange the same call setup messages (e.g., ARQ and ACF) to continue the call set-up sequence.

After the call is setup, all communications are carried over logical channels. ITU-T standard H.245 defines procedures for managing logical channels (e.g., logical channel 0 is used for the H.245 control channel, which is "open" for the duration of the call). Multiple logical channels of varying types (e.g., video, audio and data) are allowed for a single call.

(3) **Call negotiation** (H.245): ITU-T standard H.245 defines the protocol used to accomplish specific tasks (i.e., signaling entities) described as follows:

* Capability Exchange Signaling Entity (CESE): The CESE identifies the capabilities of participating entities. It may identify options and valid combinations of different

signal streams capabilities. It should be noted that all conference entities receive the capability exchange signaling entity via the gatekeeper or directly.

* Master-Slave Determination Signaling Entity (MSDSE): The MSDSE identifies which entity serves as the Multipoint Controller (MC).

(4) **Media channel setup** (H.245): The H.245 Logical Channel Signaling Entity (LCSE) opens a logical channel for each media stream between the originating and the terminating terminals. The terminating terminal sends an "open logical channel acknowledgement" to the originating terminal. A logical channel can be unidirectional or bidirectional. For bidirectional channels, the media channel setup must also be performed between the terminating terminal and the originating terminal. After acknowledgments are received by both terminals, logical channels for media streams are established (i.e., activated).

(5) **Media transport** (RTP/RTCP): Audio and video signal streams apply the Real-time Transport Protocol (RTP) specified by the Internet Engineering Task Force (IETF). Applications can use sequence number and timing information (Figure 11-62: RTP header) to eliminate duplicated packets, re-order out-of-sequence packets, synchronize multiple signal streams, and manage continuous playback despite latencies.

RTP Control Protocol (RTCP) is used to manage media streams and provide Quality of Service (QoS) feedback from receivers. The source uses QoS information to adapt encoding or buffering schemes. The RTCP uses a dedicated logical channel for each RTP media stream.

The endpoints (i.e., the originating and terminating terminals) can request changes in the bandwidth initially allocated and confirmed. The gatekeeper must process all bandwidth increase/decrease requests, and the endpoints must comply with the gatekeeper responses.

(6) **Call termination** (H.245, H.225, Q.9431and RAS): Call termination may be requested by any endpoint or by a gatekeeper. This request will result in closing media logical channels, ending the H.245 session, releasing the H.225/Q.931 connection, and provides a disconnect confirmation (to the gatekeeper) via RAS.

11.8.8.3 Other Related Standards

ITU-T standard H.323 was revised in February 1998, and is now referred to as H.323 v2. This new version addresses Wide Area Network (WAN) related issues, authentication, encryption, and security (H.235: "Security and encryption for H-series multimedia terminals"). It provides improved reliability via redundant gatekeepers, and improved scalability via cascading Multipoint Controllers (MCs) and layered video coding algorithms. The "new" H.323 also supports "media over ATM". Another important feature is that it provides a more efficient call setup via a "fast connect procedure".

The "fast connect procedure" can establish point-to-point call setup with as few as two messages. The "fastStart" element supports H.245 information in Q.931 messages. It uses Open Logical Channel (OLC) structures defined in the Q.931 setup. It also applies the OLC acknowledgement structures defined for the Q.931 response. They include: call proceeding, alerting, progress and connect. Fast connection procedures must be agreed to by both endpoints, otherwise the full H.245 standard must be applied.

Another related standard for "Voice over IP" (VoIP) is the Session Initiation Protocol (SIP), which was developed by the IETF Multi-party MUltimedia SessIon Control (MMUSIC) working group. It was proposed as being a less complex procedures for internet conferencing and telephony. It is an application level protocol, and is independent of the underlying packet protocol (e.g., TCP, UDP, X.25, or ATM). SIP provides personal mobility, name mapping and redirection, encryption and authorization functions. It adopts "HTTP-like" text based encoding (versus Q.931, ANS.1 for H.323).

Media Gateway Control Protocol (MGCP) is an alternative to H.323 and SIP for gateway control. It is based on a combination of Simple Gateway Control Protocol (SGCP) and IP Device Control (IPDC). MGCP can interwork with H.323/SIP terminals or networks. It distributes functionality between media gateways and a central controller. The media gateway is a simple, stateless translator between PSTN and IP transport. A call agent is used in MGCP. MGCP provides centralized intelligence functions: total control over media gateways, call admission and billing, signaling interfaces to PSTN, and translation for other protocols (e.g., H.323 or SIP).

Review Questions II for Chapter 11:

(12) TCP/IP can operate over several types of subnets: _____ (SLIP, RFC _____), _____ protocol (PPP, RFC_____), ____ Ethernet (RFC _____), _____(RFC2176), IEEE ____ LAN (RFC ____), _____ (HIPPI), _____ (FDDI); and _____(SMDS).

(13) SLIP is widely used for point-to-point _____ connections running TCP/IP, but SLIP is not an _____ standard. In contrast, PPP is an _____ standard, that is designed to provide a common solution for connecting a variety of _____, _____, and _____ using simple links that can transport _____ datagrams between _____.

(14) (True, False)   Three main components of a PPP are: PPP encapsulation, Link Control Protocol (LCP), and Network Control Protocol (NCP).

(15) The PPP link operation can be divided into several phases: _____ phase, _____ _____ phase, _____ phase, and _____ phase.

(16) To transport IP over SONET/SDH, certain minimum data link protocol services are required: _____ each IP datagram packet, _____ identification, and _____. PPP frames are mapped into SONET _____.

(17) Access networks can be: traditional _____, _____ (DLC), _____, _____ (BRI or PRI), _____ (DSL), or _____ (WLL).

(18) Voice digitization can result a digital bitstream of _____ kbps (by using PCM), or _____ kbps (by using MLQ).

(19) There are many reasons in implementing voice over IP (VoIP). The fundamental reason is the general trend towards _____. IP was established in _____ for experimental APARNET. The IP explosion in popularity is linked to the availability of _____ and the _____.

(20) Due to the rapid growth of ITSP networks, several issues require immediate attention: (a) IP services require _____; (b) the ability to interwork with _____; (c) _____ issue must be resolved; (d) global _____ must be generated and deployed; (e) _____ should be defined and standardized; and (f) _____ are required.

(21) ITU-T fax standards have evolved from _____ (1972) to _____ (1984), which transmits _____ signal at a rate of _____ kbps. The time required to transmit a 8½ by 11 page < (is less than) _____.

(22) ITU-T standard _____ specifies "Packet-based Multimedia Communications Systems."

Appendix 11-1

Voice Digitization

11A-1   INTRODUCTION

Typical speech signal waveforms possess signal power over the range from several tens of hertz up to 10 kHz. In fact, high-quality sound reproduction systems often cover the band from 20 Hz to approximately 40 kHz. Although the ear does not respond to frequencies above 15 kHz (the upper limit decreases as one's age increases; the human ear's sensitivity is discussed in Chapter 1), the higher frequencies do contribute to an overall sensory appreciation of sound. There are different cutoff frequencies for various systems:

- FM broadcast radio uses an upper cutoff of 15 kHz.
- AM radio uses only 5 kHz for the upper cutoff.
- The standard long-distance toll line frequency cutoff is approximately 3.3 kHz (the same as various forms of citizen-band radio).

Note that human speech energy peaks at several hundred (800 to 1000) hertz, and about 98% of the energy can be expected to lie below 3 kHz. Actual speech characteristics vary with age, sex, and country (i.e., the language being spoken). The curve in Figure 11A-1 should be interpreted as an average.

For simplicity, the speech spectrum can be represented by a continuous curve from 200 Hz to 4000 Hz. However, about 90% of speech energy, for a typical speaker, is concentrated around 1000 Hz and below. Figure 11A-1 is known as a discrete spectral representation of a speech signal. This graph is often used to indicate that a speech signal possesses many frequency components, known as harmonics. If a transmission system could carry an infinite number of harmonics, the speech quality would be perfect (i.e., no distortion). However, all systems have finite bandwidth. Only a finite number of harmonics can be carried by a practical system, therefore signal distortion is unavoidable.

For design and analysis of a voice network, the speech signal is normally assumed to have a bandwidth of 4000 Hz (4 kHz). That is, **a voice signal is treated as having a signal bandwidth of 4 kHz**. It should be mentioned that not all the human voices have a frequency spectrum identical to Figure 11A-1. For telecommunications applications, the frequency range from 200 Hz to 3200 Hz (sometimes 3400 Hz) is called the voice-(frequency) band. Any signal inside this frequency band is called an "in-band" signal. Other signals carried by a system are referred to as "out-of-band" signals. There is evidence that a human vocal sound can reach up to 10,000 Hz.

For modern communications networks, the equipment, terminals, switching machines, and transmission facilities are almost all digital. Therefore, it is necessary to convert 4 kHz analog voice signals into digital signals so that they can be transported over digital networks. Voice "digitization" is a required process for voice (speech) communications. The topics discussed in this appendix are the C-message curve, speech properties, and speech encoding.

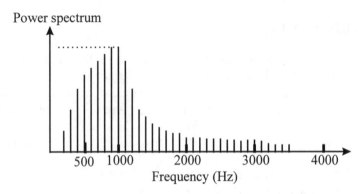

Figure 11A-1   Typical Human Speech Signal Spectral Density.

11A-1.1 The C-Message Curve

Human ears are sensitive to various frequency tones with different degrees of sensitivity. The ears can detect a 1000 Hz tone much easier than other tones. Figure 11A-2 shows typical ear sensitivities to different tones. Because of the shape of this curve, it is commonly referred to as the "C-curve", "C-message curve", or "C-message weights". This curve is often applied in studies associated with human hearing (for example, ENT physicians apply this curve for patients with hearing problems), in addition to speech signal transport. The meaning and importance of this curve is described as follows:

Around 1,000 Hz, the human ear sensitivity (see Figure 11A-2) is 0 dB. The sensitivity at 220 Hz is about −24 dB ($\equiv 1/2^8 = 1/256$; where the number "8" comes from 24 dB ÷ 3 dB = 8). This implies that the human ears can detect a 1000 Hz tone at a power level of 1 watt with the same degree of sensitivity as a 200 Hz tone with a power level of 256 watts. That is, the human ears are much more sensitive to a 1,000 Hz tone than a 220 Hz tone. Similarly, the sensitivity measured at 4,600 Hz is also about −24 dB. Therefore, the human ear has the same sensitivity to either 220 Hz or 4,600 Hz tone at any power level.

Typical measurements of attenuation are provided in Table 11A-1 that is part of Figure 11A-2. Note that beyond 5,000 Hz, attenuation continues to increase at a rate of approximately 12 dB per octave, until the attenuation reaches a value of −60 dB.

The C-message curve is important in designing a handset for any telephone service. The receiver in the handset must use sensitivity factors as "frequency weights" to compensate for the ear's sensitivities at various frequencies.

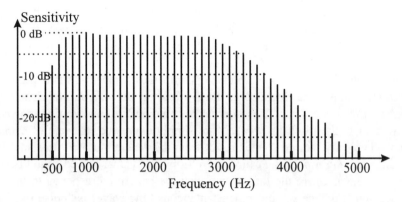

Figure 11A-2   Ear Sensitivity in Terms of Frequency.

Table 11A-1   Ear Sensitivity (Figure 11A-2).

f(kHz)	0.4	0.8	1.2	1.5	1.8	2.0	2.5	3.0	3.5	4.0	4.5	5.0
Attenuation (–dB)	11.4	1.5	0.2	1.0	1.3	1.3	1.4	2.5	7.6	14.5	21.5	28.5

11A-1.2   Speech Properties

Speech is a signal that exhibits considerable redundancy because of the physical mechanism of the human vocal tract, and the inherent structure of language. Because of the physical mechanism of the human ear, our ability to perceive speech sounds (as well as other sounds) is constrained to a dynamic range and bandwidth. By taking advantage of the redundancies and constraints of speech production/perception, it is possible to compress the bit rate needed to encode and transmit speech signals. That is, other methods besides traditional speech encoding methods [e.g., Pulse Code Modulation (PCM), Differential PCM (DPCM), etc.] can be used.

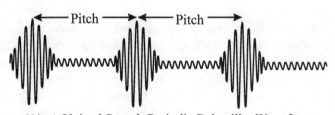

(A) A Voiced Sound: Periodic Pulse-like Waveform.

(B) A Unvoiced Sound: Noise-like waveform.

Figure 11A-3   A Voiced Sound and an Unvoiced Sound.

This section describes two properties of a speech signal. These properties are not dependent on signal frequency response (i.e., the signal frequency waveform). Human speech sounds are often categorized as being generated by either:

- *Voiced sound*: This category of sounds encompasses "voiced" sounds produced as a result of vibrations of the vocal cords. Each vibration allows a puff of air to flow from the lungs into the vocal tract. The interval between puffs of air exciting the vocal tract is referred to as the **pitch interval**. More simply expressed, the rate of excitation is the pitch. Typically, voiced sounds result from the generation of *vowels* and the *latter portions of some consonants*. A time waveform of a typical voiced sound is shown in Figure 11A-3(A), where the long-term repetitive pattern corresponds to the duration of a pitch interval. The waveform (instantaneous time wave) is "pulse-like" because of the vocal cord vibration characteristics.

    For example, if the alphabetic "a" sound is spoken, the sound waveform representing this "a" appears as the waveform shown in Figure 11A-3(A). The sound representing an "e" will also have the same waveform. The difference between the two waveforms (i.e., "a" and "e") is that they have different pitches. Therefore, if the "pitch" of a "voiced-sound" is known, then a waveform representing the human voice sound can be generated. This process is called speech synthesis.

- *Unvoiced sound*: This category of sounds include the fricatives or "unvoiced" sounds. Fricatives occur as a result of continuous air flowing from the lungs and passing through a vocal tract, constricted at some point to generate air turbulence (friction). Unvoiced sounds correspond to *certain consonants* (e.g., "s", "f", "p", "j", "x", etc.). A time waveform for an unvoiced sound is shown in Figure 11A-3(B). Notice that an unvoiced sound is a more random waveform compared to a voiced sound. It is more "noise-like" because of the turbulence at constriction points in the vocal tract. Therefore, speech transport of "unvoiced sound" can be accomplished at the receiver by using a random-noise generator, instead of actually transmitting these sounds.

An efficient way of encoding the voiced portions of speech is to encode one pitch interval waveform, and use that encoding as a template for each successive pitch interval of the same sound. Pitch intervals usually last from 5 to 20 msec for men, and from 2.5 to 10 msec for women. Since a typical voiced sound lasts for approximately 100 msec, there may be as many as 20 ($\equiv$ 100 msec/5 msec for men) to 40 ($\equiv$ 100 msec/2.5 msec for women) pitch intervals in a single sound. Although pitch interval encoding can provide significant reductions in bit rates, accurate pitch detection is very difficult. Not all voiced sounds produce a readily identifiable pitch interval as shown in Figure 11A-3(A). If the pitch gets encoded erroneously, strange sounds result. Therefore, it is important to implement a precise pitch detector for a speech encoder. In addition, a correct bit stream representing the pitch must be recovered at the receiver. Several (bit) error detection and correction methods can be applied to produce "nearly error-free" bit stream for "voiced-sound"-pitch information.

11A-2   Generation of Speech (Electrical Model): Using Speech Properties

The process of speech production can be represented by an electrical model that uses the properties of human speech. As represented by the model in Figure 11A-4, speech is generated by sound source excitation that is either (A) (pitch) pulse-like, during "voiced" segments of speech when the vocal cords are vibrating, or (B) noise-like, during "unvoiced" segments of speech because of turbulence at constriction points in the vocal tract. These pulse-like or noise-like excitations are then filtered by the vocal tract filter, which behaves like a time-varying acoustic filter. The filter represents the effects of the mouth, throat, and nasal passages, and is known as a **vocoder (voice coder).** The output of the vocal track filter is a synthesized speech signal, which may (or may not) closely emulate human speech. The quality of the synthesized speech signal depends upon: (1) the accuracy of the "pitch" used in the model, with respect to the pitch of the actual speech signal; (2) the accuracy of the "noise source" used in the model, with respect to the actual unvoiced-sound; and (3) the accuracy of the vocal track filter design, with respect to the actual language tone.

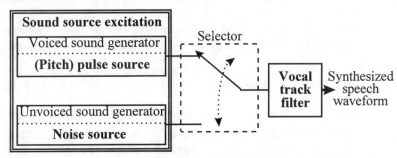

Figure 11A-4   An Electrical Model for Speech Synthesis.

The principle of a vocoder is based on **not** being required to transmit the exact (precise) waveform generated by human speech, but rather transmitting information from which a waveform can be reconstructed at the receiver which is **similar to, but not identical to**, the original waveform generated by the speaker at the transmitter. To fully understand this concept, consider listening to several different people pronouncing the same word or a sequence of words, having the following characteristics:

- One has a high-pitched voice, another a low pitch
- One speaks with a foreign accent, another has no accent
- One enunciates clearly, another slurs words
- One speaks slowly, the other quickly

Despite these prominent differences, the listener can understand practically ***all*** the speakers, providing they use the same language. This observation makes it clear that there is a variability (within limits) that can be allowed in the waveform that impinges on a listener's ear, before a loss of recognition of the spoken word occurs. Therefore, to transmit speech reproducing the precise waveform generated by the speaker is not necessary.

When using the electrical model in a vocoder, the input speech signal must be analyzed to determine whether a sound is "voiced" or "unvoiced". When the sound is "voiced", the pitch must also be estimated. The pitch estimate controls the fundamental frequency of the pulse source. These estimates control the position of the switch in Figure 11A-4 (shown as the selector) and produce appropriate waveforms that are sent to the vocal tract filter. Likewise, the vocal tract filter parameters are also estimated at the same time as the "voiced" or "unvoiced" sounds are analyzed. The output of the filter is a synthesized approximation to the speech waveform. In summary, if the following information is available: (1) the distance between "voiced-sounds" and "unvoiced-sounds"; (2) the "pitch" of the "voiced-sound"; (3) the emulation of "unvoiced-sounds"; (4) switching between the "voiced-sounds" and the "unvoiced-sounds"; and, (5) the appropriate vocal track filter parameters, then a "speech signal" that is *similar* to the "true speech" signal can be regenerated. This regenerated speech can be understood by a human listener at the receiver.

Acceptable vocoder can operate in the range 1.2 to 2.4 kbps, however, the resulting reproduced voice has a synthetic-sounding and a somewhat artificial or "machine-like" quality. As a result, vocoders are typically employed in special applications where it is acceptable to trade speech quality for the advantages of low bit rates. These applications are usually found in military communications, operator recorded messages, etc.

11A-3   Speech Encoding Technologies

There are three classes of speech encoding methods that can be applied to convert an analog speech signal into a digital speech signal. Some systems apply one of the three methods, while others may apply a combination of methods to achieve a specific signal rate. The three classes of speech encoding are briefly described as follows:

(1)   **Waveform encoding**: Waveform encoding treats speech as an analog signal, and attempts to reproduce (restore) the original signal at the receiver with acceptable quality. It does not use any of the properties of speech, other than bandwidth to establish the sampling rate. Typical methods are: Pulse-Code Modulation (PCM), Differential Pulse-Code Modulation (DPCM), Adaptive Differential Pulse-Code Modulation (ADPCM), Delta Modulation (DM), and Adaptive Delta Modulation (ADM). In summary, this waveform encoding can convert *any* **analog signal** into a digital signal (see Chapter 6 for details).

(2)   **Source model encoding (vocoding)**: This method utilizes the properties of the speech signal to preserve the actual speech information. The analysis performed by a vocoder involves breaking-up speech into its basic components and waveform segments (voiced/unvoiced speech segments, pitch, vocal filtering). In evaluating speech coding techniques, subjective measures often take precedence over mathematical measures. That is, the word or sentence intelligibility and subjective qualities of speech become important when implementing vocoder technology. Despite continued improvements, some people still consider computer-synthesized voice signals unacceptable.

(3) **Hybrid or parametric encoding**: Hybrid or parametric methods combine the features of both waveform encoding and vocoding to produce higher quality simulated speech signals. Sometimes, for simplicity, hybrid or parametric encoding is referred to as "vocoding", but interchanging these terms is not accurate.

11A-4   SPEECH ENCODING OBJECTIVES

It is desirable to encode digital speech in a way that reduces the bit rate, thereby reducing the bandwidth required to transport speech over a transmission medium. Digital modulation usually **expands** the bandwidth needed to transmit the signal. In wireline circuits and optical-fiber systems does not create a problem. However, in radio (wireless) communications, bandwidth is always limited. Once the radio channels are allocated in a given geographical area, there is no easy way to "*manufacture*" additional spectrum. Recognizing the scarcity of bandwidth resource in the radio spectrum, the FCC establishes strict bandwidth limits on radio emissions.

The reasons that the FCC must control radio emissions are:

(1) Control adjacent channel interference: If radio channels were granted to various users, they might be re-used repeatedly in a given area at the same time. This would definitely introduced *co-channel* interference and result in unacceptable speech quality (i.e., unintelligible transmission).

(2) Ensure efficient use of the resource: Controlling radio emissions will stimulate innovation of methods for using bandwidth efficiently.

As a result of controlling radio emissions, digital radio has traditionally been at a serious disadvantage compared to analog radio. Digital radio needs more bandwidth to transmit the same number of voice circuits (channels). Therefore, in cellular applications, reducing the bit rate through speech coding techniques to reduce bandwidth while maintaining "telephone voice quality" becomes a "*must*" technology. It is also desirable to have a speech coding technique with robust quality so its performance is not degraded drastically by the transmission environment (errors caused by noise and fading) or by different user characteristics (male, female, adult, child, etc.).

Another problem in wireless communication systems is explained as follows:

• Conventional PCM (Pulse Code Modulation) analog to digital conversion was designed for wireline digital systems in which engineers can deploy *regenerative repeaters* to assure virtually error-free transmission. The fact is that PCM is actually rather vulnerable to transmission errors. That is, because some bits are relatively more important than others means that specific errors can have a much greater effect on the overall transmission quality. By utilizing regenerators along the transmission path, the errors can be reduced or virtually be eliminated in PCM wireline applications.

- In mobile-radio applications, regenerative repeaters are not feasible as a method to produce error-free transmission. In fact, mobile radio often operates at error rates that would overwhelm an ordinary PCM coder. For example, if PCM is used in the wireline network with the help of regenerators and error detection/correction codes, a bit error rate of 10^{-8} is feasible. For wireless applications, if no Forward Error Control (FEC; detection/correction) codes are used, the bit error rate can approach a level of 10^{-2}.

When considering voice coding strategies to reduce the bit rate, the method used can increase the relative importance of certain bits and may increase vulnerability to errors. This effect must be considered so that robustness, in the presence of errors, is maintained. Based on this fact, the bit stream output of a speech encoder is often grouped into the following classes: (1) class-Ia bits, (2) class-Ib bits, and (3) class-II bits. (Detailed description of these characteristics is beyond the scope of this book).

11A-5   SPEECH ENCODING

It is the goal of a speech encoder to reduce the number of bits needed to be transmitted for representing a speech signal, thereby lowering the bandwidth required for transmission. A traditional PCM system requires a rate of 64 kbps to represent a single speech signal. For wireless applications, a 64 kbps rate will require a bandwidth that would be impossible for practical airway transport. By using a speech encoder, the 64 kbps rate can be reduced considerably. In turn, the wireless system can support more simultaneous users that are sharing the same transport channel. The final result is reduced communications costs for the customers. However, speech quality must always be maintained at (or above) the expectation level of the subscribers.

11A-5.1   A Channel Vocoder

The strategy of channel vocoder is to represent the frequency spectrum of a speech signal, by using samples taken from the contiguous frequency bands within the speech signal. Typically, the speech signal spectrum is divided into 16 bands (ranges): (200 to 400 Hz), (400 to 600 Hz), ..., (3200 to 3400 Hz) as shown in Figure 11A-5. This is based on a typical speech signal having significant signal energy from 200 Hz to 3400 Hz (see Figure 11A-1). Each band carries the information of the speech signal energy within the respective frequency range, and there is a Vocal Track Filter (VTF) associated with each band. The output of each VTF is represented by a group of digital bitstreams, which are fed to a Time Division Multiplexer (TDM) used to transmit the signal over long distances. Note that *a vocal track filter* consists of: (1) A BandPass Filter (BPF); (2) A rectifier; and (3) A Low Pass Filter (LPF).

The "voice"/"unvoiced" decision and pitch extraction functions are performed as parallel activities. These operations determine the fine-grain structure of the speech spectrum. As described earlier in this appendix, human speech sounds can be either "voiced" or "unvoiced" sounds. The "voiced"/"unvoiced" sound information must be recorded and transmitted to the receiver for use in restoring the speech signal. If the sound is a "voiced sound", the pitch of the sound must be extracted and encoded into a digital bitstream that is also transmitted to the receiver for the same purpose. In contrast, if the speech sound is a "unvoiced sound", this noise-like signal can be generated locally at the receiver instead of transporting it from the transmitter. This is a primary reason why bit compression is possible for speech signals.

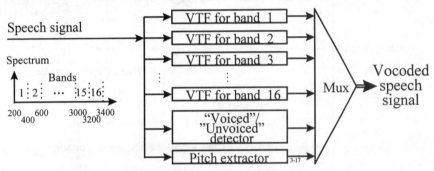

Figure 11A-5   The Encoder of a Speech Vocoder.

In the encoder, the outputs of a bank of bandpass filters are connected to a rectifier and lowpass filter. The Vocal Tract Filter (VTF) is reasonably stimulated by 16 channel sample values (16 frequency bands as shown in Figure 11A-5) taken every 20 ms. Low pass filtering limits the bandwidth of each spectral channel to about 25 to 30 Hz. The excitation signals require another 50 Hz of bandwidth, so that "vocoded speech" can be transmitted within a bandwidth of about 500 Hz. This results in a bandwidth savings of 7:1.

In summary, the encoder must perform time division multiplexing for three groups of digital bitstreams so they can be transported as one single bitstream to the receiver. These three bitstreams are:

(1)   Sub-bitstreams representing the 16 VTF output signals for the 16 spectrum bands.

(2)   The bitstream indicating whether the human speech sounds are "voiced" or "unvoiced" sounds.

(3)   A bitstream representing the pitch information for the "voiced" sounds.

The decoder used to restore "vocoded speech" signals contains three functional blocks briefly described as follows:

(1)   Demultiplexer: Separates the incoming bitstream into three bitstreams; (a) 16 channels of vocal track filtering information; (b) the "voiced" or the "unvoiced" sound indication; and, (c) the pitch associated with "voiced sounds".

(2)   Electrical mode: used to generate pulse-like or noise-like signals based on the "voiced" sound and its pitch, or the "unvoiced" sound information.

(3)   Vocal Track Filter (VTF): Consists of a BandPass Filter (BPF), a rectifier and Low Pass Filter (LPF), and speech spectrum restorer for reconstructing the original speech signals.

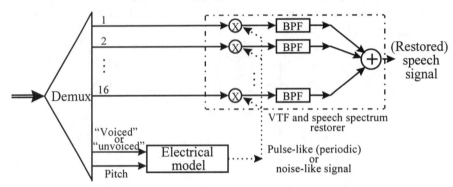

Figure 11A-6   The Decoder of Speech Vocoder.

In the decoder, the speech signal is regenerated by modulating the estimated "voiced" or "unvoiced" sound (identified by the electrical model) with the frequency samples provided by the vocal tract filter. After bandpass filtering and summation, the result is synthetic speech that reproduces the frequency spectrum of the original speaker. Despite extensive research in channel vocoders, no optimum design exists today, and channel vocoders still produce the unnatural "machine-like" speech that was characteristic of early vocoders.

11A-5.2 Linear Predictive Coder (LPC)

The performance of a vocoder system can be improved by using a vocal tract filter which has great versatility in its ability to be adjusted. The same type of filter can be used in an encoder to enable regeneration of speech not only at the decoder, but at the encoder as well. The reason this capability is needed at the transmitter is explained by referring to Figure 11A-7. The functional blocks of the encoder (shown in Figure 11A-7), which is a Linear Predictive Codec (coder/decoder), are briefly described as follows:

(1)   "Voiced"/"unvoiced" detector: Determines whether the human speech sound is a "voiced" or "unvoiced" sound. This information is used at the transmitter for estimating the restored speech signal that the receiver will eventually recover. The "voice"/unvoiced" sound information is sent to the receiver for the same purpose.

(2)   Pitch extractor: Estimates the pitch for "voiced sounds". Any human speech sound with periodic characteristic can be reproduced with an acceptable quality by estimating the pitch of the sound. The pitch information is needed by both the transmitter and receiver for speech signal restoration.

(3) rms (root mean square) estimator: Determines the signal power level that must be used. Even if the speech sounds are accurately regenerated, "machine-like" effect may occur if the sound volume is incorrectly transmitted/received. Therefore, the rms estimator provides the information needed to reproduce natural speech volume.

(4) Electrical model: See Section 11A-2 for detailed description.

(5) Linear Predictive Filter (LPF): Accepts the rms value of the original speech signal and the artificially generated speech signal from the electrical mode, uses this information to generate a (regenerated) speech signal.

(6) Error signal generator: Used to determine the errors between the true (original) speech signal and the regenerated speech signal. This error signal is minimized so that the regenerated speech signal represents the original speech signal with minimum errors. It should be noted that when a minimum error level has been obtained (typically the least square error criterion is applied to obtain the optimum result), the coefficients (C_n) representing the characteristics of the linear predictive filter are sent to the receiver for use in speech signal restoration.

(7) Multiplexer: Used to combine all the bitstreams generated by items (1), (2), (3) and (6).

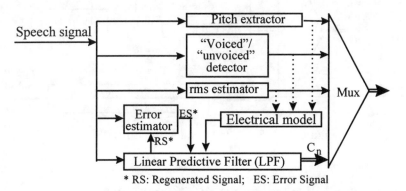

* RS: Regenerated Signal; ES: Error Signal

Figure 11A-7   The Encoder of a Linear Predictive Coder.

It is important that the encoder be able to "*hear*" how the speech will sound when it is regenerated at the decoder. This enables the encoder to generate all the necessary information, and transmit it to the receiver so that speech signal can be restored as closely to the original speech signal as possible. One task at the transmitter is to compare the original speech and its regenerated version and (as in any feedback control system) use the differences, (i.e., the error signal is derived) to adjust the filter parameters to minimize the error. This is called the *Linear Predictive Coder* (LPC) function. As in the channel vocoder encoder, the LPC encoder extracts the sound type (i.e., voiced or unvoiced) and the pitch. A single rectifier and filter is used to generate one (amplitude) signal, which is called the rms value of the speech input.

The electrical model, based on the "voiced" and "unvoiced" sound information, provides the hardware necessary to regenerate the speech. The signal that is used to set the parameters of the adjustable filter is the difference (error) signal between the original speech and its regenerated form (i.e., the filter output). This error signal is applied to a device that calculates and generates the signals need by the adjustable filter to minimize the error signal. These signals, which are essentially a model of the human vocal tract, along with the sound type, pitch, and rms speech value are time-division multiplexed and transmitted to the decoder.

At the decoder (see Figure 11A-8) these signals (the "voiced" sound or the "unvoiced" sound, the pitch of the voiced sound, and all the coefficients needed to adjust the linear predictive filter) are first demultiplexed. Then, they are used in connection with the electrical model to control the adjustable filter. The filter characteristics are adjusted for optimum voice regeneration. The quality of the LPC is "machine-like" speech, although the speech produced is intelligible and the bit rate is very low. However, LPC is not considered acceptable for telecommunications applications.

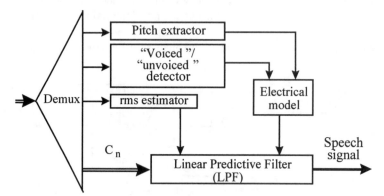

Figure 11A-8   The Decoder of a Linear Predictive Coder.

11A-5.3 Multi-Pulse Linear Predictive Coder (MP-LPC)

The Multi-Pulse Linear Predictive Coder (MP-LPC) (Figure 11A-9) was invented at AT&T-Bell Laboratories. It is a hybrid technique that combines waveform and vocoding features. The "voiced/unvoiced" detector and pitch extractor are replaced by a multi-pulse analysis function (a waveform property), but the vocal tract is still modeled by using a linear predictive filter (the vocoder approach). Instead of placing one excitation pulse per pitch period as speech proceeds, the MP-LPC uses many pulses per period and positions them dynamically according to variations in the speech signal. The vocal excitation parameters are the amplitudes (including sign) $a_1, a_2, a_3, a_4, \cdots, a_n$ placed at locations $t_1, t_2, t_3, t_4, \cdots, t_n$, for each pulse within the train.

The analysis-by synthesis procedure for determining the amplitudes and locations of the pulses from the multi-pulse excitation generator uses the error information derived by comparing the original speech and the regenerated speech. The error signal is "weighted" to take into account the human perception of the error. This process is called perceptual weighting. Amplitudes and locations of pulses are chosen to minimize the weighted error. The LPC filter coefficients and the vocal excitation parameters are time-division multiplexed and transmitted to the decoder. The vocal excitation parameters produce a multi-pulse excitation signal that is used by the LPF (along with the filter coefficients) to reproduce speech. The MP-LPC speech signal has a more "natural-sounding" quality than the "machine-like" sound of the LPC decoder.

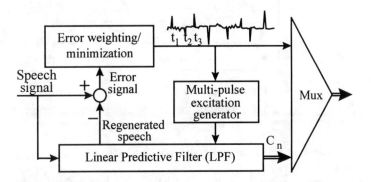

Figure 11A-9   The Encoder of a MP-LPC.

11A-5.4 Regular Pulse Excited Long Term Predictive Coder (RPE-LTP)

In a Regular-Pulse Excited-Long Term Predictive (RPE-LTP) coder, the multi-pulse excitation is replaced by regular-pulse stream excitation. Here, the spacing between the pulses is equidistant:

$$t_j = 0, \quad T, \quad 2T, \quad 3T, \quad \cdots \quad (j = 0, 1, 2, \cdots)$$

That is, for the RPE-LTP and the MP-LPC speech encoders, the error locations (spaces) have the following relationship:

$$t_2 - t_1 = t_3 - t_2 = t_4 - t_3 = t_5 - t_4 = \ldots \qquad \text{(RPE-LTP)}$$

$$t_2 - t_1 \neq t_3 - t_2 \neq t_4 - t_3 \neq t_5 - t_4 \neq \ldots \qquad \text{(MP-LPC)}$$

The spacing and pulse amplitudes are chosen to minimize the weighted error. But, the RPE-LTP requires less bits to transmit the required error space information. The LPC filter coefficients and the pulse parameters are time-division multiplexed and transmitted to the decoder. The decoder has the same form as the MP-LPC.

RPE-LPC is moderate complexity (see Figure 11A-10) compared to MP-LPC, and high quality speech can be obtained. It is used in the PAN-European GSM system. With an output rate of 13 kbps, the encoder can process 20 ms blocks of speech where each block corresponds to 260 bits.

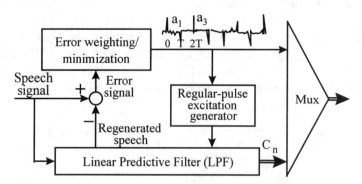

Figure 11A-10   The Encoder of a RPE-LTP.

11A-5.5   Code-Excited Linear Predictive (CELP)

The Code-Excited Linear Predictive (CELP) coder is a hybrid technique that produces high quality speech at lower bit rates (e.g., 16 kbps). Both waveform and speech properties are encoded. The essence of CELP is based on an analysis-by-synthesis codebook search. One codeword is selected which best matches the speech vector to be coded. An index to this codeword is transmitted to the receiver, along with the gain and filter coefficients. Conventional (fully forward-adaptive) CELP introduces a processing delay caused by the codebook search, of typically 40 to 60 ms. This delay is undesirable, especially when echo cancellations is involved. Echo occurs in telephone networks because of delay, and must be canceled to insure high quality speech. A backward-adaptive CELP coder is a low-delay CELP which is the proposed ITU-T standard (at 16 kbps) for network quality speech. In this system, the forward adaptation of the shape of the excitation signal is the only source of encoding delay. This reduces the processing delay to less than 2 ms.

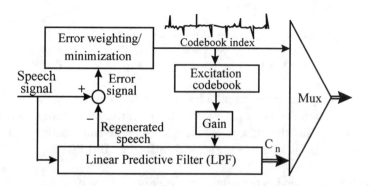

Figure 11A-11   The Encoder of Code-Excited Linear Predictive.

The North-American IS-54/IS-136 Standard [set by Telecommunications Industry Association (TIA)] uses a variation of CELP, called Vector-Sum Excited LP (VSELP). It uses a special set of codebooks that are derived from vector sums of basic excitation vectors representative of speech contained in a database. The encoder processes 20 ms blocks of speech (each block contains 159 bits) at a source rate of 7.95 kbps. It is more efficient than GSM, which has a source rate of 13 kbps.

11A-6 SPEECH ENCODING QUALITY COMPARISON

Today's wireless cellular telephone system is based on repeated use of 832 radio channels ($\equiv 2 \times 416$ RF channels; discussed in Chapter 8). These are Frequency-Modulation (FM) radio channels within the microwave radio frequency spectrum allocated by the Federal Communications Commission (FCC). This spectral band is known as the 800 (900) MHz cellular band.

To meet anticipated demand for cellular telephone service (e.g., from 2 million U.S. subscribers in 1992 to 18 millions in 1995), a new generation of digital cellular equipment is needed. These systems will use digital signal processing techniques for low-bit-rate speech coding, spectrally efficient modems, and fast adaptive equalization. High-quality speech coders that operate at the lowest possible bit rate will play a key role in implementing spectrally efficient digital cellular system. A 7.95-kbps speech coding algorithm has been selected for use in digital cellular equipment.

The Telecommunications Industry Association (TIA) has agreed to use Time-Division Multiple-Access (TDMA) technology for the new cellular system [to replace the existing Frequency Division Multiple Access (FDMA) systems], which uses the 7.95-kbps speech coding algorithm. Channel bandwidth will be kept at the current 30 kHz to ease the transition from analog to digital technology. Thus, an existing analog channel unit serving one conversation could be replaced by a digital unit serving three (or more) conversations over the same 30-kHz channel (used in the FDMA systems) without affecting adjacent analog channels. A 30-kHz channel could support data rates up to 48.6 kilobytes per second (i.e., 16.2 kbps per conversion). Taking overhead into account, the upper limit on the speech coding rate is 13 kbps.

In speech coders with low data rates, loss of information can result in serious degradation of speech quality. A plot of speech quality as a function of bit rate for several classes of speech coders is shown in Figure 11A-12. Speech quality is measured by using a subjective test scale. It is called Grade of Service (GOS) or Mean Opinion Score (MOS) with the following five measurement scales:

(1) Excellent: a score of "5".
(2) Good: a score of "4".
(3) Satisfactory: a score of "3"
(4) Fair: a score of "2"
(5) Poor: a score of "1"

A system with a MOS of 4.5 for speech signal transport is said to have a "trunk quality". A Pulse Code Modulation (PCM; either A-law or μ-law, described in Chapter 6) coder, as used in the public network, is often used as the reference for comparing different speech encoders. A PCM coder yields high quality speech most of the time, but requires a high bit rate (64 kbps). However, even with a high bit rate, a PCM system may yield a poor quality speech because of other parameters.

In comparison, Delta Modulation (DM), Adaptive DM (ADM), Differential PCM (DPCM), and Adaptive DPCM (ADPCM) systems have a widely-spread speech quality and required bit rates. For example, the high-complexity waveform coder, such as the ADPCM can provide good speech quality if the bit rate is high enough.

A high-complexity hybrid coder, such as the Code-Exited Linear Predictive (CELP) coder, yields high quality for wireless applications (i.e., with a MOS requirement of 3.5 or higher), even at relatively low bit rates. However, if their bit rates are not high enough, they can never provide good quality. The low bit rate high-complexity Linear Predictive Coder (LPC) can not provide acceptable quality.

In Figure 11A-12 also indicates that the research trends for speech encoding technology is to reduce the required bit rates and maintain good speech quality as indicated by the "shaded" zone in Figure 11A-12.

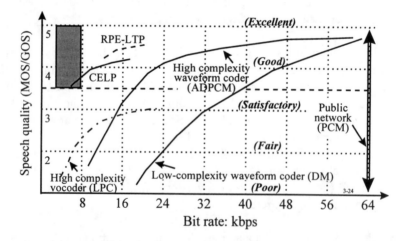

Figure 11A-12   Speech Encoding Quality Comparison.

CHAPTER 12
Network Management And Telecommunications Management Network (TMN)

Chapter Objectives

Upon the completion of this chapter, you should be able to:

- Describe the purpose of network management, telecommunications network operations, wide area network migration, and integrated platform architecture.

- Describe the Simple Network Management Protocol (SNMP) including the TCP/IP protocol suite, SNMP networks, SNMP data unit, protocol architecture, and Management Information Base (MIB).

- Discuss OSI management standards and OSI network management: OSI Management Environment (OME) organization model, OME information model, OSI management structure, OSI management services and protocols, environment model, configuration management systems, etc.

- Discuss some "mature" technology network management applications: System Network Architecture (SNA), SystemView, NetView, DECmcc, and OpenView.

- Discuss the Telecommunications Management Network (TMN): evolution of network management into TMN, TMN strategy, rationale for TMN, TMN vision/goals/functionality, TMN users/benefits/standards, ITU-T Recommendations for TMN, network management forum, and TMN architectures [e.g., functional architecture (including TMN management layers, reference model, functional blocks and reference points), TMN information architecture, and TMN physical architecture (including interfaces, interaction, etc.)].

12.1 INTRODUCTION

The definition of "network management" has been changing (evolving) since 1970's. Today, it means different things to different network users. To a public switched network owner, network management involves real-time network (alarm) surveillance, network control, automatic protection switching for restoring failed network components, eliminating the source of degraded network performance, and network traffic management.

In contrast, for a private (data) network owner, network management involves planning, implementing, and maintaining the network in its "top working condition".

Definition 12-1 (Network management): For modern telecommunications, network management is responsible for both "**long-term**" and "**day-to-day**" activities required for telecommunications services to be delivered to the customers, and assuring the quality of those services.

Network management supports telecommunications service providers in various activities which enable corporate managers to plan, organize, supervise, control, and account for the use of interconnection services. It also enables the service providers to respond to changing requirements, applications, and new technology.

12.1.1 Purpose of Network Management

The task of network management involves "setting up and running" a network, monitoring network activities, controlling the network to provide acceptable performance, and assuring high availability, quick response time, and acceptable quality is delivered to the network users. The purpose of network management is:

- To improve customer service

  * Meet service-on-demand
  * Minimize network outages
  * Response to customer troubles quickly

- To low network operating cost

  * Centralize operations
  * Automate tests on demand
  * Restore network (systems) quickly

- To increase technical support (craft) productivity

  * Identify problems in the network
  * Locate where the problem is in the network
  * To reduce false dispatches of maintenance personnel

12.1.2 Telecommunications Networks Overview

Network management technology is evolving as rapidly as telecommunications networks are changing. This section briefly describes the rapid network evolution that started in the mid 1960's. A telecommunications network is a collection of many telecommunications nodes (each node is composed of switching machines, transmission equipment and/or transmission terminals) interconnected by communications links (the connecting links can be wire, fiber, or wireless transmission facilities). A network is designed to carry the telecommunications traffic that results from Information Movement and Management (IM&M) services.

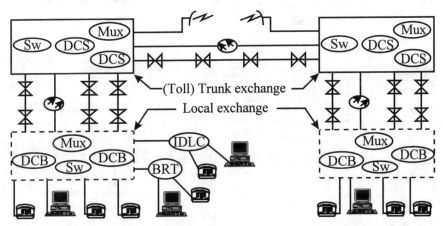

Figure 12-1   Elements of a Modern Telecommunications Network.

Network can be classified based on different characteristics. A network can be a Public Switched Telephone Network (PSTN) or a private (dedicated, or "nailed-up") network. A network can be a voice network, a data network, or an ISDN network. A PSTN typically supports voice applications, and is used by the public. Private networks originated for computer data transport and evolved into ISDN applications. For modern corporate applications, a hybrid arrangement using a combination of PSTN and private network services to meet communications needs has been adopted in many metropolitan areas.

Network nodes contain many network elements. The elements can be switches (SW for switching traffic), Digital Channel Banks (DCBs for analog-to-digital conversion, digital multiplexing, and vice versa), Integrated Digital Loop Carrier (IDLC) systems (for combining voice, data, image and video signals into a single bitstream), Add/Drop Multiplexers (ADMs or multiplexer for add and/or dropping traffic), Business Remote Terminals (BRTs; IDLC for business applications), Digital Cross-connect Systems (DCSs for consolidating/grooming traffic), and transmission facilities as shown in Figure 12-1. Switching machine are discussed in Chapter 5, IDLC, DCB and BRT are discussed in Chapter 6. The other elements are described in Chapters 6, 7 and 8. Note that part of the IDLC and BRT systems are located on the customer premises while other parts of these systems are located in the Central Office (CO) to serve as transmission terminals in the network nodes.

12.1.3 (Wide Area) Network Migration

The early generation of Wide Area Networks (WANs) were essentially a set of unconnected applications. There was no efficient way to share limited resources. In addition, the concept of network compatibility was not considered feasible. The communications environment was inflexible and non-dynamic. Networks with these characteristics are no longer appropriate (acceptable) for modern communications.

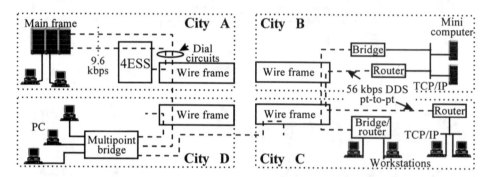

Figure 12-2   Early Network Architecture for Wide Area Network.

Network migration has several goals. Two primary goals are to (1) provide universal connectivity and (2) optimize resource utilization so that communications costs can be reduced. The evolution of network architecture is business driven, and should allow dynamic responses to rapid communications changes. Four phases (before, present, near term, and long term) briefly describe wide area network migration as follows:

- **Phase 1** (before): The "before" phase (Figure 12-2) illustrates the era in which network interconnectivity was barely possible. There are four cities in this illustration. City A is a main frame-(computer)-based network. This is an environment with a mainframe attached to a front-end processor with connections to a multipoint user community of an on-line data entry system. A "dial in" connectivity capability exists for limited remote PC applications. Note that the interface speed is typically 9.6 kbps. City B is a typical mini-computer cluster consisting of several minicomputer connected to a local area Ethernet network and linked to remote users via bridges or routers. All these connections, except for the dial up, are hardwired (i.e., dedicated private line connections). Users in City D cannot access applications in City B. Some PC users in City D can't access anything except their own local programs. Users in City

C cannot access the workstation applications in the other part of City C that is on the TCP/IP network. Management of this network is difficult and reliability is uncertain.

- **Phase 2** (present): Several changes have been made to improve network operations. In place of dedicated end-to-end hard-wired circuits, separate access requirements (rather than long-haul requirements) have been introduced for fractional T1 services. Using a common access media (e.g., T1.5; Chapter 6) for both voice and data, and using multiplexers as network access interfaces allows service providers to buy the incremented bandwidth needed to support a specific number of users for a particular time interval. With the introduction of Digital Cross-connect Systems (DCSs; discussed in Chapter 6) services like Accunet Bandwidth Manager (ABM) provides the ability to allocate bandwidth on an "as needed" basis. It also allows bandwidth deployment to handle dynamically in response to environmental changes (e.g., shifts in business, physical disasters, or increased service demands). Common "brouters" (bridge-routers) have been introduced to handle translations between different devices and protocols. In addition, LAN-based connectivity has been widely deployed. The "cost/performance" of access, reliability, flexibility, and management of the physical network have been drastically improved. However, there is no "cross elasticity" between dial-up users, or between mainframe and mini-computer applications.

- **Phase 3** (near term): Shared T1 access, brouters as interface devices, and multiplexers as physical integrators continue to be primary technologies. X.25 connectivity has been applied as a mean of expanding the dial-up environment in response to increasing demand for remote access from telecommuters and PC users. The X.25 common interface allows users to access both mainframe and mini-computer applications from a common menu that is resident in the network. Frame relay technology has been deployed to improve "LAN to LAN" connectivity. Frame relay service has been deployed in the "backbone network", thereby eliminating dedicated circuits and encouraging transition to a hybrid virtual public/private networking environment. In addition, this service provides the ability to introduce new applications at any point in the network, and the flexibility to relocate users, devices, and databases (as dictated by business) with the assurance that the network can accommodate these changes quickly and economically.

- **Phase 4** (long term): The migration to fiber-based services such as Fiber Distributed Data Interface (FDDI) for Metropolitan Area Network (MAN), and ATM and SONET/SDH for Wide Area Network (WAN) and broadband applications is clearly the future trend. Access has been further separated from backbone services. Standardized interface utilities and user application technology development allows service providers to improve network applications/services without disrupting the end users. The network will eventually evolve to a state where service providers can focus on the integration of applications that deliver audio, image, and text in "easy to use" relational packages. These applications (with higher bandwidth requirements) will be incorporated into the network utilities. The users view the network will be "**an asset that provides quick**

responses with better information", will insure telecommunications is a profitable and growing enterprise. The network will become a vital business tool touching every aspect of daily operations as well as providing enhanced services in the future. Migration of the physical network will support development of a logical that will eventually lead to universal connectivity on a global basis (see Figure 12-3).

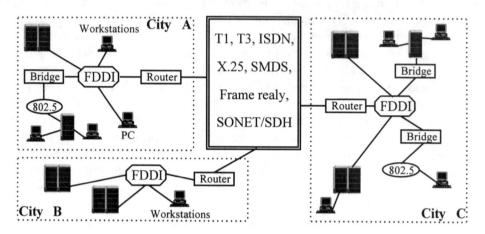

Figure 12-3 Wide Area Network (WAN) Applications.

12.1.4 Integrated Platform Architecture/Profiles

The AT&T OneVision product is an example of integrated platform. It is based on a family of network management software and services that moves customers closer to a "single-point" for monitoring and managing widely disparate network components deployed throughout a corporation. Networking components used in today's corporations include information systems (e.g., main frame, mini, and personal computers), Local Area Networks (LANs), and telecommunications networks.

Telecommunications networks typically consist of switches, Private Branch eXchanges (PBXs), modems, multiplexers, and transmission facilities. Most of these network elements are supplied by different vendors, and must be managed separately (often with costly duplication of functions). AT&T's OneVision strategy is to provide a completely interoperable network management application that covers a broad range of network and system components.

The dynamics of the network and system management applications market imposes the need for: (1) quality and reliability in a management platform, and (2) flexibility for integrating a variety of management applications. Network users are faced with the challenge of creating and operating management solutions that span multiple application domains. They also demand international Open Systems Interface (OSI) standards that facilitate interoperability of applications on a variety of equipment and management systems manufactured by different vendors.

The goal of AT&T's OneVision is to give customers quick and complete access to information about the condition of their networks. OneVision's strategy reflects an expanded view of network and systems management being a "critical enabler" for delivering end-to-end business solutions that encompass computing and communications applications, network operations, and professional services. It provides a broadest set of integrated options for managing the customer's environment. This is achieved by providing tools directly to customers, and also supplying network management services. OneVision offers a family of interoperable applications for centralized control of enterprise networks. It includes applications and solutions for both UNIX based and Window's NT operating systems.

Hewlett Packard's OpenView product is a recognized market leader in the field of private network and system management products. OpenView is considered to be a "standard". In comparison, the AT&T BaseWorX applications platform offers comprehensive "middle-ware" capabilities for facilitating the development of OSI network management and Operations support Systems (OSs) applications for management of highly complex public telecommunications networks.

An integrated platform using AT&T's BaseWorX and the HP's OpenView provides common application process management services, common communications structures, and common application programmer interfaces. This integration focuses on implementing a compatible object technology, a common data repository, user interface integration, and additional functionality identified by market needs assessment. Both systems are industry leading management platforms, and the agreement between them is intended to accelerate the availability and standardization of an "**open, integrated**, and **feature rich**" environment for management applications. This is accomplished through greater consistency between these industry leading products.

The objectives of the integrated platform are briefly described as follows:

- Bring consistency to software platforms being used to develop management solutions which span:

  * Customer Premises Management (CPM): CPM handles management entities such as computer hardware, modems, routers, bridges, LANs, and WANs.

  * Telecommunications Network Management (TNM): It manages telecommunications networks including switches and all other elements.

  * Customer Network Management (CNM): CNM combines the management aspects of CPM and TNM to support the customer's view of their network. CNM enables customers to manage their subscribed network services on an end-to-end basis.

* Integrated platform architecture: This approach provides comprehensive capabilities for developing either object-oriented applications or traditional procedural applications that cover a range of CPM, CNM, and TNM areas.

• Provide the ability for customers to take advantage of new platform features, while protecting their investment in existing applications.

• Facilitate portability of applications between platforms through a common architecture and compatible Application Programmer Interface (API).

• Facilitate interoperability of different platforms by sharing a common technology base to the extent that this is feasible for independent vendors.

• Provide long term consistency for application developers through coordinated platform evolution based on compliance with industry standards.

Definition 12-2: **Profiling** is the process of bundling modules to provide a platform that supports appropriate functions to meet the application developer's needs.

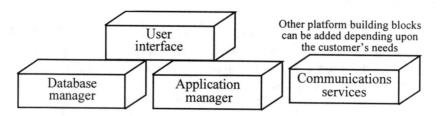

Figure 12-4   Integrated Platform Profile Core Building Blocks.

An integrated platform provides a comprehensive set of functionality and capabilities that can be configured to support needs spanning CPM, CNM and TNM environments. A set of core building blocks (Figure 12-4) is required for managing the platform and applications whether the solution is intended for TNM, CPM or CNM. These bundling blocks include a user interface, application manager, database manager, and communications services. This common core is surrounded by other modules to address the needs for specific set of functionality distinguishing one profile from another. The CPM, CNM, and TNM application architecture profiles are briefly described as follows:

• CPM application architecture profile: The application architecture for CPM uses the integrated platform building blocks to create a suitable profile for managing TCP/IP based LANs/WANs, modems, and other computing/data communications hardware. The CPM architecture profile supports the manager-agent model for constructing applications.

- **TNM application architecture profile**: The TNM profile is appropriate for developing procedural applications to manage telecommunications service provider networks. Examples of these applications include: fault (maintenance) management, configuration management, and performance management. The TNM architecture profile supports the manager-agent model for constructing applications.

- **CNM application architecture profile**: The CNM profile combines the management aspects of the CPM and TNM architecture profiles. Using this profile, the customer can view subscribed telecommunications services along with management information related to local equipment and networks. Examples of these applications include: Software Defined Network (SDN) management, leased line management, and private network management.

12.2 SIMPLE NETWORK MANAGEMENT PROTOCOL (SNMP)

One of the first efforts focused on management of TCP/IP based internetworks began in 1987 with NETMON: a protocol based on Routing Information Protocol (RIP) which "pinged" messages between devices. RIP was followed by the Simple Gateway Monitor Protocol (SGMP; late 1987), which issued a Request For Comment (RFC).

The Simple Network Management Protocol (SNMP) effort began in early 1988 and culminated in generating several RFCs (RFC1065, RFC1066, RFC1067 and RFC1098). The second phase of TCP/IP network management is Common Management Information (services) Protocol (CMIP) over TCP/IP (Common Management over TCP: CMOT). CMOT supports an easy transition to OSI-based Internets.

12.2.1 TCP/IP Protocol Suite

SNMP makes use of TCP/IP-based Internets, as specified by several Requests For Comment (RFCs) standards generated by the Internet Engineering Task Force (IETF) activities board. The TCP/IP protocol suite is briefly described in this section. TCP/IP was developed based on experience gained from the original "**store and forward**" packet switched network ARPANET (currently Internet). As a result, TCP/IP has become a "*de facto*" standard for internetworking.

SNMP is a TCP/IP standard. Internet Control Message Protocol (ICMP) is used by IP for limited network alerting procedures. It is called by IP for services, and is encapsulated by IP for delivery to the destination. Figure 12-5 represents the TCP/IP protocol suite. That is, the OSI layers can be compared to the TCP/IP architecture shown in Figure 12-5. The TCP/IP protocol suite comprises:

- A layer three Internet Protocol (IP)
- A layer four Transmission Control Protocol (TCP) or User Datagram Protocol (UDP)

- Supporting applications.

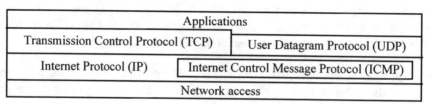

Applications	
Transmission Control Protocol (TCP)	User Datagram Protocol (UDP)
Internet Protocol (IP)	Internet Control Message Protocol (ICMP)
Network access	

Figure 12-5   TCP/IP Protocol Suite.

12.2.1.1 The Internet Protocol (IP)

IP is a "connectionless-mode" protocol that supports data transfer service between peer network entities, and the exchange of information between users connected by a set of concatenated, non-homogeneous subnetworks.

Definition 12-3: The unit of data transfer is called a **datagram** (a somewhat generic term). Datagrams consist of a fixed-format header (except the option field which has a variable length), followed by the user data field. The user data field contains the "upper-layer user information" being exchanged.

← 32 bits →			
Version	Internet header length	Type of service	Total length
Identifier		Flags	Fragment offset
Time to live	Protocol	Header checksum	
Source address			
Destination address			
Options + padding			
Data (field)			

Figure 12-6   IP Message Format (Structure).

Figure 12-6 shows the IP message format. This is a 32-bit structure, based on the width of the original ARPANET processors message format. The minimum length of the IP header is 20 octets, without options or padding. The IP data field contains the TCP header and data, or the UDP header and data. The entities of the IP message are briefly described as follows:

- VERsion (VER) field: A 4-bit field that indicates the version number of IP (e.g., "0100" for version 4 IP, i.e., IPv4).

- Internet Header Length (IHL): A 4-bit field (see Figure 12-6) indicating the header size. The minimum IP header is five 32-bit words, or 20 ($\equiv$ 32 bits/word ÷ 8 bits/octet × 5 words) octets in length.

- Type of service: An 8-bit field that is used to specify reliability, precedence, delay, and throughput parameters.

- Total length: A 16-bit field used to indicate the total length of the IP datagram (expressed in octets), including the IP header.

- Identification: A 16-bit field that provides a unique identifier for the datagram.

- Flags: A 3-bit field that is an option used to indicate whether fragmentation is permitted and/or used.

- Fragment offset: A13-bit field that indicates where in the entire datagram this specific fragment belongs. The fragment's offset position is measured in 64-bit increments from the beginning of the datagram.

- Time To Live (TTL): An 8-bit field containing Time To Live (TTL) value measured in gateway "hops" and/or seconds.

- Protocol: An 8-bit field that identifies the next protocol following the IP header (e.g., TCP).

- Header checksum: A 16-bit field containing a checksum generated over the IP header. This checksum value may be recomputed at each gateway.

- Source address: A 32-bit field containing the Internet address of the originating host.

- Destination address: A 32-bit field containing the Internet address of the destination host.

- Options: A variable length field used by the sender (source) to indicate specific features (e.g., route specification).

- Padding: A variable length "field" used to fill-out the IP header so that it fully occupies a 32-bit word.

- Data field: A variable length field, that must be a multiple of 8 bits and cannot exceed 65,535 octets for the IP header plus data (e.g., TCP header, TCP data, etc.).

The IP standard requires that all devices accept at least a 576-byte IP datagram. A typical IP address might be "192.33.4.21", and represents a particular class of address (e.g., called type A, B or C).

12.2.1.2 Internet Control Message Protocol (ICMP)

ICMP is a network layer protocol used for communication between various IP entities. ICMP messages are generated to indicate a network layer problem, such as network congestion or an unreachable application port. This protocol uses IP services. An ICMP message is sent using IP, with the ICMP message occupying the IP data field. ICMP is used for very limited network management applications. It communicates with the IP layer directly, and with higher layers indirectly. It is considered an "unreliable service" because it does not use "acknowledgment" to verify actions that are taken.

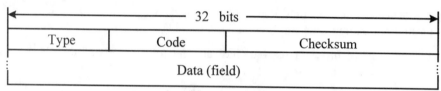

Figure 12-7   ICMP Message Format (Structure).

ICMP is categorized as being a part of the network (IP) layer as shown in Figure 12-5. However, the header used by ICMP has no datagram addresses. Therefore, ICMP must be encapsulated by IP (Figure 12-5) to be sent to its destination address. Historically ICMP has been used for very limited network management functions. Since ICMP is carried as IP data, it is subject to loss, corruption, or duplication as is the case for a datagram service (IP). The transmitter cannot tell whether the ICMP has been delivered to its intended destination because acknowledgments are not used. The ICMP message format is shown in Figure 12-7 and is briefly described as follows:

- Type: An 8-bit field used to indicate the type of ICMP message. Among 256 (= 2^8) possible combinations, the presently defined messages are: destination unreachable, time exceeded, parameter problem, source quench, redirect, echo, echo reply, time stamp, and time-stamp reply.

- Code: An 8-bit field used to specify the parameters of the ICMP message that can be encoded.

- Checksum: A 16-bit field containing checksum generated over the ICMP message.

- Data: A variable length field that carries additional information related to the ICMP message.

12.2.1.3 Transmission Control Protocol (TCP)

TCP is a Layer 4 protocol specified in standard RFC793. It uses a common encoding for the exchange of data and control information between a pair of peer TCP entities. TCP receives bit streams of information from Upper Layer Protocols (ULPs), and then forms transmission segments for communication with a distant peer entity. TCP (see Figure 12-5) has more functionality than the OSI Layer 4 protocol because there is no formal session or presentation layer in the TCP protocol architecture. Features of the presentation layer that are needed (e.g., data representation) are present in the application layer.

Connection-oriented TCP procedures may have different network Qualities of Service (QoS) characteristics. These procedures provide reliable operation even when data is lost, damaged, duplicated, disordered, and/or network congestion occurs.

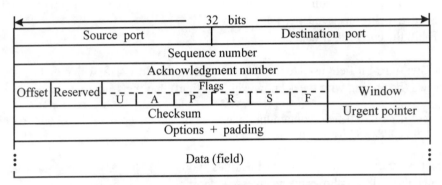

Figure 12-8   TCP Message Format (Structure).

The minimum length of a TCP message header is 20 bytes, assuming no options or padding is applied and the data field contains the applications. As shown in Figure 12-8, the first header word contains the source port and the destination port. The second word contains the sequence number. The third word is the acknowledgment number. The fourth word contains the "offset + reserved + flags + window" word. The fifth word contains the checksum and urgent pointer. The next word contains options + padding, followed by the data field. A TCP message consists of words that are 32-bits in length. The entries of the TCP message are briefly described as follows:

- Source port: A 16-bit field (the range is 0~1,023 for applications, and 1,024~65,535 for users). Servers are assigned to the range of 0~1,023, while clients are assigned to the range of 1,024~65,535.

- Destination port: A 16-bit field that contains the number (identity) of the called port.

- Sequence number: A 32-bit field used to indicate the sequence number of the data so that it can be delivered to the destination in the correct sequence. This number indicates the byte sequence number of the first octet in this TCP data block, and is incremented according to the number of octets transmitted in each TCP segment.

- Acknowledgment number: A 32-bit field used as a "piggyback acknowledgment" for the next expected TCP octet.

- Offset: A 4-bit field used to indicate the number of 32-bit words in the TCP header.

- Reserved: A 6-bit field reserved for future use (default value "000000").

- Flags: A 6-bit field used to indicate various control functions, such as the setup and termination of a session, expedited or urgent data flow, reset of a connection, or end of data. The 6 bits are assigned as follows:

* U-bit: urgent pointer field significant
* A-bit: acknowledgment field significant
* P-bit: push function
* R-bit: reset connection
* S-bit: synchronize sequence numbers
* F-bit: the end of user data

• Window: A 16-bit field used to indicate the receive window size, which is the number of octets (beginning with the acknowledgment field) that the sender will accept.

• Checksum: A 16-bit field containing the checksum generated over the IP address plus the TCP header and its length.

• Urgent pointer: A 16-bit field that identifies (points to) the first octet following the urgent data, and thus allows the receiver to determine how much urgent data is arriving.

• Options: A variable length field (maximum TCP segment size) that is currently undefined.

• Padding: A variable length field used to fill-out the TCP header so that it is a 32-bit word.

• Data field: A variable length field, that must be a multiple of 8 bits, and cannot exceed 65,535 octets (i.e., TCP header plus data).

12.2.1.4 User Datagram Protocol (UDP)

User Datagram Protocol (UDP) is a connectionless transport protocol and is similar to the ISO-8602 standard. UDP provides minimal services, and is a method that applications can use for port addressing to multiplex data over the same Internet address (similar to TCP). A different value contained in the IP protocol filed indicates that the user of the network service is UDP instead of TCP. This addressing convention ensures proper delivery of datagrams to the correct IP user.

← 32 bits →	
Source address (port)	Destination address (port)
Length	Checksum
Data (field)	

Figure 12-9   UDP Message Format (Structure).

There are applications that do not require the extensive error control functions provided by TCP. A common example of this type of an application is Simple Network

Management Protocol (SNMP). This type of application does not require "absolute" reliability. Therefore, this lower overhead UDP approach can be used. Figure 12-9 shows the UDP message format, and is briefly described as follows:

- Source address: A 16-bit field that contains the number of the calling port.

- Destination address: A 16-bit field that contains the number of the called port.

- Length: A 16-bit field that indicates the length of the UDP datagram.

- Checksum: A 16-bit field that contains the checksum generated over the UDP message.

- Data (field): A variable length, that must be a multiple of 8 bits and cannot exceed 65,535 octets (i.e., UDP header plus data).

Note that because guaranteed delivery is **not** a UDP requirement, the reliability-related fields (e.g., the sequence number and acknowledgment number) are not used in a UDP message. Therefore, the UDP header is shortened accordingly. In addition to using the UDP datagram service, SNMP implements separate acknowledgment messages (discussed later in this chapter).

12.2.2 SNMP Network (Example) and SNMP Data Unit

A typical SNMP network model is shown in Figure 12-10. As indicated, one workstation serves as a Network Management Station (NMS), and "agents" are present in all the managed devices (e.g., routers, bridges, host computers, file servers, and UNIX hosts) in the network.

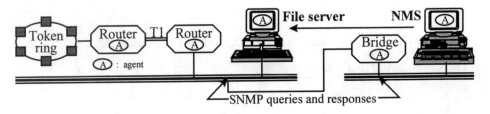

Figure 12-10   Typical SNMP Network Model.

The Network Management Station (NMS) and the routers must agree on three activities: (1) how to reference information [this function is performed by the Management Information System (MIS); discussed later in this chapter]; (2) how to exchange information [this function is handled by sending and receiving SNMP protocol messages or Protocol Data Units (PDUs); discussed later in this chapter]; and (3) how to represent information [this process is described in the Structure of Management Information (SMI); discussed later in this chapter].

The Network Management Station (NMS) is the network entity that performs management function by poling and the receiving unsolicited state messages. NMS also provides the user interface. The management software, that resides in the NMS, controls, monitors, and displays the status of the network by sending queries or requests to the agent programs residing in the managed devices.

The agent programs respond with information about the state of their Ethernet interface or the number of "bad" packets received within a specific time interval. The agents can also generate unsolicited alarms indicating failures, power up or power down states, and critical conditions. The NMS periodically broadcasts requests to obtain the status of the network (periodic queried) and the agents respond with the requested information accordingly.

12.2.3 SNMP Protocol Architecture

Simple Network Management Protocol (SNMP) was created to monitor network performance, analyze network failures, configure network devices, and perform network tests (e.g., validation, accounting, and fault detection/correction) as part of Operations, Administration, Maintenance and Provisioning (OAM&P) activities.

SNMP can be used to query entries in routing tables, the state of user interfaces, and protocol performance statistics. In this scheme, everything related to network management is essentially reduced to a set of variables, and two operations on these variables. "Traps" are also applied to convey information about specific unsolicited events. The two basic operations are:

- Get: Used to read a variable
- Set: Used to assign a value to a variable

SNMP Protocol Data Unit (PDU)	SNMP header (authentication)	UDP	IP	Network access layer

Figure 12-11   SNMP Protocol Architecture.

SNMP is an application-level protocol that resides "on top of" the User Datagram Protocol (UDP)/IP stack. The ISO ASN.1 standard defines the protocol representation via a bit encoded data stream for SNMP data units (packets). This notation specifies the basic data types, and further specifies the Basic Encoding Rules (BERs) for transmission. The SNMP protocol architecture has three main components:

(1) SNMP protocol : Specifies the protocol representation.

(2) Structure of Management Information (SMI): It specifies how the MIB is structured [i.e., how the agents (managed devices) are represented]. SMI defines:

* The syntax for representing the MIB (which is machine independent).

* The primitive types (which include integer, octet string, object identifier, and null).

SMI applies defined types including: network address (support of non-IP protocol), IpAddress (octet string of length 4), counter (integer), gauge (latch at a maximum value), and TimeTicks (integer representing hundreds of a second).

(3) Management Information Base (MIB): The information available to the SNMP network manager is defined in the MIB by standards RFC-1155, RFC-1156, and RFC-1213. MIB defines a set of variables related to both hardware and software. It depends on a hierarchy for naming network objects used to group related objects together in a tree structure (discussed later in this chapter). A variable is referenced by a path from the root (of the tree structure) to the particular variable.

The SNMP network contains Network Management Stations (NMSs), which keep a database containing a set of all the managed devices in the network, and all MIB variables. The NMS serves as a user interface, and has all the necessary tools needed to administer the network (i.e., the managed devices that have agent software). The agent software is the part of a managed device that communicates with the NMS. The agent includes a MIB that pertains to the specific device. The basic operations involve NMS sending SNMP messages, queries, and commands to agents in the network. The agents respond to these messages, and return the requested information.

12.2.4 SNMP Protocol Data Unit (PDU)

Figure 12-12 shows the SNMP message encapsulation. SNMP makes use of UDP/IP services. Each SNMP Protocol Data Unit (PDU) contains one SNMP request or response. A PDU can contain operations on as many variables as can fit into a SNMP message. If a variable is unknown to an agent, then an error message is returned to the sender. PDUs can be any of the types shown in Table 12-1, which also shows the corresponding response returned by an agent that "listens" for the request.

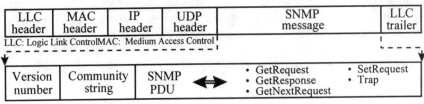

Figure 12-12   SNMP Message Encapsulation.

SNMPv2 (SNMP version 2) adds two more PDUs to those listed in Table 12-1. They are (1) GetBulkRequest, and (2) InformRequest. SNMPv2 also allows for secure operations beyond the sample authentication supported by version 1 (i.e., SNMPv1).

Table 12-1   PDU Request and Its Corresponding Response.

PDU request	Agent's response	
GetRequest	Receive GetRequest	⇒ return GetResponse
GetNextRequest	Receive GetNextRequest	⇒ return GetResponse
GetResponse		
SetRequest	Receive SetRequest; set the information	⇒ return GetResponse
Trap	Detect event	⇒ send Trap message

12.2.5 Management Information Base (MIB)

A minimum number of managed objects were included in the first Internet standard MIB (MIB-I). Devices that support the MIB are manageable by SNMP. Not all objects in the MIB are meaningful for certain devices. MIB-I was set up to include the first seven functional groups listed in Table 12-2.

Table 12-2   MIB's Groups/Objects.

Group	Object
System	All managed (by SNMP) nodes (e.g., description of device, name)
Interface	Network interface/attachments (all nodes managed by SNMP)
Address translation	IP address translation
IP	Internet Protocol
ICMP	ICMP management (mandatory for all managed nodes)
UDP	User Datagram Protocol (implemented to nodes running UDP)
EGP	All nodes (managed by SNMP) using Exterior Gateway Protocol
Transmission	Includes token ring, loopback, and network architecture
SNMP	Mandatory for all systems that support SNMP protocol entity

ICMP: Internet Control Message Protocol

Extension of MIB-I resulted in the addition of the transmission group and SNMP group (Table 12-2). The transmission group includes token ring, loopback, and network architecture. The "transmission group" definitions were introduced in the "experimental phase" of the MIB, and have since migrated to the Internet standard. The SNMP group allows a network manager to manipulate the SNMP portion of the entities that it manages.

Names for object types are defined in the Internet standard MIB and in documents that describe the Structure of Management Information (SMI). This requires compliant protocols to be defined using mechanisms where individual instances of object types (i.e., instantiations) for a particular network element are uniquely identified. Each instance of an object defined in the MIB is also identified in SNMP by a unique name called the "variable name". A total of 126 objects have been defined in these groups. The arrangement is i a hierarchical organization, with individual objects at the lowest level of the database. Entries can be grouped into tables, which in turn represent the highest level of hierarchy.

A subset of ASN.1 MIB objects has been defined for SNMP. The types are: ASN.1 basic types, NetworkAddress, IpAddress, Counter, Gauge, TimeTicks, Opaque, and Extensible. The structure of MIB implies data type; all structures are defined in standard RFC-1155, and all representations are defined in ASN.1 X.409.

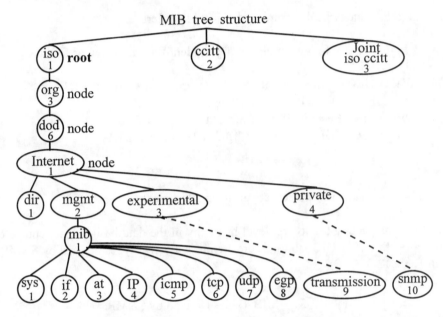

Figure 12-13   Typical MIB Tree Structure.

Example 12-1 Describe the MIB tree structure.

A typical MIB tree structure is illustrated in Figure 12-13. It can be seen that MIB elements (starting from the root) are equivalent to a tree with a trunk, branches, and leaves. An object's name in the tree is a sequence of labels along the path from the root. These variables have a specific meaning only to the network manager. All operations involve Get, Set, and Trap. The MIB is defined as:

(1) A naming structure uniquely referencing a particular variable

(2) A logical tree structure

The goal of the MIB is *"to establish a common data store for objects to be managed in a protocol-independent manner."* Two typical name sequences (derived from the tree structure in Figure 12-13) are:

- The "name" 1.3.6.1.1 represents iso.org.dod.internet.dir = "directory".

- The "name" 1.3.6.1.2.1.4 represents iso.org.dod.internet.mgmt.mib.ip = "IP".

An object identifier is a special kind of data type, that is used to identify a network management object. It represents a sequence of non-negative integer values that traverse a path in a logical MIB tree structure.

Example 12-2 Provide typical examples of object identifiers.

Referring to Figure 12-13, four examples of object identifiers are given as follows:

(A) Internet OBJECT IDENTIFIER :: = { iso(1) org(3) dod(6) 1 } = 1.3.6.1
(B) mgmt OBJECT IDENTIFIER :: = { Internet 2 } = 1.3.6.1.2
(C) mib OBJECT IDENTIFIER :: = { mgmt 1} = 1.3.6.1.2.1
(D) system OBJECT IDENTIFIER :: = {mib 1 } = 1.3.6.1.2.1.1

Example 12-3 Describe how objects are grouped into types.

Individual objects occupy the lowest level hierarchy in the data base. Object entries can be grouped together into MIB tables. There are presently five types defined by SNMP as shown in Table 12-3.

Table 12-3   MIB Tables Defined by SNMP.

MIB table type	Function/Contents
If	Status of interfaces on the agent
At	Address translation values
IP address	IP address of all interfaces on the agent
IP routing	IP destination addresses, address of next hop, number of hops
TCP connection	Status of TCP connections

Example 12-4 Describe the function of the Remote Network Monitoring (RMON) agent and (RMON) MIB.

Remote Network Monitoring (RMON) is an important stage of Internet management. The embodiment of this function is described in the RMON MIB standard RFC-1271. This MIB complements the existing MIB-II. Special devices are attached to various subnets to collect information specific to the LAN, as shown in Figure 12-14. Examples of the types of data collected include:

- Number of collisions
- "Runt" packet numbers

- Giants
- Delivered packets per second

Each subnet is required to have an attached device to monitor and collect data. The devices can be servers, workstations, and routers (Figure 12-14). These remote monitors are required to communicate with one or more Network Management Stations (NMSs).

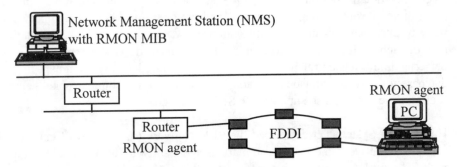

Figure 12-14   Remote Network Monitor Agent and MIB.

Example 12-5   Describe typical SNMP vendors and products.

- SNMP vendors/developers (partial list):

  * Epilogue Technologies
  * MIT
  * Performance Systems Incorporated (PSI)
  * SNMP Research
  * Carnegie Mellon University
  * Netlabs

SNMP Research, Carnegie Mellon University, PSI and others provide SNMP code (software) to manufactures. The usual procedure is for a vendor to introduce agent software first, and later work on a Network Management Station (NMS). Many products are targeted for specific operating system platforms (typically UNIX). Some developers include utilities and library subroutines that are specific to their systems. As an example, Epilogue has a MIB compiler that uses vendor specific MIB's to create tables that are accessible to SNMP. The implementations can be simple (i.e., monitor networks and isolate faults) or sophisticated (e.g., configuration management as well as performance).

- SNMP vendors/products (partial list):

  * Proteon Inc.: It has implemented the SNMP version of the MIB. In addition, Proteon has provided some specific variables in the experimental section of the

MIB and called it the "private enterprise tree". The extensions are: (1) Ethernet collisions, (2) Ethernet adapter board state, and (3) Network interface performance. Support is provided for X.25 (traditional packet switching technology), FDDI (Fiber Distributed Data Interface), and the SET command.

* Cisco Systems Inc.: It has a Network Management Station running on Sun-3s, and will be eventually ported to DEC VAX stations. Agent software for its line of multi-protocol routers, terminal servers, and protocol translators is also provided. Its NetCentral network management station software provides a dynamic real time map of each bridge, router, and terminal host connected via Ethernet, token ring, or serial line. NetCentral also incorporates Structured Query Language (SQL) database for network statistics on parameters such as error counts, packet lengths, routing tables, etc. It also supports the SET command.

* Hughes Lan Systems: It developed the 9100 Network Management Center to be used on Sun-3 workstations. It also markets agent software for terminals (servers) with PCs and LAN servers. It supports the SET command but uses a proprietary authentication system that assigns passwords to users when they log in. Tools are provided for users to support other vendor's MIB extensions. The MIB extensions used in the Hughes systems is based on "English" parameters for ease of operation (i.e., instead of using ASN.1 parameters).

* Wellfleet Communications Inc.: It markets SNMP agent software for their line of multi-protocol routers and bridges. This software runs on Sun-3 and Sun SPARC station servers. The MIB has been extended by WellFleet to include other protocols (e.g., XNS, Novell's IPX and DECnet). Support is provided for communication over Ethernet networks, with token ring, FDDI-Ethernet, and token ring Ethernet interfaces.

12.3 OPEN SYSTEM INTERCONNECTION (OSI) MANAGEMENT STANDARDS

The OSI management function is described in this section, and covers the basic organization model, management domain, and inter-model management. Descriptions of the OSI information model, potential contents, object entry and object classes, OSI management structure, systems management, manager-agent model, OSI management protocol, and OSI management services are also discussed in this section.

12.3.1 OSI Management Environment (OME) Basic Organization Model

Figure 12-15 illustrates the OSI Management Environment (OME) basic organization model. A "management domain" consists of a "manager", an "agent", and many "managed objects."

A **manager** (the role of a manager is defined later in this chapter) is the part of a distributed management application process that has responsibility for one or more management activities. A "network management user" (for example, a telecommunications system operator) interfaces with a manager.

An **agent** performs management functions on managed objects, in accordance with "management operations directives" generated by a manager. An agent may also convey "notification" (generated by the managed objects) to a manager.

A **managed object** is the OSI management view of a user communication resource. It may represent an abstracted portion of a real network component, and this component may have more than one abstraction. For example, if the network component is a LAN bridge, an abstracted object might be its Medium Access Control (MAC) layer.

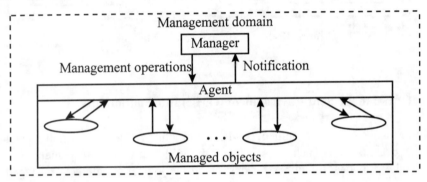

Figure 12-15   OSI Management Environment Organization Model.

The OSI organizational model (Figure 12-15) is based on a recursive architecture. That is, a management domain can consist of many (sub) domains; wherein the (sub) domain itself contains a manager and many managed objects. In this arrangement, the manager of the sub-domain also has the additional role of being an agent to the manager of the (principal) domain.

Example 12-6: Describe the OSI inter-domain management functions.

The OSI basic organization model shown in Figure 12-15 can be extended to form the model shown in Figure 12-16. Two domains (domains A and B; management systems A and B) are shown in this model. However, it should be noted that a network can consist of more than just two domains. A manager of one management system (i.e., management domain) interacts with an agent of another system, to manage the managed-objects associated with that agent. This is done by employing shared knowledge. Inter-domain management is important because many network management systems may exist in an end-to-end communication configuration. That is, management systems may exist at each customer's premises, within carriers, across international boundaries, etc. Therefore, these independent management systems must share knowledge and interact with one another.

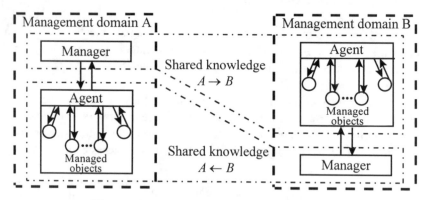

Figure 12-16　　Inter-Domain Management.

12.3.2 OSI Management Environment (OME) Information Model

The OSI Management Environment (OME) information model was initially developed by standards organizations such as ANSI and the OSI Network Management Forum. The OME model provides guidelines for describing the logical structure of managed objects and other pertinent management information about managed objects.

12.3.2.1 OME Information Model Contents and Potential Contents

The "conceptual repository" of management information is the Management Information Base (MIB) as shown in Figure 12-17. This conceptual repository is important because it is used to define the retrieval structure of the data using a consistent approach. The internal database is not required to be implemented according to MIB structure standards. However, an interface that presents the repository as a standard structure for the external (remote) retrieval is required. Hence, a standard conceptual structure is important, since it yields a common language that describes networks and their components. As shown in Figure 12-17, the contents of the MIB provides comprehensive description of the network and its performance.

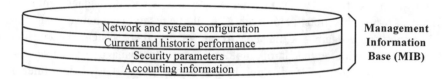

Figure 12-17　　OSI Management Environment (OME) Information Model Contents.

12.3.2.2 OME Information Model Object Entry

ANSI standards have proposed that the ITU-T Directory Services (X.500) structure be adopted for the Management Information Base (MIB). One aspect of this standard is the definition of an object entry.

Definition 12-4: An "**object entry**" is a collection of information pertaining to an "*object instance*".

The information stored in a MIB is divided into one or more "attributes" (Figure 12-18). Each attribute consists of an "attribute type" and one or more "attribute values". The attribute type corresponds to a class of information. Note that at least one attribute must contain an unambiguous name to identify the specific object instance.

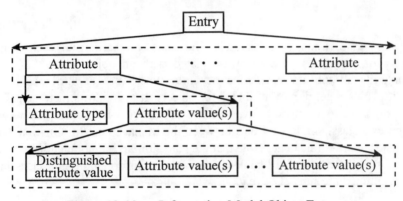

Figure 12-18   Information Model Object Entry.

Example 12-7: Describe a typical "object entry" for a modem device.

A fall-back modem object entry is provided in the following table:

Attribute No.	Attribute type	Attribute value
1	Modem	M603 (distinguished)
2	Speeds	19.2, 9.6, 4.8 kbps
3	Location	Room 4K501

12.3.2.3 OME Information Model Object Classes Example

Every object instance belongs to a class. Classes can be represented by a tree structure, as shown in Figure 12-19, because they are hierarchical. This diagram is used to illustrate an "inheritance" relationship called "refinement." For example, the *network* class is refined into *circuits*, *services*, and *network* equipment. Further refinements of each class below "Network" are possible, such as a T1 circuit, ISDN services, Add/Drop Mux (ADM), etc.

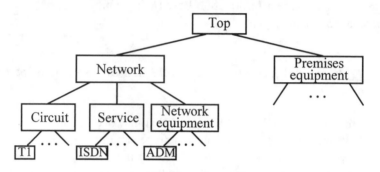

Figure 12-19   Object Classes Example.

The classifications and sub-classifications are arranged according to the inheritance of properties (attributes) associated with an object class. For example, a circuit inherits all the attributes of a network. Inheritance of attributes is important because it avoids repetition of attributes for objects. It also allows incremental additions of new properties and extendibility. Because of the inter-relationship between objects belonging to a class, similarity exists between the Management Information Tree (MIT) and the object class refinement. Note that they are similar, but not identical. That is, each class is stored according to a template that includes information as a class label (e.g., circuit), its immediate superclass (e.g., network), etc.

12.3.3 OSI Management Structure (OMS)

The OSI Management Structure (OMS) is based on the ISO OSI seven-layer reference model, which serves the System Management Application (SMA) process that allows execution of both local and remote system management functions. This service is implemented using the System Management Interface (SMI). The Management Information Base (MIB) represents the repository of information for the SMA process. An indirect means of communications between the SMA process and any of the seven layers is also supported by the MIB. The application layer (layer 7) consists of an entity expressly designed to serve SMA process. The System Management Application Entity (SMAE) utilizes the Common Management Information Protocol (CMIP) to communicate with peer entities. The SMAE, unlike lower layers, has a single line of communication with the MIB that is used to insure the execution of system functions.

OSI seven layers are generalized by layer "N" ($1 \le N \le 7$). The N-layers (for $1 \le N \le 6$) perform peer-to-peer communication in one of two ways:

(1) *N*-layer management protocol via Layer Management Entity (LME)

(2) *N*-layer protocol

The first protocol method is dedicated to management functions at the *N*-layer. The *N*-layer protocol represents an actual end-user protocol used to support the communication of information. Every *N*-layer can operate in the management mode.

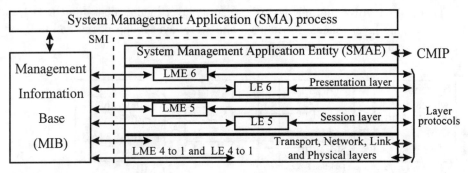

Figure 12-20   OSI Management Structure.

One way to invoke *N*-layer management functions is to employ the *N*-layer management protocol. In this arrangement, an *(N−1)*-layer will utilize its *N*-protocol, and the *(N+1)*-layers are rendered inert when communicating the *N*-layer management functions. The Layer Management Entity (LME) of the *N*-layer is applied to invoke the *N*-layer management protocol, and is a means of communicating with the MIB.

An alternate way to invoke *N*-layer management functions is to alter the *N*-layer operation. Using this method, the *N*-layer protocol parameters are placed in a state for monitoring or controlling one instance of end-user communication. This transient functionality must be indigenous to the *N*-protocol. However, only the *N*-layer is affected, and management information flows "from/to" the MIB, but without an intervening LME. The *N*-layer protocol discriminates between management information and end-user information. The end-user information is directed to its normal path [i.e., to the *(N−1)*-layer or the *(N+1)*-layer].

12.3.3.1 OMS Systems Management

As shown in Figure 12-21, System Management (SM) of the OSI Management Structure (OMS) is organized into three parts: (1) SM Functions (SMFs), (2) SM Application (SMA) process, and (3) SM Application Entity (SMAE). The SMFs correspond to SM services that are common to, and essential for achieving the following functional areas:

1. Coordinating parameter changes of several layers

2. Reading parameters of several layers

3. Changing system or network configurations

4. Transmitting accounting information

5. Downloading software

6. Requesting diagnostic tests

The SMFs involve multiple layers, or can be layer independent. Functions 1 and 2 (listed above) are layer related, functions 3 and 4 are layer independent, and functions 5 and 6 may or may not pertain to a layer.

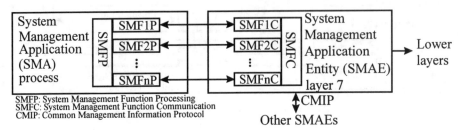

Figure 12-21   OSI Management Structure Systems Management.

Because a function must be processed and communicated for remote operations, the Systems Management Application (SMA) process is a local operation that is responsible for invoking or executing a sequence of System Management Functions (SMFs). The SMA process has access to the entire network by means of the System Management Application Entity (SMAE). It uses the same lower OSI layers as the end-users, and executes these functions remotely by using SMAE "peer-to-peer" communication via Common Management Information Protocol (CMIP). The SMAE performs formatting and other operations that are essential to CMIP communications.

12.3.3.2 Manager-Agent Model

Figure 12-22 illustrates the manager-agent model. The roles of the manager and the agent are briefly described as follows:

- **Manager's role**: Performs the part of the distributed application that issues management operation directives and receives notifications.

- **Agent's role**: Performs the part of the application process that administers the associated managed objects. The role of the agent is to respond to directives issued by a manager. It reflects (to the manager) a view of these objects, and also emits (generates) notifications indicating the behavior of these objects.

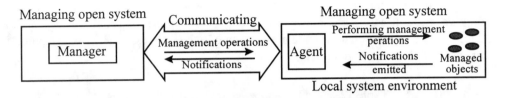

Figure 12-22   Manager-Agent Model.

12.3.4 OSI Management Services

Table 12-4 shows the OSI management services [formally called Common Management and Information Services (CMIS)] that represent the five Service Management Functional Areas (SMFAs). There are three service categories: event (and data) reporting, data manipulation, and control. These services are provided by the Common Management and Information Services Element (CMISE). Note that the entries in the table indicate the activities performed for each of the five SMFAs. The three service categories (event reporting, data manipulation, and control) are implemented by using service primitive communication between peer level Common Management Information Service Elements (CMISEs). The Common Management Information Protocol (CMIP) is used as the vehicle for communication between the two CMISEs associated with a service user entity. One of these entities is the "invoker" of the operation (defined by a primitive), and the other is the "performer" of the operation.

Table 12-4   OSI Management Services (SMFA, CMISE).

Service Management Functional Area (SMFA)	Event reporting (CMISE)	Data manipulation (CMISE)	Control (CMISE)
Fault	*Error detection*	*Error logs*	*Scheduling and execution*
Configuration	*Object creation & attribute change reports*	*Modifications, data collection & dissemination*	*Changes*
Performance	*Workload monitoring, measurement summary*	*Data collection & dissemination, performance logging*	–
Accounting	*Accounting records*	*Data collection & dissemination, audit functions*	–
Security	*Authentication, security logs*	*Encryption & key management, security logs, Authorization,*	*Access control, authentication*

The invoker can select either a "confirmed" or a "non-confirmed" type of service primitive. Several cases are shown in Table 12-5. A confirmed primitive requires the performer of an operation to provide notification of either success or an error condition in response to the invoker's request.

Table 12-5   OSI Management Service Primitives.

Service category	Service primitive	Type(s) of primitive
Event reporting	*M-EVENT-REPORT*	*Confirmed/Non-confirmed*
Data manipulation	*M-GET*	*Confirmed*
	M-SET	*Confirmed/Non-confirmed*
	M-CREATE	*Confirmed*
	M-DELETE	*Confirmed*
Control	*M-ACTION*	*Confirmed/Non-confirmed*
	M-CREATE	*Confirmed*
	M-DELETE	*Confirmed*
	M-CANCEL-GET	*Confirmed*
	M-SET	*Confirmed/Non-confirmed*
Management association	*A-ASSOICATE*	*Confirmed*
	A-RELEASE	*Confirmed*
	A-ABORT	*Non-confirmed*

A brief description of each service category listed in Table 12-5 is provided as follows:

- **Event reporting**: Polling is not used, and events are reported on an "exception basis". For example, an event is reported if an alarm is generated because the error rate exceeds a certain threshold level. However, there are also "scheduled" reports that must be periodically implemented. Scheduled reporting can be used analyze sampled data (e.g., determine the number of times an event occurred within a fixed time interval).

- **Data manipulation**: This service is used to alter the information base of a peer CMISE service use. The four services are:

  * "M-GET": used to retrieve data.

  * "M-CREATE": used to add (insert) data.

  * "M-SET": used to modify data.

  * "M-DELETE": used to remove data.

- **Control**: These service "actions" are intended to alter a managed object. The modifications can be either permanent or temporary (transient). A complementary action is available to "undo" a permanent alternation. The "M-SET" service primitive is used to change parameter values of a managed object. The "M-CREATE" and "M-DELETE" are used to add or remove the instance of a managed object.

- **Management association**: This service is used to administer the relationships between peer CMISE service users.

  * "A-ASSOCIATE": used to establish an association between peer CMISE service user.

  * "A-RELEASE": used to end an association.

  * "A-ABORT": used to invoke abrupt association releases (either peer can invoke the A-ABORT; but it is possible that information may continue to be transferred after an abort).

Two sets of nomenclatures are used for Management Association as listed below. The significance of the "A" prefix is that these services are provided by the Association Control Service Element (ACSE) of the application layer (i.e., not by CMISE). Likewise, the significance of the "M" prefix is that these services are provided by data Manipulation.

  * A-ASSOCIATE = M-INITIALIZE

  * A-RELEASE   = M-TERMINATE

  * A-ABORT   = M-ABORT

12.3.5 OSI Management Protocol

There are three types of OSI management protocols: (1) system management protocol (discussed using Figures 12-23 and 12-24), (2) *N*-layer management protocol [discussed in Figure 12-25(A)], and (3) *N*-protocol operations [discussed later in Figure 12-25(B)].

In system management, communication occurs between application layer peers (layer 7, Figure 12-23). The exchange of management information, used to perform CMISE services, is performed according to the Common Management Information Protocol (CMIP) standard. Before management information exchange takes place (or after no further exchanges are made), ACSE services are used to form and release an association. The ACSE utilizes Association Control Protocol (ACP). The normal services of all lower layers (N ≤ 6) are utilized by CMIP and ACP.

   The management communications shown in Figure 12-23 is known as a full-stack operation, which generally only exists between end user systems. Intervening stacks can be as few as two deep. However, the need may also exist to invoke system management functions for systems possessing incomplete stacks. Therefore, a "gap" (Figure 12-24) exists for the application layer protocol that does not confirm to OSI. Closure of this gap with fully functional layers is wasteful, as the upper layers only serve to communicate system management information. To avoid waste, the concept of a "thin stack" is recommended. The thin stack provides " minimum communication capabilities." Its purpose is to intercept systems management communications intended for the system in which it resides. The intercepted information is then directed to the appropriate System

Management Application (SMA) process. Protocols that permit layers 4 through 6 to be essentially inactive (i.e., the thinnest possible stack) have been implemented.

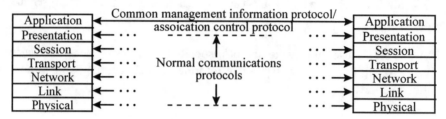

Figure 12-23   System Management Protocol.

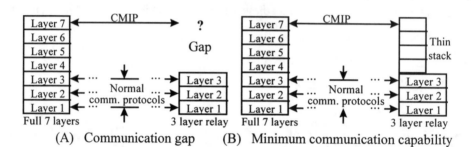

Figure 12-24   System Management with Incomplete Stacks.

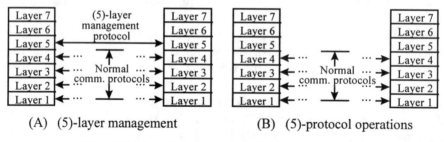

(A) (5)-layer management   (B) (5)-protocol operations

Figure 12-25   Management Information Exchange.

A second and third type of OSI management protocol that can also be applied for management information exchange are shown in Figure 12-25(A) and 12-25(B).

- (N)-layer management [N = 5 in Figure 12-25(A)] protocol application: The basic principle is that the Nth layer communicates according to the (N)-layer protocol. Normal communication services are employed by all layers below N. Prior connections must be established (for all layers of N and less) to allow management information to be exchanged at the (N)-layer.

- (N)-protocols operations [Figure 12-25(B)]: These operations are the same as used for conveying normal user information. The distinction is that the access at a specific protocol layer exploits the management capabilities built into the communication protocol.

12.4 OSI NETWORK MANAGEMENT

A network is composed of many elements. Typical network elements: are switches, Pulse Code Modulation (PCM) terminals (such as digital channel banks), Add-Drop Multiplexers (ADMs), Integrated Digital Loop Carrier (IDLC) systems, and Digital Cross-connect Systems (DCSs) that are interconnected to provide network services to end users.

The range of network management tasks is rather broad. The management tasks may start with the network element management (see Figure 12-26). The network element management task involves administration of each network element on an individual basis. Network management is responsible for the management of all the network elements presented by the element management layer. Service management is concerned with the contractual aspects of network services. Business management is responsible for the management of the total overall enterprise.

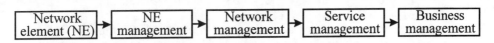

Figure 12-26   Range of Network Management Tasks

12.4.1 OSI Management Environment Model

The OSI management environment can be divided into three separate models:

(1) **Organizational model**: This model describes the ways in which network management can be administratively distributed across management domains, and the ways management systems can be distributed within a domain.

(2) **Informational model**: This model describes the manner in which managed objects are defined. An object definition includes its: class, attributes, actions, name, and inter-relationships with other objects.

(3) **Functional (or facility) model**: This model defines the functions provided by the environment that are employed to achieve the user requirements. These functions are either performed locally or remotely, through communication among the open systems.

Figure 12-27 shows five major network management functions, which are described in the following sections.

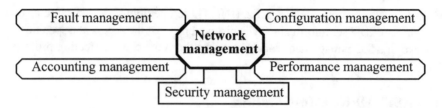

Figure 12-27   OSI Network Management Functional Model.

12.4.1.1 Configuration (and Name) Management Systems

This (configuration) function allows network managers to exercise control over, identify, collect data from, and provide data to the managed objects. Its purpose is to insure continuous network operation.

An important aspect of configuration management is the naming of managed objects and of associated inquires. The "naming" aspect is usually part of the information model description. Therefore, "naming" plays an essential background role for configuration management.

Any managed object must contain parameters necessary to perform its operations. These parameters are "set" (to specific values) whenever an object is initialized (i.e., created or placed into operation). When configuration changes (e.g., re-assigning a statistical multiplexer time slot from data to voice) entail setting parameters, other parameters may also need to be modified. For example, if a modem has been changed (re-configured) from a speed of 9.6 kbps to 19.2 kbps, other related parameters may also need to be modified.

Being of a lesser degree than a configuration change, parameter changing is termed "configuration modification". Modifications of this type are supported by the Common Management Information Service Element (CMISE) **data manipulation services** (see Table 12-5). However, configuration changes that correspond to major alternations such as "closing down" (i.e., deleting) and/or "initializing" (i.e., creating) managed objects are activities supported by the CMISE **control services** (see Table 12-5).

Configuration and name management require "data collection and dissemination" functionality. This is done on a routine basis, and also when a significant change of state is encountered within the network. The CMISE event reporting services provide the means for data collection. In summary, configuration and name management's main tasks are:

- To name managed objects
- To set and/or modify parameters
- To initialize or close-down managed objects

- To change configuration
- To collect and/or disseminate data

12.4.1.2 Performance Management Systems

Performance management is implemented to evaluate the behavior of the managed objects, track the effectiveness of communications activities, and monitor the states of all the elements involved in the network services. These evaluations represent an important aspect of network planning.

Statistical data must be collected and disseminated for performance management. Data that indicates gradual deterioration in performance can assist in proactively dealing with network errors (fault management). CMISE event reporting and data manipulation services provide a means for collecting performance data. The logged data constitutes the system state history, and is used for planning and analysis. These logs are maintained and examined with the assistance of the CMISE data manipulation services. Typical data that is monitored in performance management includes:

- Blocking probability of a switching facility
- Call completion statistics
- Call attempt statistics
- Signal propagation attenuation (loss)
- Signal propagation delay
- Echo characteristics
- Pulse spreading (dispersion) of digital services
- Frequency offset
- Out of frame (OOF) conditions
- Slip rate deviation
- Signal-to-noise ratio (S/N)
- Error rate monitoring (bit error rate)
- Error free seconds
- Severe error seconds
- Bias current deviation

12.4.1.3 Fault Management Systems

Faults are manifested as error events that prevent communication, and subsequently end users cannot meet their operational objectives. Faults can be persistent or transient. Fault management is achieved through a set of facilities that enable the detection, isolation, and correction of error conditions. The following five inter-related facilities represent a typical procedure of fault management:

(1) Trace faults: "Fault tracing" represents the process by which a fault is localized to a general portion of a user system.

(2) Accept and act upon error detection notification: "Error detection" consists of detecting the errors and notifying an appropriate manager or peer system. This initial step utilizes the OSI CMISE event reporting services.

(3) Carry out sequences of diagnostic tests: This activity is used to isolate a fault, and confirm that it is caused by a specific portion(s) of a user system.

(4) Fault correction: This is the process used to remedy a fault. Fault correction, diagnostic testing, and fault tracing are sometimes combined into "scheduling and execution".

(5) Maintain and examine error logs: Errors are logged (recorded) for two reasons: (1) Error information can be used to suggest corrective actions or assist in scheduling remedial steps, and (2) Error log records can provide data for other functions (e.g., performance management).

Maintaining, updating, and data retrieval of error logs information is the responsibility of fault management. The CMISE data manipulation services is the vehicle for performing error logging activities.

The procedure for scheduling and execution of fault resolution encompasses tracing faults, carrying out diagnostic tests (this is performed by measuring performance parameters such as system attenuation, continuation, etc.), and correcting faults. All three steps include "scheduling" activities. The fault logs are used interactively for this procedure. These logs are updated as pertinent information becomes available. For certain types of "exception" faults (e.g., those mandating immediate attention) scheduling and execution may be invoked before the fault is logged. The control services of CMISE provide assistance for scheduling and execution activities.

12.4.1.4 Security Management Systems

The purpose of security management is to protect and operate the managed objects correctly. The procedures for security management are briefly described as follows:

- Control authorization: Decisions associated with allowing access to system resources are managed by the control authorization facilities.

- Encryption and key management: The assignment and distribution of encryption keys represents one aspect of access control. Another is the administration of user/password permissions for accessing appropriate sets of managed objects.

- Control access: Decisions associated with restricting user permission are performed by the "control access" functions.

- Support authentication: Authentication represents the procedures performed to determine whether a user is qualified to access particular sets of managed objects. Access control impacts the information used for authentication. The activities relating to authentication are stored in a data log. This data is important for properly operating the authorization facilities, and other functions (e.g., performance management). The CMISE data manipulation services support control authorization, encryption and key management, and security log maintenance. The control services of CMISE can be applied to support access control, and authentication. CMISE event reporting services are required by authentication facilities and security logs.

- Security log maintenance: Security management includes maintaining and periodically examining the data contained in security logs.

12.4.1.5 Accounting Management Systems

Accounting management enables resource utilization charges and costs to be established for using particular managed objects. Two purposes of accounting management are:

(1) To inform users of the costs they have incurred and resources consumed

(2) To provide data for network planning

To achieve these two purposes (resource/cost) data must be collected and disseminated. The CMISE event reporting and data manipulation services facilitate the collection and dissemination of this data. These are special accounting event types and accounting records. Many communication operations entail the use of multiple resources. Therefore, a combined cost for the use of multiple managed objects is included in the accounting management function. Additionally, accounting limits are often important when using managed objects. The CMISE data manipulation services can be used to generate "combined costs of multiple used resources" and " set accounting limits".

12.5 NETWORK MANAGEMENT SYSTEMS/APPLICATIONS

Several "mature technology" network management applications are briefly discussed in this section. They are: System Network Architecture (SNA), SystemView, NetView, DECmcc, and OpenView. The topic of "Telecommunications Management Network" (TMN) will be described separately in a later section of this chapter.

12.5.1 System Network Architecture (SNA)

System Network Architecture (SNA) was first introduced in 1975 to interconnect IBM computers (at that time, they were IBM mainframe computers). SNA is presently one of the most widely used network architectures in the world. It is a closed system architecture, however, IBM specifies how their products connect and communicate with one another by using System Network Architecture (SNA).

12.5.1.1 Hierarchical SNA

SNA is traditionally a hierarchical network architecture (Figure 12-28) with computing machines having a primary-secondary relationship, rather than a peer-to-peer relationship. However, it is possible to implement a SNA network that is not hierarchical (discussed in a later section of this chapter). The components of a hierarchical SNA configuration are: (1) the host, which is typically a mainframe computer, (2) several communications controllers, in which network control programs reside, (3) several cluster controllers, and (4) many end devices or workstations, which serves as sources and/or targets. A host machine controls one or more communications controllers. Each communicate controller interfaces with one or more remote cluster controllers. Each cluster controller may control several workstations or devices. The functions of each of the components shown in Figure 12-28 are briefly discussed as follows:

- **Host processor**: This component can control all, or part of a network. The host processor provides capabilities such as computation, program execution, access to databases, directory services, and network management. Within the host processor, there are two sub-components:

  (1) Telecommunications Access Method (TAM): The Telecommunications Access Method logically controls the flow of data through the network, and provides an interface between application subsystems and the network. In addition, the TAM protects application subsystems from unauthorized system access by using specialized software. One example of this software is known as the Virtual Telecommunications Access Method (VTAM).

  (2) Application subsystems: This function is responsible for retrieving and updating information, processing jobs remotely, and presenting graphical information about the condition of displays and/or printers.

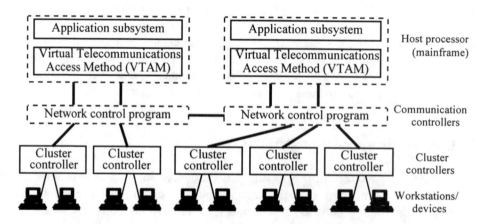

Figure 12-28   Components of a Hierarchical Network, e.g., SNA.

- **Communications controller (front-end processor)**: These controllers manage the physical network, control communications links, and route data through the network. The network control program, residing in the communications controllers, routes data and controls its flow between the front-end processors and other network resources.

- **Cluster controller**: These controllers manage the workstations' input/output operations and any other devices connected to them. Note that the cluster controllers and the communications controllers are geographically located far from each other, and are connected via various types of transmission media (e.g., twisted-pair telephone lines, coaxial cables, microwave links, optical fibers). Synchronous Data Link Control (SDLC) protocol provides a reliable data link that is carried over the transmission medium.

- **Workstations**: These elements are the input/output devices that enable end users to access the network and send/receive information.

The end-user of a System Network Architecture (SNA) is typically a person at a workstation, or an application program that submits/receives information from a network. Network Addressable Units (NAUs) are identified by unique addresses. They enable end users to send data via the a network. The NAU provides functions that synchronize communications between end users, manage the resources in each node, and control/manage the overall network. A (SNA) node is a hardware element and the associated software that supports SNA functions. It serves as one endpoint of a data link (a data station), and is connected to two (or more) links in a network. Host processors, cluster controllers, communications controllers, and workstations are all examples of nodes. The SNA path control network (Figure 12-29) is used to route data between NAUs. It also transmits data across the links between adjacent nodes, and makes use of control elements (e.g., data link control and sub-area path control) to perform these functions.

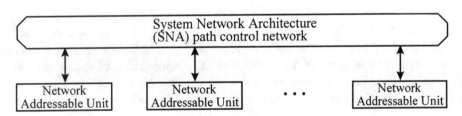

Figure 12-29   SNA Path Control Network.

An NAU can be one of three types: (1) Logical Unit [(LU) provided for end users to access the SNA network], (2) Physical Units [(PUs) reside in each SNA node to manage/monitor physical connections between adjacent nodes], and (3) System Services Control Point [(SSCP) can only reside in the host and is used to activate, control, and de-activate network resources]. An SSCP can also provide directory services to Logical Units (LUs), and assist the initiation of LU-LU sessions.

12.5.1.2 Peer-to-Peer SNA

Traditional SNA products are based on asymmetrical "primary-to-secondary" relationships. This is not desirable in an office automation environment where there is no mainframe (host) and workstations may need to communicate directly with each other. To support peer networking of workstations, Advanced Peer-to-Peer Networking (APPN) has been introduced. In APPN applications, several network nodes interconnect the end nodes (see Figure 12-30).

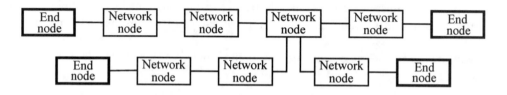

Figure 12-30   Advanced Peer-to-Peer Networking (APPN).

Each network node performs route selection and provides directory services for other APPN nodes. The network node can also be connected to a host. Each end node is an end system or workstation which can be a "source and/or target". An end node can not perform route selection. APPN supports decentralized control (rather than centralized control), and can adapt to dynamic topology changes as technology progresses. APPN provides local system definition, network configuration, and automated route selection.

12.5.1.3 APPN Management Services and Implementation

Figure 12-31 illustrates an APPN network with three focal points connected by Logical Unit Sessions (LUSs). This APPN management service is hierarchical, and a group of focal points can report to a higher-level focal point. The looped focal points, also known as "nested focal points", reduces the number of LU sessions required, and eliminates the need for each entry point to have its own session with a high-level focal point. At the lower layers of the management hierarchy, a network node and its associated nodes can be treated as a single "unit".

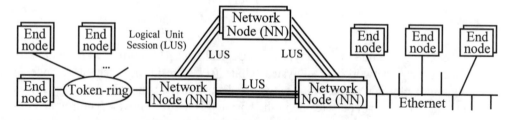

Figure 12-31   APPN Management Service using Looped (or Nested) Focal Points.

APPN can be implemented by using a fully integrated traditional SNA network. As SNA enterprise networks evolve from traditional mainframe centralized architectures to decentralized configurations, management services will apply UNIX-based alternatives (e.g., enhanced NetView or HP's OpenView management systems) to support peer-to-peer networking. In this arrangement, an SNMP platform can be managed as a service point gateway to interface between the two environments (i.e., centralized and decentralized operations).

12.5.1.4 Workstation-to-Workstation Communications

IBM has developed the LU6.2 protocol standard, which allows intelligent workstations to communicate with one another via an LU6.2 session over a LAN. Note that LU6.2 eliminates the primary-secondary orientation associated with centralized control.

Figure 12-32 shows an application example using LU6.2. This configuration is an automated office environment where PC A can establish an LU6.2 session with PC C on a "token-ring" LAN, without involving a Virtual Telecommunications Access Method (VTAM) as the host. This a "process-to-process" communications is called Advanced Program-to-Program Communications (APPC) in IBM terminology. Typical services using APPC are sever/client communication and e-mail. It should be mentioned that APPC uses some of the LU6.2 command verbs, and is limited to small networks with a limited number of stations. In a large network (e.g., hundreds of nodes distributed over a large area) customers must use a hierarchical SNA.

Figure 12-32   Communications Among Workstations.

12.5.2 SystemView

SystemView was introduced by IBM as an enterprise management framework for planning, coordinating, and operating enterprise-wide information systems. It is based on Open Systems Interconnection (OSI) concepts.

The SystemView framework consists of both software and hardware products that comply with IBM's Systems Application Architecture (SAA) and Systems Network Architecture (SNA). It can be extended to facilitate managing any vendor's products (systems) in addition to elements built by IBM. SystemView defines the user interfaces, shared data formats, enhanced automation, and managed-resource capabilities. It supports both large and small business applications, and spans a broad range of platforms (e.g., S/390, OS/2, AS/400, AIX) and LAN workgroups. It has evolved into an open client/server systems management element for all environments, and is no longer restricted to mainframe applications.

12.5.2.1 SystemView Model Example

Figure 12-33 shows an example of the SystemView model, in which presentation services represent the end user application, and information services include the contents of the database. The functional services are: business, change, configuration, operations, performance, and problems.

SystemView is both an architecture and strategy that fulfills user requirements for total system and network management by providing detailed enterprise-wide information technology management, regardless of system size or location.

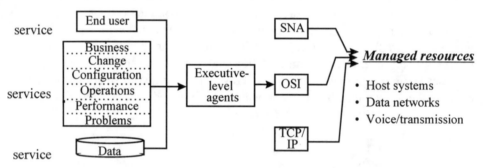

SNA: System Network Architecture   OSI: Open System Interconnection

Figure 12-33   SystemView Example Model.

12.5.2.2 SystemView Structure/Products

The high level objective of SystemView is to provide comprehensive management of an enterprise's information-technology resources. The framework that supports this activity consists of the SystemView architecture and the products that implement that framework. The SystemView structure consists of four "dimensions" that define the guidelines, standards, services, and the necessary interfaces for integrating all interconnecting systems and network applications. The four complementary dimensions are briefly described as follows:

- **End-user dimension**: This dimension defines a consistent integrated user interface. SystemView specifies IBM System Application Architecture (SAA) common user access guidelines as the standard for maintaining the same "look and feel" characteristics across various SystemView applications.

- **Application dimension**: This dimension defines the guidelines for implementing and integrating systems and network management applications. It covers the SystemView functional areas, and explains the concepts of "level and function".

- **Data dimension**: This dimension addresses the aspects of systems integration that involve modeling and sharing data. It consists of the SystemView data model (an object-oriented structure), a data object manager, and an adapter for traditional (e.g., non-object-oriented) applications. These capabilities enable data sharing among existing management applications, and future requirements. SystemView defines an Enterprise Information Base (EIB) and a Control Information Base (CIB). Data in each Enterprise Information Base (EIB) or (CIB) that is represented by a common definition can be shared between management applications.

- **Managed-resource dimension**: This dimension enables applications to exploit (use) resource without specific information about those resources. It hides the specifics for each resource by classifying and abstracting them into general and consistent classes. This allows management operations to inter-work across a broad range of resources.

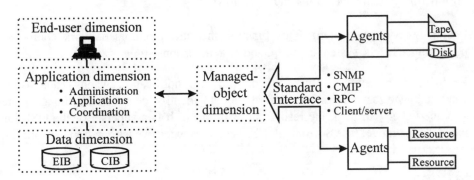

Figure 12-34   SystemView Structure.

It is impossible to accurately describe all the SystemView capabilities because elements are constantly changing as standards and technology evolve. Over 100 SystemView products are produced by several vendors, and have various levels of SystemView conformance. The following is a list of SystemView products that are commonly available:

- AIX NetView/6000 VI (manages trouble tickets)
- AIX system monitor
- ESCON manager
- LAN NetView agents
- LAN NetView manager
- NetView/MVS (Multiple Virtual System; operation system)
- NetView file transfer program (MVS and OS/400)
- OS/2 LAN server

12.5.2.3 SystemView Framework Management Functions

The management functions (e.g., business management, change management, configuration management, etc.) of the SystemView framework are briefly described as follows:

- **Business management**: This function corresponds to accounting management in the OSI management model (see Section 12.4.1.5). It addresses financial administration, business planning, and security issues.

- **Change management**: This function manages physical and logical resources by adding, deleting, and changing network devices or end users. It is similar to configuration management in the OSI model (see Section 12.4.1.1).

- **Configuration management**: This function manages network topology and the relationships between various resources.

- **Operations management**: This function manages the day-to-day enterprise information systems operations and workflow.

- **Performance management**: This function measures/monitors network component performance levels, system capacity, and system response time.

- **Problem management**: This function provides notification when problems are detected, analyzes performance information to identify degradation, and generates "trouble tickets" to track the resolution of problem. It is a superset of the OSI fault management model (see Section 12.4.1.3) contains extensive automation capabilities.

12.5.3 NetView

NetView network management functions can be modeled as a four-point conceptual structure as shown in Figure 12-35. The physical network can be either hierarchical or distributed, and each logical point may contain multiple underlying network nodes. Devices may also be connected directly to a single point, or be used in cascading networks that are not required to communicate with the focal point.

The entry point [System Network Architecture (SNA) system] provides an interface for SNA devices and applications. This point collects SNA management information and system commands from distributed SNA nodes and devices. These entry points make it possible for all of the devices in a small system to be connected directly to a single Front-End Processor (FEP). Generally, some devices are locally connected to the entry points, and others are connected to remote entry points.

The service point can process commands that are sent to non-SNA devices. It is also used to process alerts received from non-SNA devices. These devices are typically managed by using NetView/PC which contains modules produced by "third party" vendors. NetView/PC is essentially an SNA proxy agent, that communicates with NetView using Network Management Vector Transports (NMVTs). It provides alert origin information, severity ratings, probable cause analysis, and recommended actions.

Distributed management systems are attached at either collection points or entry points. Sophisticated systems (e.g., AIS SystemView and NetView/6000) controlling a TCP/IP- or CMIP-based subnetwork, typically use collection point attachment. Less advanced management systems use entry point attachment. Both approaches control SNMP-managed and CMIP-managed communication device, but have different levels of management capability.

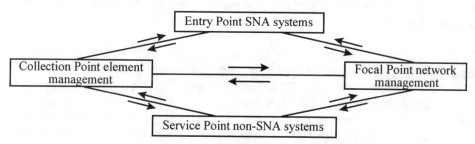

Figure 12-35   NetView Enterprise Model.

NetView is the primary vehicle for implementing SystemView. In a typical network, the Focal Point and its components reside on a mainframe. A small (but highly centralized) operation has sole responsibility for the entire operation. It uses composite network and system management consoles. However, a completely distributed configuration can also be used. For example, traditional SNA devices can be attached to the front-end processor directly via T1 circuits (T1 digital carrier systems are described in Chapter 6) or LAN interconnection, to form the entry point. NetView excels at the logical management of SNA sessions, and also provides management for other protocol structures. The rapid development of SNMP has made dependence on TCP/IP network management a serious concern for many users (i.e., compatibility and support issues).

NetView is an application process that resides on a mainframe host (see Figure 12-36). The application process is internally divided into facilities and monitors (e.g., hardware monitor, session monitor, and status monitor). The facilities are the interfaces to operator terminals used to manage networks. Facilities communicate with monitors internal to the NetView application process. Monitors are the routines used for communicating with entry points and service points (i.e., local and remote service points; both are connected via NetView/PC). The facilities often operate in conjunction with network monitors, described as follows:

- **Hardware monitor**: Originally called Network Problem Determination Applications (NPDA). It is used to collect data on failures and/or degrading conditions of SNA network physical devices.

- **Session monitor**: Originally called Network Logical Data Management (NLDM). It is used to collect data on failures and/or degrading conditions in the SNA logical network.

- **Status monitor**: Originally called VTAM (Virtual Telecommunications Access Method) Node Control Application (VNCA). It allows operators to interactively access the SNA network activity status data (includes special indication of urgent messages).

There are two types of "help facilities": (1) the "help desk", and (2) the "specific help" facility. The help desk facility provides a systematic approach to solving network problems. The specific help facility provides on-line documentation to explain commands or to define codes (e.g., alerts, recommend potential fixes). Note that the help facilities belong to a body of software that is sometimes called the Network Management Productivity Facility (NMPF).

The command (control) facility is used to invoke network management actions. The individual steps of a command action are contained within an object executable file known as the Command list (Clist). Clists can be executed manually from the operator terminal or automatically in response to network events (e.g., network alert). The definition of "open communication architecture" is a method of publishing common interfaces among various vendors. This is called the Application Programming Interface /Communications Services (API/CS).

NetView utilizes VTAM for communication with network points. That is, network management communication is overlaid on end user communications. (the same as in the previously described OSI network management). The Network Management Vector Transport (NMVT) protocol is defined (by IBM) for conveying management requests [command/Response Units (RUs)]. The NMVT protocol is analogous to ISO's Common Management Information Protocol (CMIP). The RU represents various transaction service layer protocols, which is equivalent to OSI's application layer protocol.

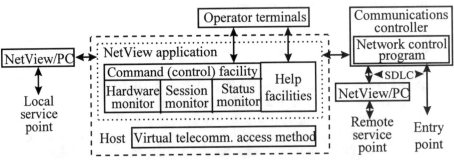

Figure 12-36   NetView Software Components and Interfaces.

Communications controllers utilize special software, known as the Network Control Program (NCP), to communicate with the remote network service point. The link layer protocol used for remote communications is the called Synchronous Data Link Control (SDLC) protocol (see Figure 12-36).

Another method for interfacing to NetView is the Application Program Interface (API), which is equivalent to accessing a service point without using NetView/PC. The API permits mainframe (e.g., System/370) applications to communicate directly with the resources of NetView, as does the NetView/PC. The applications can be programs provided by IBM, or "user composed" applications programs.

12.5.4 DEC Management Control Center (DECmcc)

The Digital Equipment Corporation (DEC) provides network managers for their Enterprise Management Architecture (EMA) system interfaces via software called the "DECmcc directory". The periphery of the DECmcc directory is structured to contain three modules (shown in Figure 12-37) described as follows:

- **Access modules**: These modules, identified as DECNet, contain the original nomenclature used for DEC's management systems. They have evolved into another form, known as DECNet phase IV. The DECNet management systems will eventually be absorbed as access modules. The "bridge" module is designed to provide interfaces for LAN network bridges.

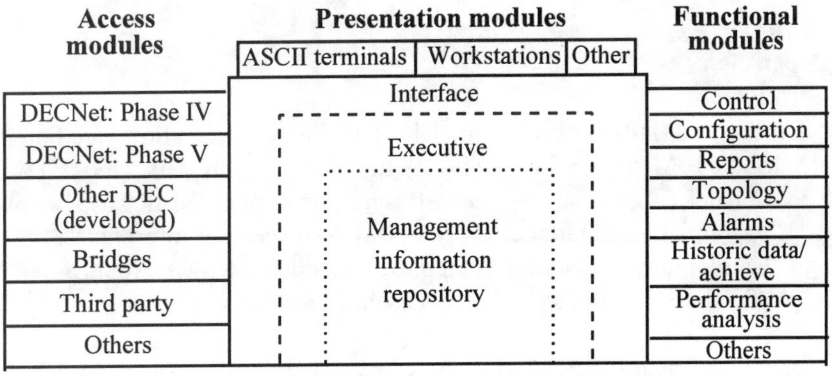

Access modules	Presentation modules			Functional modules
	ASCII terminals	Workstations	Other	
DECNet: Phase IV	Interface			Control
				Configuration
DECNet: Phase V	Executive			Reports
Other DEC (developed)				Topology
	Management information repository			Alarms
Bridges				Historic data/ achieve
Third party				Performance analysis
Others				Others

Figure 12-37   DECmcc Director/Modules.

DECNet Phase V is an elaborate management system within DEC's Digital Network Architecture (DNA) "umbrella" of DEC networks. It is designed to be backward compatible with earlier phases (e.g., X.25 networks using Phase III and Ethernet LANs using Phase IV). It is a distributed management system that has inherent "peer-to-peer management communications". Note that distributed management systems typically have lower initial investment costs than centralized systems.

The architecture of Phase V is based on the "director entity" model. An **entity** consists of a managed object (a state variable machine) and its agent (the conduit for management operations). A **director** is the Enterprise Management Architecture (EMA) software system that serves as the interface between a manager (user) and the entities. Communication between the director and an agent is handled by the appropriate access module protocol.

The OSI CMIP protocol is used by DECNet Phase V along with DECNet's Network Information and Control Exchange (NICE) protocol. The similarity of these protocols permits their co-existence. An entity's particular protocol is identified when a connection is established. The hierarchical structure of CMIP is the result of the relationship that exists between a "management system" and the "managed system".

- **Presentation modules**: These modules are used, in conjunction with a visible display, by network operators. They provide flexible input/output presentations, that can include graphics, command lines, menus, etc.

- **Functional modules**: These modules perform the processing associated with network management, and intervene between the access modules and presentation modules. Functional modules are aligned with OSI management functional areas. The modules surround a core system that has an interface used to provide inter-communication for the peripheral modules. The Enterprise Management Architecture (EMA) executive software controls the entire network management function. This executive software also supports database access for retrieval of management information. EMA is a distributed (centralization is possible, with the degree being user defined), multi-vendor and multi-carrier network management system.

12.5.5 OpenView

The Hewlett Packard (HP) OpenView model is based on the Open Software Foundation's (OSF) Distributed Management Environment (DME). The HP OpenView SNMP management model (Figure 12-38) supports single manager SNMP based networks. It provides a Graphical User Interface (GUI), SNMP Management Information Base (MIB) browsing/event monitor, IP discovery/mapping, and a direct SNMP Application Program Interface (API). These functions are briefly described as follows:

- User interface: The primary interface is X.11 window/Motif.

- SNMP MIB browser: Displays MIB contents and structure.

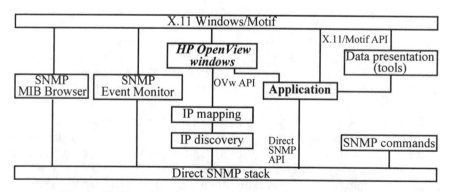

Figure 12-38   HP OpenView SNMP Management Model.

- SNMP event monitor: Multiplexes SNMP traps and events from the detection point through the appropriate applications.

- The HP discovery: This process uses Internet Control Message Protocol (ICMP) and SNMP to "discover" network nodes. It can find and display all SNMP devices, IP-addressed devices, FDDI (Fiber Distributed Data Interface), and IEEE 802.5 rings.

- IP mapping: This process displays the "discovered" nodes.

- SNMP API: The Application Program Interface (API) eliminates the need to use ASN.1 encoding for user applications by serving as an ASN.1 encoder and decoder. It also creates logical binding (known as "sessions") between managers and agents.

The HP OpenView management model provides a comprehensive solution for distributed management environments (applications). The model defines both the Simple Network Management Protocol (SNMP) and Common Management Information Protocol (CMIP). The HP OpenView model implements the Open Software Foundation's Distributed Management Environment (OSF/DME), and contains direct SNMP, XMP (X/open Management Protocol), and OSI Abstract-Data Manipulation (XDM) APIs. The features of this distributed management model are briefly described as follows:

- Management applications: Processes inputs generated by the user interfaces or network events, and prepares outputs based on appropriate management services.

- SNMP platform services: A specific implementation of the SNMP management model.

- Distribution management infrastructure: This function encompasses all aspects of the overall network and its resources.

- Ingress database: This is the system's data storage and retrieval function, and its associated data sets.

- Management protocols: This function supports SNMP, CMIP, and Common Management Over TCP/IP (CMOT).

- Metadata: This subsystem compiles and provides online access to the objects, based on the Guidelines for the definition of Managed Objects (GDMO).

- The Event Management Services (EMS): The EMS consists of three individual functional components: (1) local and remote filtering of events, (2) event logging, and (3) an interactive tool for browsing the event log.

12.5.6 X.25

Figure 12-39(A) is a simplified diagram representing the communication of two Data Terminal Equipment (DTE) elements (e.g., two host computers) using X.25 packet protocol carried by Data Circuit-terminating Equipment (DCE; e.g., modems) over a packet switched network.

An equivalent implementation using a traditional Public Switched Telephone Network (PSTN) is shown in Figure 12-39(B). In the PSTN configuration, the "initiator" of the communication activity "picks-up" a telephone handset, waits for the dial tone signal, and then dials the number of th "called party". The called party telephone set rings (at remote location) and if the call is "answered" (i.e., the remote handset is picked-up) the connection is "completed" (i.e., communications occurs). This connection is accomplished by the functions performed in two (or more) Central Offices (COs) along with the support provided by the PSTN. The interfaces between the end user stations and the "network" are: the off-hook signal, dial tone, ring signal, audible tones, and the actual voice signals of the conversation. The interface devices in this example are: the local switched and toll exchanges (if this is a long distance call).

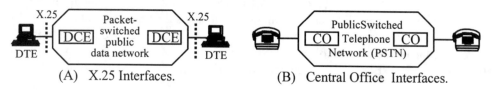

(A) X.25 Interfaces.   (B) Central Office Interfaces.

Figure 12-39   X.25 Packet Switched and PSTN Connection.

In comparison, the X.25 packet switch connection shown in Figure 12-39(B) is initiated by the physical and data link layers. Once these layer connections have been established on both sides of the network, the calling DTE sends a "call request" message (in packet form) to the network using X.25 interface protocol. The network informs the DTE on the other side (i.e., the called party) by forwarding the packet to it. After the called DTE responds by returning a "call accept" message, and the calling party receives this "acknowledgment", a "virtual circuit" (connection) is established. This allows data packets to be transferred in both directions. In this connection, the user needs to know how to access the network, but is unaware of how the packet is routed to its final destination. It is the responsibility of the network to receive the packet from the user, and reliably deliver it to the correct destination.

12.5.6.1 The X.25 Physical Layer

Figure 12-40 shows the X.25 physical layer connection of a packet-switching network (e.g., the Accunet® packet-switching network). The X.21 interface is based on an ITU-T recommendation that defines the physical connection between the Data Terminating Equipment (DTE) and the Data Service Unit (DSU). The DSU is a modem that serves as interface between the circuit-switched or dedicated line connected to the DTE. The physical connection is a synchronous full duplex interface with a 15-pin connector and is used to transfer data or control information. X.21 bis ("bis" is a Swiss/French term meaning "alternate form") is similar to EIA-232-C, but uses 25-pin connectors (i.e., X.21 specifies EIA-232-C).

In North America, ANSI recommends EIA-232-C, EIA-530, and V35 for the X.25 physical layer interface. The Data Service Units (DSUs) operate as physical layer Data Circuit-terminating Equipment (DCE). In analog leased line applications, the DSU must support modulation/demodulation (i.e., modem) functions.

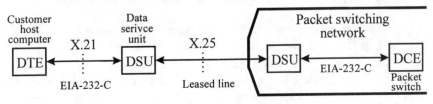

Figure 12-40   The X.25 Physical Layer.

12.5.6.2 The X.25 (Data) Link Layer

For implementing the data link layer of the X.25 interface, ITU-T recommends the Link Access Procedure Balanced (LAPB) which is a subset of the ISO High-level Data Link Control (HDLC). It is a synchronous, bit-oriented, point-to-point, full duplex protocol, which provides an error-free path between the X.25 host and the packet switch.

In addition to supporting the transfer of information frames which carry data packets, the X.25 data link layer performs the following functions:

- Initiates and terminates (data) link connections
- Provides error-free communication
- Performs flow control

12.5.6.3 Link Access Procedure Balanced (LAPB)

The data transmission unit of LAPB is a "frame", which consists of three fields: (1) the header, (2) the information payload, and (3) the trailer (see Figure 12-41). The header contains: a flag, an address field, and a control field. The payload field is used to carry the information message. The trailer contains: the frame check sequence, and a flag. The frame's functions are briefly described as follows:

- Flags: There is one flag in the header, and another in the trailer. Each has a fixed pattern of "0111 1110" (7E Hex). This special pattern is used to delimit the frame (i.e., define the boundaries of frames and obtain frame synchronization).

- Address: The code in the address field is "01" for DCE, and "03" for DTE.

Header			Information		(payload)	Trailer	
8-bit flag	16-bit address	8-bit control	(I-field)		(I-field)	16-bit frame check sequence (CRC)	8-bit flag

Figure 12-41   The Frame Structure of LAPB.

- Control field: This field is used to identify the frame type, which can be:

    * Supervisory frame: These frames are used for "acknowledgement", "flow control", and "retransmission." When a packet is received with error(s), a message of "re-transmission" is issued. Likewise, when the receiver is not ready to accept a new packet, a flow-control message is issued to control the data flow in the network so that no packets are lost.

    * Information frame: These frames contain user data.

    * Frames for "other functions": A frame may contain information (a message) for link establishment and link termination. These frames are unnumbered.

- I-field: This field carries the payload information in packet format.

- Frame check sequence: A Cyclic Redundancy Check (CRC) sequence (bit pattern) is generated at the transmitter, based on the information field data content. The CRC sequence is transmitted to the receiver, and is used to determine whether there are errors in the information data stream.

12.5.6.4 X.25 Packet-layer Protocol Functions

The packet-layer of X.25 is the third layer of the interface, and is responsible for the following functions:

- It informs the network about the destination of packets by providing information about the source and destination DTE addresses.

- It establishes and disconnects virtual circuits by assigning a logical channel number at each end of the virtual circuit, and allows data packets to use the logical channel number for DTE-to-DTE data transfer.

- It multiplexes logical channels on data links at each end of a virtual circuit, thereby allowing several users to share network resources.

- It provides a flow control function. The multiplexing capabilities include protocol function that regulate individual channels used for data packet transfer to and from the network at each interface, which is known as flow control.

Review Questions 1 for Chapter 12:

(1) Network management is responsible for both _____ and _____ activities required for telecommunications services to be delivered to the customers, and assuring _____ of those services.

(2) _____ and _____ are industry leading management platforms, and the agreement between them is intended to accelerate the availability and standardization of an _____, _____ and _____ environment for network management applications.

(3) The TCP/IP protocol suite comprises: a layer three _____, a layer four _____ or _____, and _____.

(4) _____ (ICMP) is a network layer protocol used for communications between various _____ entities. ICMP messages are generated to indicate a network layer problem, such as _____ or an _____ application port.

(5) User Datagram Protocol (UDP) is a _____ transport protocol, and is similar to the ISO-_____ standard.

(6) Simple Network Management Protocol (SNMP) was created to monitor _____, analyze _____, configure _____, and perform _____ tests (e.g., _____, _____ and _____).

(7) The MIB (Management Information Base) elements, starting from the _____, are equivalent to a tree with a _____, _____ and _____. An object's name in the tree is a sequence of _____ along the _____ from the root. These variables have a specific meaning only to the network manager. All operations involve _____, _____ and _____.

(8) In an OSI Management Environment (OME) basic organization model, a "management domain" consists of a _____, an _____ and many _____.

(9) An object entry is a collection of _____ pertaining to an _____. An information model object entry is divided into one or more _____, each consists of an _____ and one or more _____.

(10) The OSI service management functional areas include: _____, _____, _____, _____ and _____.

(11) SNA (System Network Architecture), a closed system, is presently one of the most widely used network architectures in the world. The components of a hierarchical SNA configuration are: the _____, several _____, several _____, and many _____ or _____.

12.6 TELECOMMUNICATIONS MNAGEMENT NETWORK (TMN)

Network management is the ability to monitor (from a bandwidth utilization and performance satisfaction perspective), examine, and control the operations of a telecommunications network. In Public Switched Telephone Network (PSTN) applications, network management functions include real-time network surveillance, control, and traffic management. In private network applications, network management functions include network planning, implementation, operation, maintenance, and systems management.

Network management include the following tasks: setting up and running a telecommunications network, monitoring network activities, controlling the network to provide acceptable performance [e.g., a Signal-to-Noise ratio (S/N) of 21 dB, a Bit Error Rate (BER) of 10^{-6}, a service blocking probability of 0.1%, etc.], and assuring high availability with fast response time to meet the needs of network users.

12.6.1 Evolution of Network Management into TMN

Rapid modernization of telecommunications networks has resulted in a corresponding evolution of network Operations, Administration, and Maintenance (OA&M). OA&M has advanced to include Provisioning (OAM&P), and is gradually transitioning to Network Management (NM), that then evolves into TMN.

12.6.1.1 Traditional Network Management

Traditional network management covers the following (functional) areas:

- **Network planning**: New services cannot be introduced until service planning, network planning, and operations planning have been completed.

  * Service planning: A service plan must be generated that meets customer quality and price needs. The design should define the service price, availability, and features. Marketing strategy (including advertising, service distribution, and personnel training) is another aspect of service planning.

  * Network planning: A network plan is used to determine the system, network elements, and topology required to provide the desired services.

  * Operations planning: An operations plan identifies the activities and associated processes required to operate a network that supports a specific set of services.

- **Provisioning**: This process enables various network resources to be made available for telecommunications network services (Chapter 2). It includes network element, and service provisioning activities.

- **Performance Monitoring (PM)**: This function tracks the operational status of various network elements.

- **Maintenance**: This aspect of network operations includes performing both preventive maintenance (i.e., proactive tasks to prevent service failures) and corrective maintenance (i.e., reactive tasks to repair service failures).

- **Billing**: This process tracks customer usage of network resources, and includes bill preparation/payment/collection.

- **Customer service**: The customer service center responds to individual customer needs. Typical tasks include new service orders, service revision/updates, feature adding/dropping, complaints, sales/marketing promotions, etc.

- **Database and data management**: This process is used to manage the network databases (information) efficiently, and insures the data is properly updated/maintained.

12.6.1.2 Transition from Local to Remote Surveillance

Network management has traditionally been a local activity (i.e., handled at the central office level), and is still appropriate for some applications. Network elements such as multiplexers, switches, and routers are managed locally (on site) through physical activities. These operations often require a technician to connect a test meter or "push a button" to check or modify the state of a network element. A physical alarm generated by network element(s) or a trouble report (typically based on a customer complaint) is the trigger that initiates network management actions. Clearly, this scheme is not the best strategy for providing reliable network service to users because it is a "reactive" response to a "failure" condition that has already impacted service. Therefore, this type of network management is:

- Service affecting
- People intensive (manual activities)
- Expensive
- Slow
- Error prone (human analysis)
- Unreliable and inefficient

The rapid development of microprocessor technology has facilitated the transition from local to remote surveillance-based network management. Thus, the strategy has changed from "managing components" (e.g., multiplexers and switches) on-site activities to "managing information" over a wide area via remote operations centers. This approach allows the network to be continuously monitored. Routine maintenance is scheduled, and emergency conditions are handled on a "real time" basis. The actions are "preventive", cost-effective, and responsive. This results in a much higher productivity for technical support personnel. In addition, remote automated surveillance systems allows consolidation of work centers, reduce the number of operation centers, and reduce the number of network management personnel required to operate/maintain the network. Network utilization is also improved because of higher reliability/availability characteristics, and the "per-circuit" operations costs are low.

However, this strategy is often a "task-oriented operation", based on "inflexible" systems that are expensive and difficult to maintain. Interfaces between the Operation System (OS) and network elements and between separate OSs are typically proprietary. Management information is gathered via dedicated links, and inter-operability is practically impossible. The traditional approach is to consider Operations Systems (OSs) as being physically separate entities (i.e., not part of the telecommunications network that is being managed). As a result, interconnection of OSs becomes a complex and cumbersome task that often creates "network management islands" within a non-integrated environment. Fortunately the disadvantages of this methodology have been recognized, and are being corrected in the next generation of OSs.

12.6.2 Telecommunications Management Network (TMN) Strategy

TMN, like the traditional network management techniques, uses a separate network to monitor and maintain the telecommunications networks. However, TMN enhances the quality and features of the management capabilities by supporting integration of multi-vendor products, promoting inter-operability, providing flexible operations, and allowing options for future growth.

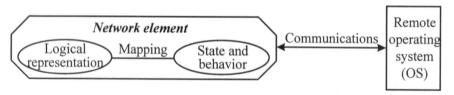

Figure 12-42   TMN Strategy using Systems Management Model.

Definition 12-5: (recommended by ITU-T and ISO): The **systems management model** maps the state and behavior of physical resources onto a well-defined set of data values (Figure 12-42). By doing so, the range of functions that have to be performed by a remote Operating System (OS) can be simplified to a set of common database management functions such as create, read, update, delete, etc. This allows TMN to provide a relatively simple platform for remote systems-based surveillance and control.

Example 12-8: Compare the operations planning strategy for traditional Network Management (NM) and Telecommunications Management Network (TMN) applications.

- Traditional NM is a "top down" analytical (task-oriented) approach. TMN is a "bottom up" object oriented approach.

- Traditional NM operating plans identify Operating Systems (OSs), and describe how they are to be used. TMN operating plans identify Network Elements (NEs) and define architectures based on flexible frameworks in which many OSs can co-exist in an integrated environment.

- Operation life cycle (planning, design and execution) of a traditional NM can take several years to be completed. TMN operating planning enables a service provider to install OSs immediately and then adapt ("fine tune") individual systems to realize its full potential.

12.6.3 Rationale for TMN

The motivation for developing TMN standards/implementation can be separated into the following three categories:

(1) **The changing telecommunications environment:** Rapid and constant change of the telecommunications environment has created network management challenges. In response to regulatory changes, many new network/service providers have been formed, with fierce competition between these providers. The complexity of the telecommunications market has also increased because of subscriber demands for additional features and capacity. As a result, interworking among equipment, networks, and services has become essential. The diverse environments that service providers must manage have the following characteristics:

  * Mix of applications: voice (speech signal), digital data, video, and images, etc.

  * Mix of networks: digital carrier systems, switches, digital trunks, digital channel banks, add-drop multiplexers, digital cross-connect systems, etc.

  * Mix of transport (inter-connection) facilities: a combination of wirelines (twisted-pair, coaxial cable), airlink (radio, satellite, cellular, wireless), waveguides, and optical fibers.

  * Emerging technologies: technology has evolved from Plesiochronous Digital Hierarchy (PDH) to Synchronous Optical Network/Synchronous Digital Hierarchy (SONET/SDH); from Plain Old Telephone Service (POTS) to Integrated Services Digital Network (ISDN), Asynchronous Transfer Mode (ATM), multimedia, cellular, Personal Communications Service (PCS); and from circuit-switching to packet switching [e.g., X.25, frame relay, Switched Multi-megabit Digital Service (SMDS), ATM, etc.].

(2) **End users' expectations**: Based on the regulatory changes, end-users have many choices for meeting their telecommunications needs. Rising customer expectations

include needs for "one-stop shopping", billing, and customer support. End users have less tolerance for network/service failures. Typical network problems include: equipment failures (can be caused by software glitches), network traffic congestion, and nature disasters. Networks, their associated resources, and distributed applications have become indispensable to end users. The present trend is toward larger, more complicated networks, that support more applications and larger number of users. Quick network/service provisioning and high reliability are essential for meeting customer expectations. As telecommunications networks grow in scale, more things can "go wrong" that may cause an entire network (or portions of a network) to fail or degrade to an unacceptable (service quality) level.

(3) **Network/service providers' needs**: The following areas offer challenges for network/service providers:

* Improve service quality: includes reducing provisioning delays, eliminating inefficient maintenance, and improving real-time traffic/congestion management.

* Improve network quality: can be achieved by using "proactive" rather than "reactive" maintenance, detecting and repairing network failures before they impact customers, and tracking failure/error conditions.

* Reduce operations costs: cost reductions can be implemented by applying expert systems, and by improving the effectiveness of technicians responding to alarm conditions and service restoration.

* Improve competitive edge: efficient operations can be achieved by consolidating work centers, allowing customers to control options, and adopting creative/ flexible tariff schemes.

* Generate and protect revenues: revenue can be generated and protected by reducing provisioning time for service, introducing new services faster, and maintaining high quality/reliable network operations.

A common set of objectives for providing "world class telecommunications operations" are listed as follows:

* Provisioning time for new services ≤ 3 days

* Directory update (to operator service) < 24 hours

* Dial tone delay: not-measurable (end user cannot perceive a delay)

* Blocking probability < 1%

* Call completion rate > 99%

* POTS/leased-line failure fixed time < 24 hours

* Customer fault report < 1 per line per year

* Customer complaints answered < 20 seconds

12.6.4 TMN Vision, Goals and Functionality

The overall vision of Telecommunications Management Network (TMN) is a network of management systems linked together to manage a variety of telecommunications networks. The set of systems and the links between them comprises TMN. TMN constantly monitors and "fine tunes" telecommunications networks. In general, TMN eliminate the need for human intervention, except for rare emergency circumstances, or special activities that require physical reconfiguration.

The initial objective of TMN is the definition of interfaces and protocols used between Operations Systems (OSs) and transmission terminals. By standardizing these interfaces and protocols, technologies can be introduced with minimum modification. This allows operational procedures to gradually change via "evolution". As technology advances, the "TMN scope" can be extended to develop recommendation for managing an entire telecommunications network. The TMN vision and goals are briefly described as follows:

- Automate network management: TMN is used to reduce the costs of operations. This objective requires machine-to-machine operational interfaces.

- Support rapid technological evolution: TMN is a long term solution that is based on standardized interfaces, which must be flexible to allow future enhancements.

- Manage multi-vendor equipment environment: TMN is a "generic concept", that requires management standards to support interoperability.

- Facilitate end-to-end management of global services: TMN will be used to optimize the flow of management information on a global basis.

- Improve customer service and interactions: TMN is intended to increase the efficiency of service provider operations and customer support.

- Ensure security: TMN controls access to management information, and includes security features that prevent unauthorized access.

- Provide integrated, inter-operable, and flexible management systems: TMN provides standards to support administration across multiple OSs. Every management system within an administration must be part of an interconnected management hierarchy, and must be able to access the management capabilities of other systems through standard (compatible) interfaces.

- Permit exchange of information between the management systems: TMN allows sharing of information among service providers (administrations) or between a service provider and a customer. It includes exchange of management information across the boundaries between different TMN environments. TMN can convert management information from one format to another, so that management information flow within the TMN environment can be easily achieved.

- Minimize changes: TMN has robust architecture that is flexible, and can adapt to future changes in telecommunications networks.

Conceptually TMN is a separate network (i.e., a management network that is logically separate from the telecommunication networks) that transports, stores, and processes information used to manage telecommunications networks/services. TMN adopts the architecture shown in Figure 12-43 to achieve interconnection between various management systems and/or telecommunications equipment. TMN specifies standard interfaces, including protocols and messages, to permit direct exchange of management information. Note that OSI open interfaces and systems management principles are the basis of TMN interface requirements. The following descriptions define the boundaries of TMN functionality:

- TMN supports a wide variety of management functions including: network planning, installation, operations, administration, maintenance, and provisioning. Management is performed by network of inter-operative systems, rather than a single monolithic manager.

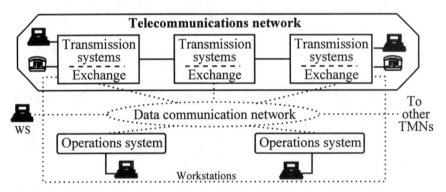

Figure 12-43   Management Information Exchanges.

- TMN provides management functions and supports communications between OSs and various parts of telecommunications networks.

- TMN provides varying levels of complexity, depending upon network management needs. TMN can connect a single OS to one piece of telecommunications equipment, or many OSs to a variety of telecommunications elements.

- TMN can use parts of the telecommunications network to support its communications needs (i.e., to carry and exchange management information).

TMN defines the interfaces and specifications of the interface protocols used between OSs and transmission terminals. The scope includes development of Recommendations for information networks that manage all aspects of telecommunications networks and services. These TMN Recommendations will be developed over a long time period, and will satisfy the needs of constantly evolving telecommunications networks and services. The subject areas covered by TMN Recommendations are:

- TMN architecture
- Interface specification methodology
- Management functions (protocol independent)
- Management information models and catalog
- Management information registration
- Management services
- Communications protocols
- System management services and management messages (protocol specific)
- Conformance requirements
- International standard profiles

12.6.5 TMN Users, Benefits and Standards

TMN provides the means for exchanging (management) information required to manage "end-to-end" telecommunications services. These services are provided by interconnecting several telecommunications networks. Potential TMN users can be any of the following entities:

- Postal, Telegram and Telephone (PTT) administrations
- Local exchange carriers
- Inter-exchange carriers
- Global service providers
- Telecommunications network/service customers
- Recognized Private Operating Agencies (RPOAs)

The benefits of TMN are unlimited. By making all internal network management functions available via standardized interfaces, service providers can rapidly deploy new telecommunications networks/services. Powerful service management capabilities can be offered to customers through interconnection of an extensive network management infrastructure. Groups of service providers have the ability to enter business-level agreements to deploy resource sharing systems that can be administered automatically through inter-operable interfaces. TMN can serve as a tool to implement the following management objectives:

- TMN supports for management of "heterogeneous" networks (e.g., mixture of PDH, SONET, and SDH), services, and equipment.

- TMN allows vendors of network elements to offer specialized systems (known as "element managers") that can be easily integrated into a service provider's management hierarchy.

- TMN promotes the internetworking between separately managed networks to provide "inter-network" services.

- TMN allows telecommunications customers, service providers, and associated administrations to access management information using a controlled and secure methodology.

- TMN allows technological and functional changes to be easily accommodated.

Standards organizations (i.e., ITU-T, ISO, ANSI, ESTI, TTC, and NM Forum) that are involved in the development of TMN standards and the recommendations for implementation guidelines are listed as follows:

- ITU-T (International Telecommunications Union-Telecommunication Standard Sector; formally CCITT)

  * Study Group 4 (SG4): TMN architecture and coordination (Rec. M-)

  * SG7: Jointly with ISO, OSI management, data network management (Rec. X-)

  * SG11: Management of ISDN, SS7, IN, Q3 protocol and services (Rec. Q-)

  * SG15: SDH management (Rec. G-)

Note that all TMN activities originally handled by SG11 and SG15 have been consolidated within SG4 (the TMN project was started by ITU-T in the fall of 1985).

- International Standard Organization (ISO): OSI systems management

- American National Standard Institute (ANSI): TMN North American applications

- European Telecommunications Standard Institute (ETSI): TMN European considerations and applications

- Telecommunications Technology Committee (TTC): TMN Japanese considerations and applications

- Network Management (NM) Forum: Inter-operability

12.6.6 ITU-T Recommendations for TMN

This section briefly describes ITU-T TMN Recommendations (i.e., the initial set of TMN documents). Figure 12-44 shows TMN architecture, methodology, terminology, and the associated ITU-T TMN Recommendations. [Specially, (1) ITU-T M.3010 covers TMN architecture; (2) ITU-T M.3020 covers TMN methodology; (3) ITU-T M.60 covers TMN terminology; (4) ITU-T M.3200 (series), M.3300 & M.3400 cover TMN management services and functions; (5) M.3100, M.3180 & G.774 cover the TMN management information model & catalog; etc.]. Note that Recommendations M.3200 consist of a series of documents.

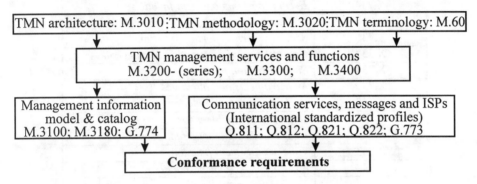

Figure 12-44   TMN Architecture, Methodology and Terminology.

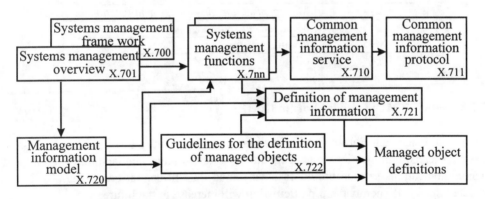

Figure 12-45   ITU-T/OSI Management Standards.

12.6.7 ITU-T/OSI Management Standards

Table 12-6 lists the TMN/OSI system management functions standards recommendation (X.---) documents and their associated functions (e.g., X.730 covers Object management function; X.731 covers State management function; X.732 covers attributes for representing relationships; X.733 covers alarm reporting function; X.734 covers event report management function; X.735 covers log control function; etc.). Figure 12-45 illustrates the relationship among various management standards/functions.

Table 12-6   ITU-T/OSI Standards and Functions.

Recommendation	System management functions
X.730	*Object management function*
X.731	*State management function*
X.732	*Attributes for representing relationships*
X.733	*Alarm reporting function*
X.734	*Event report management function*
X.735	*Log control function*
X.736	*Security alarm reporting function*
X.737	*Confidence and diagnostic test categories*
X.738	*Summarization function*
X.739	*Metric objects and attributes*
X.740	*Security audit trail function*
X.741	*Objects and attributes for access control*
X.742	*Usage metering function for accounting*
X.743	*Time management function*
X.744	*Software management function*
X.745	*Test management function*
X.746	*Scheduling function*
X.747	*General relationship model*
X.748	*Response time monitoring function*
X.749	*Management domain management function*
X.750	*Management knowledge management function*
X.751	*Changeover function*

12.6.8 Network Management Forum (NMF)

Network Management Forum (NMF) has played, and continues to fill an important role in setting telecommunications management standards. Many manufacturers/vendors and telecommunications service providers have joined this influential consortium, and it is expected that NMF membership/participation will increase in the future.

The purpose of the NMF is to promote the interoperability of information network management systems by applying common standards from various sources. The overall objective is to generate practical implementation packages known as "OMNIPoint".

Figure 12-46 shows the function of the OMNIPoint interface. In this approach, each individual management system is treated as a "black box", whose internal structure and method of communications with the resources being managed are of no concern. That is, the management system used to communicate with the managed resources may be of any type [e.g., Simple Network Management Protocol (SNMP), Common Management Information Protocol (CMIP), etc.], and the actual transport mechanisms used to carry management information may be different provided it supports the specific service.

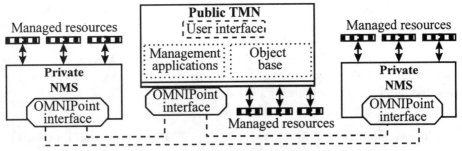

Figure 12-46   The Function of the OMNIPoint Interface.

However, communications between management systems must be clearly defined. The scheme shown in Figure 12-46 uses inter-operable interfaces that comply with the OMNIPoint specifications to support communications between the public TMN and private Network Management Systems (NMSs). The transport mechanism is typically OSI or TCP/IP, or possibly a proprietary interface for specific applications.

OMNIPoint collaborates with other standards groups (e.g., OSI regional workshops) and places emphasis on generating service management guidelines for implementing network management products. The OMNIPoint model is also referred to as Simple Network Management Protocol (SNMP) which is defined in the context of Internet applications. SNMP and TCP/IP are de facto standards, but are not as complete as the OSI standards. OSI standards are normally applied when the inter-networking problems are considered difficult. However, simpler standards (e.g., SNMP or TCP/IP) are used when appropriate.

Network Management Forum (NMF) and the ITU-T Joint Coordination Group-TMN (JCG-TMN) explore how NMF complements TMN. Emphasis is placed on conformance profiles, and International Standardized Profiles (ISPs). The overall effect of the OMNIPoint program is that TMN acceptance and implementation will be accelerated on a global basis.

12.7 ARCHITECTURES OF TMN

It is essential to develop an understanding of TMN architectures. This includes the: (1) functional architecture, (2) information architecture, and (3) physical architecture. The details of these three topics is presented separately in the following sections.

12.7.1 Functional Architecture of TMN

The functional areas of a traditional management system include: planning, installation, Operations, Administration, Maintenance and Provisioning (OAM&P) of telecommunications networks and services. The TMN management functional areas: are accounting management, performance management, fault management, security management, and configuration management. General descriptions of these functions have been previously presented in this chapter. This section concentrates on the TMN applications and viewpoint. Figure 12-47 shows the mapping between traditional management functional areas and the TMN management functional areas.

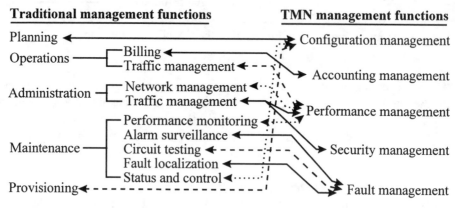

Figure 12-47   Mapping between Functional Areas.

12.7.1.1 Configuration Management

Configuration management function allows network managers to control the configuration of the telecommunications network components to meet specific service needs. The configuration of a network may be changed to alleviate congestion, isolate faults, or accommodate changing end user needs. The functions performed by configuration management are:

- Planning and engineering: This activity includes network design, network topology, and restoration planning. Setting and modifying parameters of individual network components are also performed.

- Service order management (service provisioning): This activity deals with service configuration and database manipulation/updating.

- Equipment and network provisioning: The provisioning function includes installation of equipment, initialization of resources, resource status verification, and back up testing. This ensures consistent configuration between any two devices.

- Resource allocation and management: This function covers the assignment of network/service resources, database setup, and system administration. It includes collection and dissemination of data reflecting the current state of resources. Locally initiated changes, or changes occurring due to unpredicted events, are communicated to the management systems to support resource inventory and control.

12.7.1.2 Accounting and Security Management

Accounting management activities generate, collect, and process resource usage information used to support the customer billing function. It allows network managers to determine and allocate costs/charges for the use of network resources. Accounting management supports the following tasks:

- Informing users of costs incurred and/or resources utilized
- Enables accounting limits to be set for the use of resources
- Allows costs to be combined for multiple resources
- Inventory management
- Monitoring network resource utilization

Security management provides protection against unauthorized access of systems and resources. It allows network managers to control services that protect communications resources. Security management supports the following tasks:

- Authorization mechanisms
- Resource access control
- Information encryption and/or key (seed) management
- Authentication mechanisms
- Security logs (audit trails)

12.7.1.3 Performance Management (PM)

Performance Management (PM) provides the capability to monitor and evaluate the network performance. Abnormal behavior is reported so that actions can be taken to insure the effectiveness of the telecommunications network and its elements. Performance management supports the following functions:

- Network element performance monitoring (including both current and historical performance). The PM function is used to collect and disseminate data.

- Threshold detection using collected/analyzed data to issue an alarm whenever performance thresholds are crossed. For example, if the Severe Error Seconds (SES), or the Bit Error Rate (BER) measurement has reached a specified number, an alarm is issued.

- Network traffic management permits constant surveillance of network traffic loading so that network element controls can be administrated to insure efficient operation.

- Service quality is continuously monitored to insure the appropriate level of network performance is maintained.

In summary, performance management can be used to analyze traffic patterns, which can be used to forecast the need for network re-configuration and/or network expansion. It can also be used to determine service levels and predict potential network outages, thereby minimizing the potential revenue losses.

12.7.1.4 Fault Management

Fault management allows network operators/administrators to detect problems occurring in telecommunications networks. These mechanisms are used to detect, isolate, and correct abnormal operations/conditions in any network component. Therefore, fault management support the following functions:

- Detecting and reporting network component failures: this activity notifies the proper manager so that the component failures are handled properly.

- Logging received event reports: this activity allows network component conditions to be examined so that appropriate actions are taken.

- Schedule and execute diagnostic tests: this activity allows faults to be traced so that corrective actions can be initiated. These procedures may be invoked as a result of analyzing of the event log.

- Correct multiple alarms: this type of condition is typically caused by a network failure such as loss of clock or synchronization signals.

- Identify subscribers affected by network failures: this activity allows notification of the parties impacted by the failure condition.

- Open/close trouble tickets: this activity is used to dispatch maintenance personnel and track resolution of failures.

In summary, fault management allows network operators to analyze, filter, and correlate network alarms. It can be used to localize the network faults (performance measurements and appropriate tests are run) and correct failures. Under most failures, the network will be automatically restored. In addition, fault management issues trouble tickets, tracks these tickets, and manages work assignment for maintenance personnel.

12.7.1.5 TMN Management Layers

Figure 12-48 illustrates the layered structure of TMN management; from the lowest element management layer to the highest business management layer.

- **Element management layer:** This layer interfaces with network elements for resource inventory and network configuration information. The management functions include collecting network element performance data, issuing alarm surveillance, and performing test access. Network operators can control and coordinate a subset of network element functions. This control/coordination can also be performed on a collective basis. The element management layer maintains statistics, an error log and other data about the elements within its scope of control. The element management layer manages each network element on an individual basis, and supports an "abstraction" of the functions provided by the Network Element (NE) layer.

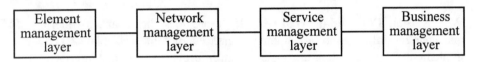

Figure 12-48   TMN Management Layers.

- **Network management layer**: This layer is responsible for the management of all network elements presented by the element management layer. This function manages elements both individually and as a set. Its key functions are to perform network/service provisioning, monitor network performance, perform network surveillance, test end-to-end service performance, analyze performance measurement data and, automatically restore network. In addition to network/service provisioning, network management also performs cessation and modification of network capabilities to support network services for customers. It must maintain all network capabilities at all times.

- **Service management layer:** The service management layer is responsible for the contractual aspects of features/functions provided by the telecommunications service provider to customers. It also controls the availability of services offered to new customers. The major tasks of the service management layer is to track and enter work items, accounting, and billing information. Designing and assigning resources (e.g., network circuits and facilities) and to maintain customer databases is also a function performed by the service management layer. This layer provides a customer interface with administrations and Recognized operating service agencies (Rosa) capabilities. It interfaces telecommunication service providers, maintains statistical data [call completion rate, incomplete connections, Quality of Service (QoS), etc.], and interacts with various services.

- **Business management layer:** This layer is responsible for the entire telecommunications business enterprise. Business management maintains aggregate data about the overall enterprise. It manages telecommunications business activities between different service providers, and supports the decision-making process for optimal investment and utilization of network resources. It supports the management of OA&M related budget, and tracks the supply and demand for OA&M staff assignments so that resource utilization is optimized.

12.7.1.6 TMN Reference Model, Functional Blocks, and Reference Points

Figure 12-49 shows the TMN reference model, the reference points (g-, f-, m-, x-, q_3 and q_x interfaces) between functional blocks, and functional blocks [WorkStation Functional (WSF) block, Mediation Functional (MF) block, Operations Systems Functional (OSF) block, Q-Adapter Functional (QAF) block, and Network Element Functional (NEF) block]. These functional blocks are briefly described as follows:

- **WorkStation Functional (WSF)** block: It provides the means to interpret TMN management information for human users, via graphical displays. The WSF is implemented by translating the management information from one interface format to another. Note that the user interface and the human operator are not considered part of Telecommunications Management Network (TMN).

- **Mediation Functional (MF)** block: Mediation Devices (MDs) are probably the most vague component of TMN. These devices may provide storage, adaptation, filtering, threshold-setting, or consolidation of operations on the data received from subtending equipment. The concept of MD is nebulous, and whether any MDs have actually been developed is questionable. Often what is referred to as an MD in the telecommunications industry is actually a "Q-Adapter" (QA; described later in this section). Mediation activities include Information Transport Functions (ITFs) and Information Processing Functions (IPFs). The ITF is responsible for protocol conversion, message conversion, signal conversion, address mapping, address translation, routing, and concentration. The IPF is responsible for execution, screening, storage, and filtering.

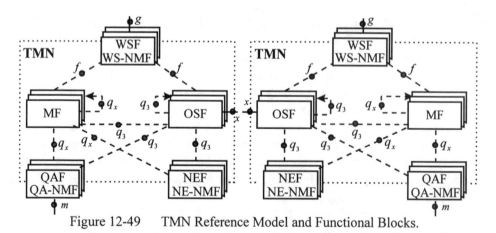

Figure 12-49   TMN Reference Model and Functional Blocks.

- **Operations System Functional (OSF)** block: The OSF will process any information related to telecommunications network/service management. This allows network managers to monitor, coordinate, and control telecommunications functions. Several types of OSFs (currently under development by the telecommunications product vendors and standards organizations), are required to manage modern telecommunications networks and services. For example, according to ITU-T M.3010 there are presently four types of OSF block that support the previously described TMN management functional layers. They are: (1) the element management, (2) the network management, (3) the service management, and (4) the business management layers. The function of OSF includes supporting manager and agent roles in accessing managed object information. The OSF also processes raw data (i.e., concentrating various data, correlating alarm surveillance information, or performing statistical performance data analysis). The OSF must react properly to incoming management information by issuing/tracking trouble tickets and re-configuring network resources automatically. Security and directory services are also functions supported by the OSF.

- **Q-Adapter Functional (QAF)** block: The QAF provides translation and conversion between a TMN reference points and a non-TMN reference points. That is, the goal of QAF is to connect a TMN system to a non-TMN system. In reality, many problems develop when mapping between TMN interfaces and existing (non-TMN) interfaces. QAF is the primary method used to integrate existing management networks into TMN.

- **Network Element management Functional (NEF)** block: The Network Element (NE) is the only node that actually resides in the managed telecommunications network. Examples of NEs are switches, Digital Cross-connect Systems (DCSs), Integrated Digital Loop Carrier (IDLC) systems, and Add-Drop Multiplexers (ADMs). The NE's primary job is to customer's traffic, rather than perform network management. However, the NE is the ultimate origin or destination of the network management supervision and control. The following tasks are performed by Network Element-Network Management Functions (NE-NMFs): protocol conversion, address mapping/translation, message conversion, traffic routing, (performance, accounting, alarm, and network status) data storage/collection, data backup, network element alarm analysis, self-testing, operations data transport via Embedded Operations Channels (EOCs), and network restoration via "self-healing" processes.

As shown in Figure 12-49, each TMN interface is an embodiment of a reference point. However, some reference points may fall within equipment. Therefore, these "internal points" are not considered interfaces because a reference point is defined as an interface connecting functional blocks that are embodied in physically separate pieces of equipment. The TMN reference points are used to delineate management functional blocks, define service boundaries between two management functional blocks, and identify the information passing between functional blocks. The classes of TMN reference point are briefly described as follows:

- **q reference point**: The "q" classification defines the points of standardized inter-operability between TMN functions on different layers (as well as within a layer) of the TMN architecture. The q reference points connect the TMN Mediation Function (MF), Operations Systems Function (OSF), Q-Adapter Function (QAF), WorkStation Function (WSF), and Network Element Function (NEF) blocks together either directly or via the Data Communications Function (DCF).

* The q$_3$ reference point connects MF to OSF, NEF to OSF, QAF to OSF, and OSF to OSF.

* The q$_x$ reference point connects MF to MF, MF to NEF, and MF to QAF.

* **m reference point**: The "m" classification typically defines the connection between a QAF and its non-TMN managed resources. It is usually a point of contact between the TMN and an older telecommunications interface. They can use Transaction Language 1 (TL1), Telemetry Byte-Oriented Serial (TBOS), Telemetry Asynchronous Block Serial (TABS), or non-TMN network management protocol (e.g., Simple Network Management Protocol (SNMP) or Common Management Information Protocol (CMIP)] as interface "languages".

* **x reference point**: The "x" classification reference point is used to designate inter-operability points between administration systems. It is used between an OSF and a similar function in another management network.

* **f reference point**: The "f" reference point designates the interface between an OSF and WSF. This is typically an "X-window" interface that a human operator uses to interact with functions of the TMN.

* **g reference point**: The "g" reference point designates the interface between a WSF and its user. It is considered to be outside the TMN boundaries, but is described in the Z.300 series of communications standards.

12.7.1.7 TMN Functional Components

Each TMN functional block (MF, OSF, QAF, NEF or WSF) consists of one or more TMN functional components briefly described as follows:

* **Management Application Function (MAF):** This component supports several TMN management services. It is part of the: (1) TMN Operations System Function (i.e., OSF-MAF), (2) Mediation Function (i.e., MF-MAF), (3) Network Element Function (i.e., NEF-MAF), and (4) Q-Adapter Function (i.e., QAF-MAF).

* **Security Function (SF):** This component provides security services that are required for TMN functional blocks to satisfy their security policy and/or user security needs. The security services are classified (independent of the TMN functional blocks) into five basic services: (1) authentication, (2) access control, (3) data confidentiality, (4) data integrity, and (5) non-repudiation. They are defined in ITU-T Rec. X.800.

* **Message Communication Function (MCF):** The MCF is limited to exchanging management information (contained in messages) with its peers. It is associated with all functional blocks having physical interfaces (Figure 12-50). The MCF consists of a protocol convergence function used for interfaces where all seven OSI layers are not

supported (i.e., a short stack). There are different MCF types, which are differentiated by subscripts (e.g., the MCFq₃ is used at the q₃ reference point), corresponding various protocol stacks supported at the respective reference point.

The communication control functions performed by the MCF are: polling, addressing, communications networking, and ensuring integrity of data flows.

The MCF supports communications of primitive functions such as command and response statements, alarm statements, alarm forwarding (reporting), test results/data collection, operational measurement data collection, upload of status report/local alarming, and protocol conversion.

The MCF requires a Data Communications Function (DCF), which is used by the TMN functional blocks for exchanging management information. The DCF serves as an information transport mechanism between management functional blocks, and supports routing, relaying, and interworking function. In general, DCF provides layers 1 through 3 of the OSI reference model (or their equivalent). The DCF can be supported by the bearer channel of the subnetworks (e.g., X.25, MANs, LANs, SS7) or the Embedded Communications Channel (ECC) in SONET/SDH applications. When different subnetworks are interconnected, the interworking functions are provided by the DCF. If DCFs are located between systems, the MCFs are associated with every point of attachment to the DCF.

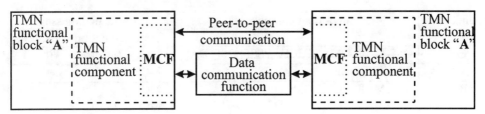

Figure 12-50   Message Communication Function (MCF).

- **Information Conversion Function (ICF):** ICF is used in intermediate systems to provide a translation mechanism between the information models (which may or may not be object-oriented) at both interfaces. ICF is mandatory for the Mediation Functional (MF) and the Q-Adapter Functional (QAF) blocks because ICF is the component that characterizes both MF and QAF.

- **WorkStation Support Function (WSSF):** The WSSF assists the WorkStation Functional (WSF) block. It provides data access/manipulation, invocation/ confirmation of actions, transmittal of notification, and hides the existence of NEFs (and other OSFs or MFs) from WSF users communicating with a particular OSF or MF. In addition, the WSSF provides administrative support for the WS,F and access for administering the OSF.

- **User Interface Support Function (UISF):** The UISF translates system information to a format that can be displayed on a monitor for the human-machine interface, and vice versa. That is, it also translates user inputs into the TMN information model. The USIF integrates various types of data from one or more sessions with OSF or MF blocks, so that the information can be presented in a correct and consistent format at the user interface. In addition, functions similar to MAF and ICF may be provided by the UISF.

- **Directory System Function (DSF):** The DSF component represents a local, regional, national, or global directory system. The directory information is stored as a set of hierarchically ordered Directory Objects (DOs) in a group of distributed DSF.

- **Directory Access Function (DAF):** The DAF component is used by any functional block to access the DSF. It is used to access TMN related information contained in the Directory Information Base (DIB). It also supports DIB maintenance activities (e.g., to read, list, search, add, modify and/or delete, information in DIB). The OSF requires this component, and other functional blocks (WSF, MD, QAF and NEF) may also use the DAF.

Table 12-7 shows the required functional components (MAF, SF, MCF, ICF, WSSF, UISF, DSF and DAF) for each functional block (WSF, MF, OSF, QAF and NEF).

Table 12-7   Required Functional Components for Each Functional Block.

Functional block	Functional components	Associated message communications functions
OSF	OSF-MAF(A/M), SF,ICF, WSSF, DSF, DAF	MCF_x, MCF_{q3}, MCF_f
WSF	SF, UISF, DAF	MCF_f
NEF_{q3}	NEF-MAF(A), SF, DSF, DAF	MCF_{q3}
NEF_{qx}	NEF-MAF(A), SF, DSF, DAF	MCF_{qx}
MF	MF-MAF(A/M), SF, ICF, WSSF, DSF, DAF	MCF_{q3}, MCF_{qx}, MCF_f
QAF_{q3}	QAF-MAF(A/M), SF, ICF, DSF, DAF	MCF_{q3}, MCF_m
QAF_{qx}	QAF-MAF(A/M), SF, ICF, DSF, DAF	MCF_{qx}, MCF_m

A: Agent;   A/M: Agent/Manager

12.7.1.8 User Access to TMN, and between TMNs

TMN users are allowed to access to certain subsets of TMN functionality. This includes access between TMNs as shown in Figure 12-51. The user can access TMN to exchange the management information related to a specific interface or a specific link. Likewise, the user can exchange management information concerning events on different links, and the status of services that are available to the user. This function is implemented in a centralized fashion, and the exchange is available at an "**x**" reference point supported at the connection between two TMNs, or a TMN and a network user. TMN typically provides users with common access to management applications for one (or more) of the following telecommunications services: (1) translation between the objects known by the user and the service (and/or network) management functions, (2) security functions, (3) protocol conversion, and (4) value added services.

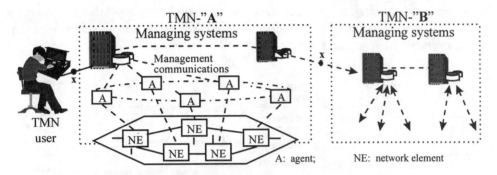

Figure 12-51   Access to TMN, Interaction between TMNs.

12.7.2 Information Architecture of TMN

There are several issues related to TMN management communications. One key issue is the specification of management information to be communicated: (1) between two Operation Systems (OSs); (2) between an OS and a Network Element (NE); (3) between two NEs; (4) between an OS and a WorkStation (WS), and (5) between a NE and a WS.

Other issues are the protocols that should be used to communicate, the exchange of management information, and the processing of this information at both ends. Besides the processing issue (which is not specified by TMN standards) the solution for handling the other issues is to use the system management model as recommended by ISO and ITU-T.

A management information model represents techniques for administering network resources and related support management activities that take place at the application level. These activities involve a variety of management application functions (e.g., storing, retrieving and/or processing information). The functions involved at this level have been previously described and are referred to as TMN functional blocks [i.e., workstation, mediation, operations system, Q-adapter and network element functional blocks (WSF, MF, OSF, QAF and NEF blocks)].

The model specifies the scope of the management information exchange in a standardized manner. The exchange involves the Data Communication Function (DCF; such as a communication network) and Management Communication Functions (MCFs, which allow particular physical components to be attached to the telecommunications network at a given interface).

12.7.2.1 The System Management Model

From a modern network management viewpoint, information about the network resource is important as the physical resource itself. The system management model is shown in Figure 12-52. This model can be applied for remote surveillance and control. The remote processes, manager and agent communicate with each other for the purposes of network management. In the model, the key elements are the design of the Management Information Base (MIB) and manipulation of the MIB through remote communications (i.e., via management operations, notifications, and communications protocols).

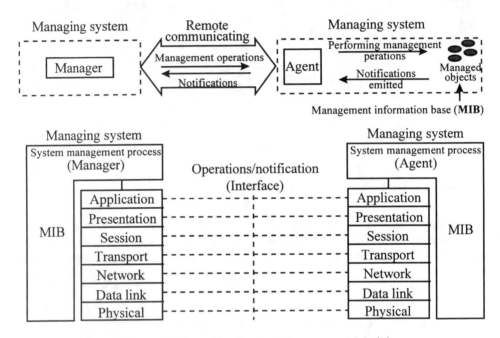

Figure 12-52   The System Management Model.

It is important for the designer of management systems or networks to consider the following: (1) the kind of management information to be accessed or reported across a specific interface (within a domain or between domains); (2) the methods used by the management processes, manager, and agent, to manipulate the MIB; and, (3) the communications protocol used between the manager and the agent.

The MIB consists of a set of management objects, along with their attributes, that are visible at the interface. The MIB provides a hierarchical database organizational model of the management information. The MIB should support multi-vendor network element environments (i.e., the MIB should be vendor-implementation independent). The design of MIB should allow fast deployment of new services and technologies in a telecommunications network. Therefore, the MIB should be modularly expandable and easily upgraded.

Management processes initiate management operations, while the 7-layer OSI stack is used for exchanging management information. Note that remote surveillance may require different choices of physical facilities, and different routing schemes. The recommendation for MIB design is to use an object-oriented (instead of a task/process-oriented) information model.

12.7.2.2 Object-oriented Design Principles for TMN Information Model

To allow effective definition of managed resources, the TMN methodology uses OSI systems management principles and is based on an objected-oriented paradigm. That is, an object-oriented management information model (e.g., the TMNE information model) is recommended. This is because an object-oriented approach defines standardized objects, provides design modularity, allows model component reuse, is easily extended, permits analysts to concentrate on the "information view" of resources, and assures quality.

By using object-oriented modeling, it is possible to generate a formal description of the problem space that is completely independent from the way it is implemented. That is, the model will not change even if the technology used to implement the system changes. In addition, if the management system is expanded to implement new management features, the model is simply expanded rather than being changed.

The information model decomposes the "system problem space" into manageable and understandable pieces. Two typical approaches have been applied for this decomposition: (1) algorithmic (e.g., the traditional top-down structured analysis), and (2) object-oriented. In the algorithmic approach, the problem space is decomposed by successively breaking down processes into sub-processes. These sub-processes are less complex and easier to handle. This approach concentrates on ordering the events in a process. In comparison, the object-oriented approach defines key abstraction in the problem space, rather than steps in a process. It emphasizes the use of agents that either cause action or are the subject of actions.

To meet required management system/network design criteria, specific object-oriented concepts must be applied. The design criteria are:

- The management system should be able to support different perspectives (views) of the same object or a group of objects.

- The management system designer should not be required to make assumption about the implementation of the design.

- The design should avoid "re-inventing the wheel" (i.e., redundancy).

- The design should allow common actions to effect different objects.

The primary concepts of object-oriented principles, which are applied to the TMN design, are: (1) abstraction for objects/managed objects; (2) encapsulation for hiding problem complexities; (3) hierarchy and inheritance for ease of extension/expansion; and (4) allomorphism (also known as polymorphism) for propriety extensions. These four concepts are described as follows:

(1) **Abstraction**: This technique provides a simple interface for a complex system, and allows particular types of resources to be placed in classes of commonality. Abstraction is a conceptual view of the managed network resources within a given context [e.g., TMN context (q_3, f and x), functional context, technology context (PDH, SONET, SDH, ATM, etc.), or managed resource abstraction context]. The different **levels** of abstraction provide different **degrees of details** about the managed systems. Therefore, by choosing the appropriate level of abstraction, the managed resource can be made generic (i.e., independent of technology, service, or vendor). The management perspective is another dimension of abstraction. Depending upon whether the manager needs to perform fault, performance, or another type of management function influences how the managed resources will be perceived.

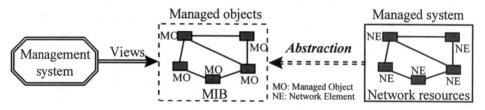

Figure 12-53   Abstraction of Network Resources.

As shown in Figure 12-53, managed objects are abstractions of network resources (network elements) that are being managed or used to support specific management functions (e.g., event forwarding or event logging). A managed object can also represent the relationship between two network resources or a combination of network resources (i.e., a subnetwork or a network). Note that it may or may not be necessary to have a "one-to-one mapping" (Figure 12-53 shows a one-to-one mapping) between Managed Objects (MOs) and Network Elements (NEs) that are, either physical or logical resources. That is, a resource (NE) may be represented by one or more Managed Objects (MOs).

When a resource is represented by multiple Managed Objects (MOs), each MO provides a different abstract view of that specific resource, and these objects may be coupled through either a physical or logical relationship. In some cases, a resource may not be represented by a managed object. Under this condition, the resource is "invisible" to the management system, and thus cannot be managed via the management interface. The abstraction concept is applied to TMN management information modeling as follows:

* Abstraction of network resources creates a model of the information that is exchanged at the management interface. That is, resources are modeled as objects and the management system views each resource as a Managed Object (MO).

* Abstractions at different levels (network, network element, etc.) and from different perspectives (fault, performance, etc.) creates different classes of Managed Objects (MOs).

* A management system exchanges information (about resources that have been modeled) in terms of managed objects.

* The definitions of managed objects must be consistent with the communications procedures used between operations system and network elements, and vice versa.

(2) **Encapsulation**: Encapsulation hides complex and proprietary implementation details, while abstraction provides a simple interface to a complex object. Thus, encapsulation is used to deal with network architecture, technology, and functionality which is continuously changing. For encapsulation to ensure that the integrity of an object is preserved, all operations performed on an object are accomplished by sending messages to the object, and having the object control how the operation is performed.

(3) **Inheritance**: Inheritance allows reuse of object class specifications, and permits incremental refinement of code. Two types of inheritance are supported by the OSI information model:

* Strict inheritance: When a subclass does **not** possess one or more of the characteristics of its parent (the superclass), this subclass must be treated as a new object class. This is necessary to preserve the modularity of the class hierarchy.

* Multiple inheritance: A subclass has the ability to inherit characteristics from more than one superclass. This enables the system to create an "instantiated subclass" from clusters of "uninstantiated" objects that were created specifically for this purpose. Reuse of objects (without modification) through encapsulation, and extensibility through abstraction/inheritance are important qualities. However, evolution of technology will add the complication of "vintages" to the management problem. That is, over time resources and management systems will be deployed that will have different versions of model implementations. Thus, this may result in different behavior characteristics for the "same" model. Therefore, some existing systems may choose to not implement the extensions (upgrades).

(4) **Allomorphism**: Allomorphism is the ability of object instances of a specific class to imitate the behavior of another object class, and allows proprietary extensions. This is a technique for managing the complexity introduced by multiple versions of models.

12.7.2.3 Objects/Managed Objects

An object is an abstraction of a physical or logical entity. A managed object (see Figure 12-54) is characterized by:

- **Attributes**: Every managed object possesses a set of attributes which are visible, but not accessible (since attributes can only be accessed through operations), via the management interface. Attributes can reflect values of parameters based on the resource being modeled. Attributes can also reflect calculated parameter values, or the state of the managed object.

- **Behavior**: Every managed object possesses behavior that is determined by the process encapsulated in the managed object.

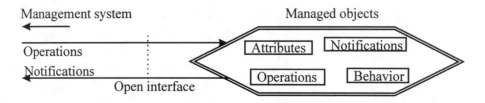

Figure 12-54   Characterization of Managed Objects.

- **Operations**: Every managed object has a set of management operations that reflect the interactions of the managed object with other functions of the management system. Managed objects typically have the major management operations defined in ITU-T Rec. X.720, which are consistent with the Common Management Information Protocol (CMIP; defines the protocol aspect of the messaging).

- **Notifications**: Every managed object may initiate an unsolicited notification, which results in a message being sent to the managing side of the interface.

Definition 12-6: A repository of Managed Objects (MOs) is defined as the Management Information Base (MIB).

Managed objects must be named, and have their relationship well defined, within a specific context to avoid ambiguity. Management system modeling must be captured in standard templates known as Guidelines for the Definition of Managed Objects (GDMO). Templates are registered with standards bodies so they can be made available to management system vendors.

Definition 12-7: An object class is a group of managed objects that share the same attributes, behavior, operations, and notifications.

Example 12-9: Describe the characterization for a typical Managed Object (MO).

The managed object characterization for a "circuit pack" is given in Figure 12-55.

Managed object class:	Circuit pack
Attributes:	Circuit pack ID, type, vendor, location
Behavior:	Does not respond if ambient temperature < 20°C
Operations:	Read and change attribute values; activate/deactivate
Notifications:	Failure alarm(s)

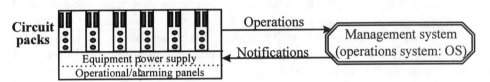

Figure 12-55   Circuit Pack Management.

The definition of a managed object is specified by GDMO templates, and should include the following parameters:

- The object must indicates its position within the inheritance hierarchy.

- The attributes (within the package structure) must be visible at the managed object boundary.

- The behavior (within the package structure) is exhibited by the managed object.

- The operations (within the package structure) are applied to the managed object.

- The notifications (within the package structure) are emitted by the managed object.

- The object must consist of a collection of mandatory packages of attributes, behavior, operations, and notifications.

- If a collection of "conditional" packages of attributes, behavior, operations, and notifications are included, the object must identify the conditions under which the package is presented.

The GDMO templates, which are defined in standard X.722, provide a common set of tools in addition to a common notation that represents various aspects of a managed object's class and naming structure. Formal definitions of the constructs that each template contains must be included in the template.

12.7.2.4 OSI Management Tree Structure

The three tree structures used in OSI management are briefly described as follows:

(1) **Inheritance tree**: This is a tree of managed object classes. The inheritance tree is used to derive new classes based on specialization. The relationship between two object classes is defined as the superclass (i.e., the parent class) and the subclass. The inheritance tree shows how subclass objects inherit attributes, properties, and behavior from their parent classes. Note that subclasses are supported by GDMO templates.

(2) **Naming tree**: This is a tree of managed object instances. All objects are "instances" of an object class, and an object class defines a template for all of its instances. The naming tree is the result of adopting a hierarchical naming scheme based on containment. The relationship between two objects is defined as the superior object and the subordinate object. An object described by subordinate objects is called the superior object. An object's name, which is related to its superior, consists of the attribute identifier, and its value.

Names are designed to be unambiguous within a specific context, which is determined by the containing object being managed. The naming context may be recursively qualified by another naming context, so the complete naming structure can be visualized as a single-root hierarchy, which is the naming tree (see Figure 12-56).

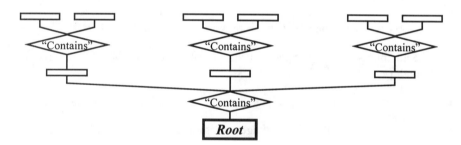

Figure 12-56   A Naming Tree.

The root (i.e., top level) of the naming tree is a null object without any associated properties, which always exists. For each object class defined, the attributes and the superior object classes (whose instances may be used in constructing the name of the object) must be identified. The relationship that defines a superior object class, and may be used in naming, is called "name binding".

Names identify individual objects unambiguously within a given context. Each superior object serves as the naming authority for the objects it contains. Three types of names are used for the object naming:

* **Relative Distinguished Names** (RDNs): These names are unique within the context of a superior object. The containing object serves as a naming authority for the objects it contains.

* **Distinguished names**: These names are unique throughout the entire hierarchy, starting at the root. They are constructed hierarchically by recursive use of relative distinguished names (RDNs).

* **Local names**: These names are unique within the context of the object instance representing the system being managed.

(3) **Object identifier tree or registration tree**: It is an ASN.1 tree structure. It is a hierarchical identification authority structure and allows unique identification of information which includes managed object classes and their constituent elements, such as attributes, behavior, notification, and so on.

Example 12-10: List the kinds of TMN operations that a management system can perform on a managed object.

Typical TMN operations on a managed object includes:

* Attribute-oriented operations: "Get" or "replace" attribute value; "replace" with default value; and, "add" or "remove" member (these operations are valid for "set-value" attributes only).

* Object-oriented operations: "Create" or "delete" message; and, take "action" on message.

* Notification operations

12.7.2.5 Manager/Agent Interactions

All (management information) exchanges between a manager and an agent are expressed in terms of a consistent set of operations and notifications (Figures 12-52, 12-54 and 12-55). These operations are realized through the use of the Common Management Information Services (CMISs) and the Common Management Information Protocol (CMIP) as specified in Recommendations X.710 and X.711.

The services offered by CMIS (confirmed or unconfirmed mode) are listed as follows:

* Provide access control (management associated services): "M-INITIALIZE" establishes management associations; "M-TERMINATE" terminates management associations; and "M-ABORT" is used for unconfirmed termination.

* Perform management operations: "M-GET" retrieves management information from a peer CMISE-service user; "M-CANCEL-GET" cancels a previously requested retrieve information request; "M-create" creates a managed object instance record in

the MIB; "M-DELETE" deletes a managed object instance from the MIB; "M-SET" changes the management information (e.g., an attribute value); and, "M-ACTION" invokes a managed object operation. All services are confirmed, except for "M-SET" and "M-Action" which can be either confirmed or not confirmed.

- Provide management notifications: "M-EVENT-REPORT" is a confirmed or non-confirmed service used to report an event about a managed object to a peer CMISE-service user.

- Scope managed objects: Scoping is used to identify an object (or objects) to which a filter is to be applied. The managed object is starting point for the selection of one or more objects to be filtered, and is known as the Base Managed Object (BMO).

- Filter managed objects: A filter (typically represented by a Boolean expression), consists of one or more assertions about the presence of attributes and/or the attribute value in a scoped managed object.

- Provide synchronization for selected objects and operations: A facility can either be "atomic" or "best effort". First it must be ascertained whether the selected managed objects can perform a specific operation successfully. The case when one or more managed objects are not confirmed, and none of them perform an operation is known as an "atomic". Conversely, if all the managed objects selected are requested to perform an operation, it is known as a "best effort".

- Link replies from managed objects: If multiple replies are sent by an agent to a managed object in response to a query, the replies must be linked.

12.7.2.6 Conformance and ISPs

Conformance specifications are standard procedures for assessing implementation compliance to standards. These specifications allow vendors to demonstrate product conformity to the standards. Conformance specifications exist for several standards including OSI communication protocols, system management functions (messages), and information models. Most of the communication protocols adopted for TMN include the Protocol Implementation Conformance Statement (PICS), and ITU-T X.724 defines the methodology for preparation of Managed Object Conformance Statements (MOCS).

TR10000 (an OSI profile) is a set of OSI standards assembled to perform particular tasks deemed valuable in the marketplace. An International Standardized Profile (ISP) is an internationally recognized specification of one or more OSI profiles. An ISP defines subsets and combinations of base standards that are used to provide functions for supporting specific application areas or performing a particular task. ISP also provides a basis for developing uniform conformance tests. Likewise, ISP specifications allow different vendors to build compatible products that can work together to support common applications.

12.7.3 Physical Architecture of TMN

The TMN physical architecture defines the management interfaces and identifies physical components used to implement the TMN. The physical architecture is concerned with the TMN standard interfaces that correspond to TMN reference points (see Figure 12-49).

12.7.3.1 A Simplified View of TMN Physical Architecture

The TMN reference model shown in Figure 12-49 can be redrawn as illustrated in Figure 12-57 to represent a simplified view of the TMN physical architecture. The building blocks of a TMN are: Operations System (OS), Data Communication Network (DCN), Mediation Device (MD), Q-adapter (QA), Network Element (NE) and WorkStations (WSs). The TMN standard interfaces correspond to TMN reference points, which are defined as a part of the TMN functional architecture. The goal of these interfaces is to ensure the compatibility of devices the are interconnected to implement a given TMN function.

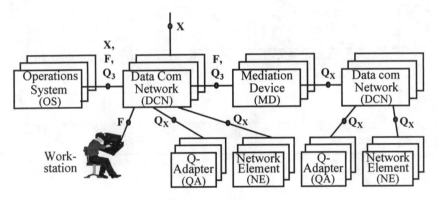

Figure 12-57   A Simplified View of TMN Physical Architecture.

12.7.3.2 TMN Interfaces and Interactions

As shown in Figure 12-57, there are three types of interfaces used in TMN physical architecture: Q, F, and X. They are briefly described here.

- **Q interface**: The Q interface is applied at the q reference points (see Figures 12-49 and 12-57). Furthermore, to provide flexible implementation, the Q class interfaces is divided into two subclasses: the Q_3 interface (applied at the q_3 reference point) and the Q_x interface (applied at the q_x reference point).

The Q_3 interface is characterized by the portion of the management information model shared between the operations system and those TMN elements to which it directly interfaces. The Q_x interface is characterized as the portion of the management information model shared between the Mediation Device (MD), Network Elements (NEs), and Q-Adapters (QAs) it supports. The q_x reference point represents the requirements derived from the interaction between the MF-MAF and other applicable MAFs (see Figure 12-49). The difference between Q_3 and Q_x interfaces are presently under study.

The information models for the Q_3 and Q_x interfaces can potentially be the same, but typically the protocol they support may have less functionality (i.e., may be less generic). Therefore, a mediation function is usually needed to provide conversion between the information models.

Table 12-8   Characteristic Comparison among X, F and Q Interfaces.

Parameter	Q_3 interface	F interface	X interface
Functional block	OSF-NEF/ OSF-MF/ OSF-OSF/ OSF-QAF	OSF-WSF, MF-WSF	OSF-OSF
Service type	Interactive (object oriented), file transfer	Interactive (object oriented)	Interactive (object oriented), store and forward file transfer
Syntax	Machine/ machine ASN.1	Machine/ machine human/machine characters	Machine/ machine ASN.1
Access control*	Optional	Optional	Mandatory
Security aspects**	Yes	Yes	Under study

* Access requirements on an activity basis   ** Other security aspects, e.g., data integrity and encryption

- **F interface**: The F interface is applied at the f reference point. The F interfaces connect workstations to the TMN building blocks (e.g., network, operations system, mediation device, Q-adapter, or another workstation) containing OSFs or MFs.

- **X interface**: The X interface is applied at the x reference point and is used to interconnect two TMNs, or a TMN with other networks/systems that have a "TMN-like" interface. The information model at the X interface sets limits on external access to the TMN. The set of capabilities made available at the X interface is referred to as "TMN access". Additional protocol requirements may be needed to provide security.

12.7.3.3 Data Communications Network (DCN)

There are different types of Data Communications Networks (DCNs). A DCN that provides the ability to share management information among various Operations Systems (OSs) is called an "OS access DC network" (Figure 12-58). A network that provides the ability to access a Central Office (CO) is known as a "DCN backbone network". A network used by Network Elements (NEs) to access other NEs in a CO is called the "NE access network". A DCN is used to support interworking of OSs within an operations center, interworking of OSs among multiple network service providers, interworking of OSs with network elements, and for interworking of management communications within a CO.

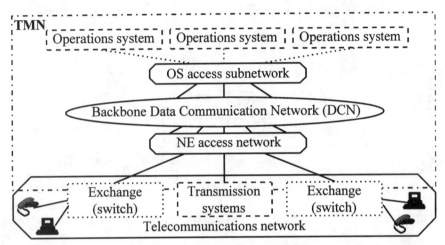

Figure 12-58   Telecommunications Network and Data Communications Network.

A cost-effective TMN design utilizes the existing telecommunications network to carry management information along with message traffic. To do this requires Embedded Communications Channels (ECCs) or Embedded Operations Channels (EOCs), and network elements that can support these functions. The ECC is provided by overhead bandwidth (bits) contained in the traffic channels. The TMN Data Communications Network (DCN) can be functionally divided into three subnetworks as shown in Figure 12-58: (1) OS-access, (2) Backbone DCN (B-DCN), and (3) NE-access network.

(1) **OS-access network**: The OS-access subnetwork provides data communications paths between Operations Systems. It also connects appropriate OSs to the Backbone DCN. Point-to-point private lines have been used to implement a simple OS-access network architecture to support "OS to OS" or "OS to EN" communications. However, this arrangement does not have the flexibility required for an OS-access network in TMN applications.

In the TMN environment, a high-speed LAN or Fiber Distributed Data Interface (FDDI) network is suitable for connecting OSs to B-DCNs, and providing communication links between OSs. To increase the throughput and reliability of an OS-access network, more than one Gateway Network Element (GNE) can be applied. An OS can be directly connected to a B-DCN (via a GNE) to meet the requirements for a specific application and increase the reliability of the OS-access network.

(2) **Backbone DCN**: Figure 12-59 illustrates an example of a Backbone Data Communications Network. A SONET ring network, a mesh network, and an intra-site LAN are interconnected. Since the Management communication Function (MCF) for the Gateway Network Elements (GNEs) performs concentration and routing functions, the selected GNEs can be utilized to implement an embedded Public Switched Telephone Network (PSTN). Note that the MCFs for the GNEs function like a simple packet switch.

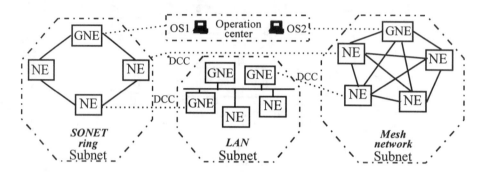

Figure 12-59   An Example Backbone Data Communications Network (B-DCN).

Figure 12-59 can be partitioned into three communications subnetworks. Each subnetwork is connected to OSs via the X.25 DCN. Communications between subnetworks (e.g., for NE-NE communications) can be accomplished via Data Communications Channel (DCC) links. The Embedded Operations Channels (EOCs) carried by interoffice digital transmission facilities are used to provide communications links between the GNEs. The GNEs and/or Mediation Devices (MDs) are used to collect and concentrate network management traffic from subtending NEs, and provide internetworking functions between the B-DCN and NE-access network. SONET management communications architectures vary depending upon the particular network configuration (e.g., communications within a site, or between sites). The architectures also vary depending upon applications [e.g., between OS and NE; NE and NE; IEC and LEC (Inter-Exchange Carrier and Local Exchange Carrier central offices); or survivable rings].

Within a site, typically drop side SONET interfaces are used to connect NEs. Thus, DCC is not supported. As an alternative, an LAN (e.g., an IEEE 802.3 LAN) can be used for intra-site management communications.

A PSTN can also be used to transport network management traffic while carrying payload information. However, this architecture has many disadvantages. First, the LEC Central Office may not be equipped with the packet switching capability for providing data communications links. Second, the speed data link presently terminated by the packet switches is 56 kbps (or lower). Thus, a multiplexer is needed to access a backbone T1 interface transport network. Therefore, the present PSTN architecture may not be flexible enough for use as a backbone data communications network.

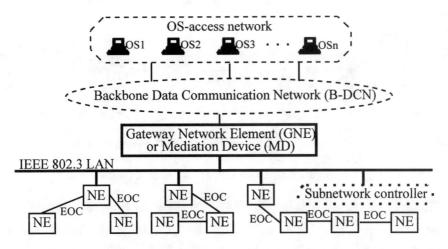

Figure 12-60   NE-Access Network via EOCs and LAN.

(3) **NE-access network**: Figure 12-60 shows a NE-access network that uses both Embedded Operations Channels (EOCs) and LAN (e.g., the IEEE 802.3 LAN) technologies. Note the Network Elements (NEs) can be gateway NEs, end-NEs, or an Intermediate NEs (INEs).

The characteristics and functions of a Gateway Network Element (GNE) are:

* Provide gateway functions: These functions include protocol conversion, message translation, address mapping, and subnetwork flow control.

* Provide access connection: The access links include the connections to a Packet-Switched Network (PSN), Operations Systems, and other gateway elements.

* Provide statistical multiplexing: This function multiplexes the network management information (traffic), and is based on "bandwidth on demand".

* Provide remote access: Remote access is provided for subtending network elements via embedded operations channels or via the operations center.

* Route tandem operations messages: Figure 12-61 illustrates a typical tandem message (or traffic) path. The message is generated at network element 1 (NE1) and is sent to NE3 via NE2. A message of this type is referred to as a "tandem message" from the NE2 viewpoint. Several other paths have been illustrated in

Figure 12-61. If the message takes one of the following path, it is a tandem path: (1) from NE1 to NE4, NE2 and then NE3; (2) from NE1 to NE2, NE5, and then NE3; (3) from NE1 to NE4, NE5, and then NE3; (4) from NE1 to NE4, NE2, NE5, and then NE2. However, the path from NE1 to NE3 is a direct path.

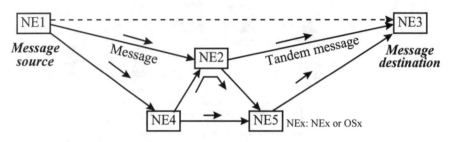

Figure 12-61   Tandem Message (Traffic) Path.

An Intermediate Network Element (INE) also has subtending network element(s). It can provide statistical multiplexing for network management traffic, and can also be used to route a tandem traffic. However, it can not provide direct access to a packet-switched network or operations systems.

An end Network Element (end-NE) can provide direct access to any type of network element, a packet-switched network, or an operations system. An end-NE can only handle its own traffic (i.e., not statistical multiplexed traffic), and can not route tandem network management traffic.

12.7.3.4 Generic NE Management Communications Function (MCF)

The Management Communication Function (MCF) performs two classes of functions, dedicated and common, which are described as follows:

- MCF common functions: This class of functions include statistical multiplexing, synchronous time division multiplexing, digital cross-connection, flow control, data collection, and gateway activities.

- MCF dedicated functions: This class of functions include parsing network management messages, interpreting and executing network management messages, and providing access to Operations Systems (OSs), technicians, and Network Elements (NEs) for supporting network management activities.

Table 12-9 lists the primary MCF functions (e.g., access to routing table, address mapping, etc.) for various Networks Elements [i.e., Gateway Network Elements (GNEs), Intermediate Network Element (INEs), and end Network Element (End-NE)].

Table 12-9   MCF Functions for GNE, INE and End-NE.

MCF Function	GNE	INE	End-NE
Access to routing table	R	R	NA
Address mapping	R	R/O	R/O
Alternative routing	R	R/O	O
Buffer status indication and report	R	R/O	R/O
Embedded operations channel (EOC) access	R	R	R
EOC idle code insertion	R	R	R
EOC monitoring	R/O	R/O	NA
EOC protection switching	R	R/O	O
EOC status indication and report	R	R	R
EOC termination	R	R	R
EOC-to-dedicated port cross-connection	O	O	O
EOC-to-EOC cross-connection	R/O	R/O	NA
Flow control	R	R/O	NA
Message conversion	R/O	R/O	NA
Message duplication	R/O	R/O	NA
MCF access	R	R	R
Protocol conversion	R	R/O	NA
Routing	R/O	R/O	NA
Statistical multiplexing	R	R	NA

NA: Not applicable; O: Optional;   R: Required; R/O: R or O depending on application.

12.7.4 Specifications of TMN Interfaces

Interfaces are the tools used by management system to interact with the network and its elements. Hence, the bulk of the TMN standards deal with interfaces. Standardizing interfaces for TMN allows network nodes to internetwork, provided protocols are specified at an appropriate level so that various applications can interact among network nodes.

The basis of TMN interfaces are a set of standards developed jointly by ISO and ITU. The principles of these standards are the use of: (1) object-oriented modeling of network resources and management services; (2) manager/agent modeling; and (3) an OSI layered communications environment. The TMN interfaces (see Figures 12-49 and 12-57) are briefly described from another viewpoint as follows:

- **Q_3 and Q_x interfaces**: This is the most complete TMN interfaces. It is used to connect a NE to an OS; an MD to an OS; a QA to an OS; or two OSs within the same TMN. The Q_x interface, which is still underdevelopment, is a modified version of the Q_3 interface. The Q_x interface has less functionality than the Q_3 interface, thus it is intended for use when cost or efficiency issues precluded a Q_3 interface.

- **F interface**: It is used for connecting a WorkStation (WS) to any other node in the network (see Figures 12-49 and 12-57).

- **X interface**: There is considerable interest in the X interface, but it is complicated and only partially developed. The X interface is used for connections between OSs of different TMNs, or between an OS in a TMN application and a non-TMN OS that supports "TMN-like interfaces".

In general, a TMN interface consists of the following two parts:

(1) Communications part: This part is concerned with the type of TMN communication protocols that are used. It is defined by a communications protocol profile.

(2) Information part: This part is concerned with the type of information passing through the TMN interfaces. It is defined by the message formats that carry information between respective systems.

12.7.4.1 TMN Interface Methodology and Considerations

TMN interface specification methodology is divided into two areas of activity: application tasks (tasks 0 through 7) and protocol tasks (tasks 8 through 13). Each application task has associated information, and a Task Information Base (TIB) contains the results of previous iterations of that represent an accumulated way of performing a particular task. Tables 12-4 and 12-10 represent the mapping between management functions and management areas (which is shown in Figure 12-47).

The following considerations must be carefully evaluated when specifying a TMN interface:

- **Define and partition the management problem space**: This activity defines the functional areas of network management. For example, establishing agreement on the minimum functionality deployed to support operations for a specific domain (e.g., alarm surveillance and performance monitoring).

- **Define the items in the problem space**: This activity includes definitions of managed objects, and the minimum functionality required to support operations in terms of atomic units.

- **Define the topics of the items in the problem space**: This activity includes selecting the method of interaction between managed objects and the information model (e.g., Recommendations X.720, X.721, and X.722). It also specifies the agreements on the application context to be used, the subset of the schema required for mapping network elements that support a particular technology, and determination of the "administration-specific" requirements for the selected schema. In addition, it determines the structure rules for naming instances of the selected managed object classes, and security requirements for the interfaces (e.g., customer network management) between different administrations.

- **Define the interaction**: This activity includes the definition of the protocol that allows managed objects to interact across open interfaces. It also specifies agreements for protocols features in the Common Management Information Service Element (CMISE), and in the lower layers required to implement management functions.

12.7.4.2 TMN Interface Specifications

TMN interface specifications cover: (1) management services (Guidelines for the Definition of Management Services; GDMS), (2) telecommunications management areas, and (3) management functions (Guidelines for the Definition of Management Function; GDMF).

(1) **Management services**: A TMN service is defined by its role, the resources used, and related TMN functions, within the scope of a particular management context. A TMN function group consists of many TMN function sets. These TMN function sets are comprised of TMN management functions that belong together, according to the management context. A TMN function set is used for management information modeling that are used with the Common Management Information Service (CMIS). A TMN function set can be reused for services applied to different managed areas. A TMN management service uses the relevant information, derived from a comprehensive description of the management context, to accomplish a specific management goal or task. The TMN management services, supported by interactions across all TMN interfaces (Q, F, and X), are listed as follows (note that these are guidelines):

  * Customer administration
  * Logistic management
  * Maintenance management
  * Network provisioning management
  * Quality of Service (QoS) and network performance administration
  * Routing and digital signal analysis administration
  * Security administration
  * Traffic management
  * Traffic measurement and analysis administration
  * Tariff, billing, and accounting administration
  * Work force management

Guidelines for the Definition of TMN Management Services (GDMS): The template for GDMS provide the following areas.

  * TMN management goals: Identifies the telecommunications user's benefits obtained by carrying out the management activities.

* TMN management service description: Identifies the specific service function.

* Management context description: Management context defines the environment where TMN management services are carried out. This includes "who manages the network", "what is managed", and "how it can be managed". The management context is described by using three components: TMN management role (e.g., planning, installation, and testing), telecommunications resources, and TMN management functions.

* TMN management scenario: These are examples of management interactions using TMN management information definitions and TMN system management services/messages.

* TMN architecture: The major TMN architecture include: management functions, management function sets (both are described in M.3400), applicable reference points (q, f and x), and applicable interfaces (Q, F and X).

(2) **Telecommunications management areas**: The managed areas include traditional telecommunications networks, mobile communications networks, and both dedicated and reconfigurable networks. The telecommunications network is a set of resources that are used to provide telecommunications services. These services are provided to customers, and are managed as a composite unit. These resources may include: a switched telephone network, switched data network, intelligent network, Common Channel Signaling (CCS7 and SS7), Integrated Service Digital Network (ISDN and Broadband-ISDN; B-ISDN), access and terminal equipment network, and transport network.

A mobile communication network utilizes frequency reuse principles to increase the number of customers served by the system. Two system components are the Switching and Control Exchanges [SCE; Mobile Switching Center (MSC); or Mobile Telephone Switching Center (MTSO)], and the Radio Base Station [RBS, Base Station (BS), or Cell Site (CS)]. Since "frequency reuse" must be applied in a mobile communications network, service areas are always divided into "cells" and "clusters of cells". Therefore, it is also necessary to apply "roaming", "handoff (or handover)" and "call delivery", techniques, which are the managed areas.

Dedicated and reconfigurable networks contain a set of leased (or hybrid; i.e., leased plus switched) and special telecommunications resources required to support voice, data, image, and video communications. This network can be reconfigured and managed by the customer and/or network operators.

(3) **Management functions**: A TMN **management function** is a cooperative interaction between an application process and a managed system, for the purpose of managing telecommunications resources. TMN management functions are the smallest functional part of a TMN management service, as perceived by the TMN user.

A TMN **management function set** is a collection of TMN management functions which contextually belong together. They are all related to a specific management capability (e.g., alarm reporting or traffic management control). A function set is the smallest reusable item of functional specification. It should be noted that a function set must be treated as a whole, just like the requirements portion of the OSI system management function.

A TMN **management function set group** consists of several TMN management function sets. It is a way to simplify listing the many TMN management function sets required satisfy a particular user's demands. TMN management function set groups are not subject to standardization.

Guidelines for the Definition of TMN Management Functions (GDMF): The template for GDMF includes the following:

* TMN management function set description: This description provides the function set name, along with a prose description of the function set capabilities.

* Management requirements: These requirements describe the goals and concepts that support the management function set.

* Function model: This is a brief description of the TMN management function set, and the capabilities associated with the TMN management function set. It also identifies the resources affected by the TMN management function set.

* TMN management functions: A TMN management function provides a detailed description of the management information that flows between the "managing system" and the "managed system".

12.7.5 TMN Reality and Issues

TMN standardization has promised to simplify network management, lower costs, and increase market size through a greater number of applications. However, the present reality is that it has been a lot of vocal support, but very few actual deployments. This may be caused by the following reasons:

• The task of specifying TMN interfaces is complex and tedious.

• It is difficult to meet all the requirements on TMN information models. Two different approaches that have been proposed, but both use: object-oriented principles, standard protocol for communications, a standard abstract syntax for management information specifications, and a standard set of information management functions (not identical). These methods attempt to integrate network management at the schema level, and are based on a remote surveillance paradigm and system management model. The two approaches are:

(1)   OSI model: Its standards are typically considered comprehensive. It is built around complex and full function technologies that promise to survive well into the future, but may be unproven.

(2)   Internet model: Its standards are typically considered evolutionary. It is built around simple/proven technologies, but initially has limited functionality.

- The initial cost for introducing TMN may be hard to justify and/or recover.

- OS developers are reluctant to design products for which there is no Network Element (NE) support. Likewise, NE developers do not want to build/develop interfaces for which there is no OS support. This is a "chicken-egg" situation, hence progress is slow and cautious.

- Presently there are very few NEs that support full stack Q-protocols.

A possible near-term solution may be the option of using Q-Adapters (QAs). Another potential approach is to use SNMP in TMN applications, because SNMP is simpler (but less powerful), and there is support for SNMP in data communications networks. Table 12-10 compares the characteristics of OSI-based TMN and SNMP.

Table 12-10   TMN versus SNMP.

Description	OSI-based TMN	SNMP
Object classes (or types)	*Collections of properties of a resource that are reusable*	*Atomic data or tables that are not reusable*
Inheritance (of object classes)	*Specialized, uses multiple and strict inheritance*	*No inheritance concept is used for object types*
Attributes (Object classes)	*May contain optional attributes that coexist with mandatory attributes*	*All variables within an object group (e.g. table) are mandatory*
Naming	*Containment relations are used in naming; with globally unique names*	*Naming is unique within a single system (containment is not used)*
Syntax	*No restrictions on the ASN.1 types for specifying syntax*	*Allows basic, simple and restricted ASN.1 constructs*
Information storage	*In both internal and leaf nodes*	*Only at the leaf nodes*
MIB structure	*Can change dynamically as nodes are added or deleted*	*Static structure*
Unique identifier	*Use RDN & DN, which is used by CMIP for node ID*	*Use registration tree, determined during the MIB design time*
MOs included	*Attributes, methods, operations, event notifications*	*Attributes only (event traps are associated with agents)*
MO add/delete	*DN may change if add/delete*	*Not possible (static ID)*
Instances (same MO)	*Stored in individual nodes*	*Combined into tables*

It may also be appropriate to consider an alternative management architecture based on distributed management, which is supported by the Common Request Broker Architecture (CORBA).

12.7.5.1 Network Management and TMN Future Trends

The overall telecommunications service provider business segment is constantly increasing in complexity. Networks are no longer easily managed or controlled, especially since there is strong motivation to move toward global networks that support a "world-wide" economy. In addition, there is intense competition in the telecommunications industry for both product vendors and service providers. These factors highlight the necessity of having automated Network Management systems that are faster, more flexible, and have greater reliability.

The future trend of TMN appears to be focused on three areas: (1) Network Management; (2) Subnetwork Management; and (3) Network Element Management (see Figure 12-62).

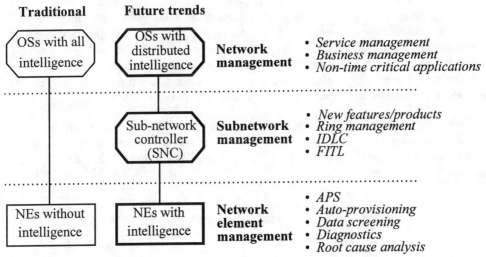

IDLC: Integrated Digital Loop Carrier system   FITL: Fiber In The Loop; APS: Automatic Protection Switching

Figure 12-62   Network Management Product Trends.

The traditional Network Management (NM) strategy is to build Operations Systems (OSs) with all the required intelligence for managing Network Elements (NEs). The Network Elements do not have any Embedded Operations Channels (EOCs), equipped with operation intelligence, to perform network management functions. In comparison, the future Network Management strategy (adopted by TMN) is to build Network Elements (NEs) with intelligence to perform root cause analysis, diagnostics, data screening, auto-provisioning, and Automatic Protection Switching (APS). For example, in SONET/SDH networks, Add-Drop Multiplexers (ADMs) can perform APS functions. The network architectures adopted for APS can be (1) 1+1 linear, (2) 1:n (1 ≤ n ≤ 14), (3) unidirectional line switched ring, (4) bidirectional line switched ring, (5) unidirectional path switched ring, or (6) bidirectional path switched ring configuration.

Figure 12-62 also illustrates that the future Network Management system can provide subnetwork management functions. For example, Fiber In The Loop (FITL), which is a subnetwork of an end-to-end network, is used as the access network, and can be managed by TMN. Likewise, Integrated Digital Loop Carrier (IDLC) systems have been widely adopted in the business areas for providing multimedia services to transport voice, image, video, and data signals. The system capacity has increased from OC-3 (155.52 Mbps) to OC-12 (622.08 Mbps), and is expected to increase in the near future (OC-48; 2.48832 Gbps, or OC-192; 9.95328 Gbps). Managing this type of high-speed subnetwork is essential for providing quality services. The self-healing SONET/SDH ring subnetworks are the fastest-growing networks in the modern communications era. Presently, the ring capacity is OC-48 (2.48832 Gbps) for longer distances, and OC-12 (622.08 Mbps) for regional applications. To implement "self-healing", ring network management must be robust.

Service management takes care of the contractual aspects of features provided by the telecommunications service provider to customer. The service management also controls the availability of services offered to new customers. The primary tasks of service management are: (1) tracking and entering work items, (2) accounting, (3) billing, (4) designing and assigning resources, (5) maintaining customer databases, etc. Business management maintains aggregate data about the overall telecommunications business enterprise, and manages business activities between different service providers.

The increased level of "intelligence" being incorporated into these products, in accordance with industry initiatives (see Table 12-11) are destined to meet the goals of providing efficient, stable, and "feature rich" multimedia communications services in a highly competitive marketplace.

Table 12-11   TMN Initiatives and Product Vendors.

TMN Initiative Project	Sponsor or vendor
PanEuropean ATM network (ATMPILOT)	*EURESCOM (year 1993)*
PanEuropean SDH network with cooperative management (METRAN)	*EURESCOM (year 1993)*
TMN-based OS for SDH networks	*NTT (Japan, year 1993)*
Guidelines for TMN specs. and implementation	*EURESCOM (year 1994)*
PanEuropean Labs & X-interface specifications	*EURESCOM (year 1994)*
Electronic bonding	*IECs/LECs (USA, 1995)*
Fiber Loop Around the Globe (FLAG)	*Submarine system (1995)*
Management of ATM trial network (JAMES)	*EURESCOM (year 1995)*
Management of Integrated SDH and ATM networks (MISA)	*RACE/ACTS (1995)*
TMN-based OS for ATM networks	*NTT (year 1995)*
Management Of Optical Network (MOON)	*RACE/ACTS (1996)*
Prospect of multi-domain management in open services environment (PROSPECT)	*RACE/ACTS (1996)*
TMN's Regulators, Users and Multi Providers EnvironmenT (TRUMPET)	*RACE/ACTS (1996)*
Trouble ticketing	*EURESCOM (year 1996)*

It should be understood that X interface is important for international service management in the European telecommunications scenario. Likewise, Q_3 interface provides a common denominator to various technologies in a multivendor network, from network management viewpoint. The acronyms used in Table 12-11 are listed as follows:

EURESCOM	European Institute for Research and Strategic Studies in Telecommunications
NTT	Nippon Telephone & Telegram
IEC	Inter-Exchange Carrier company
LEC	Local Exchange Carrier company
RACE	Research and Development in Advanced Communications in Europe
ACTS	Advanced Communication Technologies and Services (Europe)

Table 12-12 lists the projects/products of several leading TMN vendors. For example, Alcatel is the most proactive in TMN associated standards. Its management platform provides Q_3 interface, and its Mediation Device (MD) is designed for proprietary to Q_3 interface. In comparison, Lucent Technologies has developed proprietary or TL1 interfaces in domestic products, and TMN interfaces for SDH products. Two most commonly used TMN platforms are BaseWorX and OpenView. Even though BaseWorX was the first platform available for the network management industry, and has been adopted globally, Lucent has adopted Hewlett Packard's OpenView as TMN platform.

Table 12-12   TMN Projects/Products and Vendors

Project/Product	Vendor
• Most proactive in standards • Alcatel network management platform providing Q_3 • Mediation device for proprietary to Q_3	*Alcatel*
• Proprietary or TL1 interfaces (current focus) • TMN interfaces (future focus)	*Bellcore*
• Employs X.25 interfaces • Migrating to TMN standards	*Ericsson*
• Proprietary or TL1 interfaces in domestic products • Moving to TMN interfaces starting from SDH products	*Lucent*
• Native protocols is TL1 • Moving to TMN interfaces	*NTI*
• Advertises TMN compliance • Family of OSs on TMN platform	*Siemens*

Review Questions 2 for Chapter 12:

(12) Network Management (NM) is the ability to _____ (from a bandwidth utilization and performance viewpoint), _____, and _____ the operations of a telecommunications network. In PSTN applications, NM functions include real-time network _____, _____ and _____ management. In contrast, in private network applications, NM functions include network _____, _____, _____, _____ and system _____.

(13) TMN uses a _____ network to monitor and maintain the telecommunications networks. TMN enhances the quality and features of the management capabilities by supporting integration of _____ products, promoting _____, providing _____, and allowing _____ for future growth.

(14) The motivation for developing TMN standards/implementation are: (a) the changing telecommunications _____, (b) end users' _____, and (c) service providers' _____.

(15) Potential TMN users are: PTT _____, _____, _____, _____, etc. TMN supports for management of _____ networks (e.g., mixture of PDH, _____, and _____), _____, and _____.

(16) The well-established ITU-T recommendations on TMN architecture, methodology, and terminologies are: _____ covers TMN architecture; _____ covers TMN methodology; _____ covers TMN terminology; and, _____ (series), _____, and _____ cover TMN management services and functions.

(17) (True, False) Network Management Forum (NMF) has played, and continues to fill an important role in setting telecommunications management standards. Many vendors, manufactures and service providers have joined this influential consortium.

(18) The five TMN management areas are: _____, _____, _____, _____ and _____ management. Fault management is equivalent to maintenance management of traditional management function (e.g., _____, _____, and _____).

(19) The layered structure of TMN management includes the lowest layer of element management layer, _____ layer, _____ layer, and the highest _____ layer. The five TMN functional blocks are _____, _____, _____, _____ and _____.

(20) Each TMN functional block (MF, OSF, QAF, NEF and WSF) consists of one or more TMN functional components: _____, _____, _____, _____, _____, _____ or _____.

CHAPTER 13

Error Control Technologies

Chapter Objectives

Upon the completion of this chapter, you should be able to:

- Describe the rational for applying channel error control for digital communications: including the importance of bit error rates for digital services, system modeling for a noisy channel, and the concept of digital signal restoration.

- Discuss the needs for adding parity-check digits in the information data stream, and the ability to detect and/or correct potential bit error(s) in the information bitstream.

- Describe the algebra used for cyclic redundancy check codes. Define CRC code, code space, code vectors (codewords), Hamming weights, minimum distance of a code and its application, implementation of a CRC code, and a CRC code's error control capability (including the generating polynomial, generating matrix, parity-check matrix, and code syndrome).

- Define Hamming codes, BCH codes, Golay codes, Reed-Solomon codes, and convolutional codes. Describe specific CRC codes and convolutional codes used in digital cellular systems (i.e., GSM and IS-54/IS-136).

- Describe the principles of bit interleaving to control bursty errors caused by deep fading of radio transmission.

13.1 INTRODUCTION

Global communication technology is rapidly evolving from analog-based to digital-based networks. However, the signal types carried over these new networks are often mixed (i.e., some are analog while others are digital). Therefore, coding becomes a necessity for transporting different types of signals over global digital networks. Three types of coders, from an application viewpoint, have been developed for use in digital networks:

(1) **Source encoders**: Source encoders (Figure 13-1) are used to convert an analog signal into a digital signal so that it can be transported over a digital network. Examples of source encoders are PCM, DPCM, ADPCM, DM and ADM (described in Chapter 6; PCM has been used in DS1, and E1 systems).

(2) **Line encoders:** Line encoders are used to guarantee ones density for timing recovery and synchronization purposes (described in Chapter 14). From Figure 13-1, it can be seen that any signal, either digitized analog or digital (computer) data, must be fed to a line encoder before it is transmitted.

(3) **Channel encoders:** Channel encoders are used to control channel error. They can be implemented for either "detection only" or "detection plus correction" depending upon service needs. For (computer) data communications, a channel encoder is often (if not always) used. For landline applications, digitized analog speech signals do not require channel encoding since error control for these services is not critical (i.e., shown as an option in Figure 13-1).

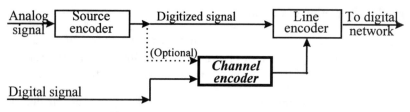

Figure 13-1 Three Types of Network Coding.

In this chapter, channel encoding is described in sufficient detail to develop an understanding of how channel codes can be applied to wireless communications. In general, the functions of channel encoders (known as channel error control methods) are two fold:

1. ***To detect erroneous bits in the data bitstream transported over a noisy channel***: There are systems in which it is only necessary to detect errors (i.e., not correct errors). In these cases the end user decides whether to accept the erroneous data or request re-transmission. Since the end user may decide to re-transmit whenever there are errors in the received data bitstream, error detection alone is adequate for this application. Several data communication systems adopt this technology.

2. ***To detect and then to correct erroneous bits***: There are applications where error correction becomes a necessity because the end user can not afford to request re-transmission. An example is wireless voice communications, in which it would be impossible to re-construct a conversation if it was necessary to re-transmit parts of the signal. That is, the sequence of transmission and the delay caused by re-transmission is unacceptable for voice communications. Thus, it is better for the system to correct as many erroneous bits as possible to the extent conversation can be understandable.

13.2 Rationale for Channel Coding

The performance of digital services are graded by measuring the Bit Error Rate (or bit error ratio, BER). The BER is always expressed as 10^{-3}, 10^{-4}, 2.5×10^{-5}, ... , etc. Customers, especially data customers, are often charged according to the contracted BER to be delivered by a service provider. The definition/meanings, and the importance of BER are described in the following examples:

Example 13-1: If the BER of a system is specified as 2.5×10^{-4}, determine the number of bits are bit errors, assuming one billion bits have been transmitted.

2.5×10^{-4} can be expressed as follows:

$$2.5 \times 10^{-4} = \frac{2.5}{10^4} = \frac{25}{10^5} = \frac{250,000}{10^9}$$

Since 10^9 = one billion, in average (statistically speaking), this system will contain 250,000 erroneous bits assuming it has received one billion bits.

Example 13-2: If the BER of a system is specified as 2.5×10^{-8}, determine the number of bits errors, assuming one billion bits have been transmitted.

The performance grade in Example 13-1 is for a typical T1 carrier system, Example 13-2 is a BER for a typical optical fiber communication system. As in Example 13-1, 2.5×10^{-8} can be expressed as follows:

$$2.5 \times 10^{-8} = \frac{2.5}{10^8} = \frac{25}{10^9}$$

Therefore, this system will contain, on average, 25 erroneous bits assuming one billion bits have been received. Hence, this system has higher reliability compared to the system in Example 13-1, with a BER of 2.5×10^{-4}.

Example 13-3: If the speed of a digital system is 100 Mbps and the BER is 2.5×10^{-4}, determine the number of bit errors received in 10 minutes.

An interval of 10 minutes is equal to 600 seconds, therefore, the number of bits received in this interval is equal to $600 \times 100 \times 10^6$ ($\equiv 600 \times 100$ Mbps) = 6×10^{10} bits. Likewise, the received bitstream can have an average of fifteen million bits in error, derived as follows:

$$6 \times 10^{10} \times 2.5 \times 10^{-4} = 15 \times 10^6.$$

It can be concluded from Examples 13-1 and 13-3 that a system with a BER of 2.5×10^{-4} is not acceptable for computer data transport because of too many erroneous bits.

Service is often classified into different "grades" for various communications applications. Each "grade of service" has a specific BER requirement. If the minimum BER requirement is not met, system performance is not considered acceptable. For voice communications, a signal BER greater than 10^{-3} is considered unacceptable. Typical wireline digital networks for voice applications have BER requirement between 10^{-4} and 10^{-5}. The BER requirements for computer data transport depends upon the service grade that is specified, and typically ranges from 10^{-5} to 10^{-9}.

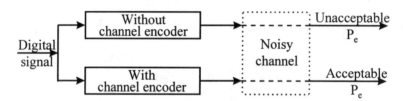

Figure 13-2   Rationale for Channel Encoders.

Figure 13-2 shows the rationale for applying a channel encoder. If the system does not use a channel encoder, the BER is often unacceptable (e.g., the channel is noisy, etc.). In a noisy environment, digits may be corrupted and/or erroneously restored. However, if a channel encoder is used, the received BER can be acceptable even under degraded conditions (i.e., the signal strength is degraded due to channel noise).

Two questions often asked are:

(1)   "Why is the calculated error performance measurement always given by P_e (probability of error), not BER?"

(2)   "Is there a difference between BER and P_e?"

Example 13-4 illustrates the relationship between P_e and BER.

Example 13-4 Illustrates the relationship between P_e and BER for a system that uses 16-FSK modulation.

Assume the system can transmit 100 sinusoidal waves in one second as shown in Figure 13-3. That is, the system can distinguish 100 unique frequencies of each sinusoidal waves. Note that, for simplicity, in this example the received signal has one erroneous wave; the transmitted frequency of ω_8 is received as ω_9. That is, the signal stream transmitted is ($\sin\omega_2 t$), ($\sin\omega_4 t$), ($\sin\omega_1 t$), ($\sin\omega_8 t$), ($\sin\omega_{15} t$), ..., ($\sin\omega_{16} t$), and the received signal stream is ($\sin\omega_2 t$), ($\sin\omega_4 t$), ($\sin\omega_1 t$), ($\sin\omega_9 t$), ($\sin\omega_{15} t$), ..., ($\sin\omega_{16} t$), where ($\sin\omega_8 t$) has been erroneously received as ($\sin\omega_9 t$).

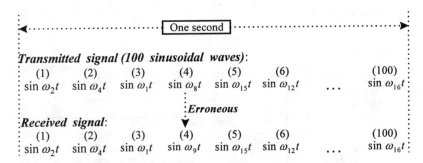

Figure 13-3   Transmitted/Received Signals of a 16-FSK System.

By definition, since 100 sinusoidal waves were transmitted and one received sinusoidal wave contains a wrong frequency, the probability of error is derived as follows:

$$P_e = \frac{Number\ of\ erroneous\ waves}{Total\ number\ of\ waves\ transmitted} = \frac{1}{100} = 10^{-2} \qquad (13\text{-}1)$$

Case 1: If the binary algorithm is used to assign the required frequencies for this 16-FSK system (Table 13-1), the transmitted signal is represented by the following data bitstream:

0001 0011 0000 **0111** 1110 1011 ... 1111

Likewise, the received signal is represented the following bitstream:

0001 0011 0000 <u>**1000**</u> 1110 1011 ... 1111

Note that the error in the received bit stream is highlighted (i.e., underlined). The system uses 16-FSK modulation (see Chapter 6), with 100 sinusoidal waves carrying 400 bits per second. There are four bits in error (i.e., transmitted: 0111; received: 1000). The system Bit Error Rate (BER) can be derived as follows:

$$BER = \frac{Number\ of\ erroneous\ bits}{Total\ number\ of\ bits\ transmitted} = \frac{4}{400} = 10^{-2} \qquad (13\text{-}2)$$

Therefore, in this case P_e is equal to BER:

$$P_e = BER \qquad (13\text{-}3)$$

Table 13-1   Binary versus Gray's Algorithms for Frequency Assignment.

Binary algorithm	Gray algorithm	Frequency assignment
0000	0000	ω_1
0001	0001	ω_2
0010	0011	ω_3
0011	0010	ω_4
0100	0110	ω_5
0101	0111	ω_6
0110	0101	ω_7
0111	0100	ω_8
1000	1100	ω_9
1001	1101	ω_{10}
1010	1111	ω_{11}
1011	1110	ω_{12}
1100	1010	ω_{13}
1101	1011	ω_{14}
1110	1001	ω_{15}
1111	1000	ω_{16}

___**Case 2**___: If Gray's algorithm (Table 13-1) is used, the transmitted signal is represented by the following bitstream:

0001 0010 0000 **0100** 1001 1110 ... 1000

Likewise, the received signal is represented by the following bitstream:

0001 0010 0000 **<u>1100</u>** 1001 1110 ... 1000

Note the error in the bit stream is highlighted (i.e., underlined). In this case, Gray's algorithm results in one bit (instead of 4) error. Hence, the system Bit Error Rate (BER) is derived as follows:

$$BER = \frac{Number\ of\ erroneous\ bits}{Total\ number\ of\ bits\ transmitted} = \frac{1}{400} = 0.25 \times 10^{-2} \qquad (13\text{-}4)$$

Examining Eq.(13-1) and Eq.(13-4), the relationship between P_e and BER for this case is as follows:

$$P_e > BER \qquad (13\text{-}5)$$

Combining Eq.(13-3) and Eq.(13-5), the general relationship between P_e and BER of a digital system can be stated as follows:

$$P_e \geq BER \qquad (13\text{-}6)$$

Therefore, the probability of error, P_e, can be considered the "worst case BER".

Another concept that is often misunderstood is the relationship between BER and the S/N (Signal to Noise ratio) for digital applications. It is technically incorrect to state: "For digital transmission, BER is used to measure performance, and S/N can be ignored." The correct statement is: "For digital transmission, performance is measured as BER, which is improved by having a high S/N ratio."

Example 13-5 illustrates the relationship between the system Signal-to-Noise ratio (S/N) and Bit Error Rate (BER; assuming the probability of error, P_e, is equal to BER).

Example 13-5 Determine the system BER if S/N = 18, and 21 dB for an optical fiber system that has the probability of error, P_e specified as follows (described in Chapter 7):

$$P_e = 0.5 \times erfc\,(0.354\sqrt{S/N}) \qquad (13\text{-}7)$$

Note: *It is important to understand that the S/N (in dB) cannot be substituted directly into a formula used for communication system analysis/design unless the formula is power budget related.* Therefore, S/N must be converted into a "unitless" value. Hence, the S/N for 18 and 21 dB are converted as follows:

$$18\ dB \Rightarrow 10^{\frac{18}{10}} = 63.096 \qquad and \qquad 21\ dB \Rightarrow 10^{\frac{21}{10}} = 125.893 \qquad (13\text{-}8)$$

Substitute the above values (individually) into Eq.(13-7) to derive the BER (assumed the probability of error is equal to BER) as follows:

For S/N = 18 dB:

$$BER = 0.5 \times erfc\,(0.354\sqrt{S/N}) = 0.5 \times erfc\,(0.354\sqrt{63.096}) = 0.5 \times erfc\,(2.82119)$$

$$= 0.5 \times \frac{e^{-2.8119^2}}{2.8119 \times \sqrt{\pi}} = 3.69 \times 10^{-5}$$

For S/N = 21 dB:

$$BER = 0.5 \times erfc(0.354\sqrt{S/N}) = 0.5 \times erfc(0.354\sqrt{125.893}) = 0.5 \times erfc(3.9720)$$

$$= 0.5 \times \frac{e^{-3.9720^2}}{3.9720 \times \sqrt{\pi}} = 3.69 \times 10^{-9}$$

Therefore, in a digital communication system, a higher S/N ratio yields better system performance (i.e., a smaller BER). Figure 13-4 summarizes the system performance (P$_e$) of typical digital optical fiber systems with respect to different S/N ratios

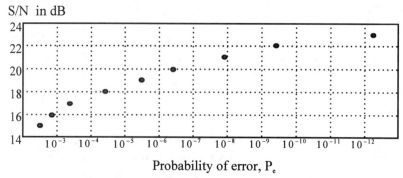

Figure 13-4   Probability of Error, P$_e$, versus S/N for Optical Fiber Systems.

13.2.1 System Model for a Noisy Channels

When analyzing, evaluating, and measuring system performance of communication systems (i.e., S/N for an analog system, and S/N plus BER for a digital system), it is necessary to model the system. As shown in Figure 13-5, a communication channel is always subject to noise corruption. Thermal noise, which behaves as Gaussian noise, appears in all systems. Other noise (e.g., shot noise, amplifier noise, background noise, impulsive noise, etc.) often appears in communication systems, but most are not Gaussian. To analyze a system with an infinite number of noise sources is not practical. Therefore, a common approach is to simplify the problem by modeling a system with a single noise source as shown in Figure 13-5.

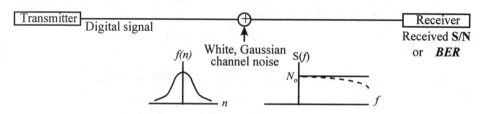

Figure 13-5   System Model of a Noisy Channel.

According to the "central limit theorem", when all of the noise sources (which are random, and statistically independent) in a communication system are represented by a single noise, this single noise must be "Gaussian". The probability density function versus noise voltage [$f(n)$], and the "white" noise power spectral density function [$S(f)$; with its power density N_o are shown in Figure 13-5. This channel modeling, using the central limit theorem, is independent of the nature of each individual noise sources. The "white" noise curve [$S(f)$] illustrates both the "strict white" noise (straight line), and the practical noise known as a "loose sense white" (indicated by the dashed curve). This model has been applied for many communication systems, and has been proven to work well.

By using the system model given in Figure 13-5 it is easier to analyze the overall system performance (S/N and BER), rather than attempting to treat each noise source separately. In addition, the properties of Gaussian noise are thoroughly understood. In summary, this approach is simple and provides sufficient accuracy for most applications. Based on this model, the system performance of a typical digital system can be expressed as a function of system Signal-to-Noise (S/N) as shown in Eq.(13-7)., or more generally as shown in the following equation (where k_1 and k_2 are system dependent):

$$P_e = k_1 \times erfc\,(k_2 \times \sqrt{S/N})$$
(13-9)

13.2.2 Noise Effect on Digital System Performance

When a digital signal is transported over a digital network, the data bitstream is transmitted as a string of various voltage values. Three common techniques used for this purpose are shown in Figure 13-6. Each technique is presented as a separate topic as follows:

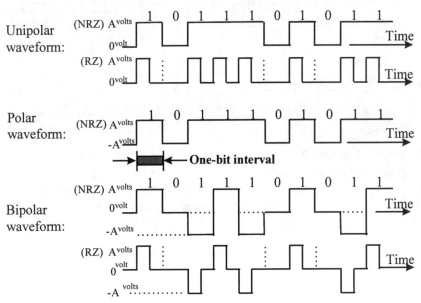

Figure 13-6   Three Waveform Representations of a Digital Signal.

- **Unipolar waveform**: Two voltage levels are used in this system: *"0"* volt and *"A"* volts. The digital (logical) "1" is transported as *"A"* volts, and the digital "0" is transported as *"0"* volt. The actual voltage for *"A"* depends on the system type and the application (e.g., "A" can be "5ᵛ", "12 ᵛ", or other values). There are two subclasses of unipolar signals:

    (1) Non-Return-to-Zero (NRZ) unipolar signals: If a voltage of "A" volts is transmitted during the entire bit interval to represent a logical "1", the signal is called a NRZ signal (i.e., the value does not return to zero during the bit interval).

    (2) Return-to-Zero (RZ) unipolar signals: In contrast, if the first part of the bit interval of a logical "1" is transported by a voltage of "A" volts, and then the voltage returns to "0" volt during the later part of the bit interval, the signal is a RZ signal. If the portion of "A" volts and the portion of "0" volt for a RZ signal are equal in time (i.e., a logical "1" has a voltage of "A" volts during 50% of the bit interval), the signal is called a 50% duty cycle RZ signal.

- **Polar waveform**: In this system, two voltages are used to transport digital signals: "+*A*" volts and "−*A* volts". A logical "1" is represented by "+*A*" volts, and a logical "0" is represented by a "−*A*" volts. There is no RZ polar signal because a polar signal does not have a zero ("0") voltage level for the signal to "return to". Thus, polar signals are always NRZ signal (i.e., it is not necessary to specify a polar signal as being a "NRZ polar signal"). Two common system applications that use this technique are:

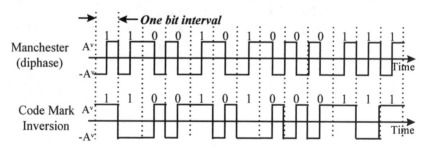

Figure 13-7   Manchester and Code Mark Inversion Codes.

(1) Ethernet LANs use Manchester code (shown in Figure 13-7): In a Manchester (also called diphase, or digital biphase) code, a logical "1" is transmitted as "−*A*ᵛ" for the first half of each bit interval, followed by "*A*ᵛ" for the second half of the bit interval. Similarly, a logical "0" is transmitted as "*A*ᵛ" for the first half of each bit interval, and "−*A*ᵛ" for the second half of the bit interval.

(2) E4 A-law digital systems (139.264 Mbps) use Code Mark Inversion (CMI) code: A CMI code transmits logical "1s" by "*A*ᵛ", or "−*A*ᵛ" for the entire bit interval following an alternating sequence (*A*ᵛ, −*A*ᵛ, *A*ᵛ, −*A*ᵛ, …). A logical "0" is transmitted as "−*A*ᵛ" for the first half of each bit interval, followed by "*A*ᵛ" for the second half of the bit interval.

- **Bipolar waveform**: This system uses three (instead of two) voltage levels to represent a digital signal: "−*A*" volts, "*0*" volt, and "+*A*" volts. A logical "*0*" is always transported as "*0*" volt. But, a logical "*1*" is represented by "+*A*" volts and "−*A*" volts following an alternating sequence (*A*v, −*A*v, *A*v, −*A*v, …; Figure 13-8). There are also two subclasses of bipolar signal:

(1) NRZ bipolar: which is the same as those of unipolar waveforms.

(2) RZ bipolar: which is the same as those of unipolar waveforms. RZ bipolar signals are used for DS1 (i.e., B8ZS), DS2 (i.e., B6ZS), DS3 (i.e., B3ZS) in the μ-law digital hierarchy, and for E1, E2 and E3 (all use HDB3 line codes) in the A-law digital hierarchy (see Chapter 6). Both BNZS (N = 3, 6 and 8), and HDB3 line codes are used for zero suppression.

The most popular waveform for digital transport application is the 50% duty cycle RZ bipolar signal (see Chapter 6). However, a unipolar signal is used to illustrate the effect of noise on digital signal transmission (Figure 13-8) because it is easier to analyze a unipolar waveform. A digital bitstream of "1011010…" is assumed to be transmitted [see Figure 13-8(A)]. The noise voltage shown in Figure 13-8(B) is a Gaussian noise that typically has an average noise voltage of zero volt (i.e., E[n] = 0; the expected value of the noise voltage is zero). However, the noise can have any instantaneous voltage of any value, positive or negative. Hence, the received signal is attenuated and corrupted by noise (i.e., the original signal is no longer a clean rectangular waveform) as shown in Figure 13-8(C).

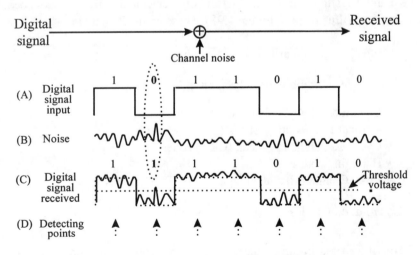

Figure 13-8   Noise Effect on Digital Signal Transport.

To understand the effect of noise on system performance, it is important to know how a receiver restores a digital bitstream from a corrupted waveform. To restore a corrupted signal, a receiver must have the following capabilities:

- ***The receiver must set a threshold voltage*** [Figure 13-8(C)] ***for the purpose of determining whether the received signal is a logical "1" or a "0"***. If the expected logical "1" should have a voltage level of "A" volts, and the expected logical "0" value should have a voltage level of zero volt, then the threshold voltage is set to be "A/2" volts. Therefore, if the received voltage is larger than the threshold voltage, a logical "1" is restored. Likewise, if the received signal is lower than the threshold voltage, a logical "0" is restored.

- ***The receiver must set detecting (or sampling) points*** [Figure 13-8(D)]. The receiver uses a clock having the same rate as the transmitter clock, and the receiver clock should be synchronized with the transmitter clock by using a zero suppression technique. At the detecting point (set by the receiver clock), the receiver determines whether the received signal is a logical "1" or a logical "0". These detection points are also known as " data strobe points".

In this example (Figure 13-8), the second bit was a "0" when it was transmitted. However, because of the large noise voltage (such as an impulse noise spike) occurring at the detecting point, the restored signal is a "1" (instead of "0" as it should be). Therefore, this is a bit error, which contributes to the overall BER measurement for this signal.

13.2.3 Various Error Control Methods

There are many ways to control (i.e., "detect" or "detect and correct") errors occurring in a digital bitstream (illustrated in Figure 13-8). These methods include:

- Even parity or odd parity calculation bits

- Block codes (adding parity-check bits)

    * Longitudinal Redundancy Check (LRC)
    * Vertical Redundancy Check (VRC)
    * Cyclic Redundancy Check (CRC) codes
    * Hamming codes
    * Bose, Chandhuri, and Hocquenghem (BCH) codes

- Convolutional codes

The parity bit algorithm is the simplest error control method. This technique is based on the following logical relationships [i.e., mod(2) operation]:

$$\text{"0"} + \text{"0"} = 0; \ \text{"0"} + \text{"1"} = 1; \ \text{"1"} + \text{"0"} = 1 \text{ and } \text{"1"} + \text{"1"} = 0 \qquad (13\text{-}10)$$

- For an "even" parity algorithm:

Total number of "*1*s" in the data bitstresm + the parity bit = 0   (13-11)

- For an "odd" parity algorithm:

Total number of "*1*s" in the data bitstresm + the parity bit = 1   (13-12)

In summary, "parity" is the process when additional bits are inserted into a long string of user information to control potential channel errors occurring in the system. Two very simple parity methods have been developed. If the total numbers of ones in the information data stream plus the parity bit (typically appended to the end of the data bitstream) is equal to an odd number of ones, it is an **"odd parity"** algorithm. Similarly, if the total numbers of ones in the information data stream plus the parity bit is equal to an even number of ones, it is an **"even parity"** algorithm.

Example 13-6: Describe a simple parity algorithm that can be used to control errors in 3-bit codewords (code vectors).

Assume eight employees of a small firm are represented by eight 3-bit codewords as follows: (000 for Mr. Baer), (001 for Ms. Dole), (010 for Mr. Fan), (011 for Ms. Cole), (100 for Ms. King), (101 for Mr. Ash), (110 for Ms. Bush) and (111 for Mr. Hart). Data is recorded daily on a computer disk to represent each employee's working records. A portion of the recorded data and the corresponding retrieved data is shown in Figure 13-9. For simplicity, in this example it is assumed that the system can only support one parity bit for every six (6) bits that are stored. It is also assumed that an *even parity* algorithm is applied. (*It should be understood there is no difference between using an even or odd parity bit algorithm from a performance viewpoint*).

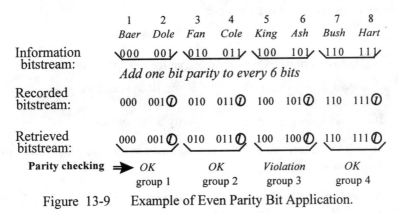

Figure 13-9   Example of Even Parity Bit Application.

For the first two names (i.e., Baer and Dole), there is only one "1" in the six-bit stream, therefore, a parity bit of "1" is applied to make the total number of *1*s even (i.e., two 1s). The calculated parity bits for each pair of names are indicated by the circled number in Figure 13-9. The same algorithm is applied to the third and fourth, the fifth and sixth, and to the seventh and eighth names [i.e., (Fan, Cole), (King, Ash), and (Bush, Hart), respectively]. These parity bits and the information bits are recorded (stored) in memory (e.g., on a computer disk) for retrieving at a later time.

When the data is retrieved from the disk for payroll purposes, the parity check is performed whenever a pair of names are retrieved. In this example, four groups of bits were retrieved and checked for parity violation. Several observations and questions associated with Figure 13-9 are presented as follows:

- The first, second, and forth groups (two names in each group) do not have a **parity violation**. Does this mean there are no bit errors in each group? The answer is No; parity checking with a result of "no parity violation" implies there are no odd number of erroneous bits. However, two bits, four bits, or even all six bits could be erroneous and still return a "no parity violation" result. If there are no errors, then the retrieved names are correct (i.e., Baer and Dole for the first group). However, if there are two, or four errors, then the names are incorrect, and there is no way to make correction. If there are six errors (i.e., the bitstream of "000 001" becomes "111 110"), then the retrieved names incorrectly refer to Hart and Bush.

- The third group (i.e., King and Ash) has a parity violation. This indicates **at least <u>one</u>** bit of the six information bits is wrong. In this example, if the 6th bit is wrong, the restored names would be (King, King). In addition, 3 or 5 erroneous bits in six transmitted bits will also cause the same parity check violation.

- If the parity violation indicates the received digital bitstream has been corrupted, what error conditions can be detected and/or corrected?

    The input names (data) to the computer were:

    > Baer, Dole, Fan, Cole, King, **Ash**, Bush and Hart.

    The action is to determine whether the output (retrieved) names are correct:

    > Baer, Dole, Fan, Cole, King, **King**, Bush and Hart.

- How effective is a simple even (or odd) parity bit algorithm?

    "This algorithm detects single bit errors. There is no error correction or multiple error detection capability".

- *There are better methods (than simple even or odd parity) for error detection/correction if there is a willingness to pay for additional hardware and complexity.*

Assuming the computer disk used in this example is a good quality product, it can be concluded that only the fifth and the sixth names (i.e., group 3; King and Ash) were incorrectly retrieved. However, there is no way to **detect and then correct** bit errors using this simple method. In summary, a simple even (or odd) parity check algorithm is not very effective. There are other error control methods that can be applied in practical systems. These methods are presented in later sections of this chapter.

13.2.4 Longitudinal and Vertical Redundancy Checks

Two slightly more effective error control methods, other than the simple odd or even parity-check method previously discussed, are the Longitudinal Redundancy Check (LRC) and Vertical Redundancy Check (VRC). It should be understood that the LRC and VRC algorithms can both be applied in a system. When either is used alone to control errors, the effectiveness is not much better than the simple even or odd parity method. Therefore, the individual configurations will not be discussed in this section.

The more effective method for error control based on combining the Longitudinal Redundancy Check (LRC) with the Vertical Redundancy Check (VRC) algorithm is described as follows. A buffer store is used at the transmitter to store the data bit stream before it is transmitted. The data stream forms a matrix containing 8 columns (assuming each data block consists of 8 bits). There are **N** rows in this matrix, assuming there are 8 × **N** bits in the transmitted bitstream. That is, the data stream is grouped into information blocks, and the blocks are placed on a "stack" as shown in Figure 13-10.

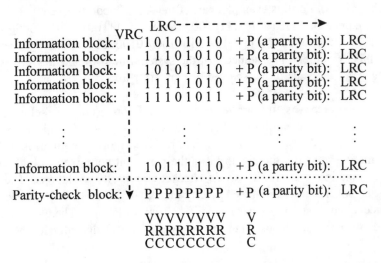

Figure 13-10   LRC and VRC Algorithms Simultaneously Applied.

The LRC and the VRC algorithm add parity check bits to the matrix as shown in Figure 13-10 by following these rules:

- For each block (one row in Figure 13-10), one parity-check bit is added using an even parity algorithm (e.g., if the information block is 00000001, the parity bit is "1";

and if the information block is 10000001, the parity bit is "0"). The parity algorithm makes the block 9 bits (9 columns in the matrix) wide. Repeat the LRC algorithm for each block (row). Note that an odd parity algorithm can also be used for LRC.

- For each column, one parity bit is added to the string of N vertical bits using an even parity algorithm. Repeat the VRC algorithm for each of the 9 columns. Note that an odd parity algorithm can also be used for VRC.

- Applying LRC and VRC results in the N x 8 information matrix becoming a (N+1) by 9 matrix. Note that the additional row is known as the "parity-check block", and the additional column is called the parity check bit.

Example 13-7 Describe how the combined LRC and VRC produces a superior error control algorithm than the simple even (odd) parity check algorithm.

Assume that a communication system applies ***LRC***, ***VRC***, and ***odd parity*** for error control. In addition, the system uses ASCII code to transmit messages. That is, a message character is represented by a 7-bit word, and an odd-parity check bit is added to form an 8-bit codeword. For example, character "a" is represented by "1100001", and the transmitted codeword including the odd-parity is "11000010" (i.e., odd parity results in an odd number of 1's). For this example, part of the ASCII code is given in Table 13-2. If the received bitstream is "11010010 11101001 01001111 11100110 01000000 11000010 01000000 11000100 11010011 11100101 11001000 01000011 10010100", decode this message. In this example, it is assumed that the system doesn't make any errors. That is, the parity check is OK, and all the received bits are error free.

The received data stream is first arranged in a matrix form (i.e., an 8-cloumn matrix). This matrix is shown in the column labeled "Received blocks" of Table 13-3. The first seven bits (i.e., the first seven columns of the "received blocks" column in Table 13-3) are the information bits, and the eighth bit is the parity bit computed as odd parity over the seven information bits. Each row is checked for parity violations. The result is indicated in the second column labeled "parity check" of Table 13-3. It can be seen that all rows, except the first row, have no parity check violations. Therefore, errors have corrupted the bits in the first block. Thus far, only LRC (parity) algorithm has been applied.

Table 13-2   Part of ASCII Code for Commonly-used Characters.

Character	a	b	d	i	I	r
ASCII	*1100001*	*1100010*	*1100100*	*1101001*	*1001001*	*1110010*
Character	s	t	!	'	space	
ASCII	*1110011*	*1110100*	*0100001*	*0100111*	*0100000*	

The complete table of ASCII is provided in Appendix 9-1 in Chapter 9.

Table 13-3   LRC and VRC Application.

Received blocks	Parity check	Corrected block	Decoded message
1_1_01001 _0_	Violation	1_0_01001	I
1110100 _1_	LRC OK	1110100	t
0100111 _1_	LRC OK	0100111	'
1110011 _0_	LRC OK	1110011	s
0100000 _0_	LRC OK	0100000	space
1100001 _0_	LRC OK	1100001	a
0100000 _0_	LRC OK	0100000	space
1100010 _0_	LRC OK	1100010	b
1101001 _1_	LRC OK	1101001	i
1110010 _1_	LRC OK	1110010	r
1100100 _0_	LRC OK	1100100	d
0100001 _1_	LRC OK	0100001	!
1001011 _0_(1)	LRC OK	1001010	
ovooooo o(2)	⇐ **VRC**		

Note (1): This (block) is the added parity block for VRC use.
Note (2): This is the result of the VRC check, **O**: VRC is OK; **v**: VRC violation.

Next, the VRC (parity) algorithm is applied. Each column of the received matrix (the first column labeled "received blocks" in Table 13-3) must also be checked for parity violations. The result is shown in the last row (block) under the column labeled "received blocks". This is the vertical redundancy check of the received signal. From this row, it can be seen that all columns, except the second (i.e., indicated by "_v_"), do not have a parity-check violation (i.e., indicated by "_o_").

From the results of the parity check (i.e., the longitudinal redundancy check plus the vertical redundancy check), it can be seen that (in the matrix) the "**second**" column has a parity violation and the "**first**" row has a parity violation. Therefore, the following conclusion can be drawn:

> *The "second" bit of the "first" information block is an erroneous bit. It should be corrected to become a logic "0" (see Table 13-3 column labeled "corrected block"). Therefore, the decoded message is*
>
> *"It's a bird!"*

As indicated in the column (Table 13-3) labeled "decoded message".

13.3 Basic Principle for Channel Control Method

The expense of error control in a digital system is a corresponding reduction in the overall system capacity for transmitting information. That is, redundancy must be added into the transmitted bitstream to detect and correct errors. In general, the following statement is true:

**"The more (bit) redundancy that is added,
results in greater error control capability."**

Before adding (bit) redundancy, the information stream must be organized into blocks of **k** bits in length. For example, in Figure 13-11, the information data stream is grouped into four-bit blocks: "0001", "1101", "1001", "1100", ..., with *k* = 4.

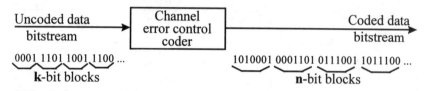

Figure 13-11   Input and Output Data Bitstreams of a Channel Encoder.

Each information block requires the addition of unique redundancy capabilities. The output of a channel error control coder is a data stream of **n**-bit blocks, where each block contains **k** information bits plus (**n** − **k**) redundant bits. The addition of redundant bits is essentially a trade-off between the bit rate and the probability of bit errors [i.e., the Bit Error Rate (BER)]. In summary, the more bits of (**n** − **k**), the better the bit error rate (i.e., a low number of errors).

The channel control code with a notation of (**n, k**) is called a block code, which uses the following parameters to indicate: (1) the transmitted codeword [also known as **code vector**] having a length of **n** digits (bits); (2) the information block which is **k** bits in length; and, (3) the added redundancy of the (**n, k**) code (known as **parity-check** bits) having a length of (**n - k**) bits.

The ratio of the number of information bits to the number of bits in the codeword (i.e., **k/n**) is called the *code rate*, or *code efficiency*. The difference (1 − k/n) is called the code *redundancy*. The encoder is said to produce an (**n, k**) block code. For example, a (7, 4) block code consists of seven data bits per output codeword, corresponding to each four bit input data word as shown in Figure 13-11. In this case, the three (3 ≡ 7 −4) extra bits are used for parity-checking. Block codes are known as "memoryless codes" because each output codeword depends on only the current k-bit source block (i.e., there is no relationship to any preceding or succeeding blocks of digits). In addition, this (7, 4) code is known a 4/7-rate code. The **code rate** (= R) important parameter of an error control code, described as follows:

(1)   A code with a large R is better efficiency code, however, the code does not have a good error control capability.

(2)   A code with a smaller R is a poorer efficiency code, however, the code provides a stronger error control capability.

13.3.1 Classification of Channel Control Codes

The coding mechanism adds redundancy by inserting extra code digits in accordance with a specific algorithm that enables the receiver to "possibly" detect and correct "channel-caused" errors (i.e., errors introduced during transport). Channel codes are usually binary, and the encoding process falls into two classes: (1) **block codes** (often called group codes), and (2) **convolutional codes** (also known as tree codes).

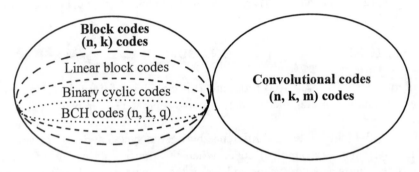

Figure 13-12   Channel Codes Classifications.

Block codes subdivide the sequence of source (binary) digits into sequential blocks of k digits (k bits for binary digits). Each k-digit block is mapped into an n-digit block of output digits, where $n > k$. Coded and uncoded blocks are compared based on the criteria that both systems use the same total time duration to transmit each "word". When the coder is computing the required parity-check bits for addition to the k-bit information block, the parity bit values are solely based on the current block of information (i.e., block codes are "memoryless").

In comparison, convolutional codes utilize memory, which is typically implemented in the form of a binary shift register having **m** storage elements (stages). The sequence of source digits (i.e., the message) is shifted into the register, one bit at a time. Appropriate outputs from various register stages are connected to "*n*" modulo-2 adders (described later in this chapter). The resultant code becomes the sequence of output bits for each message word. That is, convolutional codes are memory devices.

13.3.2 Classifications of Block Codes

In Figure 13-12, it can be seen that there are many sub-classes of block codes. The first sub-class is linear block codes, which consists of binary cyclic codes. Binary cyclic codes are also called Cyclic Redundancy Check (CRC) codes. A BCH code (independently developed by three persons: Bose, Chandhuri, and Hocquenghem) is a special type of CRC code. BCH codes are always represented by (**n, k, q**); where n and k have the same meanings as in the block codes, and **q** is the **error correction** capability. For instance, a (15, 7, 2) BCH code carries seven (7) information digits by transmitting a 15-bit codeword, and can correct up to two random errors in the codeword.

A frequently question asked is how a BCH code using the notation (n, k, q) can be distinguished from a convolutional code with a similar notation (n, k, m)? In general, when the three numbers inside the brackets are small values, they represent a convolutional code. For example, for codes designated (15, 7, 2), (15, 5, 3), (2, 1, 4) and (2, 1, 5); both (2, 1, 4) and (2, 1, 5) are convolutional codes (rather than BCH codes).

13.4 CYCLIC REDUNDANCY CHECK CODES

Cyclic Redundancy Check (CRC) codes are a special class of linear block codes that can be either systematic (unscrambled) codes, or non-systematic (scrambled) codes.

Figure 13-13 illustrates the difference between a systematic (non-scrambled) code and a non-systematic (scrambled) code. When the transmitted codeword contains the exact uncoded digits as a part of the codeword, the channel control code is a systematic. For example, when the uncoded (i.e., information) digit block is "**0001**", the transmitted code can either be "1010**0001**" or "**0001**101" as shown in Figure 13-13. Hence, the uncoded message word can be identified explicitly within the transmitted codeword. Note that the uncoded message word can be at the beginning or at the end of the transmitted codeword.

If the information message word (uncoded) can not be recognized in the transmitted codeword, the channel control code is a scrambled code. For example, the uncoded message of "0001" can not be identified within the transmitted codeword of "0101101". Similarly, the uncoded pattern of "1101" (the second message block) is not part of the transmitted codeword "1010001" in Figure 13-13.

The details of this (7, 4) CRC code will be described after the generating polynomial, *g(x)*, and the generating matrix, **G**, have been discussed.

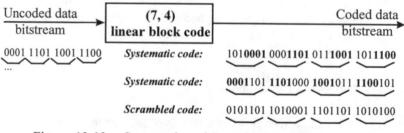

Figure 13-13   Systematic and Scrambled Linear Block Codes.

13.4.1 The Generating Polynomial and Matrix, g(x) and G

A Cyclic Redundancy Check (CRC) code (or any linear block code) can be represented by either: (1) a generating polynomial [$g(x)$], or (2) a generating matrix (**G**; shown in Figure 13-14). From the generating polynomial $g(x)$, or the generating matrix **G**, the following information can be derived:

- *The code space of the given block code*: This is the first step in designing, analyzing, encoding, and decoding a linear block code. Examples 13-8, 13-9, 13-10 and 13-11 describes this algorithm.

- *The error control capability of the given code*: This algorithm is used to decide whether a linear block code is acceptable or not from performance viewpoint.

- *The channel encoder design for the transmitter*: Simplified example is provided later in this chapter.

- *The channel decoder design for the receiver*: It's beyond the scope of this book.

Figure 13-14 illustrates a high level view of the encoder of a linear block code.

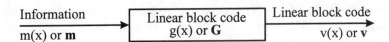

$$\text{Information} \xrightarrow{\hspace{2cm}} \boxed{\begin{array}{c}\text{Linear block code}\\ g(x) \text{ or } \mathbf{G}\end{array}} \xrightarrow{\hspace{2cm}} \begin{array}{c}\text{Linear block code}\\ v(x) \text{ or } \mathbf{v}\end{array}$$

$$m(x) \text{ or } \mathbf{m}$$

Figure 13-14   Input, Output, and System Response of Linear Block Codes.

Many generating polynomials have been developed by scientists and engineers for applications in practical communication systems. The following is a list of generating polynomials that have been used in digital networks. It should be noted that this list is for example only, and is not an exhaustive collection:

$g(x) = 1 + x + x^3$ $\qquad\qquad\qquad$ $g(x) = 1 + x + x^2 + x^4$

$g(x) = 1 + x^2 + x^3 + x^4$ $\qquad\qquad$ $g(x) = 1 + x + x^4 + x^5$

$g(x) = 1 + x + x^2 + x^4 + x^5 + x^7$ $\qquad$ $g(x) = 1 + x + x^2 + x^4 + x^5 + x^8 + x^{10}$

$g(x) = 1 + x + x^5 + x^6 + x^7 + x^9 + x^{11}$ $\qquad$ $g(x) = 1 + x + x^2 + x^3 + x^{11} + x^{12}$

$g(x) = 1 + x^5 + x^{12} + x^{16}$ $\qquad\qquad$ $g(x) = 1 + x^2 + x^{15} + x^{16}$

By knowing the generating polynomial $g(x)$, the generating matrix **G** can be determined, and vice versa. The derivation of a matrix **G** based on a polynomial $g(x)$ for a special code is described in a later section of this chapter. The derivation of a polynomial $g(x)$ based on a matrix **G** is not discussed in this book.

13.4.2 Code Space Determination

In this section, the ***code space*** of a (7, 4) CRC code is derived. This code space can be either a systematic (describe in Example 13-8) or a scrambled code (describe in Example 13-9). The definition of code space is given at the end of Example 13-9.

Example 13-8: The generating matrix G of a (7, 4) CRC channel error control code is shown in Eq.(13-3), determine the code space that has 16 (=2^4, for k = 4) entries.

$$G = \begin{pmatrix} 1\,1\,0\,1\,0\,0\,0 \\ 0\,1\,1\,0\,1\,0\,0 \\ 1\,1\,1\,0\,0\,1\,0 \\ 1\,0\,1\,0\,0\,0\,1 \end{pmatrix} \tag{13-13}$$

Note that this is a (7, 4) CRC code, therefore, the information blocks contains 4 bits each. Hence, there are 16 ($\equiv 2^4$) codewords in the code space (Table 13-4). The 16 combinations of the 4-bit information blocks are shown in the first column of Table 13-4 designated as "message code".

Three methods are commonly used to generate the code space for a linear block code:

(1) Apply the generating (generator) matrix, **G**:

$$\mathbf{v = mG} \tag{13-14}$$

where vector **m** represents the message, and **v** represents the transmitted code.

(2) Apply the generating (generator) polynomial, $g(x)$:

$$v(x) = m(x)g(x) \tag{13-15}$$

where v(x) and m(x) represent the transmitted code and the message, respectively.

(3) Apply the generating (generator) polynomial, $g(x)$:

$$f(x) = x^{n-k}m(x) \tag{13-16}$$

$$R(x) = \text{Remainder of } \frac{f(x)}{g(x)} \tag{13-17}$$

$$v(x) = f(x) + R(x) \qquad (13\text{-}18)$$

Since the generating matrix is given in Eq. (13-13), method 1 [using Eq. (13-14)] will be applied to obtain the codewords for the code space, starting with the information block (message word) "0000". By applying the formula given in Eq.(13-14), the linear block code $\mathbf{v} = (0000000)$ is derived. The actual mathematical manipulation will be illustrated using another information block, (1011).

Let the information (message word) $\mathbf{m} = (1011)$. To obtain $\mathbf{v}$ using Eq.(13-14), perform the matrix multiplication of $\mathbf{Gm}^T$. Note that $\mathbf{m}^T$ is the transpose of $\mathbf{m}$ (that is, columns become rows, and rows become columns). Since $\mathbf{m}$ [=(1011)] has only one row, the transpose of $\mathbf{m}$ ($\mathbf{m}^T$) has only one column, as shown in Eq.(13-19).

$$
\mathbf{v}^T = Gm^T =
\begin{pmatrix}
1 & 1 & 0 & 1 & 0 & 0 & 0 \\
0 & 1 & 1 & 0 & 1 & 0 & 0 \\
1 & 1 & 1 & 0 & 0 & 1 & 0 \\
1 & 0 & 1 & 0 & 0 & 0 & 1
\end{pmatrix}
\begin{pmatrix}
1 \\
0 \\
1 \\
1
\end{pmatrix}
\qquad (13\text{-}19)
$$

$$\mathbf{m}^T$$

To perform the matrix multiplication of Eq.(13-19), the simplest method is based on multiplying "column by column" of the $\mathbf{G}$ matrix by $\mathbf{m}^T$, using **mod.(2)** operation (i.e., odd number of "1s" = 1 and even number of "1s" = 0), as shown in Figure 13-15. For example, the first column of the generating matrix $\mathbf{G}$, is (1011), which is multiplied by $\mathbf{m}^T$, bit by bit as follows:

The first bit:	1 (from $\mathbf{G}$) × 1 (from $\mathbf{m}^T$) = 1
The second bit:	0 (from $\mathbf{G}$) × 0 (from $\mathbf{m}^T$) = 0
The third bit:	1 (from $\mathbf{G}$) × 1 (from $\mathbf{m}^T$) = 1
The fourth bit:	1 (from $\mathbf{G}$) × 1 (from $\mathbf{m}^T$) = 1

The result of this multiplication is shown in the first row of Figure 13-15. The sum of "1" + "0" + "1" + "1" is "1". This procedure is applied to all seven (7) columns of $\mathbf{G}$, as shown in Figure 13-15.

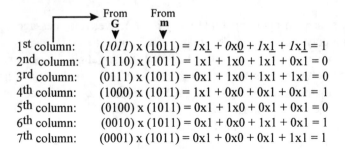

From G   From m

1st column: $(1011) \times (\underline{1011}) = 1\text{x}\underline{1} + 0\text{x}\underline{0} + 1\text{x}\underline{1} + 1\text{x}\underline{1} = 1$
2nd column: $(1110) \times (1011) = 1\text{x}1 + 1\text{x}0 + 1\text{x}1 + 0\text{x}1 = 0$
3rd column: $(0111) \times (1011) = 0\text{x}1 + 1\text{x}0 + 1\text{x}1 + 1\text{x}1 = 0$
4th column: $(1000) \times (1011) = 1\text{x}1 + 0\text{x}0 + 0\text{x}1 + 0\text{x}1 = 1$
5th column: $(0100) \times (1011) = 0\text{x}1 + 1\text{x}0 + 0\text{x}1 + 0\text{x}1 = 0$
6th column: $(0010) \times (1011) = 0\text{x}1 + 0\text{x}0 + 1\text{x}1 + 0\text{x}1 = 1$
7th column: $(0001) \times (1011) = 0\text{x}1 + 0\text{x}0 + 0\text{x}1 + 1\text{x}1 = 1$

Figure 13-15 $\mathbf{Gm}^T$ Operation.

From these calculations, $\mathbf{v}^T = (1001011)^T$ is derived (shown as the last column in Figure 13-15). Therefore, the (7, 4) CRC codeword for $\mathbf{m} = (1011)$ is $\mathbf{v} = (1001011)$. This operation is repeated a total of 16 ($\equiv 2^4$) times to derive the codeword assignments shown in Table 13-4 (i.e., the column labeled "Systematic code").

Table 13-4   Systematic and Scrambled (7, 4) CRC Code Space.

Message code	Systematic code	Scrambled code
0 0 0 0	0 0 0 0 0 0 0	0 0 0 0 0 0 0
0 0 0 1	1 0 1 0 0 0 1	0 0 0 1 1 0 1
0 0 1 0	1 1 1 0 0 1 0	0 0 1 1 0 1 0
0 0 1 1	0 1 0 0 0 1 1	0 0 1 0 1 1 1
0 1 0 0	0 1 1 0 1 0 0	0 1 1 0 1 0 0
0 1 0 1	1 1 0 0 1 0 1	0 1 1 1 0 0 1
0 1 1 0	1 0 0 0 1 1 0	0 1 0 1 1 1 0
0 1 1 1	0 0 1 0 1 1 1	0 1 0 0 0 1 1
1 0 0 0	1 1 0 1 0 0 0	1 1 0 1 0 0 0
1 0 0 1	0 1 1 1 0 0 1	1 1 0 0 1 0 1
1 0 1 0	0 0 1 1 0 1 0	1 1 1 0 0 1 0
1 0 1 1	1 0 0 1 0 1 1	1 1 1 1 1 1 1
1 1 0 0	1 0 1 1 1 0 0	1 0 1 1 1 0 0
1 1 0 1	0 0 0 1 1 0 1	1 0 1 0 0 0 1
1 1 1 0	0 1 0 1 1 1 0	1 0 0 0 1 1 0
1 1 1 1	1 1 1 1 1 1 1	1 0 0 1 0 1 1

Example 13-9: Given the generating polynomial $g(x) = 1 + x + x^3$ for a (7, 4) CRC channel error control, determine the code space.

To determine the codewords from the generating polynomial, Eq.(13-15) is applied as follows:

$$v(x) = m(x)g(x) \tag{13-20}$$

The first step in applying Eq.(13-20) is to convert the message block $\mathbf{m}$ into its corresponding polynomial $m(x)$. This may be unfamiliar to some readers, so examples are provided to illustrate this operation. If the information block $\mathbf{m} = (1101)$, its corresponding polynomial is $m(x) = 1 + x + x^3$, where "1" is the first "digit" in (1101), x is contributed by the second "digit" in (1101), x^2 is not included since the third "digit" is 0 in (1101), and x^3 is contributed by the last "digit" in (1101). The procedure is summarized in Figure 13-16. The 1st "digit" in the vector $\mathbf{m} = (1101)$ contributes to the "constant" term of the polynomial $m(x)$, the 2nd "digit" contributes to the first degree term "x", the 3rd "digit" contributes to the second degree term "x^2", and so on.

$$m \quad = \quad (\quad 1 \qquad 1 \qquad 0 \qquad 1 \quad)$$

$$\qquad \qquad \downarrow 1 \qquad \downarrow x^1 \qquad \downarrow x^2 \qquad \downarrow x^3$$

$$m(x) \quad = \qquad 1 \quad + \quad 1 \cdot x^1 \quad + \quad 0 \cdot x^2 \quad + \quad 1 \cdot x^3$$

$$\qquad \quad = \quad 1 + x^1 + x^3$$

Figure 13-16   Conversion from Vector to Polynomial [*m* to *m(x)*].

Another example is illustrated for $\mathbf{m} = (1010)$. The first "digit" of $\mathbf{m}$ is "1", thus, $m(x)$ has the "constant" term 1. Since the second and the last digits of message block $\mathbf{m}$ are both 0s, $m(x)$ doesn't contain x or x^3. Therefore, the polynomial $m(x)$ for the message block of (1010) is equal to $1 + x^2$.

Using the equation $v(x) = m(x)g(x)$, for $\mathbf{m} = (1101)$, the polynomial, $v(x)$, representing the transmitted codeword can be derived as follows:

$$v(x) = (1 + x + x^3) \times (1 + x + x^3)$$

$$= 1 + x^2 + x^6 + (x + x) + (x^3 + x^3) + (x^4 + x^4) = 1 + x^2 + x^6$$

In deriving the above result, the mod.(2) operation [see Eq.(13-16)] is applied:

$$0 + 0 = 0; \qquad 0 + 1 = 1; \qquad 1 + 0 = 1; \qquad 1 + 1 = 0 \qquad (13\text{-}21)$$

$$x + x = 0; \qquad x^2 + x^2 = 0; \qquad \dots \quad x^n + x^n = 0 \qquad (13\text{-}22)$$

The final step is to obtain the output codeword (code vector), "$\mathbf{v}$", from the codeword polynomial, $v(x)$. The (7, 4) CRC codeword polynomial is re-rewritten as follows (intended for the unfamiliar reader only):

$$v(x) = 1 + x^2 + x^6 = 1 + 0x + 1x^2 + 0x^3 + 0x^4 + 0x^5 + 1x^6$$

$$\downarrow \quad \downarrow \quad \downarrow \quad \downarrow \quad \downarrow \quad \downarrow \quad \downarrow$$

$$v \quad \longleftrightarrow \quad 1 \quad 0 \quad 1 \quad 0 \quad 0 \quad 0 \quad 1$$

Figure 13-17   Conversion from Polynomial to Vector [*v(x)* to **v**].

From Figure 13-17 the vector form of $v(x)$ can be expressed as $\mathbf{v} = (1010001)$. Next, the codeword $\mathbf{v}$ for $\mathbf{m} = (1111)$ is derived. Rewriting $m(x) = 1 + x + x^2 + x^3$, substituting $m(x)$ and $g(x)$ into Eq.(13-20), and applying Eq.(13-22), the polynomial, $v(x)$, representing the transmitted codeword is derived as follows:

$$v(x) = m(x)g(x) = (1 + x + x^2 + x^3)(1 + x + x^3) = 1 + x^5 + x^6$$

This can be rewritten as $v(x) = 1 + 0x + 0x^2 + 1x^3 + 0x^4 + 1x^5 + 1x^6$. From which (see Figure 13-17) the transmitted codeword can be expressed as $\mathbf{v}$ = (1001011) for $\mathbf{m}$ = (1111). The same procedure can be followed to complete Table 13-4 (i.e., the column designated "scrambled code").

In Table 13-4, the first column contains the 16 possible combinations of 4-bit messages (message words). The second column is the 16 corresponding systematic codewords obtained by using the generating matrix $\mathbf{G}$. The last column is the set of 16 scrambled codewords (nonsystematic words) obtained by applying the generating polynomial $g(x)$. This table contains all the possible codewords for a **(7, 4)** code, and is defined as the **"code space"** [represented by a vector $\mathbf{V}$; which contains many code vectors, $\mathbf{v}$] for the (7, 4) CRC code. Note that the terms **codeword** and **code vector** can be used interchangeably.

13.4.3 Systematic Codes from the G Matrix

The code space shown in the second column of Table 13-4, labeled "systematic code", is obtained from the generating matrix $\mathbf{G}$. It is interesting to understand why this code space is considered "systematic". In contrast, the codewords in the third column of Table 13-4 , labeled "scrambled code", was created by using the generating polynomial, $g(x)$. Two questions associated with this topic are often asked:

(1)   Is the code space generated by $\mathbf{G}$ always systematic? The answer is "No."

(2)   Is the code space generated by $g(x)$ always scrambled? The answer is "No".

The reasons behind these answers are explained in this chapter. The systematic nature of a codeword is explained first. The generating matrix given by Eq.(13-13) can be rewritten (partitioned) as follows.

$$\mathbf{G} = \begin{pmatrix} 1\,1\,0 & 1\,0\,0\,0 \\ 0\,1\,1 & 0\,1\,0\,0 \\ 1\,1\,1 & 0\,0\,1\,0 \\ 1\,0\,1 & 0\,0\,0\,1 \end{pmatrix} \tag{13-23}$$

This is a 4 by 7 matrix (i.e., 4 rows and 7 columns). Observe that the matrix has been partitioned into two parts. The second part is known as an **identity** (**unity**) matrix [a matrix having equal number of rows and columns (a square matrix) with all elements of 0s except the main diagonal, with a value of 1). The codewords generated by this type of matrix are always a systematic code. There are three possible forms of the generating matrix $\mathbf{G}$:

<u>Type 1</u>: **G** contains a unity matrix in the second half [example: **G** in Eq.(13-23)]

<u>Type 2</u>: **G** contains a unity matrix in the first half [example: see $\mathbf{G}_1$ in Eq.(13-28)]

<u>Type 3</u>: **G** doesn't contain a unity matrix at all [example: see $\mathbf{G}_2$ in Eq.(13-28)].

The first two matrix types will create systematic codes, while the third type will create a scrambled code. The general form of the type 1 generating matrix **G** can be expressed as follows:

$$G_{k\,by\,n} = \left(P_{k\,by\,r} \quad I_{k\,by\,k} \right); \quad r = n - k \tag{13-24}$$

that is,

$$G_{k\,by\,n} = \begin{pmatrix} p_{11} & p_{12} & \cdots & p_{1r} & 1 & 0 & 0 & \cdots & 0 \\ p_{21} & p_{22} & \cdots & p_{2r} & 0 & 1 & 0 & \cdots & 0 \\ p_{31} & p_{32} & \cdots & p_{3r} & 0 & 0 & 1 & \cdots & 0 \\ \vdots & \vdots & \vdots & \vdots & \vdots & \vdots & & \vdots \\ p_{k1} & p_{k2} & \cdots & p_{kr} & 1 & 0 & 0 & \cdots & 1 \end{pmatrix} \tag{13-25}$$

where

$P_{k\,by\,r}$ = parity-check matrix of matrix G

$I_{k\,by\,k}$ = identity (unity) matrix. $\tag{13-26}$

The first part of matrix **G** is the parity-check portion of the generating matrix, and the second part is the unity matrix. This is only one of the three possible forms that a generating matrix **G** can have. It is important to note that the <u>matrix **G** is a k by n</u> matrix.

That is, for an (n, k) CRC (block) code, the dimension of the generating matrix G is given as:

$$\text{Dimension of } \mathbf{G} = \textbf{\textit{k}} \text{ by } \textbf{\textit{n}}: \quad G_{k\,by\,n} \tag{13-27}$$

Example 13-10: Determine if the CRC code is systematic or scrambled for each of the following generating matrices ($\mathbf{G}_1$ and $\mathbf{G}_2$), and determine their code spaces. Note that both matrices have a dimension of (3 by 6), that can be used to generate (6, 3) codes.

$$\mathbf{G}_1 = \begin{pmatrix} 1 & 0 & 0 & 1 & 1 & 0 \\ 0 & 1 & 0 & 0 & 1 & 1 \\ 0 & 0 & 1 & 1 & 0 & 1 \end{pmatrix}; \qquad \mathbf{G}_2 = \begin{pmatrix} 0 & 0 & 1 & 1 & 1 & 0 \\ 1 & 0 & 0 & 1 & 0 & 1 \\ 0 & 1 & 0 & 0 & 1 & 1 \end{pmatrix} \tag{13-28}$$

Since both matrices are 3 by 6. A submatrix, which is a square matrix, generated by either matrix must be a 3 by 3 matrix. It is clear that the first generating matrix, G_1, consists of an identity sub-matrix (the first three columns of G_1). Therefore, the CRC derived from G_1 is a systematic code. In contrast, G_2 does not contain an identity sub-matrix, and will create a scrambled code. By applying $v = mG_1$, and $v = mG_2$, the code spaces can be derived as shown in Table 13-5.

Table 13-5   Code Spaces for G_1 and G_2 in Eq.(13-23).

Message code	Systematic code (from G_1)	Scrambled code (from G_2)
0 0 0	0 0 0 0 0 0	0 0 0 0 0 0
0 0 1	0 0 1 1 0 1	0 1 0 0 1 1
0 1 0	0 1 0 0 1 1	1 0 0 1 0 1
0 1 1	0 1 1 1 1 1	1 1 0 1 1 0
1 0 0	1 0 0 1 1 0	0 0 1 1 1 0
1 0 1	1 0 1 0 1 1	0 1 1 1 0 1
1 1 0	1 1 0 1 0 1	1 0 1 0 1 1
1 1 1	1 1 1 0 1 1	1 1 1 0 0 0

13.4.4 Another Way to Obtain a Code Space

The third method for obtaining the code space of an (n, k) code is described in this section. This method applies the generating polynomial indirectly, and consists of three steps. First, evaluate the polynomial, $f(x)$, by multiplying the message polynomial, $m(x)$, with x^{n-1} [see Eq.(13-29). Second, calculate the remainder, $R(x)$, from dividing $f(x)$ by $g(x)$ [see Eq.(13-30)]. Third, the codeword $v(x)$ is obtained by applying Eq.(13-31).

$$f(x) = x^{n-k}m(x); \quad where \ m(x) = message \tag{13-29}$$

$$R(x) = Re\,mainder \ of \ \left[\frac{f(x)}{g(x)}\right] \tag{13-30}$$

$$v(x) = f(x) + R(x) \tag{13-31}$$

Example 13-11: Determine the transmitted codeword, v, for the message word $m = (10000110)$ for an $(n, 8)$ CRC code with the generating polynomial $g(x) = 1 + x^2 + x^5$.

It should be understood that the relationship between n, k and $g(x)$ expressed in Eq.(13-27) holds for all (n, k) codes:

$$\text{Degree of } g(x) = n - k \tag{13-32}$$

In this example k = 8 and the generating polynomial, $g(x)$, has a degree of 5. Hence, the value $n = 13$ can be obtained from Eq.(13-32) (i.e., $5 = n - 8$). Given that the message word **m** = (10000110), it can be determined that $m(x) = 1 + x^5 + x^6$. By applying Eqs.(13-29), (13-30) and (13-31); $f(x)$, $R(x)$ and $v(x)$ can be derived as follows:

$$f(x) = x^{n-k} m(x) = x^{13-8}(1 + x^5 + x^6) = x^5 + x^{10} + x^{11} \tag{13-33}$$

$$R(x) = \mathrm{Re}\,mainder\ of\ \left[\frac{x^5 + x^{10} + x^{11}}{1 + x^2 + x^5}\right] = 1 + x + x^4 \tag{13-34}$$

$$v(x) = f(x) + R(x) = 1 + x + x^4 + x^5 + x^{10} + x^{11} \tag{13-35}$$

The (transmitting) codeword is obtained to be (1100110000110) for the message word **m** = (10000110), i.e., a (13, 8) CRC code. Therefore, it can be seen that a systematic code can also be derived from the generating polynomial.

Example 13-12: Derive the remainder, R(x), given in Eq.(13-29).

Eq.(13-21) and Eq.(13-22) must be used to derive the remainder, as shown in Figure 13-18.

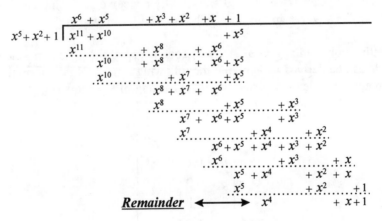

Figure 13-18   Derivation of a Remainder.

Example 13-13: Determine the transmitted codeword, **v**, for the message word **m** = (1101) for a (7, 4) CRC code with the generating polynomial $g(x) = 1 + x + x^3$.

From Eqs.(13-29), (13-30) and (13-31), $f(x)$, $R(x)$ and $v(x)$ can be derived as follows:

$$f(x) = x^{n-k} m(x) = x^{7-4}(1 + x + x^3) = x^3 + x^4 + x^6$$

$$R(x) = \text{Re}\,mainder\ of\ \left[\frac{x^3 + x^4 + x^6}{1 + x^2 + x^5}\right] = 0$$

$$v(x) = f(x) + R(x) = x3 + x4 + x6$$

The (transmitting) codeword, v, is obtained as $v = (0001101)$ for the message word $m = (1101)$. This is systematic code. Note that this systematic code is different from the one [i.e., (1001101)] obtained by using the relationship $v = mG$, as listed in Table 13-4.

13.4.5 Derivation of G from g(x)

In previous sections of this chapter several different methods were applied to derive the code space of an (n, k) code. A systematic code can also be obtained from the generating matrix G, provided G has a unity matrix as its submatrix. [see Example 13-8, and Example 13-10 (G_2)]. Example 13-10 (G_1) illustrates the derivation of a code space with scrambled codewords by using the generating matrix. Likewise, from the generating polynomial $g(x)$, can be used to derive the code, with either systematic codewords (see Example 13-11) or scrambled codewords (see Example 13-9).

Two questions often asked by engineers are: (1) "Is there a relationship between G and $g(x)$?" and, (2) "Can G be derived from $g(x)$, or vice versa?" The answers to both questions is "yes". However, in this book only cases with a known $g(x)$ are described.

If the generating polynomial $g(x)$ of an (n, k) code is given, the generating matrix G for an (n, k) code can be derived by applying the following formula. In the formula, the first part of the matrix is called the parity matrix, consisting of k vectors $(p_1, p_2, \ldots,$ and $p_k)$, and the second part is an identity matrix.

$$G = \begin{bmatrix} p_1 & 1\,0\,0\,0\cdots0 \\ p_2 & 0\,1\,0\,0\cdots0 \\ p_3 & 0\,0\,1\,0\cdots0 \\ \vdots & \vdots\,\vdots\,\vdots\,\vdots\quad\vdots \\ p_k & 0\,0\,0\,0\cdots1 \end{bmatrix} \qquad (13\text{-}36)$$

The parity vectors p_j ($j = 1$, k) can be derived from the following relationship:

$$p_j = \text{Re}\,mainder\ of\ \left[\frac{x^{n-k+j-1}}{g(x)}\right] \qquad (j = 1, k) \qquad (13\text{-}37)$$

Example 13-14: Illustrate the derivation of G from $g(x) = 1 + x + x^3$, for a $(7, 4)$ CRC code.

In this example, $n = 7$ and $k = 4$, therefore Eq.(13-37) can be rewritten as follows:

$$p_j = \text{Re}\,mainder\,of\left[\frac{x^{7-4+j-1}}{g(x)}\right] = \text{Re}\,mainder\,of\left[\frac{x^{j+2}}{1+x+x^3}\right] \quad (j = 1, 4) \quad (13\text{-}38)$$

From which, the following polynomials and vectors can be obtained:

$$p_1 = \text{Re}\,mainder\,of\left[\frac{x^{1+2}}{1+x+x^3}\right] = 1 + x \quad\Rightarrow\quad \boldsymbol{p_1} = (110) \quad (13\text{-}39)$$

$$p_1 = \text{Re}\,mainder\,of\left[\frac{x^{2+2}}{1+x+x^3}\right] = x + x^2 \quad\Rightarrow\quad \boldsymbol{p_2} = (011) \quad (13\text{-}40)$$

$$p_1 = \text{Re}\,mainder\,of\left[\frac{x^{3+2}}{1+x+x^3}\right] = 1 + x + x^2 \quad\Rightarrow\quad \boldsymbol{p_3} = (111) \quad (13\text{-}41)$$

$$p_1 = \text{Re}\,mainder\,of\left[\frac{x^{4+2}}{1+x+x^3}\right] = 1 + x^2 \quad\Rightarrow\quad \boldsymbol{p_4} = (101) \quad (13\text{-}42)$$

Substituting the above four parity vectors, $\boldsymbol{p_1}$ through $\boldsymbol{p_4}$, into Eq.(13-36), the generating matrix $\mathbf{G}$ can be derived as follows:

$$\mathbf{G} = \begin{pmatrix} 1\,1\,0 & 1\,0\,0\,0 \\ 0\,1\,1 & 0\,1\,0\,0 \\ 1\,1\,1 & 0\,0\,1\,0 \\ 1\,0\,1 & 0\,0\,0\,1 \end{pmatrix} \quad (13\text{-}43)$$

Therefore, it can be seen that the generating matrix, $\mathbf{G}$, given in Eq.(13-43) is identical to the generating matrix shown in Eq.(13-13) for a (7, 4) CRC code.

13.4.6 CRC Name Explanation

The methods used to obtain the code space of an (n, k) CRC code has been discussed throughout previous sections of this chapter. CRC codes are considered "special linear block codes". The naming of this type of code is not obvious. The code space derived in Example 13-8 is used to explain the reason that this type of code is called a Cyclic Redundancy Check (CRC) code. Note that only the systematic CRC (not scrambled CRC) code space is examined for this purpose.

Table 13-6   The Code Space of a (7, 4) CRC Code.

Message code	Systematic code	Code No.
0 0 0 0	0 0 0 0 0 0 0	1
0 0 0 1	**1 0 1 0 0 0 1**	2
0 0 1 0	1 1 1 0 0 1 0	3
0 0 1 1	0 1 0 0 0 1 1	4
0 1 0 0	0 1 1 0 1 0 0	5
0 1 0 1	*1 1 0 0 1 0 1*	6
0 1 1 0	1 0 0 0 1 1 0	7
0 1 1 1	0 0 1 0 1 1 1	8
1 0 0 0	1 1 0 1 0 0 0	9
1 0 0 1	0 1 1 1 0 0 1	10
1 0 1 0	0 0 1 1 0 1 0	11
1 0 1 1	1 0 0 1 0 1 1	12
1 1 0 0	1 0 1 1 1 0 0	13
1 1 0 1	0 0 0 1 1 0 1	14
1 1 1 0	0 1 0 1 1 1 0	15
1 1 1 1	1 1 1 1 1 1 1	16

In Table 13-6, there are 16 ($\equiv 2^4$ for $k = 4$) codewords in the code space for a (7, 4) CRC code. To understand the naming of a CRC code, two questions must be answered:

(1)   Are the 16 different codewords independent? Answer = No
(2)   Can a codeword be derived from another codeword? Answer = Yes

The reasons for these answers are given as follows. Two codewords from the code space, shown in Table 13-6, are arbitrarily selected to support these explanations. They are codewords Nos. 2 and 6 (highlighted in Table 13-6).

•   Arbitrarily starting from the codeword No. 2: $v_2 = (1010001)$, shift the right-most bit, a logical "1", to the position before the left-most bit, also a logical "1". That is, (1010001) becomes (1101000) [$\equiv v_9$], which is the codeword No. 9 in the **same** code space as shown in Figure 13-19.

Codeword No. 2:	$v_2 = (1010101)$	
Shifted by 1 bit:	$= (1101000)$	$\Rightarrow$ v_9
Shifted by one more bit:	$= (0110100)$	$\Rightarrow$ v_5
Shifted by one more bit:	$= (0011010)$	$\Rightarrow$ v_{11}
Shifted by one more bit:	$= (0001101)$	$\Rightarrow$ v_{14}
Shifted by one more bit:	$= (1000110)$	$\Rightarrow$ v_7
Shifted by one more bit:	$= (0100011)$	$\Rightarrow$ v_4
Shifted by one more bit:	$= (1010101)$	$\Rightarrow$ v_2

Figure 13-19   Cycling a (7, 4) Codeword Bit-by-Bit.

By shifting this newly created v_9 codeword following the same procedure, the codeword v_9 becomes $v_5 = (0110100)$ as shown in Figure 13-19. Continuing to shift the current codeword one bit at a time, it can be seen that v_5 becomes v_{11}; v_{11} becomes v_{14}; v_{14} becomes v_7, v_7 becomes v_4; and, finally v_4 returns back to v_2. (see Figure 13-19).

In summary, starting with codeword No. 2, $v_2 = (1010001)$, by shifting one bit at a time, the following codewords can be obtained:

$$v_2 \Rightarrow v_9 \Rightarrow v_5 \Rightarrow v_{11} \Rightarrow v_{14} \Rightarrow v_7 \Rightarrow v_4 \Rightarrow v_2$$

Note that these codewords are not "independent"; they are related.

- Let codeword No. 6, in Table 13-6, be the starting codeword. Applying the same procedure that was used for v_2, the following codewords can be obtained:

$$v_6 \Rightarrow v_3 \Rightarrow v_{10} \Rightarrow v_{13} \Rightarrow v_{15} \Rightarrow v_8 \Rightarrow v_{12} \Rightarrow v_6$$

From the above exercises, it can be concluded that these two groups of codewords [(1) v_2, v_9, v_5, v_{11}, v_{14}, v_7, and v_4; and (2) v_6, v_3, v_{10}, v_{13}, v_{15}, v_8, v_{12}] are redundant, because a single codeword can be used to generate six other codewords by cycling the bits (one bit at a time). That is, by cycling the bits in the codeword v_2, the six other codewords are essentially redundant. Hence, the name "Cyclic Redundancy Check" is appropriate. Based on the above derivations, all of the codewords in Table 13-6 can be generated from v_2 and v_6, with the exception of v_1 and v_{16}. The codewords, v_2, v_6, v_1, and v_{16}, are called the "**seeds**" of the (7, 4) CRC code represented by the generating matrix, **G** [Eq.(13-13)].

It should be understood that besides v_2, any codeword from the group (v_9, v_5, v_{11}, v_{14}, v_7) can be used as the "seed" to generate the other codewords in the group. Likewise, any codeword from the group (v_3, v_{10}, v_{13}, v_{15}, v_8, v_{12}), besides v_6 can be the "seed" used to generate other codewords in this group.

13.4.7 Parity-Check Matrix H

At the transmitter (channel encoder) either the generating polynomial, $g(x)$, or the generating matrix, **G**, can be used to create any codeword for an (n, k) code. It has also been shown that **G** can be derived from $g(x)$ for some special codes. The generating matrix and the generating polynomial are used to design the code space and the encoder (discussed later in this chapter) for the transmitter.

A frequently question asked is: "What is used by the receiver for decoding?" The answer is the parity-check polynomial, $h(x)$, or the parity-check matrix **H**, which are equivalent to $g(x)$ and **G**. That is, for Forward Error Control (FEC), the principle of the transmitter is based on **G** or $g(x)$, the receiver is based on **H** or $h(x)$.

Using the parity-check matrix **H**, the error syndrome matrix **S** can be derived by using Eq.(13-44), where **r** = the received codeword; $r(x)$ = the received code polynomial; **S** = the error syndrome matrix; $s(x)$ = the error syndrome polynomial; and $g(x)$ = the generating polynomial. Note that the first relationship in Eq.(13-44) is used if vectors and matrices are adopted to describe the decoder characteristics. Similarly, the second equation in Eq.(13-44) is used if polynomials are adopted to characterize the decoder.

$$\mathbf{S} = \mathbf{rH^T} \qquad or \qquad s(x) = \mathrm{Re}\,mainder\ of \left[\frac{r(x)}{g(x)}\right] \tag{13-44}$$

- If **S** $\neq$ **0** (zero or null vector), or if $s(x) \neq 0$:

  Then, the received codeword is not valid [i.e., the received codeword has error(s)].

- If **S** = **0** (zero or null vector), or if $s(x) = 0$:

  Then, the received codeword is assumed to be valid. When the received codeword is "valid", it can be codeword has no errors, or it can be a codeword that contains several errors, but appears to be a valid codeword (i.e., the receiver recognizes this codeword as one of the possible codewords sent by the transmitter).

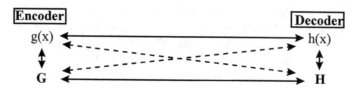

Figure 13-40   Relationship among **G**, **H**, $g(x)$ and $h(x)$.

Another question frequently asked is: "Is there a relationship between **G** and **H**, or $g(x)$ and $h(x)$?" The answer is "yes", and Figure 13-40 indicates:

(1) If **G** is given, then **H** can be derived from it, or vice versa. The generating polynomial $g(x)$ can also be derived from **G** (previously described), and the parity-check polynomial $h(x)$ can be obtained indirectly from **G**.

(2) If **H** is given, then $h(x)$ and **G** can be derived. Likewise, $g(x)$ can also be derived from **H**.

(3) If $g(x)$ is given, then **G** can be derived. Likewise, $h(x)$ and **H** can be obtained indirectly.

(4) If $h(x)$ is given, then **H** can be derived. Likewise, $g(x)$ and **H** can be obtained indirectly.

In this book, only the relationship between **G** and **H** is given for some specific codes. The general expression for the generating matrix **G** is given by Eq.(13-36), which consists of two parts: (1) a parity matrix, and (2) an identity matrix. For discussing the relationship between **G** and **H**, Eq.(13-36) is rewritten as Eq.(13-45):

$$G_{k \, by \, n} = \begin{pmatrix} p_{11} \, p_{12} \cdots p_{1r} & 1 \; 0 \; 0 \; \cdots \; 0 \\ p_{21} \, p_{22} \cdots p_{2r} & 0 \; 1 \; 0 \; \cdots \; 0 \\ p_{31} \, p_{32} \cdots p_{3r} & 0 \; 0 \; 1 \; \cdots \; 0 \\ \vdots \quad \vdots \quad \vdots & \vdots \; \vdots \; \vdots \qquad \vdots \\ p_{k1} \, p_{k2} \cdots p_{kr} & 1 \; 0 \; 0 \; \cdots \; 1 \end{pmatrix} = \left(P_{k \, by \, r} \quad I_{k \, by \, k} \right); \quad r = n - k \qquad (13\text{-}45)$$

The parity-check matrix **H** is given as follows ($p_{r \, by \, k}^{T}$ is the transpose of $p_{r \, by \, k}$):

$$H_{(n-k) \, by \, n} = \left(P_{r \, by \, k}^{T} \quad I_{r \, by \, r} \right); \qquad r = n - k \qquad (13\text{-}46)$$

Example 13-15: The generating matrix **G** of the (7, 4) CRC code is given in Eq.(13-47), determine **H**, the parity-check matrix.

$$\mathbf{G} = \begin{pmatrix} 1\,1\,0 & 1\,0\,0\,0 \\ 0\,1\,1 & 0\,1\,0\,0 \\ 1\,1\,1 & 0\,0\,1\,0 \\ 1\,0\,1 & 0\,0\,0\,1 \end{pmatrix} \qquad (13\text{-}47)$$

It should be understood that Eqs.(13-45) and (13-46) are true for systematic codes only. Hence, the generating matrix G is written into two parts as shown in Eq.(13-46).

First the parity matrix, $p_{r \, by \, k}$, is extracted from Eq.(13-47) as follows:

$$\mathbf{P}_{k \, by \, r} = \begin{pmatrix} 1 & 1 & 0 \\ 0 & 1 & 1 \\ 1 & 1 & 1 \\ 1 & 0 & 1 \end{pmatrix} \qquad (13\text{-}48)$$

Second, the transpose of $p_{r \, by \, k}$ (into $p_{r \, by \, k}^{T}$) is obtained as follows:

$$\mathbf{P}_{r \, by \, k}^{T} = \begin{pmatrix} 1 & 0 & 1 & 1 \\ 1 & 1 & 1 & 0 \\ 0 & 1 & 1 & 1 \end{pmatrix} \qquad (13\text{-}49)$$

Finally, the parity-check matrix **H** can be derived by substituting Eq.(13-49) into Eq.(13-46), as follows (note the right half of **H** is an identity matrix):

$$\mathbf{H}_{r \, by \, n} = \begin{pmatrix} 1 & 0 & 1 & 1 & 1 & 0 & 0 \\ 1 & 1 & 1 & 0 & 0 & 1 & 0 \\ 0 & 1 & 1 & 1 & 0 & 0 & 1 \end{pmatrix} \qquad (13\text{-}50)$$

In summary, for the matrices represented in Eqs.(13-48), (13-49), and (13-50), the dimensions of the parity matrix is obtained as $r = n - k$ ($\equiv 7 - 4 = 3$; for this example). Therefore, the second half of the parity-check matrix **H** [Eq.(13-50)] is an identity matrix of 3 by 3 (r by r). The dimensions of matrices, such as **G** or **H**, follow these rules:

- The generating matrix **G** dimensions are **_k_ by _n_**.

- The parity-check matrix **H** dimensions are **(_n−k_) by _n_**.

- The degree of the generating polynomial *g(x)* is **(_n − k_)**.

13.5 ERROR CONTROL CAPABILITY

Linear block codes have unique error control capabilities. An (n, k) code can be a double-error detecting code, a single error correcting code, triple-error detection, double-error detection and single-error correction, or other configurations. The (7, 4) CRC discussed throughout this chapter is used to illustrate the error control capability of a linear block code.

Before evaluating the error control capability of a linear block code, two terms (1) the Hamming weight of a codeword, and (2) the minimum distance of a block code, must be defined (definitions 13-1 and 13-2).

Definition 13-1: The Hamming weight of a codeword (code vector) **v** is given by:

$$Weight \ of \ v = W(v) = \sum_{i=1}^{n} 1's \ in \ v \qquad (13\text{-}51)$$

The total of "*1*s" in any codeword (or code vector) **v** is called the Hamming weight [W(**v**)] of the code vector **v**. For example, if **u** = (11010010) and **v** = (10101000), then W(**u**) = 4 and W(**v**) = 3.

Definition 13-2: The minimum distance, d_{min}, of a code **V** is given by:

$$d_{min} = minimum \ of \ [W(v \ \varepsilon \ V)] \qquad for \ any \ non\text{-}zero \ v \qquad (13\text{-}52)$$

That is, "*in the code space, V, besides the codeword with a zero Hamming weight (i.e., all 0's codeword), the minimum Hamming weight among all the Hamming weights is called the **minimum distance of the code**'*". Definition 13-2, Eq(13-52), is somewhat abstract, hence it is not easy to thoroughly understand the definition of the minimum distance of a specific linear block code.

Definition 13-2 is illustrated using the (7, 4) CRC code, which has the code space shown in Table 13-7. This table is the code space of the (7, 4) CRC code with a generating polynomial of $g(x) = 1 + x + x^3$. As shown, one codeword has a Hamming weight of "0", seven have a Hamming weight of "3", seven have a Hamming weight of "4", and one has a Hamming weight of "7". By Definition 13-2 [expressed in Eq.(13-52)], this (7, 4) CRC code has a *"minimum distance of 3"*.

Table 13-7   Code Space and Hamming Weights.

Message code	Systematic code	Hamming weight
0 0 0 0	0 0 0 0 0 0 0	0
0 0 0 1	1 0 1 0 0 0 1	3
0 0 1 0	1 1 1 0 0 1 0	4
0 0 1 1	0 1 0 0 0 1 1	3
0 1 0 0	0 1 1 0 1 0 0	3
0 1 0 1	1 1 0 0 1 0 1	4
0 1 1 0	1 0 0 0 1 1 0	3
0 1 1 1	0 0 1 0 1 1 1	4
1 0 0 0	1 1 0 1 0 0 0	3
1 0 0 1	0 1 1 1 0 0 1	4
1 0 1 0	0 0 1 1 0 1 0	3
1 0 1 1	1 0 0 1 0 1 1	4
1 1 0 0	1 0 1 1 1 0 0	4
1 1 0 1	0 0 0 1 1 0 1	3
1 1 1 0	0 1 0 1 1 1 0	4
1 1 1 1	1 1 1 1 1 1 1	7

The error control capability of an (n, k) linear block code is described as follows:

- If a code is used solely for detecting errors (i.e., not correcting errors), the maximum number of erroneous bits a code can detect is given by:

$$E_{detected} = d_{min} - 1 \qquad (13\text{-}53)$$

- If a code is used for correcting errors, after detecting them, the maximum number of errors this code can correct is given by:

$$E_{corrected} = \left[\frac{d_{min} - 1}{2} \right] \qquad (13\text{-}54)$$

where [ ] is the truncated integer, for example, [4.0] = 4, and [5.5] = 5.

For the (7, 4) CRC code with a generating polynomial of $g(x) = 1 + x + x^3$, and a minimum distance, $d_{min} = 3$, the corresponding $E_{detected}$ and $E_{corrected}$ can be obtained as follows: $E_{detected} = 3 - 1 = 2$, and $E_{corrected} = [(3 - 1)/2] = 1$. Therefore, this (7, 4) CRC code can **detect** two random bit errors (caused by channel noise) in the bitstream, but it can only **correct** a single bit error.

Note that the "price" for using this code is 75% overhead [$\equiv$ (7 −4)/4]. That is, 3 parity-check bits are added to protect 4 information bits, which allows detection of double errors, or correction of single errors. Hence, *error control (detect and/or correct) is a costly feature in modern telecommunications networks*!

It is interesting to know how the minimum distance (d_{min}) is used to evaluate error control capability. Let Figure 13-41 represent the code space of a (7, 4) CRC code. Each "shaded" circle is one codeword (or code vector) in the code space, which is three-dimensional. Both the transmitter (encoder) and the receiver (decoder) use this code space for encoding and decoding functions.

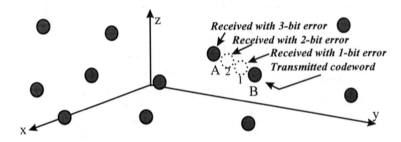

Figure 13-41   Code Space and Minimum Distance.

Recall that in the (7, 4) CRC code, the minimum distance (d_{min}) is 3. Assume that codewords "A" and "B" are separated by a "3-circle" distance (since d_{min} = 3). In the following three descriptions it is assumed that the codeword transmitted occupies the "B" location in the code space, and the codeword is corrupted by channel error(s).

(1)   The first case assumes that codeword "B" has one bit in error when it is received. Therefore, the received codeword no longer occupies the received code space position "B", and has moved one circle away from the "B"-ball location (see Figure 13-41). For simplicity, the received codeword is assumed to have moved towards codeword "A" (the location shown by a dashed circle labeled "1"). Circle "1" is "one away" from "B" and "two away" from "A". The receiver (decoder) has the code space registered in its circuitry. Because positions "1" and "2" do not belong to the code space, the receiver can detect this situation. Hence, a (7, 4) CRC code can detect one-bit random errors. After detecting a one-bit random error, the decoder will attempt to correct this error, and bring circle "1" back to a valid location in the code space. The probability of circle "1" being corrected by being returned to the "B" position is definitely higher than for circle "1" being moved to the "A" position. Hence, a (7, 4) CRC code is *a single error correction code*.

(2)   The second case assumes two bits are in error when codeword "B" is received. Therefore, the codeword transmitted from location "B" will move to the circle "2" location. This location is ***not*** valid, thus the receiver will be able to identify it as an erroneous codeword. Circle "2" is "two-away" from "B", and only "one-away" from codeword "A". After the decoder has detected the erroneous codeword, it will attempt to correct this error. The probability that circle "2" is brought back to position "B" is much smaller than being moved to position "A". Therefore, although this erroneous codeword actually originated at the codeword "B" position, it is very difficult to justify moving it from position "2" to position "B", instead of moving it to position "A". Thus, it is concluded that the (7, 4) CRC code can detect two errors (***a double-error detection code***), but can not correct two errors!

(3)   Assume there were three bits in error when a codeword located at position "B" was transmitted over a noisy channel. Since the distance between codeword "B" and codeword "A" is three, the erroneous codeword "B" will "**land**" on the same location as codeword "A" (see Figure 13-41). Therefore, the "erroneous codeword" will be restored as codeword "A" because the received codeword is "*without any error*". In effect, the received codeword is assumed to be codeword "A". Therefore, the (7, 4) CRC code is ***not*** a triple-error detecting code!

In summary, the (7, 4) CRC code with a generating polynomial of $g(x) = 1 + x + x^3$, or a generating matrix given in Eq. (13-18), can be used to:

- Detect up to two random errors in the data bitstream
- Correct any single random error in the data bitstream

However, it can not detect/correct 3 or more errors in the data bitstream.

From this example, it can be concluded that if a code has a large d_{min}, it will be able to detect and/or correct more erroneous bits. By applying Eq.(13-53) and Eq.(13-54), the relationship between the code minimum distance, d_{min}, and the error control (detection, or detection/correction) is derived as shown in Table 13-8 and Figure 13-42.

Table 13-8   Minimum Distance and Error Control Capability.

Minimum distance	m-bit detectable	n-bit correctable
3	2	1
4	3	1
5	4	2
6	5	2
7	6	3
8	7	3
9	8	4
10	9	4

Minimum distance	d_{min}	Detectable bits	Correctable bits
●⋯⋯● →	3	2	1
●⋯⋯● →	4	3	1
●⋯⋯● →	5	4	2
●⋯⋯● →	6	5	2

Figure 13-42   Error Control Capability for (n, k) code.

13.6 CRC IMPLEMENTATION

The design and implementation of an (n, k) CRC code uses conventional logical circuit elements such as "AND" gates, "OR" gates, "Exclusive OR" gates, shift registers, counters, and buffer. For this reason, combined with its mathematical characteristics, the CRC code is one of the most common methods used for channel error control codes in modern communications networks.   This section briefly describes the design of an encoder for an (n, k) CRC code.

Example 13-16: Describe the major building blocks of an encoder for the (7, 4) CRC code, with a generating polynomial of $g(x) = 1 + x + x^3$, for generating a systematic code.

It should understood that this example is not intended to show the exact design of a (7, 4) CRC encoder. It is used to illustrate the concept of sequential circuit design. [an exact coder/decoder design implementation can be obtained from a typical error control textbook (e.g., "Error Control", written by S. Lin and Costellio, ISBN 0-13-283796-x, published by Prentice-Hall, Inc. Englewood Cliffs, New Jersey)]

The degree of the generating polynomial, $g(x)$, equals **_3_**. Therefore, the encoder requires **_three_** 1-bit shift registers: r_1, r_2 and r_3 (see Figure 13-43; a typical shift register performs as a one-bit memory device). The "1" term in the generating polynomial $g(x)$ indicates that there is always an input connected to the data input port of the first shift register (r_1). The term "x" in $g(x)$ indicates that an exclusive OR gate must be used at the output of the **first** shift register to represent "x" (i.e., "$x1$"). There is no second-degree term "$x2$" in $g(x)$, hence the output of the **second** shift register (r_2) does not require an exclusive OR gate. The **third** shift register (r_3) requires an exclusive OR gate because there is a third-degree term "$x3$" in $g(x)$.

A buffer is used to store the information in the incoming data stream, and feeds 4-bit information blocks to the cyclic circuit (i.e., the sequential circuit containing the three shift registers in Figure 13-43) and the output selector. During the first half of the control signal period, the output selector selects the message block as the output bit stream. In this example the first 4 bits are the information block $\mathbf{m} = (1011)$. These four bits are also used by the cyclic circuit to generate the three parity-check bits (100). During the second half of the control signal period, the cyclic circuit has already generated the three parity-check bits, $p = (100)$, which are selected by the output selector to complete the output codeword, $\mathbf{v} = (1001011)$. This procedure is repeated for every information block.

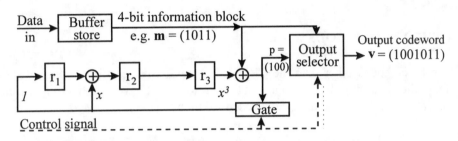

Figure 13-43   The Encoder of (7, 4) CRC: $g(x) = 1 + x + x^3$.

As previously mentioned, in addition to the simplicity of the circuit design, the algebra used to analyze a CRC code is straight forward. Therefore, many communications systems use CRC for error control. Figure 13-44 shows a block diagram for a CRC-16 encoder. The CRC-12, CRC-16, and CRC-ITU/T channel error control codes are widely used in the data communications industry. Before providing a brief description of these three CRC codes, definition 13-3 must be understood.

Definition 13-3: The double-error detecting, or single error correcting (7, 4) CRC code with the generating polynomial $g(x) = 1 + x + x^3$, is also called a CRC-3 since the degree$[g(x)] = 3$ [i.e., $g(x)$ is a 3rd-degree polynomial].

- CRC-12: This code has a generating polynomial $g(x) = 1 + x + x^2 + x^3 + x^{11} + x^{12}$. It is used in a 6-bit character synchronous data system. Since the degree of the polynomial $[g(x)]$ is 12, this technique assumes the common name CRC-12. It can detect bursty errors up to 12 bits in length. The CRC-12 encoder has 12 one-bit shift registers (numbered from 1 to 12 as shown in Figure 13-44).

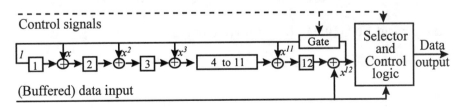

Figure 13-44   CRC-12 Encoder for Data Communications.

- CRC-16: This code has a generating polynomial $g(x) = 1 + x^2 + x^{15} + x^{16}$, and is used in an 8-bit character synchronous data systems. It can detect bursty errors up to 16 bits in length.

- CRC-ITU-T: This code has a generating polynomial $g(x) = 1 + x^5 + x^{12} + x^{16}$, and is used in European 8-bit character synchronous data systems. It can detect bursty errors up to 16 bits in length.

13.7 OTHER BLOCK CODES

There are block codes other than the CRC codes previously described. Some of these codes (e.g., the Hamming, BCH, Golay, and Reed-Solomon) have been used in practical communications systems, and are briefly described in this section.

13.7.1 The Hamming Codes

Hamming codes are "scrambled" (non-systematic) codes. They have been classified into two major groups: (1) single-error correction codes, and (2) double-error detection codes. The relationship between the following parameters: n, k, $n - k$, and s [i.e., the degree of the Hamming generating polynomial $g(x)$] for both types of Hamming codes are given in Table 13-9(A). The derivation of the code vector from $m(x)$ and $g(x)$ is illustrated in Examples 13-17 and 13-18. The most popular Hamming generating polynomials are listed for reference purposes in Table 13-9(B).

Example 13-17: Determine the code vector **v** for a message word **m** = (1011), if the Hamming single-error correction code with $g(x) = 1 + x + x^3$ is applied.

Because this is a single-error correction Hamming code, g(x) should be used as the generating polynomial to produce the codewords for transmission.

Since $s = 3$ [i.e., the degree of g(x) = 3], from Table 13-9(B), $g(x) = 1 + x + x^3$.

From Table 13-9(A), it can be determined that

$$n = 2^s - 1 = 2^3 - 1 = 7; \quad and \quad k = 2^s - s - 1 = 2^3 - 3 - 1 = 4.$$

For message word **m** = (1011), v(x) is derived follows:

$$v(x) = m(x)g(x) = (1 + x^2 + x^3)(1 + x + x^3) = 1 + x + x^2 + x^3 + x^4 + x^5 + x^6$$

From which it can be determined that the codevector for the message word [**m** = (1011)] is **v** = (1111111), which is a (7, 4) scrambled code.

Table 13-9(A) Generating Polynomials for Various Hamming Codes.

Parameter	Single-error correction	Double-error detection*
n	$2^s - 1$	$2^s - 1$
k	$2^s - s - 1$	$2^s - s - 2$
$n - k$	s	$s + 1$
Message	$m(x)$	$m(x)$
Polynomial	$g(x)$	$p(x) = (1 + x)g(x)$
$v(x)$	$m(x)g(x)$	$m(x)p(x)$

* Double-error detection plus single-error correction.

Table 13-9(B)   Polynomials for Generating Polynomials in Table 13-9(A).

s	Polynomial $g(x)$
3	$1 + x + x^3$
4	$1 + x + x^4$
5	$1 + x^2 + x^5$
6	$1 + x + x^6$
7	$1 + x^3 + x^7$
8	$1 + x^2 + x^3 + x^8$
9	$1 + x^4 + x^9$

Example 13-18: Determine the code vector **v** for a message word **m** = (111) if the Hamming double-error detection code with $g(x) = 1 + x + x^3$ is applied.

Because this is a double-error correction Hamming code, p(x) should be used as the generating polynomial to produce the codewords for transmission. That is, from Table 13-9(A), the polynomial $p(x)$ must be first derived from the following equation:

$$p(x) = (1 + x)g(x) = (1 + x)(1 + x + x^3) = 1 + x^2 + x^3 + x^4$$

Second, since $g(x) = 1 + x + x^3$ [obtained from Table 13-9(B)], the $s = 3$. Hence, n and k can be derived as follows:

$$n = 2^s - 1 = 2^3 - 1 = 7; \quad and \quad k = 2^s - s - 2 = 2^3 - 3 - 2 = 4.$$

Having derived $p(x)$, one can obtain the output code vector polynomial as follows:

$$v(x) = m(x)p(x) = (1 + x + x^2)(1 + x^2 + x^3 + x^4) = 1 + x + x^4 + x^6$$

Finally, the code vector for the message word **m** = (111) is given by:

$$\mathbf{v} = (1100101)$$

which is a (7,3) scrambled code.

From Examples 13-9, 13-12, 13-17, and 13-18, it can be seen that $g(x)$ has been used for both ordinary CRC code, and Hamming code designs. The following codes can also be generated by the same polynomial, $g(x) = 1 + x + x^3$:

- Double-error detection, systematic (7, 4) CRC

- Double-error detection, scrambled (7, 4) CRC

- Single-error correction, systematic (7, 4) CRC

- Single-error detection, scrambled (7, 4) CRC

- Single-error correction, scrambled (7, 4) Hamming code

- Double-error detection plus single-error correction, scrambled (7, 3) Hamming code

13.7.2 BCH Codes

BCH codes are also scrambled codes that have a format of (n, k, q), with **_q-error correction_**. For example in a (7, 4, 1) BCH code, the information block length is 4 digits, the codeword length is 7 digits (= 4 information bits + 3 parity bits), and any single bit error can be **_corrected_** since $q = 1$. This code is very much like the (7, 4) CRC code discussed in Examples 13-8, 13-9, and 13-12 (i.e., a single-error correction or a double-error detection code). Similarly, a (15, 5, 3) BCH code can correct any 3 errors if 10 parity-check bits are added to a 5-bit information block. The code vector of a (n, k, q) BCH code has the following constraints:

$$A \text{ length } n = 2^s - 1 \text{ } (s = \text{an integer: see Table 13-10)} \qquad (13\text{-}55)$$

$$\text{Degree } [g(x)] = m \leq sq = n - k \qquad (13\text{-}56)$$

$$d_{min} \geq 2q + 1 \qquad (13\text{-}57)$$

Table 13-10 Generating Polynomials for Some BCH Codes.

(n, k, q)	Generating polynomial $g(x)$	s
(7, 4, 1)	$1 + x + x^3$ $(m = 3)$	3
(15, 11, 1)	$1 + x + x^4$ $(m = 4)$	4
(15, 7, 2)	$1 + x^4 + x^6 + x^7 + x^8$ $(m = 8)$	4
(15, 5, 3)	$1 + x + x^2 + x^4 + x^5 + x^8 + x^{10}$ $(m = 10)$	4

Example 13-19: Design a BCH double-error correction code for transmitting 7-bit blocks of information data, and determine the (transmitting) code vector **v** if the message word **m** = (1010101) [i.e., m(x) = $1 + x^2 + x^4 + x^6$).

Given that k = 7 and q = 2, implies a (15, 7, 2) BCH code must be applied (see Table 13-10). Hence, this code has the following generating polynomial:

$$g(x) = 1 + x^4 + x^6 + x^7 + x^8$$

The code vector can be obtained as follows:

$$v(x) = m(x)g(x) = (1 + x^2 + x^4 + x^6)(1 + x^4 + x^6 + x^7 + x^8)$$

$$= 1 + x^2 + x^6 + x^7 + x^8 + x^9 + x^{10} + x^{11} + x^{12} + x^{13} + x^{14}$$

that is,

$$v(x) = 1 + x^2 + x^6 + x^7 + x^8 + x^9 + x^{10} + x^{11} + x^{12} + x^{13} + x^{14}$$

$$= 1 + 0x + 1x^2 + 0x^3 + 0x^4 + 0x^5 + 1x^6 + 1x^7 + 1x^8 + 1x^9 + 1x^{10} + 1x^{11} + 1x^{12} + 1x^{13} + 1x^{14}$$

$$\mathbf{v} = (\; 1 \quad 0 \quad 1 \quad 0 \quad 0 \quad 0 \quad 1 \quad 1 \quad 1 \quad 1 \quad 1 \quad 1 \quad 1 \quad 1 \quad 1 \;)$$

Thus, the (transmitting) code vector assigned for the message word $\mathbf{m} = (1010101)$ is $\mathbf{v} = (101000111111111)$, which is a scrambled code.

Example 13-20: Verify the BCH codes with the respective $g(x)$ shown in Table 13-10 are (15, 11, 1), (15, 7, 2), and (15, 5, 3).

From Eq.(13-55) with $s = 4$, it can be determined that the length of the codeword, n, is:

$$n = 2^s - 1 = 2^4 - 1 = 15$$

- For $g(x) = 1 + x + x^4$, by applying Eq.(13-56) with $m = 4$, $s = 4$, and $q = 1$, the relationship between m, s, q, and k is given as follows:

$$Degree\ of\ [g(x)] = 4 \leq sq\ (= 4 \times 1 = 4) = n - k = 15 - k$$

From which the message word length can be derived as:

$$k \leq 11$$

Therefore, the BCH code is (15, 11, 1) with a minimum distance of:

$$d_{min} \geq 2q + 1 = 3$$

- For $g(x) = 1 + x^4 + x^6 + x^7 + x^8$, by applying Eq.(13-51) with $s = 4$, $m = 8$, and $q = 2$, the relationship between m, s, q, and k is given as follows:

$$Degree\ of\ [g(x)] = 8 \le sq\ (= 4 \times 2 = 8) = n - k = 15 - k$$

From which the message word length can be derived as:

$$k \le 7$$

Therefore, the BCH code is (15, 7, 2) with a minimum distance of:

$$d_{min} \ge 2q + 1 = 5$$

• For $g(x) = 1 + x + x^2 + x^4 + x^5 + x^8 + x^{10}$, by applying Eq.(13-51) with $s = 4$, $m = 10$, and $q = 2$, the relationship between m, s, q, and k is given as follows:

$$Degree\ of\ [g(x)] = 10 \le sq\ (= 4 \times 3 = 12) = n - k = 15 - k$$

From which the message word length can be derived as:

$$k \le 5$$

Therefore, the BCH code is (15, 5, 3) with a minimum distance of:

$$d_{min} \ge 2q + 1 = 7$$

• Considering the possibility of $q = 4$; applying Eq.(13-56):

$$n - k = 15 - k \ge sq\ (= 4 \times 4 = 16)$$

From which the message word length would be derived as:

$$k \le -1$$

which is impossible. Therefore, for a BCH code with $s = 4$, the three available codes are (15, 11, 1), (15, 7, 2) and (15, 5, 3), but not (15, k, 4). That is, the maximum error correction capability is q = 3.

Definition 13-4: A polynomial $m(x)$ of lowest degree (i.e., irreducible) with binary coefficients is a **minimum polynomial**.

Theorem 13-1: A t-error correcting BCH (n, k, t) code has a generating polynomial of

$$g(x) = LCM\ [m_1(x), m_3(x), m_5(x), \ldots, m_{2t-1}(x)] \tag{13-58}$$

where the symbol LCM[ ] represents the Least Common Multiplier of [ ], and the minimum polynomials $m_i(x)$, for $n = 15$, are given as follows:

$$m_1(x) = 1 + x + x^4 \tag{13-59}$$

$$m_3(x) = 1 + x + x^2 + x^3 + x^4 \tag{13-60}$$

$$m_5(x) = 1 + x + x^2 \tag{13-61}$$

Example 13-21: For $s = 4$ (i.e., $n = 2^4 - 1 = 15$), as shown in Table 13-10, derive the generating polynomials for (15, 11, 1), (15, 7, 2) and (15, 5, 3) BCH codes.

(1) For single-error correcting (15, 11, 1) BCH code: $t = 1$, thus, $2t - 1 = 1$. Therefore, Eq.(13-58) becomes:

$$g(x) = \text{LCM}\,[m_1(x)] = 1 + x + x^4$$

(2) For double-error correcting (15, 7, 2) BCH code: $t = 2$, thus, $2t - 1 = 3$. Therefore, Eq.(13-58) becomes:

$$g(x) = \text{LCM}\,[m_1(x), m_3(x)] = \text{LCM}\,[(1 + x + x^4), (1 + x + x^2 + x^3 + x^4)]$$

$$= 1 + 2x + 2x^2 + 2x^3 + 3x^4 + 2x^5 + x^6 + x^7 + x^8 \tag{13-62}$$

$$= 1 + x^4 + x^6 + x^7 + x^8 \tag{13-63}$$

In simplifying Eq.(13-62) to (13-63), the relationship given in Eq.(13-17) is used. That is:

$$2x = x + x = 0, \qquad 2x^2 = x^2 + x^2 = 0, \ldots$$

(3) For triple-error correcting (15, 5, 3) BCH code: $t = 3$, thus, $2t - 1 = 5$. Therefore, Eq.(13-58) becomes:

$$g(x) = \text{LCM}\,[m_1(x), m_3(x), m_5(x)]$$

$$= \text{LCM}[(1 + x + x^4), (1 + x + x^2 + x^3 + x^4), (1 + x + x^2)] \tag{13-64}$$

which can be simplified as:

$$g(x) = 1 + x + x^2 + x^4 + x^6 + x^8 + x^{10} \tag{13-65}$$

In addition to the BCH codes shown in Table 13-10, there are other (n, k, q) BCH codes available for use in modern telecommunication systems. Table 13-11 lists lower order codes for n up to 1023. Table 13-11 is composed of three sub-tables:

(1) Table 13-11(A) for $n = 7, 15, 31, 63$, and 127 (part).

(2)   Table 13-11(B) for n = 127 (part), and 255.
(3)   Table 13-11(C) for n = 511, and 1023 (part).

Table 13-11(A)   (Part of) (n, k, q) BCH Codes

(n, k, q) BCH codes			(n, k, q) BCH codes			(n, k, q) BCH codes		
n	*k*	*q*	*n*	*k*	*q*	*n*	*k*	*q*
7	4	1	63	57	1	127	120	1
			63	51	2	127	113	2
15	11	1	63	45	3	127	106	3
15	7	2	63	39	4	127	99	4
15	5	3	63	36	5	127	92	5
			63	30	6	127	85	6
31	26	1	63	24	7	127	78	7
31	21	2	63	18	10	127	71	9
31	16	3	63	16	11	127	64	10
31	11	5	63	10	13	127	57	11
31	6	7	63	7	15	127	50	13
						127	43	14
						127	36	15

Table 13-11(B)   (Part of) (n, k, q) BCH Codes

(n, k, q) BCH codes			(n, k, q) BCH codes			(n, k, q) BCH codes		
n	*k*	*q*	*n*	*k*	*q*	*n*	*k*	*q*
127	29	21	511	475	4	255	139	15
127	22	23	511	466	5	255	131	17
127	15	27	511	457	6	255	123	19
127	8	31	511	448	7	255	115	21
			511	430	9	255	107	22
255	247	1	511	421	10	255	99	23
255	239	2	511	412	11	255	91	25
255	231	3	511	408	12	255	87	26
255	223	4	511	394	13	255	79	27
255	215	5	511	385	14	255	71	29
255	207	6	511	376	15	255	63	30
255	199	7	511	367	16	255	55	31
255	191	8	511	358	18	255	47	42
255	187	9	511	349	19	255	45	43
255	179	10	511	340	20	255	37	45
255	171	11	511	331	21	255	29	47
255	163	12	511	322	22	255	21	55
255	155	13	511	313	23	255	13	59
255	147	14	511	304	25	255	9	63

Table 13-11(C)   (Part of) (n, k, q) BCH Codes

(n, k, q) BCH codes			(n, k, q) BCH codes			(n, k, q) BCH codes		
n	**k**	**q**	**n**	**k**	**q**	**n**	**k**	**q**
511	502	1	511	241	36	1023	1013	1
511	493	2	511	238	37	1023	1008	2
511	484	3	511	229	38	1023	993	3
511	475	4	511	220	39	1023	983	4
511	466	5	511	211	41	1023	973	5
511	457	6	511	202	42	1023	963	6
511	448	7	511	193	43	1023	953	7
511	430	9	511	184	45	1023	943	8
511	421	10	511	175	46	1023	933	9
511	412	11	511	166	47	1023	913	11
511	408	12	511	157	51	1023	903	12
511	394	13	511	148	53	1023	893	13
511	385	14	511	139	54	1023	883	14
511	376	15	511	130	55	1023	873	15
511	367	16	511	121	58	1023	863	16
511	358	18	511	112	59	1023	858	17
511	349	19	511	103	61	1023	848	18
511	340	20	511	94	62	1023	838	19
511	331	21	511	85	63	1023	828	20
511	322	22	511	76	85	1023	821	21
511	313	23	511	67	87	1023	808	22
511	304	25	511	58	91	1023	798	23
511	295	26	511	49	93	1023	788	24
511	286	27	511	40	95	1023	778	25
511	277	28	511	31	109	1023	768	26
511	268	29	511	28	111	1023	758	27
511	259	30	511	19	119	1023	748	28
511	250	31	511	10	121	.	.	.

Example 13-22: Compare a (7, 4) CRC code with a (63, 24, 7) BCH code (Figure 13-45).

Assuming the message field has a length of 63 (BCH) or 49 (CRC) bits, the BCH and CRC codes can be compared as follows:

- **Percentage overhead**: 162.5% [= (63 – 24)/24] for BCH code; 75% [= (49 – 28)/28] for CRC code. Thus, BCH code is more "expensive" than CRC code.

- **Error correction capability**: A BCH (63, 24, 7) code can correct 7 erroneous bits (random or bursty) within a 63-bit stream. A (7, 4) CRC can correct a single error within a 7-bit block. When 49 bits are transmitted using CRC, seven (7) blocks are received. Only if the seven errors are evenly distributed (one bit error per each 7-bit block), can all seven erroneous bits be corrected like the (63, 24, 7) BCH code. However, if two or more errors occur in the same 7-bit block (as shown in Figure 13-45) they are not correctable. It is clear that the BCH code is more powerful than the CRC code, but the tradeoff is additional overhead bits must be added to the transmitted bitstream for BCH codes.

49 or 63 bits

Information bit stream: $\mathbf{m} = (1010\ 1010\ 1010\ 1010\ 1010\ ...\ 1010)$

(1) **BCH code:** $\mathbf{v} = (10\underline{001101010}11000100111\ ...\ 110)$: correctable

$= (1000\underline{110}1011\underline{000100}111\ ...\ 110)$: correctable

$= (\underline{1}0001101\underline{01}1000\underline{01}00111\ ...\ 1\underline{10})$: correctable

$\Big\{$ *% overhead = (63 - 24)/24 = 162.5%*

Seven-error correction

(2) **CRC code:** $\mathbf{v} = (0011010\quad 0011010\ ...\ 0011010)$: correctable

$= (0011010\quad \mathbf{0011010}\ ...\ 0011010)$: not correctable

$= (0011010\quad \mathbf{0011010}\ ...\ 0011010)$: not correctable

$\Big\{$ *% overhead = (49 - 28)/28 = 75%*

7 single error correction

Figure 13-45   BCH versus CRC Codes.

13.7.3 Golay Code

A Golay code is a special (23, 12) linear block code, that is also a scrambled code. It is the only known code that can correct any combination of three or less random errors in a block of 23 digits. It has been applied in several digital communications systems that are deployed in the field. This code has two generating polynomials, $g_1(x)$ and $g_2(x)$, which are shown in Eq.(13-66) and Eq.(13-67). The Golay code can be generated by either polynomial. Two famous decoders designed for the systems using Golay code: (1) Weldon's systematic search decoder, and (2) Kasami error-trapping decoder. (The decoders of error control codes, including Golay codes, are beyond the scope of this book).

$$g_1(x) = 1 + x^2 + x^4 + x^5 + x^6 + x^{10} + x^{11} \tag{13-66}$$

$$g_2(x) = 1 + x + x^5 + x^6 + x^7 + x^9 + x^{11} \tag{13-67}$$

and,

$$(1 + x)\,g_1(x)\,g_2(x) = 1 + x^{23} \tag{13-68}$$

Example 13-23: Determine the Golay (transmitting) code vector, using $g_1(x)$ in Eq.(13-66), for the message word **m** = (101010101010).

Applying Eq.(13-15), the code vector, $v(x)$ can be derived as follows:

$$v(x) = m(x)g_1(x) = (1 + x^2 + x^4 + x^6 + x^8 + x^{10})(1 + x^2 + x^4 + x^5 + x^6 + x^{10} + x^{11})$$

$$= 1 + x^4 + x^5 + x^7 + x^9 + x^{10} + x^{14} + x^{17} + x^{18} + x^{19} + x^{20} + x^{21}$$

that is,

$$\mathbf{v} = (10001\ 10101\ 10001\ 00111\ 110)$$

It can be seen that Golay code is a (23, 12) scrambled code.

Example 13-24: Compare the (23, 12) Golay code in Example 13-23, assuming it can correct triple errors, with a (7, 4) CRC having a single-error correction capability.

Referring to Figure 13-46, it is assumed that 21 (CRC) or 23 (Golay) bits are transmitted over two separate systems: one applies Golay code, while the other applies CRC code.

Information bit stream:

$$\overbrace{}^{\textbf{\textit{21 or 23 bits}}}$$
$$\mathbf{m} = (1010\ 1010\ ...\ 1010)$$

(1)   **Golay code: v** = (10**001** 10101 10001 00111 110): correctable

         = (1000**1 10**101 10001 00111 110): correctable

         = (10001 1010**1 1000**1 00111 110): correctable

$\left\{ \begin{array}{l} \textbf{\textit{\% overhead = (23 - 12)/12 = 92\%}} \\ \\ \textbf{\textit{Triple error correction}} \end{array} \right.$

(2)   **CRC code: v** = (0011010 0011010 0011010): correctable

         = (001101**0 0**011010 001101**0**): not correctable

         = (0011010 **0011**010 0011010): not correctable

$\left\{ \begin{array}{l} \textbf{\textit{\% overhead = (21 - 12)/12 = 75\%}} \\ \\ \textbf{\textit{3 single error correction}} \end{array} \right.$

Figure 13-46   Comparison between CRC and Golay Codes.

- **Percentage overhead**: 92% [= (23 − 11)/11] for Golay code; 75% [= (21 − 12)/12] for CRC code. Thus, Golay code is more "expensive" than CRC code.

- **Error correction capability**: A Golay (23, 11) code can correct 3 erroneous bits (random or bursty) within a 23-bit stream. A (7, 4) CRC can correct a single error within a 7-bit block. When 21 bits are transmitted using CRC, three (3) blocks are received. Only if the three errors are evenly distributed (one bit error per each 7-bit block), can all three erroneous bits be corrected like the (23, 11) Golay code. However, if any two or three errors occur in the same 7-bit block (as shown in Figure 13-46) they are not correctable. It is clear that Golay code is more powerful than the CRC code, but the tradeoff is the additional overhead bits that must be added to the transmitted bitstream of the Golay codes.

13.7.4 Reed-Solomon Code

Reed-Solomon codes are specific non-binary BCH codes. For **q-error** correction, a Reed-Solomon code has the following parameters:

- Codeword length $n = t - 1$ (13-69)

- $t = 2m$ [2 = prime number]   (13-70)

- Parity-check digits = $n - k = 2q$ (13-71)

- Minimum distance $(d_{min}) = 2q + 1$ (13-72)

In contrast, general no-binary BCH codes (not discussed in this book) with q-error correction have the following parameters:

- Codeword length $n = ts - 1$ (s = integer)   (13-73)

- $t = pm$ [p = prime number]   (13-74)

- Parity-check digits = $n - k \leq 2qs$ (13-75)

- Minimum distance $(d_{min}) \geq 2q + 1$ (13-76)

To understand the concepts of Reed-Solomon code, Galois field arithmetic [GF($2m$)] and primitive elements [α; of GF($2m$)] must be fully understood.

Definition 13-5: The symbol "0" and "1" together with modulo-2 addition and multiplication, shown in Eqs.(13-72) through (13-80), and Eq.(13-17), is called a Galois field of two symbols [i.e., GF(2)].

Mod(2) addition	*Mod(2) multiplication*	
$0 + 0 = 0$	$0 \cdot 0 = 0$	(13-77)
$0 + 1 = 1$	$0 \cdot 1 = 0$	(13-78)
$1 + 0 = 1$	$1 \cdot 0 = 0$	(13-79)
$1 + 1 = 0$	$1 \cdot 1 = 1$	(13-80)

Definition 13-6: A field with $2m$ symbols, "0", "1", α, α^2, α^3, α^4, α^5, ..., α^{2^m-2} together with the relationship shown in Eq.(13-81), is called GF($2m$).

$$\alpha^{2^m-1} = 1 \qquad\qquad (13\text{-}81)$$

Example 13-25: List the symbols of a GF(2).

The 16 symbols of a GF(2^4) are 0, 1, α, α^2, α^3, α^4, α^5, ..., α^{14}, and with $\alpha^{15} = 1$.

Theorem 13-2: To perform addition and multiplication of a GF($2m$), a minimum (primitive) polynomial with a degree of m, must be used. Any symbol higher than α^m can be reduced to a symbol with a lower power. For example, $p(x) = x^4 + x + 1$ (see Table 13-13), is used to perform the operations in a GF(2^4), and symbols α^4, α^5, ..., and α^{14} can be reduced to 1, α, α^2, α^3, and their combination.

Example 13-26: Explain how Table 13-12 is generated for a GF(2^4).

Table 13-12   Sixteen (16) Elements of a GF(2^4).

Element	Element	Element	Element
0	α^3	$\alpha^7 = \alpha^3 + \alpha + 1$	$\alpha^{11} = \alpha^3 + \alpha^2 + \alpha$
1	$\alpha^4 = \alpha + 1$	$\alpha^8 = \alpha^2 + 1$	$\alpha^{12} = \alpha^3 + \alpha^2 + \alpha + 1$
α	$\alpha^5 = \alpha^2 + \alpha$	$\alpha^9 = \alpha^3 + \alpha$	$\alpha^{13} = \alpha^3 + \alpha^2 + 1$
α^2	$\alpha^6 = \alpha^3 + \alpha^2$	$\alpha^{10} = \alpha^2 + \alpha + 1$	$\alpha^{14} = \alpha^3 + 1$

Since the minimum polynomial used in GF(2^4) is $p(x) = x^4 + x + 1$ (Theorem 13-2, and Table 13-13), the following relationship holds:

$$\alpha^4 + \alpha + 1 = 0 \qquad\qquad (13\text{-}82)$$

that is,

$$\alpha^4 = \alpha + 1 \qquad\qquad (13\text{-}83)$$

By applying Eq.(13-78), the following simplification can be obtained:

$\alpha^5 = \alpha^4 \times \alpha = (\alpha + 1) \times \alpha = \alpha^2 + \alpha$

$\alpha^6 = \alpha^4 \times \alpha^2 = (\alpha + 1) \times \alpha^2 = \alpha^3 + \alpha^2$

$\alpha^7 = \alpha^4 \times \alpha^3 = (\alpha + 1) \times \alpha^3 = \alpha^4 + \alpha^3 = (\alpha + 1) + \alpha^3 = \alpha^3 + \alpha + 1$

$\alpha^8 = \alpha^4 \times \alpha^4 = (\alpha + 1) \times (\alpha + 1) = \alpha^2 + 2\alpha + 1 = \alpha^2 + 1$

...

Table 13-13   (Partial List) Primitive Polynomials, p(x), of a GF(2^m).

m	p(x)	m	p(x)
3	$1 + x + x^3$	14	$1 + x + x^6 + x^{10} + x^{14}$
4	$1 + x + x^4$	15	$1 + x + x^{15}$
5	$1 + x^2 + x^5$	16	$1 + x + x^3 + x^{12} + x^{15}$
6	$1 + x + x^6$	17	$1 + x^3 + x^{17}$
7	$1 + x^3 + x^7$	18	$1 + x^7 + x^{18}$
8	$1 + x^2 + x^3 + x^8$	19	$1 + x + x^2 + x^5 + x^{19}$
9	$1 + x^4 + x^9$	20	$1 + x^3 + x^{20}$
10	$1 + x^3 + x^{10}$	21	$1 + x^2 + x^{21}$
11	$1 + x^2 + x^{11}$	22	$1 + x + x^{22}$
12	$1 + x + x^4 + x^6 + x^{12}$	23	$1 + x^5 + x^{23}$
13	$1 + x + x^3 + x^4 + x^{13}$	24	$1 + x^2 + x^7 + x^{24}$

Definition 13-7: The symbol α is called the primitive element of a GF(2^m).

Theorem 13-3: The generating polynomial of a q-error correction Reed-Solomon code is given as follows:

$$g(x) = (x + \alpha)(x + \alpha^2)(x + \alpha^3)(x + \alpha^4) \bullet\bullet\bullet (x + \alpha^{2q}) \qquad (13\text{-}84)$$

Example 13-26: Determine the generating polynomial, $g(x)$, for a triple-error-correcting Reed-Solomon code. Show that the message word has a length of 9 bits. Then, derive the (transmitted) codeword, **v**, for a message word **m** = (101010101).

For a triple-error-correcting Reed-Solomon code, $q = 3$. From Eq.(13-84), the corresponding generating polynomial is given as follows:

$$g(x) = (x + \alpha)(x + \alpha^2)(x + \alpha^3)(x + \alpha^4) (x + \alpha^5)(x + \alpha^6)$$

where

$$(x + \alpha)(x + \alpha^2) = x^2 + (\alpha + \alpha^2)x + \alpha^3 = x^2 + \alpha^5 x + \alpha^3$$

Note that $\alpha + \alpha^2 = \alpha^5$ (from Table 13-12)

$$(x + \alpha^3)(x + \alpha^4) = x^2 + (\alpha^3 + \alpha^4)x + \alpha^7 = x^2 + \alpha^7 x + \alpha^7$$

Note that $\alpha^3 + \alpha^4 = \alpha^3 + \alpha + 1 = \alpha^7$ (from Table 13-12)

$$(x + \alpha^5)(x + \alpha^6) = x^2 + (\alpha^5 + \alpha^6)x + \alpha^{13} = x^2 + \alpha^7 x + \alpha^{13}$$

Note that $\alpha^5 + \alpha^6 = \alpha^2 + \alpha + \alpha^3 + \alpha^2 = \alpha^3 + \alpha = \alpha^9$ (from Table 13-12)

Thus, the generating polynomial of the triple-error-correcting Reed-Solomon code is derived as follows:

$$g(x) = (x^2 + \alpha^5 x + \alpha^3)(x^2 + \alpha^7 x + \alpha^7)(x^2 + \alpha^7 x + \alpha^{13})$$

$$= x^6 + \alpha^{10}x^5 + \alpha^{14}x^4 + \alpha^4 x^3 + \alpha^6 x^2 + \alpha^9 x + \alpha^6 \qquad (13\text{-}85)$$

In accordance with Eqs.(13-69), (13-70), and (13-71), this triple-error-correcting Reed-Solomon code has the following parameters:

$$n = t - 1 = 2^m - 1 = 2^4 - 1 = 15$$
$$n - k = 2q = 2 \times 3 = 6$$

Thus,

$$k = \text{message word length} = 9$$

The message word $m(x)$ [for $\mathbf{m}$ = (101010101)], and the (transmitted) codeword $v(x)$, respectively, are expressed as:

$$m(x) = 1 + x^2 + x^4 + x^6 + x^8$$

$$v(x) = m(x)g(x) = (1 + x^2 + x^4 + x^6 + x^8)(x^6 + \alpha^{10}x^5 + \alpha^{14}x^4 + \alpha^4 x^3 + \alpha^6 x^2 + \alpha^9 x + \alpha^6)$$

$$= x^{14} + \alpha^{10}x^{13} + \alpha^3 x^{12} + \alpha^2 x^{11} + \alpha^2 x^{10} + \alpha^{11}x^9 + \alpha^3 x^8 + \alpha^{11}x^7 + \alpha^{11}x^6$$

$$+ \alpha^{11}x^5 + \alpha^{14}x^4 + \alpha^{14}x^3 + \alpha^9 x + \alpha^6$$

That is, the codeword $\mathbf{v}$ = ($\alpha^6 \alpha^9$ 0 $\alpha^{14}\alpha^{14}\alpha^{11}\alpha^{11}\alpha^{11}\alpha^3\alpha^{11}\alpha^2\alpha^2\alpha^3\alpha^{10}$ 1) is used for transmission.

The minimum distance of this triple-error-correcting Reed-Solomon code is 7 [= $2q$ + 1 = 2 × 3 + 1; from Eq.(13-72)].

Example 13-27: Compare the triple-error correcting (15, 9) Reed-Solomon code, described in Example 13-26, with a (7, 4) CRC code.

- **Percentage overhead**: 67% [= (15 − 9)/9] for a triple-error correcting (15, 9) Reed-Solomon code, and 75% [= (21 − 12)/12] for CRC code. Thus, Reed-Solomon code is less "expensive" than CRC code.

- **Error correction capability**: A Reed-Solomon (15, 9) code can correct 3 erroneous bits (random or bursty) within any 15-bit stream. A (7, 4) CRC can correct a single error within a 7-bit block. When 21 bits are transmitted using CRC, three (3) blocks of 7-bit codeword are received. Assuming three erroneous bits are received, only if the errors are evenly distributed (I.e., one bit error per each 7-bit block), can the three erroneous bits be corrected like the (15, 9) Reed-Solomon code. That is, if any two or three errors occur in the same 7-bit block, as shown in Figure 13-47, they are not correctable. It is clear that Reed-Solomon code is more powerful than the CRC code.

$$\overbrace{\textit{15 or 21 bits}}$$

Information bit stream: $\mathbf{m} = (1010\ 1010\ 1010)$

(1) **Reed-Solomon code:**

$\mathbf{v} = (\underline{\alpha^6 \alpha^9}\ 0\ \alpha^4 \alpha^{14} \alpha^{11} \alpha^{11} \alpha^{11} \alpha^3 \alpha^{11} \alpha^2 \alpha^2 \alpha^3 \alpha^{10}\ 1)$: correctable

$= (\alpha^6 \alpha^9\ 0\ \alpha^4 \alpha^{14} \alpha^{11} \alpha^{11} \underline{\alpha^{11} \alpha^3 \alpha} {}^{11} \alpha^2 \alpha^2 \alpha^3 \alpha^{10}\ 1)$: correctable

$\left\{ \begin{array}{l} \textit{\% overhead = (15 - 9)/9 = 67\%} \\ \textit{Triple error correction} \end{array} \right.$

(2) **CRC code:**

$\mathbf{v} = (00\mathbf{1}101\mathbf{0}\quad 001101\mathbf{0}\quad \mathbf{0}011010)$: correctable

$= (\mathbf{0}01101\mathbf{0}\quad 001101\mathbf{0}\quad \mathbf{0}011010)$: not correctable

$= (\mathbf{0}011010\quad 001101\mathbf{0}\quad \mathbf{0}011010)$: not correctable

$\left\{ \begin{array}{l} \textit{\% overhead = (21 - 12)/12 = 75\%} \\ \textit{2 single error correction} \end{array} \right.$

Figure 13-47   Comparison between Reed-Solomon and CRC codes.

In summary, a triple-error correcting (15, 9) Reed-Solomon code is superior to a (7, 4) single-error correcting CRC code. The tradeoff is higher complexity of coder/decoder circuits. Note that the description of circuit design is beyond the scope of this book.

13.8 A BRIEF DESCRIPTION OF CONVOLUTIONAL CODES

The (n, k) block codes previously described are considered "memoryless devices" because the encoding of a block of message word [i.e., encoding $\mathbf{m} = (1010)$ into a 7-bit codeword of $\mathbf{v} = (0011010)$] is based solely on the current message word block, not on any previous or subsequent message blocks. In contrast, a (n, k, m) convolutional code is a "memory device". The encoding of a k-bit message block is based on: (1) the current message block, and (2) the previous m message blocks.

A (n, k, m) convolutional code can be implemented by a linear sequential circuit that has the characteristic illustrated in Figure 13-48. Within the sequential circuit, there are **k** input ports, **n** output ports, and **m**-bit of memory. The relationship between inputs and outputs is given by the following convolution:

$$\mathbf{v} = \mathbf{u} * \mathbf{g} \qquad (13\text{-}86)$$

Eq.(13-86) is the short-hand notation of the convolution, $\mathbf{v}$, of two sequences $\mathbf{u}$ and $\mathbf{g}$. The operation of the convolution function in Eq.(13-86) is expressed as follows:

$$v_j^{(r)} = \sum_{i=0}^{m} u_{j-1} g_i^{(r)} \qquad \textit{for all } j \geq 0 \textit{ and } r = (1, n) \qquad (13\text{-}87)$$

That is, $\mathbf{v}$ is the convolution of $\mathbf{u}$ and $\mathbf{g}$, where $\mathbf{g}$ is the generating sequence of the (n, k, m) convolutional code.

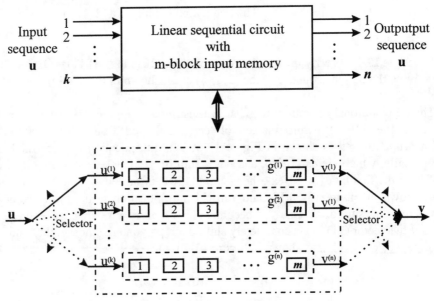

Figure 13-48   A (n, k, m) Convolutional Code.

Example 13-28: Given the encoder (i.e., the sequential circuit shown in Figure 13-49) for a (2, 1, 3) convolutional code with the generating sequences indicated in Eq.(13-88) and (13-89), determine the output sequence $\mathbf{v}$, if the input sequence is $\mathbf{u} = (\ldots 10111 \ldots)$.

$$g^{(1)} = (1011) \qquad (13\text{-}88)$$
$$g^{(2)} = (1111) \qquad (13\text{-}89)$$

The output sequences $v^{(1)}$ and $v^{(2)}$ can be obtained from the following convolutions:

$$\mathbf{v}^{(1)} = (10111) * (1011) = (10000001) \qquad (13\text{-}90)$$
$$\mathbf{v}^{(2)} = (10111) * (1111) = (11011101) \qquad (13\text{-}91)$$

Next, by bit-interleaving $\mathbf{v}^{(1)}$ and $\mathbf{v}^{(2)}$, the final output sequence $\mathbf{v}$ is obtained as follows:

$$\mathbf{u} = (\ldots 1101000101010011\ldots)$$

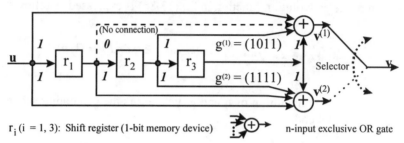

r_i (i = 1, 3): Shift register (1-bit memory device)   n-input exclusive OR gate

Figure 13-49   The Sequential Circuit of a (2, 1, 3) Code.

Example 13-29: Verify the (digital) convolution, $(10111) * (1011) = (10000001)$, used in deriving the output sequence of the (2, 1, 3) code, shown in Eq.(13-90).

The convolutional operation of $\mathbf{g}^{(1)} * \mathbf{u}$ is illustrated in Figure 13-50. The vector $\mathbf{g}^{(1)}$ stays "as is" [i.e., (1011)], while $\mathbf{u}$ is convoluted (i.e., flipped) from (10111) into (11101), and lined-up with $\mathbf{g}^{(1)}$ as shown in Figure 13-50(A). Multiplication is performed "bit-by-bit" vertically, which yields (1000), and has a sum of "1" [1+0+0+0 = 1; mod(2) operation]. This is the first bit of $\mathbf{v}^{(1)}$. Next, the vector (11101) is shifted to its left by one bit position, as shown in Figure 13-50(B), and vertical multiplication results in a vector of (0000), which has a sum of 0. This "0" becomes the 2nd bit of $\mathbf{v}^{(1)}$. This procedure is continued until the vector (11101) is completely shifted out [beyond the most-right hand bit position of the vector (1011)], as shown in Figure 13-50(Z).

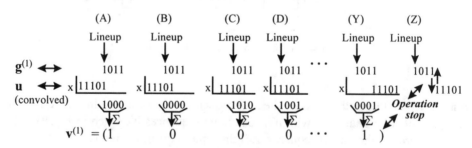

Figure 13-50   Convolutional Operation of $\mathbf{g}^{(1)}$ and $\mathbf{u}$.

13.9 CODES USED FOR DIGITAL CELLULAR NETWORKS

The channel encoder used in GSM and IS-54/IS-136 applications is presented in this section. Both GSM and IS-54 (IS-136) use a combination of CRC and convolutional codes to control channel errors resulting from noisy airway environments.

13.9.1 GSM Error Control

Speech (Voice-Frequency; VF) signals are typically sampled and encoded into an 8-bit companded PCM signal. These PCM bits are buffered and delivered to the speech encoder every 20 ms. In this 20 ms interval there are 160 samples that are processed as a group. This 20 ms interval is equivalent to 1280 bits [i.e., 8 bits every 125 µs, and 8 bits × (20 ms)/(125 µs) = 1280 bits]. These 1280 bits are converted from an 8-bit companded signal into a 13-bit linear signal having 2080 bits per 20 ms (1280 × 13/8 = 2080, as shown in Figure 13-51). This step is required because a traditional speech encoder cannot accept a nonlinear signal (i.e., an 8-bit companded signal is a nonlinear signal). After being processed by the speech encoder, the 20 ms speech signal is compressed from 2080 bits to 260 bits per 20 ms. These 260 bits of data are **not** equally important from speech reconstruction viewpoint because they consist of the following three groups of information:

(1)   In every 20 ms interval, 36 bits are used to represent the linear predictive filter parameters of the speech encoder.

(2)   In every 5 ms interval, 9 bits are used to represent the long term prediction parameters of the speech encoder.

(3)   In every 5 ms interval, 47 bits are used to represent the regular pulse excited parameter of the speech encoder.

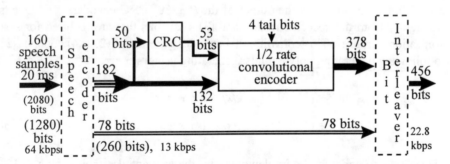

Figure 13-51   Channel Error Control Coders for GSM.

Therefore, among the 260 bits (per 20 ms) from the output of the speech encoder, some bits are considered to be more important than the others. The GSM standards committee has decided to group the 260 bits into two classes:

• **Class-I bits**: This class contains 182 bits (out of the total 260 bits) that are considered important for speech signal restoration. Because these bits can be corrupted by channel noise when transmitted over the radio link, they must be protected by error channel codes to achieve an acceptable reconstructed speech signal quality. These 182 bits are further divided into two sub-groups:

* **Class-Ia**: This group contains 50 bits that are the most significant of all of the 260 bits at the output of the speech encoder. They are strongly protected by applying both a CRC channel error control code and a convolutional code.

* **Class-Ib**: This group contains 132 bits. They are not as important as Class-Ia bits, but are more important than Class-II bits. Therefore, Class-Ib bits are protected by a convolutional code, which is actually better than the CRC code.

• **Class-II bits**: There are 78 bits that are classified as Class-II bits. This class of bits have a limited effect on the restored speech signal if they are corrupted by channel noise. However, because of bandwidth limitations, Class-II bits are not protected by either CRC code or convolutional codes.

There are 50 bits of Class-Ia information from the speech encoder that are fed into a CRC encoder. The CRC code used in this system is a (53, 50) CRC code, sometimes called a 3-bit CRC code because 3 additional bits are added to the information stream to achieve error control (i.e., detection/correction function). Another reason that this (53, 50) CRC code is called CRC-3 is that the degree of the generating polynomial [see in Eq.(13-92)], for this code is 3.

$$g(x) = 1 + x + x^3 \tag{13-92}$$

Three sets of information are fed into a 1/2 rate convolutional encoder (shown in Figure 13-51): (1) 53 bits from the output of the (53, 50) CRC encoder, (2) 132 bits of Class-Ib signals from the speech encoder, and (3) 4 tail bits that are required for system synchronization purposes. This convolutional encoder generates a (2, 1, 4) code, based on the two following generating polynomials (generating vectors):

$$\mathbf{g}^{(1)} = (11001); \qquad g(x) = 1 + x^3 + x^4 \tag{13-93}$$

$$\mathbf{g}^{(2)} = (11011); \qquad g(x) = 1 + x + x^3 + x^4 \tag{13-94}$$

This (2, 1, 4) code can be implemented by the sequential circuit shown in Figure 13-52. There are four one-bit memory devices (r_1, r_2, r_3 and r_4: shift registers) since $m = 4$. The notation $\oplus$ represents an exclusive OR gate with three or four inputs. The output $\mathbf{v}^{(1)}$ is derived from the generating vector $\mathbf{g}^{(1)} = (11001)$, and the output $\mathbf{v}^{(2)}$ is derived from the generating vector $\mathbf{g}^{(2)} = (11011)$, using Eq.(3-81) (i.e., $\mathbf{v} = \mathbf{u} * \mathbf{g}$). The output $\mathbf{v}$ is then generated by bit-interleaving $\mathbf{v}^{(1)}$ and $\mathbf{v}^{(2)}$ via the selector function.

A "1" in the generating vector [$\mathbf{g}^{(1)}$ or $\mathbf{g}^{(2)}$] indicates that the output of a shift register is connected to its corresponding exclusive OR gate, while a "0" implies no connection (as represented by dashed lines in Figure 13-51). Four important characteristics can be derived from the circuit block diagram of a GSM system shown in Figure 13-51:

(1) A digitized speech signal fed to a wireless speech encoder has a speed of 64 kbps.

(2) At the output of the speech encoder, the speech signal has a speed of 13 kbps.

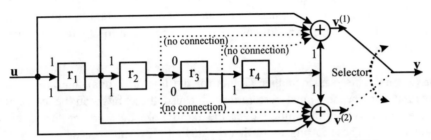

Figure 13-52   A (2, 1, 4) Convolutional Coder for GSM.

(3) The convolution code used in the GSM system is (2, 1, 4) (i.e., a code rate of ½), and its output contains 378 bits [= 2 × (53 + 132 + 4)] per 20 ms. This data stream of 378 bits represents 182 Class I bits (including Classes Ia and Ib bits). Clearly, it is costly [i.e., an overhead of 196 bits (= 378 − 182); 108% (= 196/182)] to implement error control (error detection and correction) for a digital signal.

(4) The number of bits in the output of the bit-interleaver is 456 bits per 20 ms interval. Therefore, a digitized speech signal (with error protection capability) for wireless (radio cellular) transmission has a speed of 22.8 kbps. In comparison, the transmission speed is 64 kbps without any error protection capability. Hence, the tradeoff is complicated circuit design, but it is a worthwhile investment.

13.9.2 IS-54/IS-136 Error Control

The IS-54/IS-136 (note that IS-136 is the new name for IS-54) error control technique is similar to the GSM system. The speech signal is sampled and encoded into an 8-bit companded PCM signal, and μ-law (instead of the A-law) companding is used in IS-54 systems. The PCM bits are buffered and delivered to the speech encoder every 20 ms. During this 20 ms interval 160 samples are processed as a group. This 20 ms interval is equivalent to 1280 bits, which must be converted from an 8-bit companded signal into a 13-bit linear signal containing 2080 bits per 20 ms interval (Figure 13-53). After being processed by the speech encoder, the 20 ms speech signal is compressed into 159 bits per 20 ms. These 159 bits consist of the following three groups of information:

(1) In every 20 ms interval, 43 bits are used to represent the linear predictive filter parameters of the speech encoder.

(2) In every 5 ms interval, 7 bits are used to represent the long term prediction parameters of the speech encoder.

(3) In every 5 ms interval, 22 bits are used to represent the regular pulse excited parameter of the speech encoder.

Of the 159 bits (per 20 ms) in the output of the speech encoder, some bits are considered more important than others. Therefore, the IS-54 standard committee has grouped these 159 bits into two classes: (1) Class I, including Class Ia and Class Ib, and (2) Class II. This is necessary to ensure proper error control (detection/correction) functions are implemented.

- **Class-I bits**: This class contains 77 bits (of the total 159 bits) that are considered important for speech signal restoration. Because these bits can be corrupted by channel noise when transmitted over the radio link, they are protected by error channel codes. These 77 bits are further divided into two sub-groups:

  * **Class-Ia**: This group contains 12 bits that are the most significant of the 159 bits produced by the speech encoder. They are protected by both CRC channel error control and convolutional codes.

  * **Class-Ib**: This group contains 65 bits. They are not as important as the Class-Ia bits, but are more important than Class-II bits. Therefore, they are protected by a convolutional code.

- **Class-II bits**: There are 82 bits classified as Class-II bits. The Class-II bits will have a limited effect on the restored speech signal if they are corrupted by channel noise. However, because of bandwidth limitations they are not protected by CRC or convolutional codes.

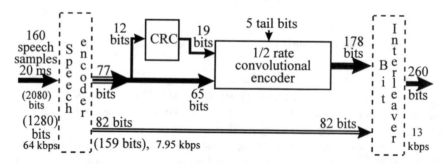

Figure 13-53   Channel Error Control Coders for IS-54/IS-136.

A description of the CRC and the convolutional codes used by IS-54/IS-136 to protect the Class-Ia and the Class I-b bits is provided in this chapter. Twelve bits of Class-Ia information from the speech encoder are fed into a CRC encoder. The CRC code used in this system is a (19, 12) CRC code. It is also called a 7-bit CRC code because its generating polynomial [see Eq.(13-95)] has a degree of 7.

$$g(x) = 1 + x + x^2 + x^4 + x^5 + x^7 \qquad (13\text{-}95)$$

Three sets of information are fed into a 1/2 rate convolutional encoder: (1) 19 bits from the output of the (19, 12) CRC encoder, representing the Class Ia bits, (2) 65 bits of Class-Ib signals from the speech encoder, and (3) 5 tail bits (required for system synchronization). This IS-54/IS-136 convolutional code is a (2, 1, 5) code, based on the two following generating polynomials (generating vectors):

$$\mathbf{g}^{(1)} = (111101); \quad g(x) = 1 + x^2 + x^3 + x^4 + x^5 \qquad (13\text{-}96)$$

$$\mathbf{g}^{(2)} = (101011); \quad g(x) = 1 + x + x^3 + x^5 \qquad (13\text{-}97)$$

This (2, 1, 5) code can be be implemented by the sequential circuit shown in Figure 13-54. There are five one-bit memory devices (r_1, r_2, r_3, r_4 and r_5: shift registers) since m = 5. The notation $\oplus$ represents an exclusive OR gate with three or four inputs. The output $\mathbf{v}^{(1)}$ is derived from the generating vector $\mathbf{g}^{(1)}$ = (11001), and the output $\mathbf{v}^{(2)}$ is derived from the generating vector $\mathbf{g}^{(2)}$ = (11011), using Eq.(3-81) (i.e., $\mathbf{v} = \mathbf{u} * \mathbf{g}$). The output $\mathbf{v}$ is then generated by bit-interleaving $\mathbf{v}^{(1)}$ and $\mathbf{v}^{(2)}$ via selector function.

A "1" in the generating vector [$\mathbf{g}^{(1)}$ or $\mathbf{g}^{(2)}$] indicates that the output of a shift register is connected to its corresponding exclusive OR gate, while a "0" implies no connection (as represented by dashed lines in Figure 13-54).

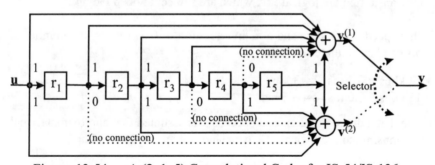

Figure 13-54   A (2, 1, 5) Convolutional Coder for IS-54/IS-136.

Four important characteristics can be derived from the circuit block diagram of a GSM system shown in Figure 13-53:

(1)   A digitized speech signal fed to a wireless speech encoder has a speed of 64 kbps.

(2)   At the output of the speech encoder, the speech signal has a speed of 7.95 kbps.

(3)   The convolution code used in the IS-54 system is (2, 1, 5) (i.e., a code rate of ½), and its output contains 178 bits [= 2 × (19 + 65 + 5)] per 20 ms. This data stream of 178 bits represents 77 Class I bits (including Class Ia and Class Ib). Clearly, it is costly [i.e., an overhead of 101 bits (= 178 − 77); 131% (= 101/77)] to implement error control (error detection and correction) for a digital signal.

(4)   The number of bits in the output of a bit-interleaver is 260 bits per 20 ms interval. Therefore, a digitized speech signal (with error protection capability) for wireless (radio cellular) transmission has a speed of 13 kbps. In comparison, the transmission speed is 64 kbps without any error protection capability. Hence, the tradeoff is complicated circuit design, but it is a worthwhile investment.

13.10 BIT INTERLEAVING FOR BURSTY ERROR CONTROL

When a digital signal is transported over a radio channel, signal fading is a common occurrence. The typical duration of a fading condition may last from 0.5 to 1 ms. During this fading interval, approximately 3 to 11 bits of the digital signal may subject to errors. If the condition is severe, it is known as "**deep fading**".

*   With a speed of 22.8 kbps and a fading duration of 0.5~1.0 ms, the number of bursty errors can be calculated as follows:

    * 22.8 kbps × 0.5 ms /2 = 5.7   bits
    * 22.8 kbps × 1.0 ms /2 = 11.4 bits

    (Note that a divisor of 2 is used because it is assumed that approximately half of the bits transmitted are logical "1", which are subject to deep fading.)

*   With a speed of 13 kbps and a fading duration of 0.5~1.0 ms, the number of bursty errors can be calculated as follows:

    * 13 kbps × 0.5 ms /2 = 3.3 bits
    * 13 kbps × 1.0 ms /2 = 6.5 bits

    (Note that a divisor of 2 is used because it is assumed that approximately half of the bits transmitted are logical "1", which are subject to deep fading.)

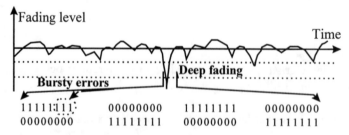

Figure 13-55   Deep Fading (of Radio Transmission) and Bursty Errors.

Figure 13-55 shows the fading level (e.g., 10-dB, 20-dB fading) of a typical received signal. The contents of the digital bitstream before and after the "**deep fading**" interval is shown. For simplicity, it is assumed that 64 bits are transmitted during this interval, and a three-bit bursty error occurred because of deep fading. The channel error control codes described throughout this chapter can not correct a three-bit bursty error. Therefore, a technology known as **bit interleaving** is applied to "**spread**" (i.e., convert) bursty errors into random errors. Random errors are typically single **correctable** errors (after bit interleaving function) that are spread over several separate code blocks.

A bit interleaver is a buffer (store) that consists of *m* "n-bit" shift registers (note that *m* can be equal to *n*). It accepts a data stream as its input, and data stream is assumed as follows:

$$x = (a_{11}, a_{12}, \ldots, a_{1n}, a_{21}, a_{22}, \ldots, a_{2n}, \ldots, a_{m1}, a_{m2}, \ldots, a_{mn}) \tag{13-98}$$

$$G = \begin{bmatrix} a_{11} & a_{12} & a_{13} & \cdots & a_{1n} \\ a_{21} & a_{22} & a_{23} & \cdots & a_{2n} \\ a_{31} & a_{32} & a_{33} & \cdots & a_{3n} \\ \vdots & & & & \vdots \\ a_{m1} & a_{m2} & a_{m3} & \cdots & a_{mn} \end{bmatrix} \tag{13-99}$$

The structure within the bit interleaver can be visualized as a matrix, with dimensions of "*m* by *n*", as shown in Eq.(13-94). The bits are fed into the buffer (store) "row by row" (i.e., horizontally). The first bit is stored in row No. 1 and column No. 1; the second bit is stored in row No. 1 and column No. 2; and the nth bit is stored in row No. 1 and the last (n^{th}) column of the matrix. When the data is extracted from the buffer (store), it is read "column by column" (i.e., vertically).

The output bitstream from the bit interleaver appears in the following sequence:

$$y = (a_{11}, a_{21}, \ldots, a_{m1}, a_{12}, a_{22}, \ldots, a_{m2}, \ldots, a_{1n}, a_{2n}, \ldots, a_{mn}) \tag{13-100}$$

Example 13-30: Illustrate the effect of using a bit interleaver to control bursty errors for the bitstream (10101010 10101010 10101010 10101010 10101010 10101010 10101010 10101010).

At the transmitter, the digital data bitstream is fed into the bit interleaver (assumed to be an 8 by 8 buffer store in this example) "row by row" (i.e., horizontally) as shown in Figure 13-56(A), and Eq.(13-101).

$$G_{\text{Interleaver}} = \begin{pmatrix} 1 & 0 & 1 & 0 & 1 & 0 & 1 & 0 \\ 1 & 0 & 1 & 0 & 1 & 0 & 1 & 0 \\ 1 & 0 & 1 & 0 & 1 & 0 & 1 & 0 \\ 1 & 0 & 1 & 0 & 1 & 0 & 1 & 0 \\ 1 & 0 & 1 & 0 & 1 & 0 & 1 & 0 \\ 1 & 0 & 1 & 0 & 1 & 0 & 1 & 0 \\ 1 & 0 & 1 & 0 & 1 & 0 & 1 & 0 \\ 1 & 0 & 1 & 0 & 1 & 0 & 1 & 0 \end{pmatrix} \tag{13-101}$$

The output bitstream from the bit interleaver will be transmitted over the radio channel [read out of the buffer store "column by column" (i.e., vertically)] as shown in Eq.(13-102):

$$d_{transmitted} = (11111\textbf{111}\ 00000000\ 11111111\ 00000000$$
$$11111111\ 00000000\ 11111111\ 00000000) \qquad (13\text{-}102)$$

Assume that the deep fading of the radio channel has caused a three-bit bursty error in the first 8-bit block, highlighted by "**000**" in Figure 13-56(B). The erroneous received signal bitsream is shown in Eq.(13-103).

$$d_{received} = (11111\textbf{000}\ 00000000\ 11111111\ 00000000$$
$$11111111\ 00000000\ 11111111\ 00000000) \qquad (13\text{-}103)$$

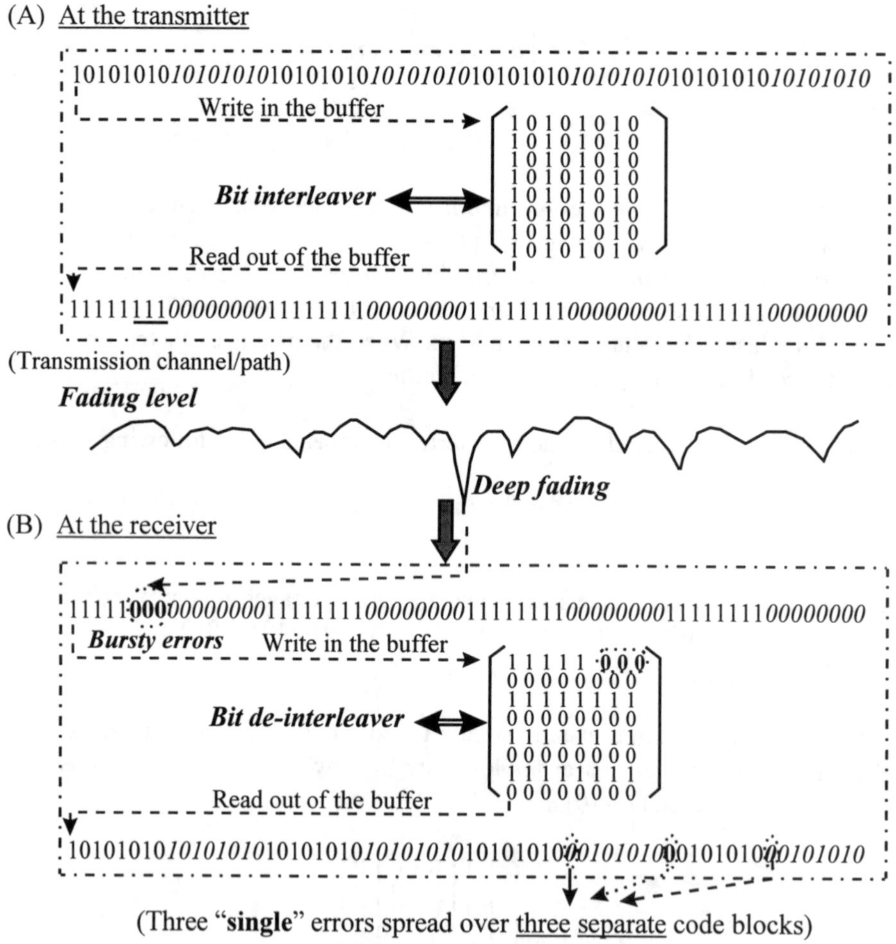

(A) <u>At the transmitter</u>

(Transmission channel/path)

(B) <u>At the receiver</u>

(Three "**single**" errors spread over <u>three</u> <u>separate</u> code blocks)

Figure 13-56   Bit Interleaver and Bit De-interleaver.

From Eq. (13-103), it can be seen that the first block of the received digital data bitstream is an erroneous block. If a conventional CRC and/or convolutional code is applied to control (detect/correct) this block containing three bits in error, the decoder will be unable to correct these errors. Therefore, before applying the decoder a "bit de-interleaver" is used. The received digital data bitstream is fed into the bit de-interleaver "row by row" (i.e., horizontally) as shown in Figure 13-56, and Eq.(13-104).

$$\mathbf{G}_{\text{de-interleaver}} = \begin{pmatrix} 1 & 1 & 1 & 1 & 1 & 0 & 0 & 0 \\ 0 & 0 & 0 & 0 & 0 & 0 & 0 & 0 \\ 1 & 1 & 1 & 1 & 1 & 1 & 1 & 1 \\ 0 & 0 & 0 & 0 & 0 & 0 & 0 & 0 \\ 1 & 1 & 1 & 1 & 1 & 1 & 1 & 1 \\ 0 & 0 & 0 & 0 & 0 & 0 & 0 & 0 \\ 1 & 1 & 1 & 1 & 1 & 1 & 1 & 1 \\ 0 & 0 & 0 & 0 & 0 & 0 & 0 & 0 \end{pmatrix} \qquad (13\text{-}104)$$

The data is extracted from the bit de-interleaver (i.e., read out of a buffer store) "column by column" (i.e., vertically) as shown in Figure 13-56. Therefore, the output digital data bitstream of the bit de-interleaver (to be fed to the error control decoder) becomes:

$$d_{\text{stream-to-decoder}} = (10101010\ 10101010\ 10101010\ 10101010$$
$$10101010\ \underline{0}0101010\ \underline{0}0101010\ \underline{0}0101010) \qquad (13\text{-}105)$$

It can be seen from Eq.(13-105) that the three-bit bursty error has been spread across three separate blocks, each containing a single error. Typically, single errors can be detected/corrected by a CRC or convolutional codes. Therefore, the receiver has accomplished the goal of applying bit-interleaving to "**spread**" the bursty errors into detectable/correctable single bit errors. Note that the buffer store sizes at the transmitter and receiver must be properly designed to implement this function.

As a general rule, "***the larger the buffer size, the better the error detect/correct capability becomes***." The tradeoff is increased system "delay" time which is detrimental in speech signal transmission. This is particularly true in "wireless" systems where other equipment also contributes to the system delay, and thus results in undesirable (unacceptable) echo conditions (see Chapter 1).

Example 13-31: Describe applications of a channel encoder for wireless service.

As shown in Figure 13-57, the channel encoder, including the CRC and the convolutional codes [(19, 12) CRC code and (2, 1, 5) convolutional code for IS-136; and (53, 50) CRC code and (2, 1, 4) convolutional code for GSM] is located in Base Station (BS) (i.e., the base station transceiver equipment). Following the channel encoder is the bit interleaver used to control bursty errors.

A question often asked is: "Should the channel encoder be located in the Mobile Switching Center (MSC) instead of the base station?" The answer is "**No**", because a channel encoder adds redundancy in the digital data bitstream. If it is placed in the MSC, then the T1 digital carrier system (see Chapter 6 for detailed description; Vol. 1) between the MSC and the base station will have lower capacity for carrying speech signals.

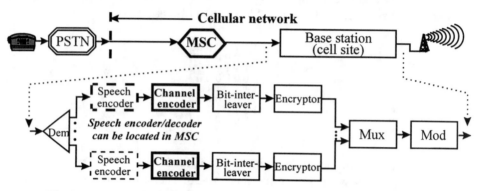

Figure 13-57   Channel Encoder Application in a Wireless Network.

It has been clearly stated, "*channel encoding requires a larger bandwidth due to the additive bit redundancy.*" In wireless applications (see Chapter 8 for detailed description) the bandwidth is scarcely. Any way to save channel bandwidth is preferable.

Two questions frequently asked are: (1) "Can the speech encoder be placed in the MSC rather than the base station?", and (2) "If a speech encoder is placed in the MSC, what are the advantages and disadvantages?"

The answer to the first question is "Yes", some wireless systems implement speech encoders in the base station while others locate speech encoders in the MSC. The answer to the second question is explained in Example 13-32.

Example 13-32: Compare a wireless system that has a speech encoder in the MSC with a wireless system with a speech encoder located in the base station. Assume both systems use T1 digital carrier systems to connect the MSC and the base station, and use speech encoders that support digital speech at 8 kbps.

Figure 13-58 illustrates the two architectures for implementing a speech encoder in a wireless system: (1) the speech encoder within the base station, and (2) the speech encoder within the MSC.

(1)   **A speech encoder within the base station**: This is the traditional method for implementing the speech encoder. T1 digital carrier systems have been deployed in digital networks since 1961. T1 technology is mature, and the equipment (e.g., the mulitplexer and the transmitter for handling twenty-four 64 kbps digital signals; and the demultiplexer at the receiver) required for transmitting various digital signals is

widely available. Therefore, when cellular networks were introduced in the mid 1970s, it was decided to use T1 carrier systems as the facilities for connecting the MSC to base stations. Locating speech encoders within the base station does not disturb this well-established network architecture (i.e., T1 technology). However, the maximum T1 capacity for speech signal transmission is 24 voice channels. Therefore, the bandwidth savings (from 64 kbps to 8 kbps) offered by the speech encoder is not utilized. Note that practical wireless systems typically use 22 channels (out of 24 channels) for speech signals.

(2)   **A speech encoder within the MSC**: This is a relatively new method for implementing speech encoders in wireless systems. It takes advantages of the bandwidth savings offered by the speech encoder. That is:

The maximum T1 capacity = 24 × (64 kbps)/(8 kbps) = 192 voice channels

Therefore, the potential capacity increase over traditional T1 is eight fold (i.e., 192 vs. 24). This factor is extremely attractive.

However, the technology for implementing the multiplexer/demultiplexer are new, and need to be "proven in". Because of the added complexity of the equipment design needed to carry more voice signals, the system requires more bandwidth for implementing control signals (i.e., data link control channels). Therefore, the actual capacity gain may not be factor of 8. However, it is believed that the capacity gained is sufficient to offset the costs of the "new" equipment.

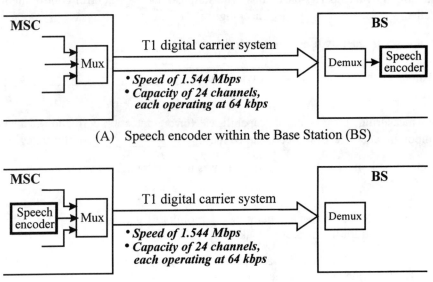

(A)   Speech encoder within the Base Station (BS)

(B)   Speech encoder within the MSC

Figure 13-58   Architectures for Speech Encoders in Wireless Applications.

Review Questions for Chapter 13

(1) From a system application viewpoint, there are three types of coders which are used in various parts of a communication network. The coder that converts an analog signal into a digital signal is called a source encoder. The other two types of coders are _____ encoders and _____ encoders.

(2) (True, false) Networks used for voice signal transport do not apply channel (error) control code in landline applications (i.e., applications other than wireless).

(3) Determine (statistically) the number of bits that may be erroneously decoded (from "1" to "0" or from "0" to "1") if a system has an average rate of 1.544 Mbps and has transmitted data for 10 minutes with a bit error rate of 10^{-5}.

(4) (True, false) For a receiver to restore a digital data stream accurately, it must receive an incoming data stream with a high density of waveform transitions (from "1" to "0", and "0" to "1") to achieve timing synchronization. That is, a digital system must apply "zero suppression (substitution)", in addition to providing clocks with high accuracy.

(5) To transmit a digital bitstream of "11101 ... ", five possible waveforms can be used. They are _____, _____, _____, _____, and _____.

(6) There are many ways to detect and/or correct erroneous bits in a received data stream. The most common scheme is to add extra bits to the information data stream, known as parity-check bits. The simplest and easiest error control method is called _____ or _____ parity checking.

(7) Name six frequently used error control codes: _____ (CRC), _____, _____, _____, _____, and _____ codes. Among them, wireless systems typical apply _____, _____, and/or _____ codes.

(8) In measuring error control capabilities (error detection/correction), the most important characteristic used is called the _____ of the code.

(9) Determine k in a (9, k) CRC code that uses the generating polynomial:

$$g(x) = 1 + x + x^2 + x^4$$

(10) A (13, 8) CRC code has a generating polynomial of $g(x) = 1 + x^2 + x^5$. Determine the codeword for the message block of $\mathbf{m} = (10101011)$.

(11) Determine whether the received codeword, $\mathbf{r} = (0111110)$ is a valid codeword for a (7, 4) CRC code with the generating matrix $\mathbf{G}$ is given by Eq.(13-13).

(12) In addition to error control code (e.g., CRC, Reed-Solomon, BCH, convolutional codes, etc.), to control bursty errors more effectively in wireless systems _____-_____ is often used.

CHAPTER 14

Timing and Synchronization

Chapter Objectives

Upon the completion of this chapter, you should be able to:

- Define frames, time slots, timing/synchronization, and describe the importance of timing and synchronization of a digital system/network.

- Discuss clock, frequency, time standards, and associated standards organizations [e.g., US National Bureau of Standards (NBS), the US Naval Observatory (USNO), the Bureau International de l'Heure (BIH)].

- Discuss the levels of synchronization needs, and describe frame synchronization examples (e.g., DS1, SONET/SDH frame synchronization schemes/requirements).

- Discuss network synchronization methods: including master-slave, mutual synchronization, external reference, pulse stuffing, and independent clock techniques for network timing and synchronization.

- Discuss US clock hierarchy (strata 1, 2, 3, and 4), clock accuracy and slip rate requirements, timing recovery techniques (phase locked loop, zero suppression, and scrambling), the Global Positioning System (GPS) and its applications, and synchronization for public-switched and private networks.

14.1 INTRODUCTION

In the past two decades, telecommunications customers have continuously requested increasing speeds for information transport services over telecommunications networks. Since digital networking offers many advantages over analog networking (e.g., ease of multiplexing, integrating different signal types, better transmission quality, and improved network security)this has been the "technology of choice" for offering high-speed services. Multimedia, ISDN, and IP applications demand digital networking technologies be deployed widely throughout global networks.

Definition 14-1 From a timing and synchronization viewpoint, a digital network is a time-sharing network that divides the available transport time (capacity or bandwidth) into smaller divisions that are shared among many telecommunications end users.

Implementation: To implement the digital network time-sharing capability, the following steps are required to offer the so-called "Time Division Multiplexing" (TDM) capability:

(1) **Divide time into smaller units called "frames"** (see Figure 14-1). In many modern telecommunications applications, the following terms have been widely adopted:

- **A frame**: The term "frame" is applied generically in many telecommunications fields. A frame typically has an interval of 125 μs (based on the Nyquist sampling rate for a voice signal at 8 kHz; 1/8000 of a second = 125 μs).

- **Multiframe**: Several definitions of the term "multiframe" have been adopted in telecommunications applications:

    * For SONET/SDH applications when transporting DS1 (1.544 Mbps), E1 (2.048 Mbps), DS1C (3.152 Mbps), or DS2 (6.312 Mbps) signals, a "multiframe" has an interval of 500 μs (i.e., four 125 μs frames).

    * For wireless applications, a "multiframe" can be either a 20 ms (160 frames), 10 ms (80 frames), 5 ms (40 frames), or 4 ms (32 frames) interval.

(2) **Allocate time slots (within frames)**: Before sharing the system bandwidth (capacity) among users, a digital network always divides a "frame" into several time slots (TSs; timeslots), as shown in Figure 14-1.

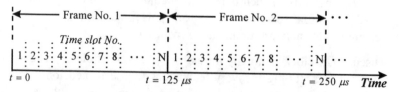

Figure 14-1   Frames and Time Slots (Timeslots).

Example 14-1: Describe four commonly-used frames/timeslot methodologies shown in Figure 14-2.

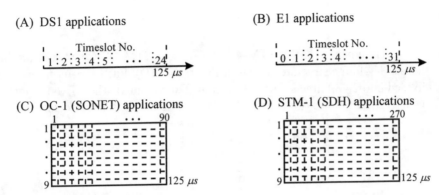

(A) DS1 applications

(B) E1 applications

(C) OC-1 (SONET) applications

(D) STM-1 (SDH) applications

Figure 14-2   Examples of Frame Structures Used in Digital Transport.

These methodologies are described as follows:

(1) The μ-law digital signals (DS1, DS1C, DS2, DS3 and DS4; Chapter 6) are based on the DS1 frame structure shown in Figure 14-2(A). Each 125-μs frame interval is divided into 24 time slots. For most digital applications the 24 time slots are used for 24 channels to carry 24 voice or voiceband data signals (64 kbps each). That is,

$$DS1 = (1\ bit\ overhead + 24\frac{timeslots}{frame} \times 8\frac{bits}{timeslot}) \times 8000\frac{frames}{second}$$

$$= 8\ kbps\ \text{overhead} + 24 \times 64\ kbps = \textbf{1.544 Mbps} \qquad (14\text{-}1)$$

(2) The A-law digital signals (E1, E2, E3 and E4; Chapter 6) are based on the E1 frame structure shown in Figure 14-2(B). Each 125-μs frame interval is divided into 32 time slots (note that the time slots are numbered from 0 through 31). In most digital networks, only 30 out of 32 timeslots are assigned to carry voice (or voicegrade data). The two remaining time slots are assigned for network signaling applications. However, there are systems that use 31 out of 32 timeslots for data transport. The E1 signal rate can be derived as follows:

$$E1 = (2 \times 8\ bits\ overhead + 30\frac{timeslots}{frame} \times 8\frac{bits}{timeslot}) \times 8000\frac{frames}{second}$$

$$= 128\ kbps\ \text{overhead} + 30 \times 64\ kbps = \textbf{2.048 Mbps} \qquad (14\text{-}2)$$

(3) The SONET signals (OC-1, OC-3, OC-12, OC-48 and OC-192; Chapter 6) are based on the OC-1 frame structure shown in Figure 14-2(C). Each 125-μs frame interval is divided into 810 time slots (= 9 rows by 90 columns). The OC-1 signal rate can be derived as follows (note that SONET signal rates are modular, also shown):

$$OC-1 = 9 \times 90\frac{bytes}{frame} \times 8\frac{bits}{byte} \times 8000\frac{frames}{\sec ond} = \textbf{51.84 Mbps} \qquad (14\text{-}3)$$

$$OC\text{-}N = N \times 51.84 \textbf{ Mbps} \qquad (14\text{-}4)$$

(4) The SDH signals (STM-1, STM-4, STM-16 and STM-64; Chapter 6) are based on the STM-1 frame structure shown in Figure 14-2(D). Each 125-µs frame interval is divided into 2,430 time slots (= 9 rows by 270 columns). The STM-1 signal rate can be derived as follows (note that SDH signal rates are modular, also shown):

$$STM-1 = 9 \times 270\frac{bytes}{frame} \times 8\frac{bits}{byte} \times 8000\frac{frames}{\sec ond} = \textbf{155.52 Mbps} \qquad (14\text{-}5)$$

$$STM\text{-}N = N \times \textbf{155.52 Mbps} \qquad (14\text{-}6)$$

System capacity is divided into many time slots (channels) used for carrying either subscriber information or network associated control signaling. It is clear that a digital system must be able to identify all time units (e.g., frame boundaries, time slot boundaries, and byte boundaries). In addition, the system must detect the start or the end point of a "bit". These functions in digital networking are called "***network timing and synchronization***" activities.

There are three levels of synchronization in a digital system: (1) "bit", (2) "frame", and (3) "network" synchronization. Implementation of synchronization requires "clocks" for any network element [e.g., Private Branch eXchanges (PBXs), digital switching machines, Digital Cross-connect Systems (DCSs), Add-Drop Multiplexers (ADM), Integrated Digital Loop Carrier (IDLC) systems, regenerators, Echo Cancelers (ECs), etc.). That is, digital signal transmission (unlike analog transmission) requires each signal to be available at a precise time for transmission/switching functions. Therefore, "synchronized" and "accurate" clocks are required throughout digital networks.

14.2 TIME, FREQUENCY AND CLOCK

Four basic units of scientific (science, engineering) measurement are: (1) length, (2) mass, (3) time, and (4) temperature. Each unit has its own standard. The quantity involved in the "time" measurement is the "time interval". The international standard for "time" is based on the definition of a "**second**".

Various time scales, besides "seconds", have been developed to keep track of daily activities. For example, "astronomical time" and "atomic time" are two well-established time standards. There are methods for reconciling them for basic time measurement applications. National and international standardized "time scales" enable precise time and frequency dissemination to provide the necessary "timing reference" for activities such as synchronization of digital communications networks.

For many years astronomers used "mean solar time" as the time standard. Mean solar time was based on the "rotation of the earth about its axis", with respect to the **sun**. The "Universal Time" (UT0) was a time scale derived from mean solar time. Later derivations of UT1 and UT2 (with corrections) provide more accurate time standards. With the development of atomic clocks, timing accuracy has been improved considerably, and eventually led to the advent of **Coordinated Universal Time** (UTC).

14.2.1 Time Standards

Several national and international organizations are devoted to the development and maintenance of standards for time, time intervals, frequency, and clock sources. In the USA, two organizations that provide time and frequency information are:

(1) National Institute for Standards and Technology (NIST): The NIST develops and maintains atomic frequency and time standards by disseminating frequency and time indicators via "radio broadcasts". It controls distribution of frequency and time for the US National Bureau of Standards (NBS).

(2) U.S. Naval Observatory (USNO): This organization conducts regularly astronomical observations for determining UT1, and keeps accurate clocks running for US Department of Defense (DOD) applications. The USNO controls distribution of Precise Time and Time Interval (PTTI) via US navy radio stations, satellites, and radio navigation systems [known as Long Range Navigation (LORAN C)] that are operated and maintained by the US Coast Guard.

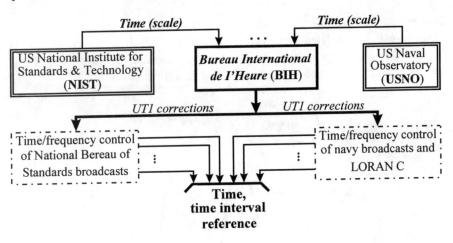

Figure 14-3   Coordination between National and International Time Scales.

The Bureau International de I'Heure (BIH) in Paris is an organization responsible for coordination of time and frequency information from several (national) time/frequency standards organizations (e.g., US NIST and USNO) for international applications. The BIH evaluates the time/time interval information collected from all the national organizations, and determines the necessary corrections. Figure 14-3 illustrates this time coordination function. For example, the NIST and USNO (other time standard organizations from other nations can perform the same task) provide time scale information to the BIH. After appropriate corrections, the BIH delivers the UT1 corrections to the NIST and the USNO for "corrected" time and frequency distribution to their users. By international consent, *"all UTC time scales must agree with the UTC time scale operated by the BIH to within ±1 ms"*.

14.2.2 Basic Terms used for Frequency and Clocks

Frequency is one of the most often used term in the in telecommunications field. It is generally defined as the number of events that occur per unit of time.

Example 14-2: (1) Figure 14-4 (A) is a diagram that illustrates an event that occurs 100,000 times every second, determine the "frequency"; and (2) Figure 14-4(B) indicates that it takes 1.5 ms for the waveform (event) to move from point "O" to point "G", determine the "frequency".

(1)   The event starts from "A", continues through "B", "C", and "D", and then return to "A" 100,000 times (turns) within one second. By definition, the frequency is 10^5 Hz [Hertz (Hz), or cycle per second (cps)].

(2)   From point "O" to "E", the waveform (event) repeats itself the first time. That is, the waveform has completed one cycle from "O" to "E". Thus, from "O" to "G", the event repeats three cycles, which takes 1.5 ms. Therefore, one cycle requires 0.5 ms. By definition, the frequency can be obtained as follows:

$$f = \frac{1 \; cycle}{0.5 \; ms} = 2 \times 10^3 \; cps = 2 \; kHz \tag{14-7}$$

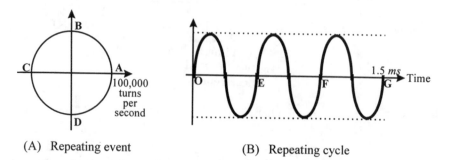

(A) Repeating event   (B) Repeating cycle

Figure 14-4 Definition of Frequency.

Definition 14-2: "**Second**", the basic unit of time; defined by the number of periods emitted for a certain resonant frequency of the element "**cesium**".

Definition 14-3: "**Clock**", a device that counts the number of seconds occurring from an arbitrary starting time. A clock requires three components: (1) a frequency source (i.e., a source of countable events), (2) an accumulator to count the number of events, and (3) display of counts (Figure 14-5).

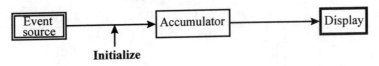

Figure 14-5   Three Components of a Basic Clock.

Three parameters that are associated with clock error are:

(1) Clock accuracy

(2) Clock stability

(3) Accuracy of timing initialization (clock synchronization)

Example 14-3 (clock accuracy): Figure 14-6(A) shows a reference clock at City "A that controls the transmitted data rate. What is the data rate? At City "B" (which is located some distance away from City "A"), three different clocks [Figure 14-6(B), (C), and (D)] are used to recover the data signal transmitted by City "A". Determine the clock accuracy (note that the clock at City "A" is considered the reference clock).

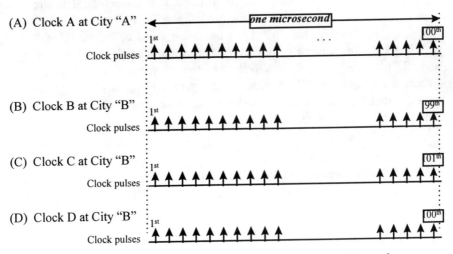

Figure 14-6   Reference Clock and Clock Accuracy Example.

(A)   Since there are 100 clock pulses in a one-microsecond (µs) interval, as it is shown in Figure 14-6(A), one hundred (100) bits will be generated by the clock at City "A". Therefore, the data rate of the transmitted signal is 100 Mbps [= 100 bits/(1µs)].

(B)   Due to the clock accuracy difference between clock sources, clock "B" at City "B" generates only 99 clock pulses in a 1µs interval. Thus, the received data stream will be restored at a rate of 99 Mbps [= 99 bits/(1µs)]. By definition, clock "B" has an accuracy of:

$$Clock\ B\ accuracy = \frac{100 - 99}{100} = \frac{100\ Mbps - 99\ Mbps}{100\ Mbps} = 10^{-2} \qquad (14\text{-}8)$$

(C)   Similarly, clock "C" at City "B" has a timing "inaccuracy". That is, the restored data stream is different because there are 101 Mbps (instead of 100 Mbps) during a 1µs interval. The accuracy of clock "C" is derived as follows:

$$Clock\ C\ accuracy = \left|\frac{100 - 101}{100}\right| = 10^{-2} \qquad (14\text{-}9)$$

(D)   However, if clock "D" is used at City "B", the restored data stream will exactly match the rate that was transmitted. The accuracy of clock D is derived as follows:

$$Clock\ D\ accuracy = \frac{100 - 100}{100} = 0 = 10^{-\infty} \qquad (14\text{-}10)$$

This example illustrates several important aspects of clocks used in a digital system: (1) Every clock's accuracy is specified its accuracy with respect to a reference clock, (2) Clock accuracy specified with respect to the transmitted clock is a good practice, since the goal of any communication link is to transport the data stream with a minimum number of errors, (3) A clock is "undesirable" if it is running either to fast or too slow (e.g., clocks "B" and "C" have the same accuracy of 10^{-2}), and (4) If the receiver's clock has the same accuracy as the transmitter's clock [as illustrated by clocks "A" and "D"], the number of bits restored is exactly equal to the number of bits transmitted. That is, clock "D" has an accuracy of $10^{-\infty}$, based on the fact that the transmitter's clock has good accuracy with respect to the Primary Reference Clock (PRC) (to be discussed later in this chapter).

__Definition 14-4__ **Frequency accuracy**: The frequency accuracy of a signal is the degree of deviation of a given frequency, with respect to its designated value. Let f_N be the designated (nominal) frequency of a signal source. The given frequency of the signal source is f, and Δf is the frequency deviation $= |f - f_N|$. Note that the absolute value is used because both a "too fast" and "too slow" signal source is undesirable. The frequency accuracy requirement of a signal source is specified by either the value of Δf or $\Delta f/f_N$.

A frequency source may change its physical characteristics over a long period of time, and thus change its accuracy. This "systematic drift" is the dominant source of long-term clock instability. Long term instability is typically one direction (i.e., either getting faster, or slower as time goes on). In comparison, random noise will introduce jitter in the output frequency of a signal source which causes short-term (e.g., temporary) instability.

Definition 14-5 Stability: Stability is a measurement of "the rate of change" of a clock's frequency, with respect to its nominal frequency, over a given time interval. It is generally specified over more than one time intervals, and is calculated for both (1) short-term stability measurement, and (2) long-term stability measurement. The theoretical unit of stability measurement is Hz/second. However, "relative" drift (i.e., $\Delta f/f$ per unit time) is also commonly used (Figure 14-7) in designing/analyzing a telecommunications system/network.

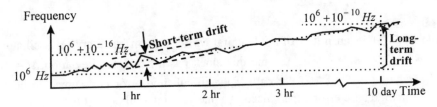

Figure 14-7   Short-term and Long-term Drift of a Frequency Source.

Example 14-4 Describe how short-term and long-term clock stability is determined.

Figure 14-7 illustrates a clock with a nominal frequency of 10^6 Hz that has both short-term drift and long-term drift. The relative drifts of (1) a short-term instability when the clock source is measured (with a frequency of 10^{-16} Hz) approximately one hour after its initial installation, and (2) a long-term instability after 10 days of operation (Figure 14-7) are determined as follows:

$$\text{Short-term drift (instability)} = \frac{\Delta f}{f} = \frac{10^{-16}}{10^6} = 10^{-22} \text{ /hr} \qquad (14\text{-}11)$$

and,

$$\text{Long-term drift (instability)} = \frac{\Delta f}{f} = \frac{10^{-10}}{10^6} = 10^{-16} /(10 \text{ day}) \qquad (14\text{-}12)$$

Definition 14-6 _Reproducibility_ and **_settability_** (of a frequency or clock): Reproducibility is used to determine whether a device (with the same design) can produce the same frequency as a reference source. It is also used to measure the degree of frequency accuracy of a source. Settability is an indication of the range that the frequency of a source can be adjusted over to obtain the "desired" reference frequency.

Definition 14-7 **Time Interval Error** (TIE) and **Maximum Time Interval Error** (MTIE): TIE is a measure of the variation in time delay for a given timing signal, with respect to a reference (ideal) timing signal, over a specific time interval. MTIE = max {TIE$_i$, i = 1, N for N different measurements}. The difference between a specific (given) clock time and the true time, ΔT, can be expressed as follows:

$$\Delta T = T_{eo} + \frac{\Delta f}{f} \cdot T + \frac{1}{2} aT^2 \qquad (14\text{-}13)$$

where

$$
\begin{aligned}
T_{eo} &= \text{Initial time setting error} \\
\Delta f &= \text{Frequency error} \\
f &= \text{Reference (ideal) frequency} \\
T &= \text{A true time interval} \\
a &= \text{The relative (time) drift rate}
\end{aligned}
$$

Example 14-5: The transmitter of a T1 digital carrier system has a crystal oscillator for generating a 1.544 MHz clock. Assume this clock has a frequency deviation $\Delta f = 10^{-10}$ Hz, and a relative drift of 10^{-9} per day. If the initial time error is assumed to be 1 ns, determine the time base error experienced in a one year interval.

The time base error is derived by applying Eq.(14-13) as follows:

$$\Delta T = 1ns + \frac{10^{-10}}{1.544 \times 10^6}(365 \times 24 \times 60 \times 60) + \frac{1}{2} \cdot \frac{10^{-9}}{24 \times 60 \times 60} \cdot (365 \times 24 \times 60 \times 60)^2 = 5.8 \; s$$

Note that in the above calculation, all time units have been converted into "seconds".

Definition 14-8 **Clock configurations** (operation modes): If the oscillator of a clock is not locked to an external synchronization reference, or it can not "hold to a previously set reference", the clock is operating in "***free-run mode***". If the oscillator of a clock is not locked to an external reference, but it maintains its clock accuracy with respect to a previously set frequency reference that has been synchronized to a reference source, the clock is operating in "***holdover mode***".

14.2.3 Frequency Sources

Three types of frequency sources are: (1) mechanical, (2) electronic and (3) atomic. However, for modern telecommunications applications, mechanical and electronic methods are not appropriate. Atomic frequency sources are commonly used for communication network synchronization, and quartz crystal oscillators are generally used as backup timing sources, and for internal time base applications.

- **Quartz crystal frequency sources (clocks)**: A quartz crystal clock is a mechanical frequency source that vibrates when excited by an electric potential. The most attractive characteristic of a quartz crystal clock is its mechanical and chemical stability. The property that links mechanical and electrical effects in crystals is called the *"piezoelectric effect"*. Figure 14-8 shows the building blocks [Oscillator electronics operating quartz crystal, an Automatic Gain Control (AGC) amplifier, and an output amplifier] of a quartz crystal clock. The performance achieved by a quartz crystal clock is a function of the crystal aging rate and temperature dependence. A good quartz crystal clock has a typical aging rate of $(10^{-8} \sim 10^{-11})$ per day. A quartz crystal clock can be used to generate megahertz frequencies. An electronic frequency multiplier must be used to derive higher frequencies.

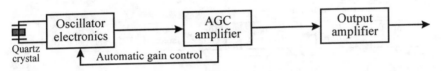

Figure 14-8   A Quartz Crystal Clock with an AGC Amplifier.

- **Cesium frequency sources (clocks)**: The basic principle of using cesium as an atomic clock is that *"its atoms release energy in the form of radiation at a specific resonant frequency."* The most important characteristic of an atomic clock is that its natural frequency is immune to temperature and other environmental factors affecting mechanical clocks. Figure 14-9 shows the building blocks of a cesium frequency source. The frequency-determining element is the atomic resonator, which contains a cavity holding the atomic material and a means of detecting changes in the state of the atoms. A microwave frequency that is very close to the resonance of the atomic resonator, is coherently generated by the Voltage-Controlled Crystal Oscillator (VCXO). An atomic resonance is in the Giga-Hertz (GHz) frequency range, typically 1000 times higher than frequencies generated by a quartz crystal clock. For a cesium oscillator, the atomic resonant frequency is 9,192,631,770 Hz.

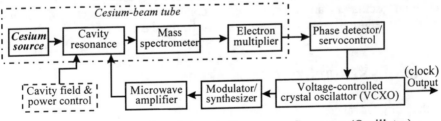

Figure 14-9   Cesium-Based Atomic Frequency Generator (Oscillator).

Cesium standard clocks are used worldwide, wherever high reproducibility and long-term stability are required for digital communications. Cesium frequency sources do not experience any systematic long-term drift, and a frequency stability of one part per 10^{14} is possible at sampling times of less than one hour and up to several days. To control the short-term stability of cesium frequency standards, the stability of the quartz oscillators within cesium frequency sources must be well controlled. Cesium frequency standards are the predominant clock sources in modern telecommunications networks because they provide clock accuracy to within a few microseconds per year.

- **Rubidium frequency sources (clocks):** When Rubidium (Rb) gas is contained in a cell at low pressure, Rb can be used as an atomic frequency source. The resonant frequency of rubidium is 6,834,682,613 Hz. Figure 14-10 shows the building blocks of a rubidium frequency source.

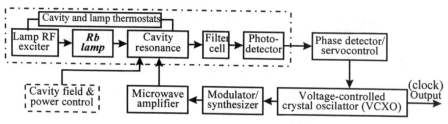

Figure 14-10   Rubidium-Based Atomic Frequency Generator (Oscillator).

Unlike a cesium resonator, the frequency generated by rubidium oscillators vary in their resonant frequency in the order of 10^{-9}, since the resonators may have different characteristics (e.g., gas composition, temperature, and pressure), and excitation light intensity. Rubidium oscillators experience frequency drift and aging, similar to crystal oscillators. Therefore, initial calibration and periodic re-calibration of Rb sources are required. However, the overall stability of rubidium oscillators is very good. A stability performance of better than 10^{-11} (nearly 10^{-13}) can be achieved for sampling times at one-second and up to one day. Long-term frequency stability is affected by long-term drift, typically about one part in 10^{11} per month. Similar to cesium oscillators, the short-term stability of rubidium frequency standards depend upon the stability of the quartz oscillators within the rubidium frequency sources. Currently, rubidium oscillators are used in digital communications systems where medium stability is required, and clock cost/size must be reduced.

14.3 VARIOUS SYNCHRONIZATION NEEDS

As technology advances, the demand for broadband ISDN/multimedia services is increasing and communication networks (public or private) are evolving towards all-digital configurations. There are many advantages (Chapter 6) of transporting information over digital networks. However, there are also several problems (issues) associated with digital communications. To achieve good quality of Information Movement and Management (IM&M), these issues must be resolved. Three important issues are:

(1) **Timing recovery**:

A digital transmission system must carry a digital bitstream, represented by a unipolar, polar, or bipolar waveform (Chapters 6 and 13). The signal must be transported from its source (the transmitter) to its destination (a receiver) with acceptable quality. In all practical systems the waveform will be degraded considerably over the distance. Therefore, the receiver must restore this degraded waveform (representing the digital bitstream) to its original digital signal format.

If the signal destination is a computer or a terminal, the restored signal can then be delivered directly to its intended "end user" (e.g., terminal) which can interpret the bitstream directly. However, if the information carries voice traffic, the restored digital signal must be converted into an analog format before delivery to the "end user" (e.g., subscriber). In either case, the restored digital signal must "**resemble**" the original signal transmitted by the source. If it is not "exactly identical", the introduced errors should be minimized. To achieve this goal, the receiver clock must be accurate with respect to the clock used at the transmitter. Likewise, the phase relationship of the receiver clock and the transmitter clock must be kept within a deterministic range. The technology used to achieve this goal is called the "**timing recovery scheme**."

(2) **Network synchronization**:

Global communication has become a "must" in today's society. Various networks (public or private; switched or dedicated) need to be interconnected. Therefore, synchronization among these networks is essential for achieving digital transmission with acceptable performance [e.g. Bit Error Rate, Bit Error Ratio (BER), Signal-to-Noise ratio (S/N)]. Clocks used for signal generations and signal restoration must meet rigid specifications to ensure network synchronization. In general, network synchronization solution starts with the needs for network primary reference clocks.

(3) **Frame synchronization**:

All digital signals are formatted into specific time units, known as frames (previously defined in Figure 14-1). The commonly used time unit for a frame is 125-μs. Since a digital bitstream typically contains bits from various users, it is necessary to identify each individual user. A "marker" (i.e., the framing interval) is used for this purpose. By establishing the frame interval, the receiver can separate the bitstream into different bundles, and deliver each bundle of digital bits to its intended user. A framing pattern, consisting of many frame bits, is always required in a bitstream to achieve "**frame synchronization**".

These three issues are described in this chapter. First, the relationship between a digital bitstream and its frame synchronization scheme is reviewed by examining a DS1 signal (the most frequently-used digital signal in North America). Doing this will build the foundation for understanding the need for, and the concepts of frame synchronization.

14.4 FRAME SYNCHRONIZATION EXAMPLES

A brief discussion of frame synchronization is given in this chapter to illustrate this technique. Figure 14-11 represents a 125 µs DS1 frame carrying one framing bit and 24 channels, with in each channel (timeslot) containing 8 bits [≡ (24 × 8) + 1 = 193 bits].

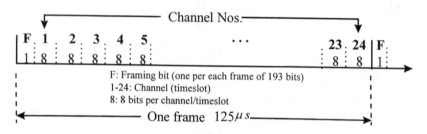

Figure 14-11   DS1 Signal Format.

Table 14-1   DS1, T1 and T1.5.

Signal designation	System	Service	Voice capacity
DS1 or digroup signal	T1 (carrier)	T1.5	24

The first bit of a DS1 signal is the framing bit. This framing bit serves as a marker or "flag" that delimits the 125 µs interval. A digital signal that carries 24 voice channels (or a combination of voice and data signals) with a signal rate of 1.544 Mbps is known as (North American) Digital Signal-level 1 (DS1) signal. A DS1 signal is also called a digroup signal (Table 14-1). In an analog system, 12 voice channels are multiplexed into a high-speed signal that is transmitted as a Frequency Division Multiplexed (FDM) signal, known as a "group signal". Therefore, a DS1 signal carrying 24 voice channels has a capacity of two "group signals". Hence the name "di-group" is applied to a signal carrying 24 digitized Voice-Frequency (VF) signals. This signal is carried on a twisted pair of copper wire (for one direction of transmission) called a T1 (digital) carrier system. T1 is a "four-wire facility" (a separate pair of wires for each direction of transmission) with a typical repeater span of 6,000 ft. The service provided by DS1 is called T1.5 service (see Table 14-1). The DS1 signal rate is derived as follows:

$$[\,1 + (24 \times 8)\,] \times 8000 = 1.544 \; Mbps$$

where 1 is the single framing bit per 125-µs interval; 24 represents the 24 voice channels carried by one DS1; each channel (or sometimes called one **timeslot**) contains 8 bits; and 8000 samples in one second are converted from analog voice into an 8-bit PCM digital signal. If the 24 channels are non-voice digital data traffic, time is **quantized** into **frames** of 125 μs each, and there are 8000 frames in every one-second interval. Note that there are 193 [≡ 1 + (24 × 8)] bits per frame. That is, a DS1 signal has a 193-bit frame.

It should be understood that DS1 signals can be multiplexed to form higher rate signals. These higher rate signals can then be transmitted over coaxial cable, digital radio systems, or optical fiber networks (Chapter 6; Vol. 1 of this book).

14.4.1 Superframe and Frame Pattern of a DS1 Signal

To understand the purpose of the framing bit, assume that a DS1 signal is designed to carry 24 voice customers signals that have been digitized. Before transporting any of the customer's information, a bit value of "1" (i.e., logical "1") is generated as the framing bit for Frame No. 1. This bit is then followed by 8 bits of information from customer No. 1; 8 bits of information from customer No. 2; 8 bits of information from customer No. 3, . . .; and finally 8 bits of information from customer No. 24. For the 2nd frame, the framing bit value is "0" (i.e., logical "0") which is followed by 24 customers' bits (8 for each customer); for the 3rd frame, the framing bit value is "0" which is followed by 24 customers' bits (8 for each customer); etc. as shown in Figure 14-12. This sequence is repeated every 12 frames (i.e., each 1.5 ms interval). A structure of 12 frames is called a **superframe**. The ensemble of the 12 framing bits of a superframe is known as the **framing pattern**. A DS1 signal that has this signal format is called a SuperFrame (SF) DS1 signal. Note that the Extended SuperFrame (ESF) signal is discussed later in this chapter.

From Figure 14-12, it can be seen that the frame contents of frame Nos.1 through No.5, and frame Nos.7 through No.11 consists of 1 framing bit and 24 channels each carrying 9 customer information bits. However, frame Nos. 6 and 12 contain 1 framing bit and 24 channels each carrying 7 information bits. Note that the 8th bit of each channel in frame Nos.6 and 12 are used for signaling, and this technique is known as rob-bit signaling (which performs data link functions; i.e., carrying control signals). That is, the 8th bit positions which would "normally" carry customer information are "robbed" and replaced with signaling data.

From Figure 14-12, it can be seen that the framing bit pattern (the first bit of each 125-μs frame) of a SF DS1 signal is given by the following sequence:

$$1\ 0\ 0\ 0\ 1\ 1\ 0\ 1\ 1\ 1\ 0\ 0$$

This sequence was adopted when the T1 carrier system was originally designed in the early 1960's. At the time, it was observed that the PCM algorithm used to convert 24 voice signals into a digital bitstream possessed a very high probability of **not** containing this particular bit pattern sequence. Therefore, the chance of false frame synchronization due to the information bitstream having this pattern is extremely rare. The 12-bit framing pattern used to implement frame synchronization can be separated into two parts:

(1) **Terminal framing bits**, F_T – the six framing bits from the six odd numbered frames are given as follows:

   1 0 1 0 1 0   for frame Nos.1, 3, 5, 7, 9, and 11 (i.e., odd frames).

(2) **Signal framing bits**, F_S – the six framing bits from the six even numbered frames are given as follows:

   0 0 1 1 1 0   for frame Nos.2, 4, 6, 8, 10, and 12 (i.e., even frames).

Frame No.

1	⌐1¬	24 x 8 = 192 bits : I
2	⌐0¬	24 x 8 = 192 bits : I
3	⌐0¬	24 x 8 = 192 bits : I
4	⌐0¬	24 x 8 = 192 bits : I
5	⌐1¬	24 x 8 = 192 bits : I
6	⌐1¬	24x7 = 168: I & 24x1 = 24 bits: S
7	⌐0¬	24 x 8 = 192 bits : I
8	⌐1¬	24 x * = 192 bits : I
9	⌐1¬	24 x 8 = 192 bits : I
10	⌐1¬	24 x 8 = 192 bits : I
11	⌐0¬	24 x 8 = 192 bits : I
12	⌐0¬	24x7 = 168: I & 24x1 = 24 bits: S

I = Information   S = Signaling (A or B channels)

Figure 14-12   DS1 Signal SuperFrame (SF) Format.

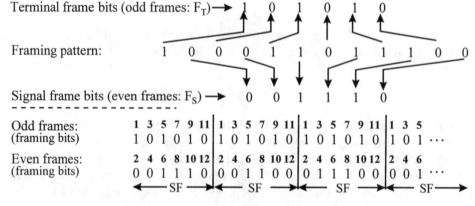

Figure 14-13   (SF) DS1 Frame Pattern.

Instead of memorizing the framing pattern "100011011100" shown in Figure 14-12, it is easier to remember the framing pattern of the DS1 SF structure signal by referring to the "terminal frame bits, F_T" and the "signal frame bits, F_S". That is, by examining the bottom half of Figure 14-13, it can be seen that the framing bits of the odd frames have a pattern of "...101010101010101..." (alternating "1s" and"0s"). while the framing bits of the even frames have a pattern of "...000111000111000 ..." (alternating three "0s" and three "1s"; except the first two "0s"). For the odd frames, note that frame No.1 always contains a "1" as the framing bit. For the even frames, the boundary between two SFs (Frames No. 12 and No.2) is identified by a single "0" immediately followed by two more "0s" (i.e., a string of three "0s").

14.4.2 Frame Pattern Detection for a DS1 Signal

The receiver uses the 12-bit framing pattern (Figures 14-12 and 14-13) to establish DS1 frame synchronization. ***Once frame synchronization has been established, the receiver can correctly distribute all the 8-bit information bytes to their intended customers***.

When a digital system is first "powered up", a valid framing pattern is generated at the transmitter as part of the digital signal (e.g., DS1), which contains idle channels to fill up the 24 timeslots within the 125-µs frame. The 12-bit framing pattern see Figures 14-12 and 14-13) is continuously generated and inserted in its proper location.

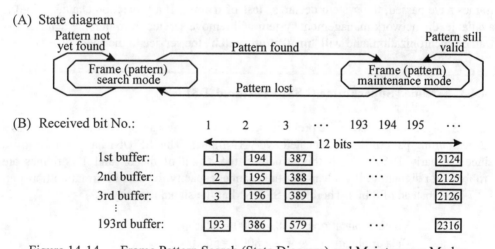

Figure 14-14   Frame Pattern Search (State Diagram) and Maintenance Modes.

During the power-up/testing period, the receiver starts up in the frame search mode as shown in Figure 14-14(A). It should be understood that this model framing pattern search is a conceptual approach only. That is, the model is only used to convey how a framing pattern can be located. The receiver collects 12 bits, with each pair of consecutive bits spaced 193-bits apart [see Figure 14-14(B)]. Theoretically, the receiver needs 193 12-bit buffers. The 1st, 194th, 387th, ..., and 2124th bits are stored in the 1st buffer [Figure 14-14(B)]. Similarly, the 2nd, 193rd, 388th, ..., and 2125th bits are stored in the 2nd buffer; the 3rd, 194th, 389th, ..., and 2126th bits are stored in the 3rd buffer; ..., etc. This procedure is continued until each buffer has stored 12 bits.

The receiver compares the 12 bits that are stored in each buffer, with a reference framing pattern (i.e., 100011011100). This process is performed simultaneously to reduce frame search time. If the 12-bit received pattern matches the reference framing pattern, frame synchronization is declared. If a valid framing pattern has been inserted in the proper position at the transmitter, one of the 193 buffers [see Figure 14-14(B)] will contain the framing pattern. The receiver will then enter into the frame maintenance mode. The 12 bits of the established framing bit positions are continuously checked against the framing reference pattern. The system remains in frame maintenance mode provided the framing pattern is still valid. After frame synchronization is established, when a timeslot (or timeslots) is ready for transmission the information bits are multiplexed into the bitstream as defined by the valid framing pattern.

While in frame maintenance mode, if the framing pattern is "lost" for several consecutive frames, the system will revert to the frame search mode. The frame search procedure will restart, and if the framing pattern cannot be found the system will stay in frame search mode. For most digital systems, a pre-determined allotment of "mis-framing" is allowed. If the framing pattern can not be found after a certain number of frames have passed, the system declares **"loss of frame"**. If a protection channel (line) is available, the network management system will remove service from the line that has lost frame synchronization, and will "**protection switch**" the service to the spare line.

14.4.3 Extended SuperFrame (ESF)-structured DS1

The DS1 signal described in the previous section is known as an SF DS1 signal, and has a 12-bit framing pattern that is repeated every 12 frames. This SF DS1 has been deployed since the early 1960's. With this structure, the 8th bit of the 6th and 12th frames are "robbed" for signaling. It is clear that the channel capacity for data information transport is "7 bits" instead of 8 bits. Therefore, SF DS1 has the signal capacity of

Voice applications: $8 \times 8000 = 64$ kbps
Data application: $7 \times 8000 = 56$ kbps

Late 1980's, the industry has realized that the full 8-bit per channel (i.e., clear 64 kbps) is essential for modern data communications. Therefore, DS1 has evolved to another format [Extended Superframe (ESF) structure]. Various DS1 signals are:

(A)   SF DS1 (12 frame structure with rob-bit signaling)
(B)   ESF DS1 (24-frame structure) which is implemented in two different ways:

(1)   Clear Channel (CC; 64 kbps)-structure DS1

(2)   DS1 with A, B, C and D-channel signaling capability

(A) SuperFrame (SF) structure

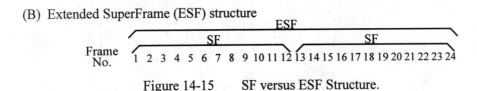

(B) Extended SuperFrame (ESF) structure

Figure 14-15   SF versus ESF Structure.

The general ESF structure is illustrated in Figure 14-15, where SF is compared with ESF structure. The two ESF implementation is described as follows:

(1) Clear Channel (CC; 64 kbps) structure DS1 signal:

Figure 14-16 illustrates the CC DS1. Several characteristics of the CC DS1 and SF DS1 signal should be understood. First, an SF-structured DS1 utilizes rob-bit signaling. In each superframe, one information bit is "robbed" from each of the 24 channels during frame No. 6 and 12. That is, the least significant bit in each of the 24 channels is replaced by signaling information. This bit replacement activity occurs every 6 frames. For an ESF structured DS1 signal, rob-bit signaling is not used [which is known as Clear Channel (CC) DS1; another variation of ESF DS1 is described in Figure 14-17], and a framing pattern of six bits (0 0 1 0 1 1) is extended across two superframes.

From Figure 14-15, it is clear that the 24 framing bit positions carry two 12-bit framing patterns when the SF structure is applied. The 24 "marker bits" allocated in the framing bit positions over the 24-frame interval are utilized in a completely different fashion for an ESF-structured DS1, compared to an SF-structured DS1. The DS1 ESF structure is described as follows:

A. The bits occupying the framing bit position (i.e., the 1st of every 193 bits) in frames No. 4, 8, 12, 16, 20, and 24 are used to carry the framing pattern "001011".

B. The bits occupying the framing bit position in frame Nos. 1, 3, 5, 7, 9, 11, 13, 15, 17, 19, 21, and 23 are used to carry control signals (known as signaling bits). These bits are referred to as the data link or the Data Communication Channel (DCC). They perform the functions that were implemented by the "robbed bits" (in frame Nos. 6 and 12 of every SuperFrame) in the SF-structured DS1.

C. The six remaining bits occupying the framing bit position of frame Nos. 2, 6, 10, 14, 18 and 22 contain Cyclic Redundancy Check (CRC) value computed over the 24 bits, and are used for error detecting/correcting.

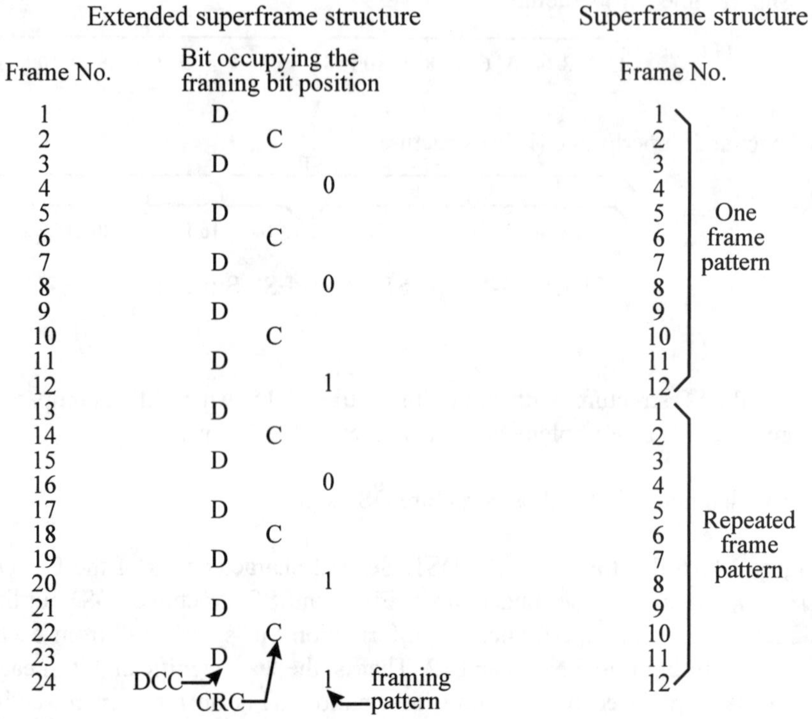

D ≡ Data link or signaling;   C ≡ Cyclic Redundancy Check (CRC)

Figure 14-16   Extended SuperFrame (ESF) DS1 Format.

For the ESF-DS1 signal, the framing pattern is no longer 12 bits in length. Instead, it has a length of six bits, and rob-bit signaling is not required for this arrangement (i.e. none of the customer information are over-written with signaling).

(2) DS1 with A, B, C and D-channel signaling capability

There is another type of modified DS1 signal (Figure 14-17) that adopts the ESF structure shown in Figure 14-15. However, the system still utilizes "robbed bits" for signaling. The frames that "robbed bit" signaling take place are frame Nos. 6, 12, 18 and 24. The bits robbed from frame No.6 is referred to as "A" channel signaling. Likewise, the bits robbed from frames No.12, 18, and 24 are called "B", "C", and "D" channel signaling respectively. Generally speaking, if a network supports an intelligent signaling network (e.g., CCS7 or SS7) a Clear Channel (CC; without robbing bits) ESF DS1 structure is used. For example, ATM cells can be carried by the CC ESF

DS1. For other applications, either SF DS1 or ESF DS1 with "A", "B", "C", and "D"-channel signaling is appropriate.

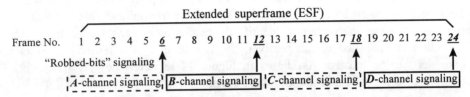

Figure 14-17   Extended Superframe DS1 with A, B, C and D-channel Signaling.

14.4.4 SONET/SDH Frame Synchronization

A SONET signal (like DS1) must carry a framing pattern within its bitstream. The generation of the framing pattern is an important task of the transmitter. Likewise, the receiver must establish frame synchronization before it can recover the bitstream. After frame synchronization has been established, the receiver performs all its other functions. Some of these functions, such as resetting a scrambler, locating the STS-1 pointer bytes (H1, H2; described in Chapter 6 vol. 1 of this book), locating the VT pointer bytes (V1, V2; described in Chapter 6), and locating other STS-1 transport overhead bytes (described in Chapter 6), are briefly described as follows:

In Chapter 6, it was indicated that an STS-1 (OC-1) signal has a framing pattern of **F628 hex** (F628H; 11110110 00101000) contained in the two framing bytes *A1* and *A2*. One significant difference between this framing pattern and a DS1 signal is illustrated as follows. The pattern F628 is concentrated within a 125-µs frame interval (Figure 14-18) but the framing pattern (100011011100) of a SF DS1 signal is distributed over 12 frames (a 1.5 ms interval). For an ESF-structured DS1, the framing pattern of "001011" is distributed over 24 frame [an interval of 3 ms (24 × 125 µs = 3 ms)].

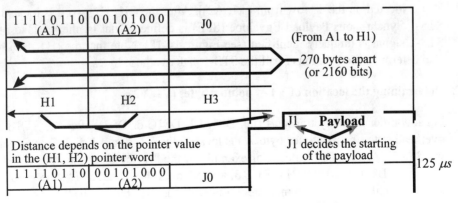

Figure 14-18   STS-1 Frame Bytes (Pattern) and Frame Structure.

At the transmitter, the 16-bit frame pattern contained in the A1, A2 framing bytes of the STS-1 (OC-1) signal is generated and placed in the first two bytes of every 125-μs frame (Figure 14-18). It should be recalled that the framing pattern bits (i.e., the first row of the section overhead bytes) are **not** scrambled at the transmitter. This is because the receiver uses the framing pattern to identify the beginning of each 125-μs frame. Once this location is identified at the receiver, the bits used by the receiver to reset the descrambler can be located. As shown in Figure 14-18, after the A1, A2 pattern is located, the receiver can make the following decisions.

A. Resetting (scrambler) function:

The scrambler (at the transmitter) must be reset every 125 μs. The Most Significant Bit (MSB) of the byte following the section trace byte (the *J0* byte) of the Nth STS-1 of an STS-N signal is used to perform the resetting function. That is, the MSB of the first byte after the first row of the section overhead (Figure 14-17) of an STS-N signal is used to reset the scrambler to an initial value of "1111111". Recall that the SONET/SDH scrambler is a seven-bit (sequential circuit) scrambler represented by a generating (generator) polynomial of $1 + X^6 + X^7$. Similarly, the descrambler (at the receiver) must be reset by the same the bit (the MSB after the 1st row of section overhead bytes), and to the same initial value (1111111), every 125-μs frame. Therefore, the location of the framing bytes, A1 and A2, is extremely important. They allow every byte in the transport overhead, including the section overhead bytes to be accurately located. Without this framing pattern, (i.e. if the framing pattern was scrambled) the bit used to reset the scrambler and the descrambler could not be located in the bitstream.

B. Determining the location of STS-1 pointer bytes (H1 and H2):

After the (A1, A2) framing pattern of "F628H" is identified, the receiver is said to have "established frame synchronization". The STS-1 pointer (H1, H2) has a **fixed** phase with respect to the STS-1 frame. That is, the first byte of the pointer (*H1*) is located 270 bytes (= 3 rows × 90 bytes per row) from *A1* in an STS-1 signal [(H1, H2) is located on the 4th row from (A1, A2)]. After the (H1, H2) word is located, the STS-1 Synchronous Payload Envelope (SPE) is defined. That is, the payload of the STS-1 signal is uniquely identified (see Figure 14-18). Note that the (H1, H2) bytes also determine the locations of all the STS-1 path overhead bytes.

C. Determining the location of VT-n pointer bytes (V1, V2):

For low-order tributary transport (i.e. DS1, E1, DS1C or DS2), after the STS-1 path overhead byte (the path trace byte *J1*) is located, the VT-n (n = 1.5, 2, 3 or 6) pointer word (V1, V2) can be located. For example, if the "H4 byte" in the Path OverHead (POH; J1, B3, C2, G1, F2, H4, F3, K3, and N1 byes) has a value of "xxxxxx00" (x = don't care), then the byte immediately following the "J1" byte is the "V1" byte. If the "H4 byte" in the POH has a value of "xxxxxx01", then the byte immediately following the "J1" byte is the "V2" byte. The (V1, V2) word is then used to determine the location of the VT-n payload.

D. Determining all other STS-1 transport overhead bytes:

All transport overhead bytes (SONET section and line overhead bytes; or SDH regenerator section and multiplex section overhead bytes) have a fixed phase with respect to the frame pattern. For example, the section error monitoring byte (B1) or the line error monitoring byte (B2) can be located after the A1 byte is identified. In an STS-1 signal, the B1 byte is located 90 bytes after the A1 byte, and the B2 byte is located 360 bytes after the A1 byte.

The achievement of SDH frame synchronization mimics that of SONET. For example, the importance and the functions of the (A1, A2) framing pattern of F628H ("1111011000101000") is identical to the SONET applications.

14.5 NETWORK SYNCHRONIZATION FUNDAMENTALS

Both generic approaches (concepts) and specific applications (examples) of network timing/synchronization methods are presented in this chapter. These synchronization techniques can be separated into "disciplined" and "non-disciplined" categories as follows:

- Disciplined techniques: In this approach, each network node requires clocks that are synchronized to a reference signal (e.g., Figures 14-19 and 14-20). Three commonly used disciplined techniques are:

    * Master-slave synchronization
    * Mutual synchronization
    * External reference synchronization

- Non-disciplined techniques: In this approach, the clocks are asynchronous and operate independent of any control or reference signal. The "slip rate" of the clock is determined by the accuracy between any two clocks used at the transmitting and receiving nodes. The slip rate is also a function of the buffer (size) used in the network nodes. Two common non-disciplined techniques are:

    * Pulse stuffing synchronization
    * Independent synchronization

14.5.1 Master-slave Synchronization Concept

The master-slave configuration is a popular synchronization scheme. In this arrangement a reference signal (i.e., the master clock) is distributed to all receiving nodes using a tree-structure. A generic master-slave structure is shown in Figure 14-19.

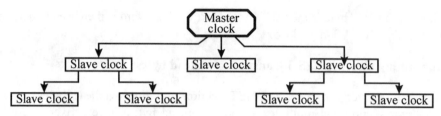

Figure 14-19   Master-Slave Synchronization Arrangement.

Timing signals, along with data, are distributed to different nodes via transmission paths. Timing at the receiving node is recovered from the incoming data bitstream, using the "ones density" obtained from zero suppression (either line code or scrambler), as described later in this chapter (Sections 14.8.2 and 14.8.3). It should be understood that a slave clock can also serve as the master clock for downstream locations in a clock hierarchy (i.e., used for generating the next rank of clock and timing signals; Figure 14-47). One important issue in the master-slave scheme is the maintenance of timing distribution in the event of a link failure. Several techniques developed for the timing distribution restoration are described as follows:

- Fixed hierarchical approach: In this approach, all nodal clocks in the network must be prioritized in a fixed hierarchical fashion. In the event of a link failure, the slave node is capable of locking itself to the highest-rank clock (other than the failed link). A unique characteristic of this master-slave approach is that control transfer signals between nodes are not required.

- Loosely coupled approach: This approach utilizes (1) a phase-locked oscillator that can store the node's previous input frequency in memory, (2) a high-quality backup oscillator that provides plesiochronous operation in the event of timing link failure, and (3) an external reference (e.g., LORAN C) that serves as a backup timing source. Therefore, in this approach each node can maintain high-frequency accuracy even in the event of a timing link fault. In addition, no control signals are needed to rearrange the clock distribution network.

- Self-organizing approach: In this approach, to provide automatic rearrangement, control signals must be transferred from one node to another. The control information carries the performance status of the clock signal. In addition, the control signal provides: (1) the designation of the node serving as the master reference for the local clock, (2) the number and quality of the links involved in the timing distribution [i.e., the path from the reference (master) clock to the local clock], and (3) the rank of the local clock.

14.5.2 Mutual Synchronization Concept

Mutual synchronization (Figure 14-20) is also known as a "frequency averaging" approach. Each nodal clock must adjust its frequency to reduce the timing error between itself and the other clocks. As illustrated in Figure 14-20 every local clock receives clock information from other nodes in the network. A weighted sum of phase errors for all incoming clocks is used as the control signal to adjust the local clocks.

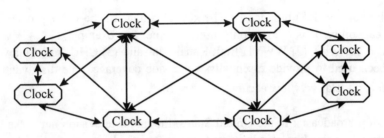

Figure 14-20   Mutual Synchronization Approach.

The mutual synchronization approach is primarily used outside the USA, and is not widelx adopted. One unique advantage of mutual synchronization is that no single clock in the network is essential. Another beneficial characteristic is its ability to rapidly adapt to system changes and clock drift.

14.5.3 External Reference Synchronization Concept

Global Positioning System (GPS) and LOng RAnge Navigation (LORAN C) are two frequently used external timing (clock) references (Figure 14-21). GPS or LORAN-C timing signals are provided to all nodal clocks from a point outside the communication networks.

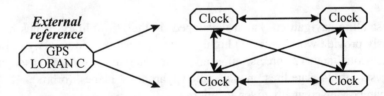

Figure 14-21   External Reference Synchronization Approach.

Efficient dissemination of precise timing and/or frequency is essential in this synchronization approach. Numerous systems have been developed for this purpose, and are described as follows:

- Low Frequency (LF) and Very Low Frequency (VLF) broadcasts: Excellent stability and good coverage are two advantages of this system. LF and VLF broadcasts can achieve an accuracy of 1 part in 10^{11} frequency stability, and 500 μs or better timing stability. There are more than 20 LF/VLF stations worldwide that provide dissemination of time and frequency. For example, OMEGA (i.e., 1×10^{-11}) operating in the VLF band, and LORAN-C (i.e., 5×10^{-12}) operating in the LF band utilize several stations collectively to provide good earth coverage.

- High-Frequency (HF) broadcasts: The key advantage of the HF approach is its long-range capability. It is a commonly used scheme. For example, (1) WWV from Fort Collins (Colorado), (2) WWVH from Kauai (Hawaii), (3) CHU from Ottawa (Canada) have been used to provide essentially worldwide coverage. One disadvantage of this system is its relatively low accuracy of 1×10^{-6}.

- Television broadcasts: In the United States, the major television networks use atomic oscillators (e.g., cesium or rubidium) to generate broadcast network reference signals. A telecommunications node can calibrate a local precise oscillator by measuring the difference between the local oscillator and a received television signal. This scheme can obtain an accuracy of ($10^{-9} \sim 10^{-11}$).

- Satellite system: Satellite time and frequency dissemination provides true global coverage. Unlike terrestrial systems, satellite transmission avoids ionospheric effects. Three different modes of satellite have been developed by using: (1) several geostationary satellites to broadcast time signals [e.g., The National Institute for Standards and Technology (NIST) in the USA], (2) communication satellites, and (3) navigation satellites carrying time standards (e.g., TRANSIT with an accuracy of 3×10^{-10}, and GPS with an accuracy of 5×10^{-12}).

Example 14-6: Describe the fundamental concepts of the Global Positioning System (GPS).

GPS is a satellite navigation system developed by the US military. It has been used to continuously provide worldwide: (1) highly accurate position and velocity information in three dimensions, and, (2) precise time and time interval. The outer space segment of GPS consists of 24 satellites in six sub-synchronous planes (orbits). At least four satellites can be viewed at any given location.

The two carrier frequencies used by each of the 24 satellites to transmit data are known as the *L1* (1,575.42 MHz) and the *L2* (1,227.6 MHz) bands. Each satellite utilizes an onboard atomic clock as a frequency reference. Spread spectrum technology is used to transmit the 50 bps navigation message in a 20 MHz bandwidth, therefore the arrival time can be measured with very high precision.

Figure 14-22 illustrates the receiver configuration used for "time and frequency" applications. The Time Transfer Unit (TTU) receives: (1) a stable reference time and frequency signal (i.e., 1 pps and 5 MHz) received from a local clock source, and (2) satellite signals received from the L1 and L2 bands.

The data received by TTUs from GPS satellites are detected and then processed: (1) to determine satellite position, and (2) to estimate time arrival of the satellite signal. The expected value after correction for atmospheric and relativistic errors is compared to the actual time of arrival. This difference is typically displayed as the local time error, and used to correct the local time and frequency standard.

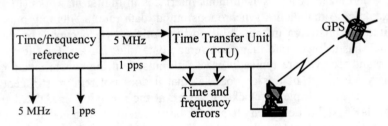

Figure 14-22   GPS Receiver Configuration.

The difference between GPS time and the user station time (x) is expressed by Eq.(14-14). In Eq.(14-14), "a" represents the satellite to user transmit time (Figure 14-23), which is estimated from satellite ephemeris (i.e., position) and atmospheric propagation correction data; "b" represents the time difference between GPS time and onboard satellite time; and "c" represents the difference between the user station time and the time received/measured from the GPS by the Time Transfer Unit (TTU).

$$x = a - b - c \qquad (14\text{-}14)$$

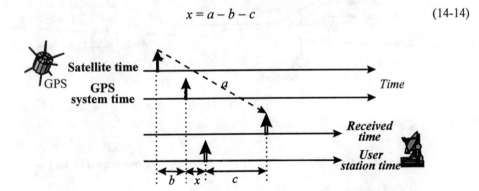

Figure 14-23   Time Relationship: Satellite, GPS and User.

14.5.4 Pulse Stuffing Synchronization Concept

The digital signals generated by using Time Division Multiplexing (TDM) are not synchronous with respect to each other.

As illustrated in Figure 14-24, the signals entering the multiplexer of a TDM system may not be generated by a single clock (i.e., the n input signals may be derived from n different clocks). The "read" clock, X, at the transmitter has a much higher rate than the "write" clocks (clocks 1, 2, ..., n). Considering the timing jitter and frequency differences, some signals must be "pulse stuffed" at the multiplexer to obtain synchronization between all incoming signals. That is, pulse stuffing is often used as a form of synchronization for asynchronous interfaces in digital networks (Figure 14-25). In this example, to maintain a synchronous output data rate, a "dummy pulse" must be inserted into the bitstream in the 8th bit position of the byte occupied by digital signal No.2, which has a lower rate than the average data rate. Buffers (elastic stores) at the transmitter and receiver are typically used with pulse stuffing synchronization schemes. The primary advantage of this approach is that it does not require stringent frequency tolerance for each multiplexer clock. However, at the receiving end, the demultiplexed TDM signals must be destuffed. It should be understood that destuffing also causes timing jitter and results in degraded performance.

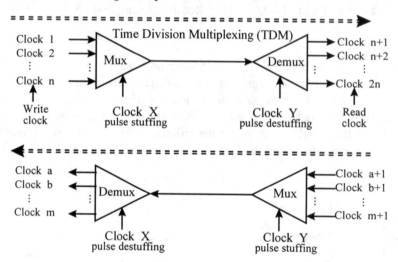

Figure 14-24   Pulse Stuffing/Destuffing Synchronization Approach.

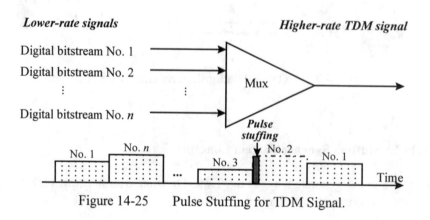

Figure 14-25   Pulse Stuffing for TDM Signal.

14.5.5 Independent Clock Synchronization Concept

The basic principle of this approach is the use of buffer stores to compensate for the differential phase in system clocks. In addition, a highly stable reference (e.g., atomic clocks) is used at each node of the network.

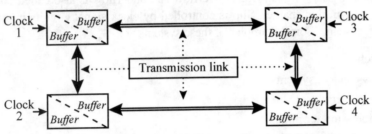

Figure 14-26   Independent Clock Synchronization Approach.

The main advantage of independent clock synchronization is that the nodal timing and frequency remain unaffected in the event of link degradation or failure. However, in these cases buffer overflow or underflow will cause time and frequency slips.

14.6 NETWORK SYNCHRONIZATION TECHNOLOGIES

Telecommunications signals require frequency sources or clocks for use in timing information signals. With regard to signal transmission, the transmitters must be "*locked*" to the receiver equipment clocks in a "***master-slave***" operation. In digital systems or networks, even if the clocks are extremely stable at both ends (transmitter and receiver), a finite amount of instability will still occur in the received signal. This instability is caused by external disturbances and changes in physical parameters (characteristics) of the transmission links. The resulting clock instability is referred to as "*timing jitter*". Therefore, network synchronization circuitry is required which typically includes phase-lock loops in the transmitter and receiver timing elements. A phase detector is used to continuously measure the phase difference between local and line clocks. The primary causes of timing jitter are:

- Noise/interference disturbing the synchronization circuitry
- Changes in the (transmission) path length
- Changes in the velocity of propagation
- Irregular timing information
- Doppler shifts (mobile unit system only)

This section describes the purpose of network synchronization. In addition, architecture, attributes, features, and **different levels of synchronization** are presented. Synchronization of switched and private networks are also compared.

14.6.1 Purpose of Network Synchronization

Network synchronization is the fundamental technology that ensures accurate **information transfer** between the myriad of synchronous time division systems is performed **without** buffer overflow, or underflow. Buffer overflow or underflow introduces **degradation** into the information message signal. Buffer overflow and underflow is also called "*slip*", which is described later in this chapter. Slip is controlled by clock signal circuits in synchronous time division systems. Some examples of these systems are:

- Switches
- Cross-connect systems
- Multiplexers
- Compression terminals
- Echo canceling terminals

Digital communications equipment using "autonomous" frequency sources (clocks) must be connected to a timing network architecture, especially in Public Switched Telephone Networks (PSTNs). Timing shifts caused by instabilities in the frequency of line clocks, are temporary and can be absorbed by elastic stores (buffers). However, in the case of an autonomous timing architecture, the clock rates of two clocks can never be exactly the same regardless of the accuracy designed into the frequency sources. Therefore, digital networks are never exactly synchronous, but they are actually plesiochronous or mesochronous (i.e., about, almost, nearly, quasi, or pseudo synchronous).

Example 14-7: Describe the clock operations of two autonomously timed digital switches (clock 1 timing switch No.1 and clock 2 timing switch No.2) as shown in Figure 14-27.

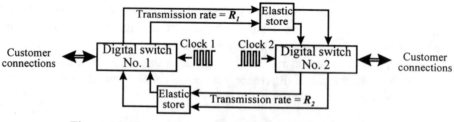

Figure 14-27   Autonomously Timed Digital Switches.

The outgoing clock for each direction of transmission is established by the clock in the digital switch. That is, the incoming clock at each switch interface contains transmission line induced jitter and frequency offset. Therefore, the interface of each digital link must utilize an elastic store to remove timing jitter. The elastic store of switch No. 1 is written to using the recovered line clock (with a rate of R_2), but is read from using the local rate

R_1. If the recovered line clock rate R_2 is different from R_1, the elastic store will either overflow or underflow as follows:

(1) If $R_2 > R_1$, the elastic store at switch No.1 overflows and will cause a loss of data.

(2) If $R_2 < R_1$, the elastic store underflows and will cause extraneous (dummy) data to be inserted into digital bitstream entering switch No.1.

Clearly, disruptions in the digital bitstream caused by underflow or overflow of an elastic store cause timing "slips". That is, if overflows and underflows correspond to "timeslots" processed by switches and/or transmission equipment, then a "slip" is defined as the "deletion" or "repetition" of "timeslots". Therefore, when digital information is transmitted over communication networks, the "bits", "timeslots", and "frames" must be synchronized.

14.6.2 Major Attributes of Network Synchronization

There are many attributes associated with network synchronization. Three major attributes are briefly described as follows:

(1) Network synchronization is a shared resource *since it provides background support technology for network applications*. For example, in a telephone central office the clock system of a switching machine often controls both:

- the timing of thousands of circuits (voice or non-voice traffic) that terminate on the switch.

- the timing of all the synchronous equipment located in the central office.

Thus, all private and switched services are dependent on the performance of the clock contained in the switch.

(2) Network synchronization can be manifested as subtle problems:

- If a customer's application is predominantly voice, synchronization is often not a problem. This is because voice service is tolerant of synchronization slips.

- If a customer's application includes voiceband data, digital data, facsimile, or similar services, the customer may experience unsatisfactory performance. Therefore, the "digital revolution" of telecommunications will *tax* the capabilities of existing network synchronization schemes.

- Resolving synchronization problems is often difficult and costly. Synchronization references can pass through a series of clocks and transmission facilities, and it may cross the boundaries of existing transmission systems, switching machines, and Operations Systems (OSs).

(3)   Network synchronization implies interdependency:

- A customer typically starts with a self-contained, private data network. This network can operate as a "timing island", referencing all clocks from a single selected timing source (clock) that may have a significant frequency offset. However, because all clocks in an isolated network are referenced to the same source, the offset is often inconsequential.

- However, if a digital gateway is established between synchronous networks, they must be upgraded to eliminate any frequency offsets.

14.6.3 Implementation of Network Synchronization

In the US, the current applications of network synchronization include: (1) AT&T and other Inter-Exchange Carrier (IEC) national telecommunications networks, (2) customer private digital networks, (3) Bell Operating Company (BOC) networks, and (4) many independent telephone companies' networks.

These networks have evolved into nearly "all-digital" operations. The services and applications provided by these networks are placing increasing demands on performance, operations, and verification of the synchronization network. This evolution demands new modeling, specifying testing methods that ensure consistent performance, and standard requirements for interfaces. In addition, network designers must use new planning tools and methodologies to meet the needs created by the accelerated growth of large private digital networks.

In the case of AT&T, a new synchronous network with 17 Primary Reference Clocks (PRCs) has been recently deployed. More (e.g., hundreds) of these PRCs are expected to be added in future networks. They provide synchronization timing references at critical locations (e.g., 4ESS toll offices) throughout the national network. Further discussion of PRCs and applications are covered later in this chapter. A new Timing Monitoring System (TMS) has also been deployed to verify that the critical timing reference is distributed with high precision.

These 17 PRCs [also known as Primary Reference Sources (PRSs)] are located in various parts of the AT&T network. Fifteen (15) are located in the continental United States, one is in Hawaii, and the other is in Puerto Rico. They are synchronized by the Global Positioning System (GPS) master clock which is located in Boulder, Colorado.

14.6.4 Three Levels of Synchronization

Three levels of synchronization are: bit-level, frame-level, and time-slot level.

(1) Bit-level synchronization deals with physical layers, and involves timing issues:

- Clock insertion
- Clock recovery
- Transmission line jitter
- Sampling windows in eye patterns
- InterSymbol Interference (ISI)
- Ones density

(2) Frame level synchronization

Frame-level synchronization refers to both the transmitter and receiver achieving proper phase alignment. This is necessary at the beginning and the end of a group of bits so they can be uniquely identified. This description refers to a frame interval of 125 μs, as described in the earlier sections of this chapter. A "125 μs frame interval" is defined as follows:

- For the DS1 signal family (North American digital hierarchy): *A group of bits consisting of* twenty-four 8-bit bytes (i.e., time slots associated with subscriber circuits), and a single framing bit, for a total of 193 bits per frame.

- For the CEPT-1 signal family (ITU-T digital hierarchy): *A group of bits consisting of* thirty-two 8-bit bytes (i.e., timeslots associated with subscriber circuits) for a total of 256 bits per frame.

(3) Time-slot synchronization

Time-Slot (TS) level synchronization deals with the processing of time slots (i.e., channels). TSs are sent (from a source node) at a uniform rate to the receiver (with a fixed delay). The time slots are "time-division multiplexed" into a 125 μs frame by a digital system located at the **source node,** and transported by a digital transmission system to another system located at the **receiving node**. Under perfect conditions, the time slots are sent from the source node at a uniform rate, and delivered to **the receiving system buffer**. The receiving system reads the time slots with a fixed delay, and assuming that no random or systematic offset of the receiving node clock occurs (with respect to the sending clock) processing continues without variation in the buffer, thereby ensuring complete time slot integrity.

14.6.5 Synchronization Clock Hierarchy

Clocks are categorized into a hierarchy based on their relative performance levels. They are divided into synchronization performance groups known as stratum levels. The levels are numbered stratum 1, 2, 3, and 4 (Table 14-2, which describes the applications of clock hierarchy). Each stratum (from 1 to 4) has a progressively less accurate, less robust, and (typically) lower cost clock design and implementation.

Table 14-2   Strata and Applications (Figure 14-28).

Stratum	*Applications*
1	• Network reference (Primary Reference Clock; PRC)
2	• Trunk exchange switch • DCS (Digital Cross-connect System)
3	• Local exchange switch • DCS • DPBX (Digital Private Branch eXchange) • Multiplexer
4	• DPBX • PCMux (PCM Mux) • EXM [EXchange Mux: Central Office Terminal (COT) equivalent]

The four clock strata (stratum 1, 2, 3 and 4; Table 14-2) are described as follows:

• **Stratum 1** clocks are network source clocks, and are also known as Primary Reference Clocks (PRCs) or Primary Reference Sources (PRSs). That is, Stratum 1 clocks (primary and secondary; Figure 14-30) are used as the source clocks of primary network nodes (e.g., a trunk exchange office housing 4ESS equipment). Stratum 2, 3, and 4 clocks are typically receivers of stratum 1 timing, and are usually part of switching or transmission equipment.

• **Stratum 2** clocks are typically found in toll (trunk) switching machines (e.g., 4ESS or 5ESS offices), and certain Digital Cross-connecting System (DCS) equipment [DCS may be classified into two categories: (1) wideband DCS, and (2) broadband DCS. Broadband DCS requires Stratum 2 or better quality]. That is, a 4ESS machine requires a clock with a Stratum 2 or better quality.

• **Stratum 3** clocks are found in local switches (e.g., 1AESS or 5ESS offices), Digital Cross-connecting System (DCS) equipment (Wideband DCS requires Stratum 3 or better quality), certain Digital Private Branch eXchanges (DPBXs), and T1 (digital carrier system) multiplexers.

• **Stratum 4** clocks are found in most T1 multiplexers, digital PBXs, channel banks used for implementing Pulse Code Modulation (PCM; typically used to convert analog voice signal into digital signals), EXchange Multiplexers (EXM; typically used to multiplex digitized voices and voiceband data into a low-rate digital signals such as 1.544 Mbps or 2.048 Mbps for distant transport), and Central Office Terminals (COTs).

Figure 14-28 shows an example of the synchronization clock hierarchy used in AT&T digital networks. The clock hierarchy has 17 (at the present time, and expected to expand in the future) Primary Reference Clocks (PRCs), which are synchronized by the

Global Positioning System (GPS). Note that GPS-based synchronization is achieved by a 24-satellite linked synchronous network. Any downlink node that synchronizes with GPS must be able to link to four satellites simultaneously. These PRCs are used to generate clocks of stratum 2 quality. Stratum 2 clocks are used to generate stratum 3 clocks, which in turn are used to generate stratum 4 clocks.

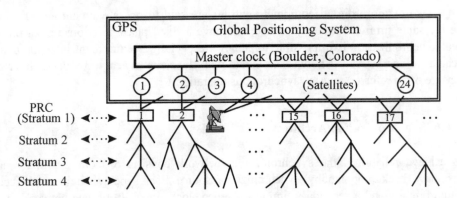

Figure 14-28   Typical AT&T Synchronization Architecture.

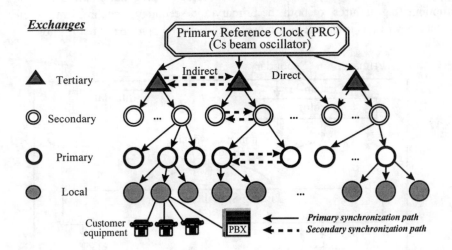

Figure 14-29   Hierarchical Structure of Network Synchronization System.

The reference clock (Figure 14-29) is a cesium (Cs)-based oscillator with a frequency uncertainty of not more than one part in 10^{11} deviation. It is normally located near the geographical center of the synchronized network. The synchronizing signals are distributed from "top down" in accordance with the switching network hierarchy (i.e., from PRC to tertiary exchanges, secondary exchanges, primary exchanges, and then local exchanges) as shown in Figure 14-29. If a primary synchronization path (indicated by "solid" lines in Figure 14-29) fails, a secondary path (indicated by "dash" lines in Figure 14-29) should be available as a back-up. The secondary path may originate from the same network node (exchange) as the primary synchronization path, but is carried over a different transmission route (diversely routed). As an alternative, the secondary path may originate from a different node (exchange).

Two or more digital equipment entities are said to operate synchronously if they use the same timing frequency source, and have a fixed phase relationship. In practice, ideal synchronization is impossible to achieve, especially if equipment is geographically located far apart. Even if networks operate with the same **average** frequency over time, they are often referred to as a "synchronous operation".

14.6.6 Synchronization Architecture

To achieve reliability, the synchronization network consists of both a primary and a secondary (backup or standby) synchronization source. Each synchronization node receives both a primary and a secondary timing reference clock signal. In private networks, this is not always possible because of limited interconnectivity and/or budget constraints. In addition to the **primary** and the **secondary** timing reference clocks, each node is equipped with an **internal clock** which can bridge (using automatic switching) short disruptions (e.g. failures) of both the primary and secondary synchronization references. The accuracy of this internal clock must be at least ± 20 ppm (parts per million).

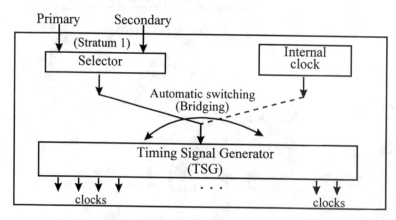

Figure 14-30   Building Integrated Timing Supply.

The architecture shown in Figure 14-30 is known as a Building Integrated Timing Supply (**BITS**) clock, which has been widely used in North American digital networks (especially SONET networks). The Timing Signal Generator (TSG) typically receives reference clock information from a stratum 1 clock, and generates all necessary clock signals for the equipment at the same node as well as "down stream" exchange offices. If both the primary and secondary reference clock sources fail, the internal free-running clock can temporarily serve as the reference clock source. The BITS configuration also reduces the following:

- Multiple clock dependency
- Administration and maintenance overhead
- Phase hits
- Jitter
- Wander
- Errored seconds

Within a building (e.g., central office), a single clock is designated as the BITS, which has the highest accuracy (typically, stratum 1). In normal operation, the Timing Signal Generator (TSG) selects a stratum 1 clock for use as the primary clock. If this primary clock does not meet stratum 1 quality, TSG then selects the secondary clock (which is preferably also a stratum 1 clock). If both the primary and the secondary clocks perform poorly or fail, the TSG automatically switches to a backup internal timing source.

BITS provides all the synchronization references required for a central office building: (1) DS1 (1.544 MHz) and DS0 (64 kHz) in North America; (2) E1 (2.048 MHz) and 64 kHz E0 in the ITU-T networks; and, (3) 2.048 MHz, 1.544 MHz and 64 kHz in the international gateway exchanges. That is, all the network equipment within the building (central office) receives timing reference signals from the BITS clock.

The BITS clocks (generated in critical locations) are used to derive the necessary timing signals for all the locations within the network, in accordance with the accuracy requirements listed in Table 14-3. The scheme of providing clocks to all the locations (other than the critical locations) is known as the "inter-building timing supply" (Figures 14-28 and 14-29 show the clock hierarchy).

14.6.7 Clock Accuracy

The accuracy for the four stratum clocks is summarized in Table 14-3. The minimum ·clock accuracy requirement, worst-case slip rate (derivations of worst slip rates and the importance of meeting the clock accuracy is given in later sections of this chapter), and the holdover for the first 24 hour period is listed for each stratum clock.

Table 14-3   Stratum Clock Compatibility Requirements.

Stratum	*Minimum accuracy*	*Worst-case slip rate*	*Holdover (first 24 hrs)*
1	1.0×10^{-11}	2.52/year	Not applicable
2	1.6×10^{-8}	11.06/day	1.0×10^{-10}
3	4.6×10^{-6}	132.48/hour	255 slips
4	3.2×10^{-5}	15.36/minute	Not applicable

Stratum 1 is a free running clock, and does not use a timing reference to derive its timing. Stratum 1 must maintain a frequency accuracy of better than 1.0×10^{-11}. Stratum 1 sources typically consist of an ensemble of primary cesium atomic standards. However, PRCs need not be implemented with primary atomic standards. For example, AT&T PRCs contain an ensemble of secondary atomic standards (rubidium) that are synchronized to the Global Positioning System (GPS).

The slip-rate contribution of a single free-running Stratum 1 clock is negligible. A network that derives timing from two free-running Stratum 1 clocks (which both maintain a frequency accuracy of 1.0×10^{-11}) will experience (at most) two slips per year. These slips are caused by the inherent inaccuracy of the clocks. In comparison, a network with timing traceable to only one clock and with no external connectivity, does not experience slips caused by timing inaccuracies of its source clock. That is, because there is only one clock source there is no basis for differences (slips) even though there are timing inaccuracies.

The usual mode of operation of a receiver is to extract timing from the clock source reference. In this mode, the receiver must handle short-term reference instability (timing jitter), and be able to bridge short reference interruptions. For example, when the source reference experiences a short-term impairment, stratum 2 and stratum 3 receivers must maintain timing to within 10 μs. The receiver clocks cause less than 1,000 ns of time-keeping error (resulting from reference switching or other transient events) with respect to their timing sources. However, stratum 4 clocks do not have any stringent time-keeping requirements.

Another mode of receiver clock operation is running while all external timing references have been lost. "Holdover" is the capability to maintain frequency accuracy with no external timing references. Table 14-3 lists holdover requirements. Note that for Stratum 4, the clock immediately enters the free-run condition when timing references are lost. The free-run condition refers to a clock's stability based only on the performance of its own internal oscillators. *All clocks must be able to lock to a free-running clock of the same stratum level.*

14.6.8 Slip Rate Requirements

Understanding slip rate requires an awareness of the meaning and importance of the clock accuracy listed in Table 14-3. For a communication system, clock accuracy is relative. That is, clock accuracy is based on a hierarchical relationship. If a receiver has a clock with exactly the same rate as the clock at the transmitter (i.e., the transmitter's clock can be used as the reference clock), for a point-to-point transport the receiver clock has an accuracy of infinity (i.e. there is no timing difference). The importance of a clock's relationship to the slip rate is illustrated in Figure 14-30. In this example, the following assumptions are made to illustrate the importance of a clock:

(1) The transmission rate is 10 Mbps

(2) The total bitstream of information requires 1 minute to transmit

(3) The receiver clock has an accuracy of 10^{-7}.

In one minute, this transmitter sends out 600,000,000 bits (= 60 seconds × 10 × 10⁶ bits per second). The first scenario (nominal; Figure 14-31) assumes that the receiver clock has an accuracy of infinity. That is, the clock at the receiver has the exact same rate as the clock at the transmitter, and they are in a perfect synchronization. Therefore, the decoded (restored) signal will contain 600,000,000 bits, which is the same as the number of bits transmitted.

In the second scenario, if the receiver clock is assumed to have an accuracy of 10^{-7}, which can be expressed as follows:

$$\text{Clock accuracy} = 10^{-7} = \frac{1}{10,000,000}$$

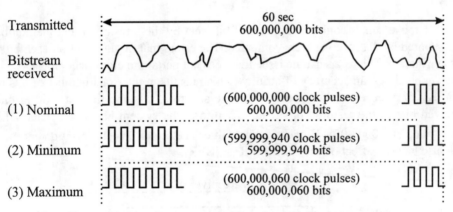

Figure 14-31   Importance of Receiver Clock Accuracy.

Since the receiver clock has an accuracy of 10^{-7}, and the recovered bitstream is generated by the clock source at the receiver, then the following two extreme cases can occur:

(1) In one worst-case scenario (maximum; Figure 14-31), the number of clock pulses generated by the receiver clock (frequency source) may be 10,000,001 pulses per second (= 10 Mbps + 10 Mbps × 10^{-7}). This is one extra clock pulse from its nominal rate of 10,000,000 clock pulses per second (because the data rate is assumed to be 10 Mbps). Therefore, the restored bitstream will contain extra digits.

(2) In another worst-case scenario (minimum; Figure 14-31), the number of clock pulses generated may be 9,999,999 per second (= 10 Mbps − 10 Mbps × 10^{-7}). This is one less clock pulse from its nominal rate of 10,000,000 clock pulses per second. Therefore, the restored bitstream will contain extra digits.

As shown in Figure 14-32, because of the variations in the receiver clock accuracy, the number of bits restored in one minute can be between 599,999,940 and 600,000,060 bits. As previously indicated, if the clock has an accuracy of infinity, the receiver will restore the exact number of bits (600,000,000 bits in one minute) that were transmitted by the information source. However, if the clock accuracy is 10^{-7} (as in this example), 60 bits of information will be either **deleted** or **repeated** in one minute, and the restored bitstream is inaccurate. The importance of clock accuracy is obvious because a typical conversation lasting 10 minutes could loose 600 bits of user information.

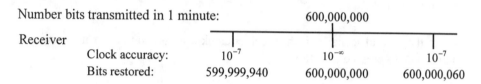

Figure 14-32   Effect of Receiver Clock Accuracy on Bit Restoration.

In this example, only the number of bits sent by the transmitter and the number of bits restored by the receiver were compared. The errors that might occur on each bit were not considered. This is a separate issue that does not pertain to clock accuracy. Even if the receiver clock has an accuracy of infinity (which results in the exact number of bits being restored) these received bits could have several errors. Assume there are 60 erroneous received bits in the restored bitstream. Therefore, the system has a calculated BER of 10^{-7} ($\equiv 60/600,000,000$). However, clock jitter (i.e. clock synchronization inaccuracy) will also have an affect on the Bit Error Rate (BER).

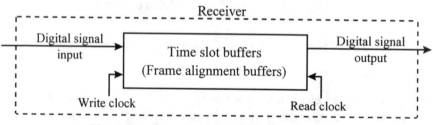

Figure 14-33   Receiver Time Slot Buffers.

With a thorough understanding of the importance of clock accuracy, the definition of **slip rate** can be presented. To understand the worst-case slip rate, the function of the receiver buffer store must be explained. Figure 14-33 represents a receiver buffer. Ideally the receiver buffer should never experience any overflow or underflow, but this is practically impossible.

A "slip" can result if the time slot buffer exceeds an overflow or underflow condition. This condition may be caused by receiver clock (either the write or the read clock) inaccuracy, relative to the transmitter clocks. When a slip occurs in a DS1 or a CEPT-1 (E-1) bitstream, an entire 125 μs frame of information is either repeated or deleted. Therefore, "slip" is defined as the *deletion or repetition of a frame*. The worst-case slip rate is defined as follows.

$$\textbf{Slip rate} = \frac{Number\ of\ frames\ delected\ (or\ repeated)}{unit\ time} \quad (14\text{-}15)$$

For example, to derive the slip rate of a stratum 4 clock [which has a minimum clock accuracy of 3.2×10^{-5} (see Table 14-3) and a worst case slip rate of 15.36 slips/min] the procedure begins by analyzing the clock accuracy:

$$Clock\ accuracy\ of\ 3.2 \times 10^{-5} = \frac{3.2}{10^5}$$

$$= \frac{3.2\ bits\ delected}{10^5\ bits\ transmitted} = \frac{3.2\ sec\ delected}{10^5\ sec\ transmitted} \quad (14\text{-}16)$$

Note that the above analysis only considers the case of deletion. The case of repetition can be derived using the same methods. Hence, from Eq.(14-16), the following statement can be made:

If 10^5 sec of information is transmitted $\rightarrow$ (implies that)
3.2 seconds of information (or 3.2 × 8000 frames) may be deleted.

Note that there are 8000 frames per second for any digital data stream (PDH, SONET or SDH). That is, 8000 × 125 μs = 1 second.

Since 3.2 × 8000 = 25,600; the previous statement can be modified as follows:

If 10^5 sec of information is transmitted $\rightarrow$
25,600 frames of information may be deleted.

Since 10^5 seconds is equal to 1666.67 minutes ($\equiv 10^5$ s/60), for a stratum 4 clock with an accuracy of 3.2×10^{-5}, the above statement becomes:

If 1666.67 ___min___ of information is transmitted $\rightarrow$
25,600 ___frames___ of information may be deleted.

This statement can further be simplified by dividing both numbers (1666.67 and 25,600) by 1666.67 (1666.67/1666.67 = 1 minute and 25,600/1666.67 = 15.36 frames). Hence, the following derivation (result) can be obtained:

> **If 1 _min_ of information is transmitted →**
> **15.36 _frames_ of information may be deleted.**

Applying the definition given in Eq.(14-15), the following conclusion can be drawn:

> **A stratum 4 clock with an accuracy of 3.2×10^{-5}**
> **has a worst-case _slip rate of 15.36 slips per min_.**

The slip rates for the other three strata clocks (Table 14-3) can be derived using the same approach. It should be emphasized that the overall impact of slips on system operation is dependent upon the customer's application and the type of service.

Example 14-8 Compare the worst case bits loss when an OC-12 SONET signal (see Figure 14-34) is transmitted for one hour when a stratum 4, instead of stratum 1, clock is used.

One OC-12 frame
$= 9 \times 1,080 \times 8 = 77,760 \, bits$

Figure 14-34   SONET OC-12 Signal Frame.

One frame of OC-12 signal contains 77,760 bits as calculated in Figure 14-34.

- If a stratum 1 clock with a worst-case slip rate of 2.52 slips per year (Table 14-3) is used, the possible worst-case number of bits lost during one hour of OC-12 signal transmission can be derived as follows.

$$Slip \ rate = 2.52 \ \frac{slips}{year} = 2.52 \ \frac{frames \ of \ bitstream}{year}$$

$$Bits \ lost \ in \ one \ hour = 2.52 \times \frac{77,760 \ bits}{365 \times 24 \ hr} \times 1 \ hr = 22 \ bits$$

- If a stratum 4 clock with a worst-case slip rate of 15.36 slips per minute (Table 14-3) is uses, the effect on one hour of OC-12 transmission is:

$$Slip \ rate = 15.36 \ \frac{slips}{m} = 15.36 \ \frac{frames \ of \ bitstream}{m}$$

$$Bits \ lost \ in \ one \ hour = 15.36 \times 77,760 \ bits \ / \ m \times 1 \ hr \ (i.e., 60 \ m) = 71,663,616 \ bits$$

Clearly, clock accuracy is important when restoring digital bitstreams.

14.7 SONET/SDH SYNCHRONIZATION REQUIREMENTS

SONET/SDH Network Elements (NEs) must be synchronized with a stratum 3 or better quality clock. If a SONET/SDH NE can not be synchronized with a clock of stratum 3 quality, the element must be equipped with an internal oscillator having a minimum accuracy of ± 20 ppm (parts per million). The use of this free-running internal clock is shown in Figure 14-30.

Networks for SONET/SDH applications must furnish timing signals which meet the stability requirements shown in Figures 14-35 and 14-36. Figure 14-35 shows the requirement of short term stability for an STS-N or an STM-N output signal. For 1 second of observation time, the maximum root mean square (rms) phase instability must be better than 3 *ns*. For up to 100 seconds of observation time, the requirement is 10 dB per decade (i.e., 30 *ns* for each ten second increment of observation time). Beyond 100 seconds of observation time, the maximum *rms* phase instability must be 300 *ns* or better, independent of the length of the observation time.

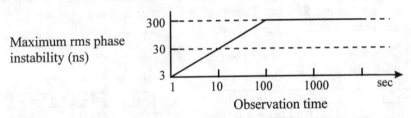

Figure 14-35   STS-N (STM-N) Short-term Stability Requirement.

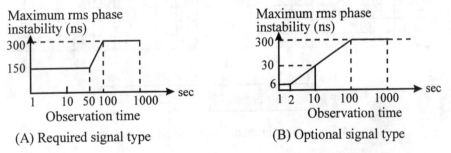

(A) Required signal type   (B) Optional signal type

Figure 14-36   Timing Reference Signal Short-term Stability Requirement.

Figure 14-36 shows the short term stability requirement of the timing reference signal furnished by the network provider. Figure 14-36(A) shows the required signal type, and Figure 14-36(B) shows the optional signal type. For the required signal type [Figure 14-36(A)], within 50 seconds of observation, the maximum phase instability must be 150 *ns* or less. The requirement is 10 dB per decade with observation periods of 50 to 100 seconds. Beyond 100 seconds of observation, the instability must be 300 *ns* or less. For the optional signal type [Figure 14-36(B)], the requirements for an observation interval of 1~2 seconds, the maximum phase instability must be 6 *ns* or less. The requirement is 30 *ns* for each 10 second interval for observation periods of 10 to 100 seconds. Beyond 100 of observation, the instability must be 300 *ns* or less. In summary, beyond 100 seconds of observation time, the maximum rms phase instability requirement is 300 *ns* or less for any signal.

14.7.1 Synchronization Status

For SONET/SDH applications, bits 5 to 8 of the S1 byte (S1 was originally the Z1 byte of the line or multiplex section overhead) of an STS-N/STM-N signal are allocated for synchronization status messages. Figure 14-37(A) shows the transport overhead bytes of an STS-3c signal, and Figure 14-37(B) shows the overhead for an STM-1 signal. Note that originally there were three unassigned Z1 bytes, and they were called growth bytes to prepare for future needs. In the present SONET/SDH standards, one (circled in Figure 14-37) of the three growth bytes (Z1, Z1 and Z1) has been assigned as S1 and is used to carry synchronization status. However, Synchronization Status Message (SSM) only occupies the last four bits of the S1 byte. Therefore, the first four bits of the S1 byte are still "unassigned" in the present standards.

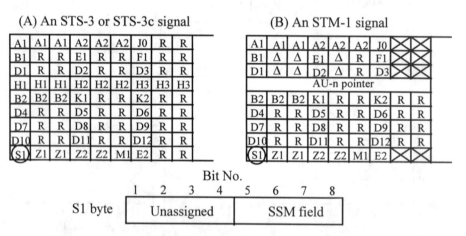

Figure 14-37   Synchronization Status Message Byte (S1).

Table 14-4 lists the Synchronization Status Messages (SSMs) in the present SONET/SDH standards. If SSM = 0000, the synchronization quality is unspecified or unknown. This is applicable for synchronous networks that comply with various regional standards (e.g., the A-law and the μ-law PDH digital signal hierarchies discussed in Chapter 6). If SSM = 0010, 0100, or 1000, synchronization of the network is implemented according to ITU-T Rec. G.811 or G.812 specifications. These three codes correspond to "general", "transit", and "local" applications respectively. When SSM =

1011, the synchronization specification is applied to the Synchronization Equipment Timing Source (SETS), as specified in SETS standards. If SSM = 1111, this field is not used for synchronization (i.e., restricted use; see Table 14-4). The remaining ten codes, as listed in Table 14-4, are reserved for future applications.

Table 14-4   Synchronization Status Messages.

SSM S1 byte bits 5~8	SDH sync quality level description	Notes
0 0 0 0	Quality unknown (Existing sync. network)	* Synchronization equipment timing source
0 0 0 1	Reserved	
0 0 1 0	G.811	
0 0 1 1	Reserved	* * This message may be emulated
0 1 0 0	G.812 transit	by equipment failure, and can
0 1 0 1	Reserved	be emulated as MS AIS.
0 1 1 0	Reserved	This message restriction is
0 1 1 1	Reserved	mandatory because the receipt
1 0 0 0	G.812 local	of an MS AIS is not necessarily
1 0 0 1	Reserved	interpreted as an indication
1 0 1 0	Reserved	of a physical failed sync
1 0 1 1	SETS*	source interface port.
1 1 0 0	Reserved	This restriction allows this
1 1 0 1	Reserved	state to be recognized without
1 1 1 0	Reserved	interaction with the MS AIS
1 1 1 1	Do not use for sync**	detection process.

MS AIS: Multiplex Section Alarm Indication Signal (also known as AIS-L; AIS-Line)

14.8 CLOCK AND TIMING RECOVERY

Timing reference performance can include a significant number of disruptive events. For example, in ITU-T Recommendation G.821, the end-to-end performance objective for Severely Errored Seconds (SES) is not more than *175 per day*. Error events disrupting the clock may occur on DS1 transport in the range of *1 to 100 events per day* depending on service type, distance, and other factors. Obviously, these constant degradations adversely affect the overall synchronization performance of a network.

Example 14-9: Describe the operation of a Primary Reference Clock (PRC) Timing Monitoring System (TMS).

As shown in Figure 14-38, a computer is used to control and monitor the rubidium-based oscillators used in a Primary Reference Clock (PRC). The computer verifies oscillator performance relative to one another, and with respect to the Global Position Satellite (GPS) timing signal.

The interaction between the PRC, the computer, and the Timing Monitoring System (TMS) is used to select the DS1 (1.544 Mbps) inputs from other network nodes, and clock them via TMS. The timing outputs of the PRC are a pair of DS1 primary rate digital signals. The computer performs control, performance verification, and error recovery functions. All DS1 signals, and other digital rates (i.e., DS1C of 3.152 Mbps, DS2 of 6.312 Mbps, DS3 of 44.736 Mbps, E1 of 2.048 Mbps, E2 of 8.448 Mbps, E3 of 34.368 Mbps, and E4 of 139.264 Mbps) are synchronized in 125-μs frames. By mapping the DS1 signals into a DS3, and then clocking this DS3 level signal in the network using the same PRC, the network is said to be synchronized. This technique establishes synchronous processes among all switching systems and transmission media used in building the network (i.e., coaxial cables, fibers, microwave radio and satellites).

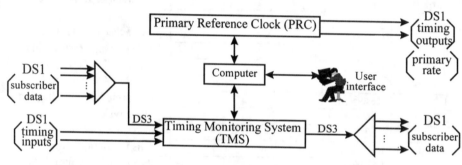

Figure 14-38   PRC Timing Monitoring System (TMS).

Figures 14-31 and 14-32 illustrate the importance of the clock accuracy at the receiver. For acceptable performance, a clock must meet its accuracy, slip, and jitter requirements. In addition, the clock must be in sync with the information data stream. This is called the *timing recovery scheme* in a digital network. Timing recovery, clock functions and operations, the desired characteristics of a received signal waveform, and various ways to achieve zero suppression of a digital bitstream are discussed in the following sections.

14.8.1 Clock Functions and Operations

Two basic functions performed by a receiver clock are briefly described as follows:

(1) Recover a good estimate of the original source node timing from the incoming reference.

(2) Maintain good time-keeping with respect to the source clock (in the absence of a reference) by using initial estimation and prediction.

There are three operational modes of a receiver clock: (1) ideal operation, (2) stressed operation, and (3) holdover operation. They are defined as follows:

(1) **Ideal operation**: In ideal operation, the receiver clock experiences no interruptions of the incoming timing reference. Under these conditions, the clock should operate in strict phase lock with the incoming reference. *Note that this is not typical in real network operation.*

(2) **Stressed operation**: This reflects the performance of a receiver clock under actual network conditions. In this mode of operation there are timing interruptions characterized as follows:

- The stability of the output timing signal behaves as a "white-noise" frequency modulation process for long observation periods.

- A frequency offset will result between the receiver clock and its reference.

(3) **Holdover operation**: This refers to the infrequent times when a receiver clock loses all its external timing references for a significant period of time (e.g., not a momentary or transient interruption). In a holdover mode, the key components of the receiver clock are **frequency drift** and **initial frequency offset**. Table 14-3 shows the holdover requirements for strata 2 and 3 clocks. Note that a Stratum 1 clock does not have holdover requirements because it continuously operates in the free-run mode.

14.8.2 Timing Recovery

Timing recovery at the receiver addresses two issues: (1) *where to obtain the reference clock*, and (2) *how to synchronize this clock to a nearly true and accurate phase*. Figure 14-37 shows that even if the receiver clock has an accurate rate (as required by the network) the restored signal can still contain in erroneous bits.

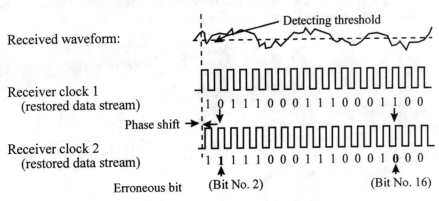

Figure 14-39   Importance of Clock Phase Synchronization.

The example in Figure 14-39 assumes that the receiver clock conforms to the rate accuracy specified by the network. However, note that receiver clock No. 1in Figure 14-39 has a different start-up point compared to receiver clock No. 2. These two clocks are said to have different phases. The received digital signal waveform, transported over a noisy long-distance facility, will have the waveform appearance shown at the top of Figure 14-39.

In this example it is assumed that clock No. 1 has a true and accurate phase. That is, the decoded signal obtained from the received waveform represents the transmitted signal provided the system is error free (i.e., system noise is negligible). By using this clock No. 1 to decode the received signal, the restored data stream is decoded as "101110001110001100". This is obtained by using the rising-edges of the receiver clock No. 1 as the reference for determining whether the received waveform (voltage) is larger or smaller than the detection threshold. If the received voltage at the rising-edge of the clock is larger than the threshold, the bit is declared to be a logical "1". Conversely, if the received voltage is smaller than the threshold, the bit is declared to be a logical "0".

Assume that a receiver clock (i.e., clock No.2) has the same exact rate as receiver clock No. 1, but is not synchronized to the same position. As a result, receiver clock No.2, has a phase difference with respect to receiver clock No. 1. If the rising edges of clock No. 2 are used to decode the received waveform, the restored digital signal is decoded as "111110001110001000". Note that the two erroneous bits, bit Nos. 2 and 16, are highlighted in the restored data stream. These errors occurred because receiver clock No.2 did not obtain proper synchronization with respect to the reference clock.

Referring to Figure 14-39, receiver clock No. 1 is "in sync" with the digital data stream, which is obviously a desirable characteristic of a receiver clock. That is, the receiver clock must be properly aligned with the bit positions of the transmitted (or received) waveform to accurately restore the bit values (i.e., "0" or "1") of the data stream. To accomplish this, a Phase Locked Loop (PLL) is often used at the receiver. A PLL "locks" the receiver clock to the bit positions of the received (incoming) data stream, as shown in Figure 14-40. The receiver clock is generated from either an external or an internal clock. Before this clock was applied to the PLL, its rising edges did not line-up correctly with the bit positions of the transmitted data stream (i.e., the clock was not "in sync").

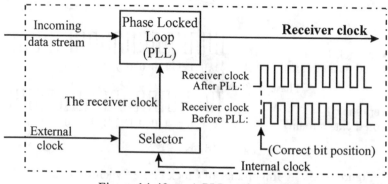

Figure 14-40   A PLL at the Receiver.

If the incoming data stream (waveform) has appropriate characteristics (i.e. has sufficient "0" to "1" transitions) and it is applied to the PLL, the receiver clock will have its phase "locked" to the correct position (Figure 14-40). This phase locked receiver clock can be used to decode the incoming data stream and accurately restore the bit values. Erroneous bits caused by an incorrectly phased clock, as shown in Figure 14-39 are eliminated when the PLL technique is used.

Two commonly asked questions regarding data bitstreams are reviewed as follows:

(1) **What are the desired characteristics of a received digital bitstream waveform?**

Figure 14-41 shows two possible digital bitstream waveforms. The top waveform (A) does not possess sufficient "ones density" (i.e. it does not have enough "1 to 0" or "0 to 1" signal transitions). A digital signal with this property is not desirable. In comparison, the waveform (B) in Figure 14-41 has adequate "ones density" (transitions). Digital signal in Figure 14-41(B) can be used to lock a receiver clock to the correct position (phase) as shown in Figure 14-40. This allows accurate restoration of the bit values in the bitstream.

(2) **Can digital signals that have very few transitions be converted to formats that have many transitions?**

The answer to question No.2 is "yes." In fact, there are several techniques that can be applied to achieve this goal. These methods are called "zero suppression" or "zero substitution". Two most popular Zero Code Suppression (ZCS) methods are:

* Line encoding
* Bit scrambling

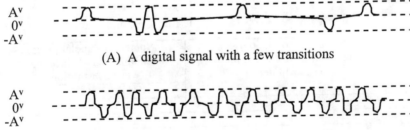

(A) A digital signal with a few transitions

(B) A digital signal with plenty of transitions

Figure 14-41   A Desired Digital Bitstream.

14.8.3 Line Encoding to Guarantee Ones Density

Table 14-5 lists the line codes (also known as transmission codes) that are commonly used in the modern digital networks. A line code is *"a technique that a digital system uses at the transmitter to convert a digital data bitstream (with too many consecutive zeros) into a bitstream that has sufficient transition (logical "1" to "0", and "0" to 1") so that the receiver can utilize these transitions to synchronize its clock to the reference clock (i.e., the transmission clock)*". In summary, <u>*zero suppression techniques are used to guarantee adequate ones density in the digital bitstream*</u>. Of the many line codes, B3ZS is frequently employed since DS3 dominates the PDH long-haul network in North America. Likewise, and E1, E2 and E3 dominate ITU-T network applications, and uses the HDB3 line code. These are also the most difficult line codes to understand and implement.

Table 14-5   Commonly-used Line Codes.

Signal	Line code
DS1	Alternate Mark Inversion (AMI) or Bipolar 8-Zero Substitution (B8ZS)
DS2	Bipolar 6-Zero Substitution (B6ZS)
DS3	Bipolar 3-Zero Substitution (B3ZS)
FDDI	4B/5B substitution
Ethernet	Manchester code
E1, E2, and E3	High Density Bipolar 3 (HDB3)
E4	Code Mark Inversion (CMI)

FDDI: Fiber Distributed Data Interface

- **B3ZS**: This line code allows only two consecutive zeros to be transmitted over a digital network. That is, it replaces any three consecutive zeros by one of the four pre-determined patterns (shown in Table 14-6). Each of the four pre-determined patterns introduce a bipolar violation in the **3rd** bit position Thus, a B3ZS code is often written as "00V, +0V, or –0V", where "+" represents a positive voltage, "–" represents a negative voltage, and a "V" represents a bit with bipolar **V**iolation.

Table 14-6   B3ZS Line Code Substitution Patterns.

The polarity of the pulse preceding the 3-zeros to be substituted	Number of bipolar pulses (both + and –) since the last substitution	
	Odd	Even
–	00– (00**V**)	+0+ (+0**V**)
+	00+ (00**V**)	–0– (–0**V**)

Figure 14-42 illustrates a binary signal (100011000001110011...) having few transitions (i.e. too many consecutive zeros in its bitstream) can be converted into a waveform with plenty of transitions by applying B3ZS encoding. When the receiver (shown in Figure 14-40) receives this signal, its clock can easily be locked to the correct timing position (i.e., phase). As a result, the restored data stream will correctly represent the transmitted bitstream sequence. As shown in Figure 14-42, the B3ZS code is a 50% duty cycle Return to Zero (RZ) signal. When a signal maintains its peak voltage value for 50% of its bit-interval, and then returns to a 0-volt level for the remainder of the bit interval, it is referred to as a RZ signal with a 50% duty cycle. Note that a 50% duty RZ signal is better for timing recovery than a NRZ (Non-Return to Zero) signal.

The application of the B3ZS line code is illustrated in Figure 14-42. The waveform shown represents the signal transmitted to the receiver. It is clear that there are more transitions in the B3ZS encoded waveform than the original binary bitstream. Therefore, the received digital bitstream will assist the receiver's Phase Lock Loop (PLL) circuit in achieving timing (clock) synchronization, and allows accurate bitstream restoration.

To decode the B3ZS waveform back into its original binary bitstream requires the following rules be applied: (1) a bipolar "+" or "−" voltage is decoded as a logical "1", except when a bipolar violation (i.e., a "+" following a "+", or a "−" following a "−") occurs; then the position with the violation and two preceding bits are decoded into three "0s"; and (2) a "zero" voltage is always decoded as a logical "0".

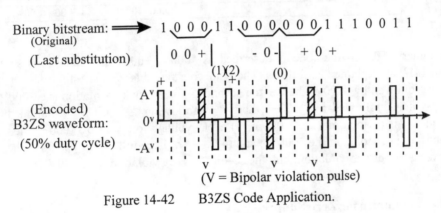

Figure 14-42   B3ZS Code Application.

The line code High Density Bipolar 3 (HDB3; 3 consecutive zeros is allowed in the bitstream) line code, is used for E1, E2 or E3 transport, and functions exactly the same as B3ZS. HDB3 can also be classified as a B4ZS code (because HDB3 allows 3 consecutive zeros in the digital bitstream, but HDB3 substitutes 4 consecutive zeros with one of the four pre-determined patterns listed in Table 14-7).

- **HDB3**: This line code allows only three consecutive zeros to be transmitted over the digital network. It replaces any four consecutive zeros by one of the four pre-determined patterns (shown in Table 14-7). Each of the four pre-determined patterns introduces a bipolar violation in the **4th** bit position. Thus, a HDB3 code is often written as "000V, +00V, or −00V", where a "+", a "−" and a "V" have the same meanings as in the case of B3ZS line code (i.e., bipolar Violation; see preceding B3ZS description in this section). The substitution and application of the HDB3 line code is identical to those used for B3ZS.

The operations (coding and decoding) of HDB3 are exactly the same as the B3ZS code. For example, to decode the HDB3 coded waveform back into the original bitstream requires the following rules be applied: (1) a bipolar "+" or "−" voltage is decoded as a logical "1", except when a bipolar violation (i.e., a "+" following a "+", or a "−" following a "−") occurs; then the position with the violation and the three (instead of two in B3ZS) preceding bits are decoded into four (instead of three in B3ZS) "0s"; and (2) a "zero" voltage is always decoded as a logical "0".

Table 14-7   HDB3 Line Code Substitution Pattern.

The polarity of the pulse preceding the 4-zeros to be substituted	Number of bipolar pulses (both + and −) since the last substitution	
	Odd	Even
−	000− (000V)	+00+ (+00V)
+	000+ (000V)	−00− (−00V)

In summary, HDB3 line code is described as "000V, +00V, or −000V)" as shown in Table 14-7, as explained as follows. There are four possible zero substitutions: (1) a "−" voltage followed by "000−"; hence, the second "−" is a bipolar violation (i.e., 000V); (2) a "−" voltage followed by "+00+"; here, "+" following "−" has no violation, but the second "+" is a violation (i.e., +00V); (3) a "+" voltage followed by "000+"; hence, the second "+" is a violation (i.e., 000V); and (4) a "+" voltage followed by "−00−"; here, "−" following "+" has no violation, but, the second "−" is a violation (i.e., −00V).

14.8.4 Scrambler for Zero Suppression

An alternate way to suppress a string of zeroes in a data stream is to apply the technique known as "bit scrambling". A scrambler is a pseudo random noise generator that is implemented by using one-bit memory devices. Seven one-bit memory devices (e.g., shift registers or "flip flops") are required (Figure 14-43) for scrambling a bitstream to provide zero suppression. This algorithm is described by a generating (generator) polynomial of $g(x) = 1 + x^6 + x^7$ used for SONET/SDH networks.

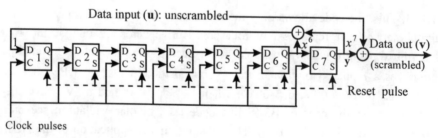

Figure 14-42   Scrambler used in SONET/SDH Networks.

When ATM cells are transported over SONET/SDH facilities, a scrambler algorithm given by the polynomial $g(x) = 1 + x^{43}$ is use. The scrambler for ATM applications requires 43 one-bit shift registers configurated as a sequential circuit.

The scrambler's sequential circuit is a pseudo-random (pseudo-noise) sequence generator. The scrambler used in SONET/SDH digital networks, based on the generator polynomial of $g(x) = 1 + x^6 + x^7$, produces the pseudo random sequence (y) shown in Figure 14-44 when a string of logical "00000000000000000..." is input to the scrambler.

<u>1111111</u>0000000100000110000101000111100100010110011101010011111010
0001110001001001101101011011111011000110100101110111001100101010
<u>1111111</u>0000000100000110000101000111100100010110011101010011111010
0001110001001001101101011011111011000110100101110111001100101010 ⋯

Figure 14-44   Pseudo Random Sequence (y) Generated by $g(x) = 1 + x^6 + x^7$.

The relationship between the input unscrambled data (u) the scrambled output data (v), and the pseudo random sequence (y) is given by the following equation:

$$v = u \bullet \bar{y} + \bar{u} \bullet y \tag{14-17}$$

where "$\bullet$" is a logical "AND" and "+" is a logical "OR" operation, and $\bar{y}$ is the "inverted" signal of y. Eq.(14-11) is known as mod(2) operation or an "exclusive ORing" operation [$v = u \oplus y$]. That is, four operational cases are given by:

$$v = u \oplus y = 0 \oplus 0 = 0 \qquad v = u \oplus y = 0 \oplus 1 = 1,$$
$$v = u \oplus y = 1 \oplus 0 = 1 \qquad v = u \oplus y = 1 \oplus 1 = 0. \tag{14-18}$$

This mod(2) operation can be extended to more than two input signals (u, y, ..., etc.). If the sum of all input signals is an "odd" number of "1s", the output is "1". Conversely, if the sum of all input signals is an "even number of 1's", the output is "0".

An STM-N signal must have sufficient bit timing content (i.e., transitions) at the Network Node Interface (NNI). A suitable bit pattern that prevents long sequences of either "1"s and "0"s, can be provided by using a scrambler. A frame-synchronous scrambler of sequence length 127 (see Figure 14-44; this sequence has a random pattern of 127-bits as indicated by the bitstream between the first group of seven "underlined" "1s" and the second group of seven "underlined" "1s"), operating at the appropriate line rate, and based on the generating polynomial, $g(x) = 1 + x^6 + x^7$, is typically used.

The scrambler must be reset (Figure 14-43, the "S" port) to "1111111" on each occurrence of the most significant bit of the byte following the last byte of the first row in the STM-N Section OverHead (SOH; see Figure 14-45). This bit, and all subsequent bits to be scrambled, are added (modulo 2) to the output from the "x^7 position" (see Figure

14-43) of the scrambler [i.e., using Eq.(14-17)]. The scrambler runs continuously throughout the complete STM-N frame interval. ***Note that the first row of the STS-N/STM-N section (regenerator section) overhead bytes (9 × N bytes, including the A1 and A2 framing bytes) is not scrambled*** (see Sections 14.4.4 and 14.7.1 of this chapter).

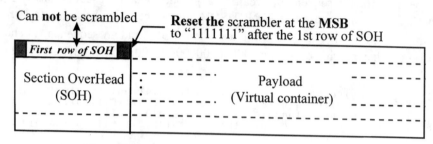

Figure 14-45   SDH STM-N Frame Structure.

14.8.5 Timing Configuration

Various timing configurations for SONET/SDH applications are shown in Figure 14-46. Five possible configurations that can be adopted for SONET/SDH networks are briefly defined as follows. The "box" in each of the five configurations represents a SONET/SDH network node (e.g., a 4 ESS central office).

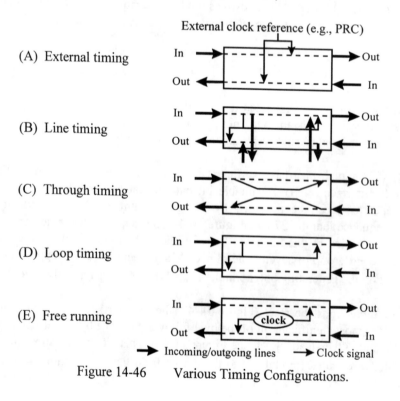

Figure 14-46   Various Timing Configurations.

(1)   External timing: In the external timing configuration [Figure 14-46(A)] a Primary Reference Clock (PRC) with stratum 1 quality and a minimum (clock) accuracy of 10^{-11} (see Table 14-3(is used as the source to derive all the clock signals.

(2)   Line timing: In the line timing configuration [Figure 14-46(B)], the clock signals are derived from the incoming optical signal. This derived clock is then applied to the outgoing optical lines.

(3)   Through timing: In the through timing configuration [Figure 14-46(C)], the clock signals are derived from the incoming optical signal. However, this derived clock is only applied to the outgoing optical line for the same transmission direction.

(4)   Loop timing: In the loop timing configuration [Figure 14-46(D)], the clock signals are derived from the incoming optical signal. This derived clock is then applied to the outgoing optical lines. This is similar to line timing. The difference between loop timing and line timing is that loop timing is only applicable to a SONET/SDH Network Element (NE) configured as a terminal-mode element [i.e., mux-demux point-to-point applications; Figure 14-47(A)]. In contrast, line timing is used when a SONET/SDH NE is configured as an Add/Drop Multiplexer [Figure 14-47(B)].

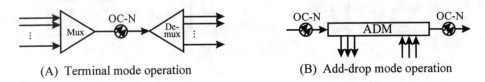

(A) Terminal mode operation   (B) Add-drop mode operation

Figure 14-47   Terminal-Mode and Add-drop Mode (ADM) Configurations.

(5)   Free running: In the free running configuration [Figure 14-46(E)], timing is supplied by an internal clock source.

       When a network element is used as a point-to-point application (e.g., a multiplexer at one end and a demultiplexer at the other end), the device is configurated as "terminal mode", and the loop timing configuration is typically used. In the Add-Drop Multiplexer (ADM) mode, the device can drop and/or add electrical/optical signals, and the line timing configuration is typically used.

14.9 PUBLIC SWITCHED AND PRIVATE NETWORK SYNCHRONIZATION

A hierarchical source-receiver method of clock synchronization (Figure 14-48) has been adopted for both public switched and private networks. A node containing the most stable clock *timing reference* is identified as the *source node* [Node (A) in Figure 14-48]. The source node [Node (A) in Figure 14-48] timing (clock) reference is transmitted to other equivalent [Node (C) in Figure 14-48] or less stable [Nodes (B) and (D)] receiver nodes. Within the receiver node, a clock circuit known as the "receiver clock" accepts and locks on to the timing reference signal provided by the source node. The receiver node, in turn, may transmit timing to other nodes and, thereby, become a "source node" for other receivers [Node (B) in Figure 14-48, is a "receiver node" with respect to Node (A), and Node (B) also serves as a "source node" for Node (E)]. Therefore, timing is distributed via a hierarchy of nodes that strictly follows "source-receiver" relationships between pairs of nodes.

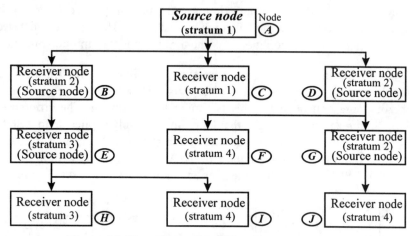

Figure 14-48   Hierarchical Synchronization.

The general definition of a receiver clock is: "*a clock whose timing output is controlled by the timing signal received from a source clock of equal or higher quality.*"

A receiver clock unit consists of the following elements:

- A timing ensemble of oscillators.

- A servo-mechanism circuit to control and monitor the performance of the oscillators with respect to the timing reference.

The role of a receiver clock is to recover a "good estimate" of the source node's timing based on *an incoming timing reference*. This requires the receiver clock to perform two basic functions: (1) reproduce the source clock's timing from a reference signal (i.e., the zero-suppressed incoming bitstream), even if it is degraded; and (2) maintain an adequate time-keeping function in the absence of a timing reference.

14.9.1 Public Switched Network Synchronization

The Primary Reference Clock (PRC) reference is transmitted from each primary node to its neighboring nodes (called secondary nodes) that do not contain a PRC. A PRC simultaneously monitors the timing signals it receives from at least two other PRC nodes (as well as the secondary nodes) to obtain long-term stability data. The long-term timing stability of each PRC location is tracked and verified to an accuracy of 10^{-13}. In a typical application, a set of duplicated rubidium oscillators provides short-term timing stability. For this arrangement, the daily stability of a disciplined rubidium clock is equivalent to the daily measurement stability of the GPS satellite that it tracks.

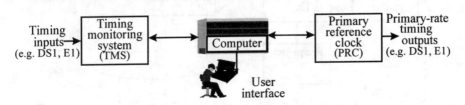

Figure 14-49   Verifiable Timing Distribution.

As reliable timing elements, rubidium oscillators can provide the best cost to performance tradeoff. In comparison, quartz oscillators **cannot** obtain the daily stability performance that is equivalent to GPS. Finally, cesium oscillators provide no significant stability advantage, and are very costly. Figure 14-49 illustrates the interconnectivity of a PRC, computer controller, and TMS (Time Monitoring System). The TMS is used to select digital signal inputs and clocks from other nodes for timing monitoring. The outputs of the PRC are a pair of digital primary-rate timing signals (e.g., 1.544 MHz DS1 or 2.048 MHz E1). The computer-aided user interface performs administrative, control, performance verification, and error recovery functions. These functions, including on-line documentation and self diagnostics, are displayed in a user-friendly manner to minimize the need for special training of field personnel.

The timing distribution architecture for switched network synchronization is shown in Figures 14-50 and 14-51. Figure 14-50 represents to a primary node, and Figure 14-51 represents a secondary node.

(1) **Primary-node applications**: In this application, the PRC provides a timing reference for the stratum 2 clock that is distributed by a digital switch (e.g., 4ESS) or a Digital Cross-connect System (DCS). In turn, this stratum 2 clock provides a timing reference (using primary and secondary paths) for all the other clocks in that node. The equipment controlled by stratum 2 clocks provide traffic-carrying (e.g., DS1 or E1 signals) digital inter-building (e.g., between central offices) timing reference distribution. It also provides direct input, for intra-nodal timing, via a device known as a Clock Distribution Unit (CDU). A CDU is used to supply multiple timing outputs to all the equipment in the node which require timing reference signals, and frequency-locked clocks for analog Frequency Division Multiplexing (FDM) equipment. This arrangement can be extended to non-AT&T public switched networks, or sometimes private networks. The clock rates generated by a CDU are typically 8 kHz and 1.544 MHz in North America, 8 kHz and 2.048

MHz in ITU-T networks, and 8 kHz, 1.544 MHz and 2.048 MHz for international gateway applications.

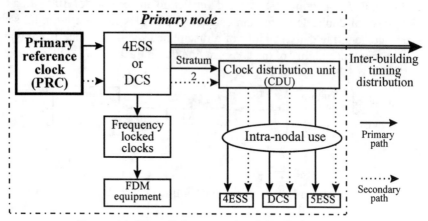

Figure 14-50   Primary-node Timing Distribution.

(2) **Secondary node applications**: In a secondary node **that does not contain a PRC**, the stratum 2 clock receives its DS1 (or equivalent) timing reference from diverse remote primary nodes via a Digital Signal Cross-connect (DSX) panel (i.e., DSX1 if DS1 signals are used). A 4ESS or a DCS can be used to terminate the timing reference from the primary node. Thereafter, the intra-nodal reference distribution function is performed by a Clock Distribution Unit (CDU) are the same as the primary node (see Figure 14-50). Note that this arrangement requires primary and secondary paths, and can also be extended to non-AT&T networks.

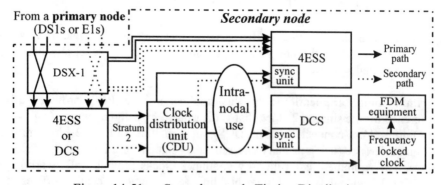

Figure 14-51   Secondary-node Timing Distribution.

14.9.2 Verification Methodology

Four levels of switched network synchronization verification have been generally adopted service providers. These levels are briefly described as follows:

(1) First level verification: This is a GPS verification process performed by various laboratories. This high-level (level 1) verification results in long-term changes in synchronization network operations (e.g., upgrading of steering algorithms). The laboratories that perform the ongoing verification are:

- The National Institute of Standards and Technology (formally the National Bureau of Standards)

- The Naval Observatory

- The Network Synchronization Laboratory (Lucent-Bell Labs, Holmdel, N.J.)

(2) Second level verification: Within the PRC itself, the relative timing instability (uncertainty) of clock elements in the system is determined. This detects short-term daily timing instability and marginal performance in any of the clocking elements.

(3) Third level verification: This is known as primary tier (long-term) verification. It determines the long-term time uncertainty (noise characteristics) of each primary node.

(4) Fourth level verification: This is known as secondary tier verification. The signals returned from the secondary nodes are monitored by several PRCs to determine the performance of the secondary nodes.

This methodology is typically used in AT&T network application, but can also be applied in non-AT&T networks (e.g., MCI or Sprint networks). The timing elements in this system are usually rubidium oscillators and a GPS receiver.

14.9.3 Primary Reference Clock (PRC) Performance

Figure 14-52 illustrates the performance of the AT&T PRC (these PRC performance requirements have also been adopted by several other service providers that own switched public networks) compared to ANSI standards. The time-keeping error relative to the Universal Time Coordinator (UTC) is shown on the ordinate (y-axis), and the observation time (in seconds) is shown on the abscissa (x-axis) of the graph in Figure 14-52. For example, ANSI and ITU-T specify a maximum time-keeping error of 3,000 *ns* for less than one day, and the typical PRC performance is better by more than two orders of magnitude, (i.e. 25 *ns* or less).Four performance characteristics (cases 1-4) that correspond to Figure 14-52 are described as follows:

- *Case (1)*: The ANSI and ITU-T specifications allow long-term frequency accuracy of 1×10^{-11} (as indicated by the slope in Figure 14-52). It also specifies a maximum daily timing instability of 3,000 ns (as indicated by the horizontal asymptote).

- *Case (2)*: PRC time-keeping performance is based on the rubidium-based (disciplined) oscillators in holdover mode (defined in Section 14.2.3; Definition 14-8).

This reflects a failure condition in which no steering is applied by the GPS. The PRC can maintain a long-term frequency accuracy of 1×10^{-11} for a minimum period of 2 weeks without steering from GPS as shown by the dashed slope in Figure 14-52.

- ***Cases (3) & (4)***: PRC performance under normal conditions is shown by Case (3) which assumes the PRC 3-σ (about 99.7%) time error specification, and Case (4) which shows typical performance.

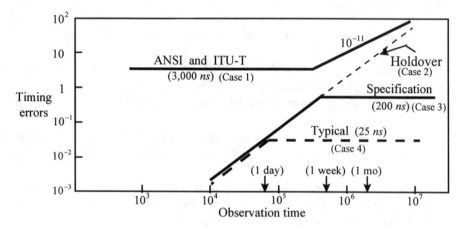

Figure 14-50   PRC/UTC Performance Comparison.

The AT&T timing interface performance objectives (these timing interface performance objectives have also been set by several other service providers that own switched public networks) for SONET/SDH networks are listed in Table 14-8.

Table 14-8   AT&T New Timing Interface Performance Objectives

Timing interface	Daily stability		Weekly stability	
	Time (ns)	Frequency ($\times 10^{-13}$)	Time (ns)	Frequency ($\times 10^{-13}$)
Primary node	60	7	60	1
Secondary node	70	8	185	3

14.9.4 Private Network Synchronization

Because of the network coverage of a private network is typically smaller than a switched public network, private network synchronization plans follow the hierarchical source-receiver method shown in Figure 14-53. In addition, private networks demonstrate the following characteristics, that are different from a switched public network:

- Complex and unconstrained
- Excessive cascading
- Lack of provision for hierarchical architecture
- Lack of diversity
- Limited connectivity

These characteristics clearly show the differences between public switched and private networks. These differences are summarized as follows:

- The overall performance of private networks are significantly impacted by the synchronization performance of Customer Premises Equipment (CPE). This is because most CPEs use stratum 4 clocks.

- The stratum 4 clock was originally designed to be used as a "receiver clock" for terminating timing (i.e., **not** as a "source clock").

- Many CPEs are placed in tandem, and each can handle a large amount of traffic. As a result, stratum 4 clocks take on the role of source clocks.

- Synchronization difficulties in private network cause serious transmission impairments such as error bursts and phase hits (i.e., not just excessive slips).

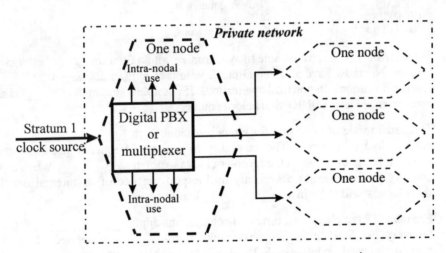

Figure 14-51   Private Network Hierarchical Source-receiver
Synchronization Method.

Review Questions for Chapter 14:

(1) Name five synchronous time division systems: _____ ; _____ ;
     _____ ; _____ ; and _____ .

(2) The three levels of synchronization considered when a network timing and
     synchronization plan is deployed are: _____ -; _____ -; and,
     _____ - synchronization.

(3) The DS1 (SF structure) has a framing pattern of _____ . The DS1 (with a
     ESF structure) has a framing pattern of _____ . The SONET/SDH has framing
     pattern of (A1, A2) = _____ , or (A1, A2) = _____ hex.

(4) A PRC (or PRS) must have a stratum ___ quality clock. There are ___ strata which
     define the telecommunications synchronization hierarchy. Stratum __ clock has the
     highest accuracy, and stratum __ has the lowest accuracy.

(5) Match the various strata with typical NE applications:

Application	Clock
(A) Trunk exchange switch	Stratum 1: _____
(B) Local exchange switch	
(C) PRC	Stratum 2: _____
(D) DCS	
(E) EXM	Stratum 3: _____
(F) DPBX	
(G) PCMux	Stratum 4: _____

(6) SONET/SDH NEs must be able to synchronize with a Stratum ___ or better clock. If
     not, the NE must have an internal clock with a minimum accuracy of ± ____ ppm
     (parts per million). In practical applications, if possible a stratum __ (____) is always
     recommended as a SONET/SDH clock source.

(7) The usual mode of operation for a receiver clock is to _____ from the
     source clock's reference. The capability to maintain frequency accuracy after all
     timing references is lost in the receiver clock is known as _____ . When a clock's
     stability performance is based only on the performance of its internal oscillators,
     this clock is said to be in a _____ condition.

(8) For non-SDH applications, time division systems apply _____ for timing
     recovery. For SDH timing recovery applications, _____ is applied. The generator
     polynomial used to define an SONET/SDH scrambler is g(x) = _____ .

(9) Network synchronization techniques can be classified into: _____ (e.g.,
     _____ , _____ and _____ synchronization), and _____
     (e.g., _____ and _____ synchronization) techniques.

(10) Assume that a clock with an accuracy of 10^{-8} is used to restore a data stream. If the
     data speed is 500 Mbps, the worst-case minimum number of bits received during 1
     minute of transmission is _____ bits. If the clock with a slip rate of 10 slips per day,
     and the data speed is 2.5 Gbps, the number of bits, (the worst case situation) that
     will not be recovered during one hour of data transmission is _____ (bits/hr).

References

- **General Communication Topics:**

1. D. Smith, "Digital Transmission Systems", Van Nostrand Reinhold, 1985
2. Taub & Schilling, "Principles of Communication Systems", 2nd Ed., McGraw-Hill, NY, 1986
3. Rainer Handel, Manfred N. Huber, and Stefan Schroder, "ATM Networks: Concepts, Protocols, Applications", Addison-Wesley Publishers Ltd. 1994
4. Taub & Schilling, "Wireless Communications: Principles & Practice", 2nd Ed., McGraw-Hill, NY, 1996
5. Chow, Ming-Chwan, "Understanding SONET/SDH: Standards and Applications", 1st Ed., Andan Publisher, NJ, 1996
6. Sexton, Mike, and Reid, Andy, "Broadband Networking: ATM, SDH, and SONET", Artech House, Inc. MA, 1997
7. Chow, Ming-Chwan, "Understanding Wireless: Digital Mobile, Cellular and PCS", 1st Ed., Andan Publisher, NJ, 1998
8. J. Bellamy, John, "Digital Telephony", Wiley & Sons
9. B. Sklar, "Digital Communications" , Prentice Hall
10. SONET Rates and Formats, ANSI T1.105
11. Fiber Optic Communications, J. Palais, Prentice Hall

- **ITU-T Recommendations:**

12. E.163, "Numbering Plan for the Global Telephone Network"
13. E.164, "Numbering Plan for the ISDN Era"
14. G.701, "Vocabulary of Digital Transmission and Multiplexing, and Pulse Code Modulation (PCM)"
15. G.702, "Digital Hierarchy Bit Rates"
16. G.704, "Synchronous Frame Structure used at 1544, 6312, 2048, 8448 and 44 736 kbit.s"
17. G.707, "Network Node Interface for the Synchronous Digital Hierarchy"
18. G.726, "40, 32, 24, 16 kbit/s Adaptive Differential Pulse Code Modulation (ADPCM)"
19. G.729, "Coding of Speech at 8 kbit/s using Conjugate-Structure Algebraic-Code-Excited Linear-Prediction"
20. G.731, "Primary PCM Multiplex Equipment for Voice Frequencies"
21. G.732, "Characteristics of Primary PCM Multiplex Equipment Operating at 2048 kbit/s"
22. G.733, "Characteristics of Primary PCM Multiplex Equipment Operating at 1544 kbit/s"
23. G.734, "Characteristics of Synchronous Digital Multiplex Equipment Operating at 1544 kbit/s"
24. G.735, "Characteristics of Primary PCM Multiplex Equipment Operating at 2048 kbit/s and Offering Synchronous Digital Access at 384 kbit/s and/or 64 kbit/s"
25. G.736, "Characteristics of a Synchronous Digital Multiplex Equipment Operating at 2048 kbit/s"
26. G.741, "General Consideration on Second Order Multiplex Equipment"

27. G.747, "Second Order Digital Multiplex Equipment Operating at 6312 kbit/s and Multiplexing Three Tributaries at 2048 kbit/s"

28. G.751, "Digital Multiplex Equipment Operating at the Third Order Bit rate of 34 368 kbit/s and the Fourth Order Bit Rate of 139 264 kbit/s and Using Positive Justification"

29. G.753, "Third Order Digital Multiplex Equipment Operating at 34 368 kbit/s and Using Positive/Zero/Negative Justification"

30. G.754, "Fourth Order Digital Multiplex Equipment Operating at 139 264 kbit/s and Using Positive/Zero/Negative Justification"

31. G.755, "Digital Multiplex Equipment Operating at 139 264 kbit/s and Multiplexing Three Tributaries at 44 736 kbit/s"

32. G.775, "Loss Of Signal (LOS), Alarm Indication Signal (AIS) and Remote Defect Indication (RDI) Defect Detection and clearance Criteria for PDH Signals"

33. G.780, "Vocabulary of Terms for Synchronous Digital Hierarchy (SDH) Networks and Equipment"

34. G.783, "Characteristics of SDH Equipment Functional Blocks"

35. G.784, "SDH Management"

36. G.785, "Characteristics of a Flexible Multiplexer in a SDH Environment"

37. G.791, "General Consideration on Transmultiplexing Equipment"

38. G.797, "Characteristics of a Flexible Multiplexer in a PDH Environment"

39. G.802, "Internetworking between Networks Based on Different Digital Hierarchy and Speech Encoding Laws"

40. G.803, "Architecture of Transport Networks Based on the SDH"

41. G.804, "ATM Cell Mapping into Plesiochronous Digital Hierarchy (PDH)"

42. G.810, "Definitions and Terminology for Synchronous Networks"

43. G.811, "Timing Characteristics of Primary Reference Clocks"

44. G.812, "Timing Requirements of Slave Clocks Suitable for Use as Node Clocks in Synchronous"

45. G.842, "Interworking of SDH Network Protection Architectures"

46. G.861, "Principles and Guidelines for the Integration of Satellite and Radio Systems in SDH Transport Networks"

47. G.901, "General Consideration on Digital Sections and Digital Line Systems"

48. G.941, "Digital Line Systems Provided by FDM Transmission Bearers"

49. G.950, "General Considerations on Digital Line Systems"

50. G.951, "Digital Line Systems Based on the 1544 kbit/s Hierarchy on Symmetric Pair Cables"

51. G.952, "Digital Line Systems Based on the 2048 kbit/s Hierarchy on Symmetric Pair Cables"

52. G.953, "Digital Line Systems Based on the 1544 kbit/s Hierarchy on Coaxial Pair Cables"

53. G.954, "Digital Line Systems Based on the 2048 kbit/s Hierarchy on Coaxial Pair Cables"

54. G.955, "Digital Line Systems Based on the 1544 & 2048 kbit/s Hierarchy on Optical Fiber Cables"

55. G.957, "Optical Interfaces for Equipment and Systems Relating to the SDH

56. G.961, "Digital Transmission System on Metallic Local Lines for ISDN Basic Rate Access"

57. G.971, "General Features of Optical Fiber Submarine Cable Systems

58. G.972, "Definition of Term Relevant to Optical Fiber Submarine Cable Systems"

59. G.981, "PDH Optical Line Systems for the Local Network"

Answers for Review Questions

Chapter 8:

(1) higher, shorter (2) infrared, optical wireless, wireless optics (3) Mobile switching center, base station, mobile unit (4) speech encoding, channel encoding, encryption, multiplexing, modulation, radio management, speech encoding (5) home, office, mobile, outdoor/travel (6) terminal mobility, personal mobility, service profile management (7) large signal attenuation, random phase, multi-path transmission (delay spread), deep fading (8) antenna gain, antenna directivity, front-to-back ratio, front-to-side ratio, beamwidth, maximum input power, operating frequency range (9) 3-to-6, 6-to-11 (10) diversity (technique), bit-interleaving, 2, selective (11) cellular, PCS (12) frequency reuse, cellularization (13) CDMA, FDMA, TDMA (14) amplitude, frequency, phase, amplitude, frequency, phase, quadratural amplitude modulation (15) π/4-DQPSK, (Gaussian) minimum shift keying (MSK) (16) types of services, types of technology, network evolution, infrastructure availability, time to market, obtaining sites due to microcell requirements, clearing the spectrum (17) IS-95, PCS1900, IS-136, W-CDMA (18) True (19) large capacity, good coverage (large or small), frequency reuse, easy to budget power, roaming and call delivery are available (20) AMPS(NAMPS), TACS, J-TACS(N-TACS), RTMS, C-Netz, NMT, RC2000, IS-136 TDMA, GSM TDMA, IS-95 CDMA, IMT-2000 (21) cdmaOne, cdma2000, cdmaOne (22) cdma2000, W-CDMA, UWC-136 (23) True (24) Wireless Intelligent Network (WIN), MSC, BSs, HLRs, VLRs, PSTN

Chapter 9:

(1) True (2) take turns, full-duplex (3) a selected group of, all (4) serial, parallel, processing time (5) frame, framing, start, framing, stop, framing, message block, characters (6) sync characters, header, characters, trailer (7) ITU-T, ANSI, ISO, IEEE, EIA (8) X.200 physical, data link, network, chained layers, transport, session, presentation, application, end-to-end (9) Protocol Control Information, sequence number, CRC, Protocol Data Unit (10) True (11) True (12) EIA-232-D (13) False (14) True (15) stop-and-wait, continuous ARQ, selective continuous ARQ, go-back-N continuous ARQ (16) High-level Data Link Control, Link Access Procedure-Balanced, Link Access Procedure on D-channel, Medium Access Control, frame relay (17) bit, selective, address, control, payload, Frame Check sequence (FCS) (18) polling, contention, broadcast, hear (19) Carrier Sense Multiple Access (CSMA), Listen-While-Talking (20) Sprintnet, Tymnet, Datapac, Transpac, Accunet Packet Switched Service (21) B, voice, video, audio, image, data, D, 16, 64, network signaling (22) routers, LANs, throughput, connection-oriented, connectionless, FECN, BECN

Chapter 10:

(1) small, medium, interfaces, computers, terminals (2) terminals, PCs, workstations, facsimiles, printers, storage devices (3) False (4) interconnections, bus, star, radial ring, hybrid (5) 802.1, 802.2, 802.3, 802.5, 802.6 (6) Logical link control, medium access control, physical (7) Destination Service Access Point (DSAP), Source SAP (SSAP), control, information (payload) (8) unacknowledged connectionless, connection-oriented, (unnumbered, supervisory), acknowledged connectionless (9) 802.3, Carrier Sense Multiple Access/Collision Detection, preamble, start frame delimiter, destination address, source address, length, LLC data, pad, frame check sequence (10) preamble, destination address, source address, type field, data, frame check sequence (11) token ring, shielded twisted pair, differential Manchester, IEEE 802.5 (12) Ethernet, token ring (13) False (14) interoperability (15) data link, LANs, transparently, flow (16) network, dissimilar, similar, addressing schemes, maximum packet size, error recovery, different time-outs, routing techniques (17) all seven layers, incompatible propriety (18) brouter, bridge, router, trouter, router, terminal server (19) system resources management, data security management, user-to-user communication management, fault tolerance management, user-to-user file transfer, software, hardware (20) service(s), file server, terminal server, terminal concentrators, disk servers, printer servers, control kernel, network interface, file system, system service, system extensions (21) configuration, fault, performance, access control, accounting (22) cheaper, more reliable, error free, more flexible, easily growable, interworkable, more accessible

3

Chapter 11:

(1) FTP, Telnet, SMTP, SNMP, HTTP, ARPARNET (2) False (3) http://www.isi.edu/rfc-editor (4) host, networks, routers (5) application/process, (5,6 and 7), host-to-host, 4, Internet, 3, network interface, (1,2) (6) listens, opens, hand-shaking (7) Network Operating System (NOB), "brain", devices (8) IPv6, IPv4 (9) misinserted packets, packets delivered out of sequence, higher layer (10) network id (net-id), host id (host-id), class bits, subnet id bits, 136.85.51.17 (11) a list of names, path, root, dots, com, edu, net, org, int, gov, mil, us, uk (12) Serial Line IP, 1055, Point-to-Point Protocol, 1661, DIX, 894, SONET, 802, 1042, High Performance Parallel Interface, Fiber Distributed Data Interface, Switched Multimegabit Data Service (13) serial, internet, internet, hosts, bridges, routers, multi-protocol, peers (14) True (15) dead, link establishment, authentication, network layer protocol (16) framing, protocol, addressing, Synchronous Payload Envelope (SPE) (17) twisted-pair wires, Digital Loop Carrier, cable modem, Integrated Services Digital Network, Digital Subscriber Line, Wireless Local Loop (18) 64, 5.3/6.4 (19) lower costs for services, browsers, World-Wide Web (20) standards for achieving interoperability, PSTNs, regulatory, numbering plan, network management, billing tariffs (21) Group 1, Group 4, digital, 56, 10 seconds (22) H.323

Chapter 12:

(1) long-term, day-to-day, the quality (2) AT&T's BaseWorX, HP's OpenView, open, integrated, feature rich (3) IP, TCP, User Datagram Protocol (UDP), supporting applications (4) Internet Control Message Protocol, IP, network congestion, unreachable (5) connectionless, 8602 (6) network performance, network failures, network devices, network, validation, accounting, fault detection/correction (7) root, trunk, branches, leaves, labels, path, Get, Set, Trap (8) manager, agent, managed objects (9) information, object instance, attributes, attribute type, attribute values (10) fault, configuration, performance, accounting, security (11) host, communication controllers, cluster controllers, end devices, workstations (12) monitor, examine, control, surveillance, control, traffic, planning, implementation, operations, maintenance, management (13) separate, multi-vendor, inter-operability, flexible operations, options (14) environment, expectations, needs (15) administrations, local exchange carrier, inter-exchange carrier, telecom network/service customers, heterogeneous, SONET, SDH, services, equipment (16) M.3010, M.3020, M.60, M.3200, M.3300, M.3400 (17) True (18) configuration, accounting, performance, security, fault, fault location, alarm surveillance, circuit testing (19) network management, service management, business management, workstation, mediation, operations system, Q-Adapter, network element management functions (20) management application function, security function, message communication function, information conversion function, workstation support function, user interface support function, directory system function, directory access function

Chapter 13:

(1) line, channel (2) True (3) 1544×10^6 (bits / s) $\times 10 \times 60$ s $\times 10^{-5} = 9,264$ bits (4) True (5) NRZ unipolar, RZ unipolar, (NRZ) polar, NRZ bipolar, NZ bipolar (6) even, odd (7) cyclic redundancy check, Hamming, Golay, BCH, Reed-Solomon, convolutional, CRC, convolutional, Reed-Solomon (8) minimum distance (9) $n - k = 9 - k = 4 \Rightarrow k = 5$ (10) $v(x) = m(x)g(x) = (1+x2+ x4+ x6+x7)(1+x2+x5) = 1+x5+x8+x11+x12 \Rightarrow m = (1000010010010)$ (11) syndrome $S = rHT = (111) \neq (000) \Rightarrow r$ is not a valid codeword (12) bit-interleaver

Chapter 14:

(1) switch, DCS, ADM, compression terminal, echo canceler (2) bit, frame timeslot (3) 100011011100, 001011, 1111011000101000, F628 (4) 1, 4, 1, 4 (5) C, (A, D), (B, F), (E, G) (6) 3, 20, 1 (PRC) (7) extract timing, holdover, free-running (8) line encoding, scrambler, $g(x) = 1+x6+x7$ (9) disciplined, master-slave, mutual, external reference, non-disciplined, pulse stuffing, independent (10) 10-8 $\times$ 500 $\times$ 106 $\times$ 60 = 300 bits/min ; 10/24(hr) $\times$ 2.5 $\times$ 109/8000 = 130 bits/hr

Abbreviations and Acronyms

A	Agent
A/M	Agent/Manager
AA	Authoritative Answer
ABM	Accunet Bandwidth Manager
AC	Access Control
ACF	Access Control Field
ACF/ARJ	Admission Confirm/Reject
ACK	Acknowledgment
ACP	Association Control Protocol
ACSE	Association Control Service Element
ACSP	Asynchronous Communications Server Program
ACTS	Advanced Communications Technologies and Services (Europe)
ADCCP	Advanced Data Communications Control Procedure
ADM	Adapt Delta Modulation (or Add-Drop Multiplexer)
APCM	Adaptive Pulse Code Modulation
ADPCM	Adapt Differential Pulse Code Modulation
ADSL	Asymmetric Digital Subscriber Line
AFP	Apple File Protocol
AIN	Advanced Intelligent Network
AL	Application layer
AM	Amplitude Modulation
AM	Administrative Module
AMI	Alternate Mark Inversion
AMP	Active Monitor Present
AMPS	Advanced Mobile Phone Service
ANI	Automatic Number Identification
ANSI	American National Standards Institute
API	Application Programmer Interface
API/CS	Application Programming Interface/Communications Service
APPC	Advanced Program-to-Program Communications
APPN	Advanced Peer-to-Peer Network
ARIB	Association of Radio Industries and Business (Japan)
ARP	Address Resolution Protocol
ARPA	Advanced Research Project Agency (ARPA or DAROA)
ARQ	Automatic Repeat/Quest
ARQ	Admission Request
ARR	Automatic Repeat & Request
AS	Autonomous System
ASC	Accredited Standards Committees
ASCII	American Standard Code for Information Interchange
ASE	Application Service Element
ASK	Amplitude Shift Frequency
ATIS	Alliance for Telecomm Industry Solutions
ATM	Asynchronous Transfer Mode
ATP	Apple Talk Protocol

5

AU	Access Unit
BBN	Bolt, Beranck and Newman
BCC	Block Check Character
BCD	Binary Coded Decimal
BCH	Bose, Chandhuri and Hocquenghem
B-DCN	Backbone Data Communications Network
BECN	Backward Explicit Congestion Control Notification
BER	Basic Encoding Rule
BER	Bit Error Rate (or Ratio)
B-ISDN	Broadband ISDN
BIH	Bureau International de I'Heure
BISYNC	BInary SYNChronous communications
BMO	Base Managed Object
BOC	Bell Operating Company
BP	Baseband Processor
BPF	Band Pass Filter
BPRZ	Bipolar Return-to-Zero
BPSK	Binary (Basic) Phase Shift Keying
BRI	Basic Rate Interface
BRT	Business Remote Terminal
BS	Base Station
BS	Back Space
BSD	Berkeley System Distribution
BWD	Bandwidth Distance
C	Combined
C/R	Command/Response (retained for HDLC compatibility)
CAD	Computer Aided Design
CAM	Computer Aided Management (or Manufacturing)
CATT	China Academy of Telecommunications Technology
CATV	Community Antenna Television
CC	Clear Channel
CCS	Common Channel Signaling
CCS7	Common Channel Signaling 7
CDG	CDMA Development Group
CDMA	Code Division Multiple Access
CDPD	Cellular Digital Packet Data
CDU	Clock Distribution Unit
CELP	Code Excited Linear Predictive
CEPT	Conference of European Posts and Telecommunications
CESE	Capability Exchange Signaling Entity
CF	Confirm
CIB	Control Information Base
CIR	Committed Information Rate
CLNP	Connection Less Network Protocol
CLS	Connection-oriented Network Service
CM	Control Module
CMI	Code mark Inversion
CMIP	Common Management Information (service) Protocol

CMIS	Common Management Information System
CMISE	Common Management Information Service Element
CMOS	Common Management Operating (Optical) System
CMOT	Common Management over TCP
CNM	Customer Network Management
CO	Central Office
COCF	Connection-Oriented Convergence Function
CORBA	Common Request Broker Architecture
COT	Central Office Terminal
CPE	Customer Premises Equipment
CPM	Customer Premises Management
CPU	Control Processing Unit
CR	Carriage Return
CRC	Cyclic Redundancy Check
CS	Cell Site
CS	Communications Service
CSM	Communications System Management
CSMA	Carrier Sense Multiple Access
CSMA/CD	Carrier Sense Multiple Access/Collision Detection
CTS	Clear-to-Sent
DA	Destination Address
DAF	Directory Access Function
DAT	Duplicated Address Test
DCB	Digital Channel Bank
DCC	Data Communications Channel
DCE	Data Computer Equipment
DCE	Data Circuit-terminating Equipment
DCF	Data Communications Function
DCS	Digital Cross-connection System
DDCMP	Digital Data Communications message Protocol
DE	Discard Eligibility indicator
DEC	Digital Equipment Corp.
DECNet	Digital Equipment Corps'
DES	Data Encryption Standard
DHCP	Dynamic Host Configuration Protocol
DIB	Directory Information Base
DISC	Disconnect
DLCI	Data Link Connection Identifier
DLL	Data Link Layer
DM	Disconnected Mode
DM	Delta Modulation
DN	Directory Number
DNA	Digital Network Architecture
DNS	Domain Name System
DO	Directory Object
DOD	Direct Outward Dialing
DOD	Department of Defense
DOD-STD	Department of Defense Standards

DPCM	Differential Pulse Code Modulation
DPSK	Differential Phase Shift Frequency
DQDB	Distributed Queue Dual Bus
DSAP	Destination Service Access Point
DS-CDMA	Direct Sequence CDMA
DSF	Directory System Function
DSI	Digital Speech Interpolation
DSL	Digital Subscriber Line
DSM	Distributed System Management
DSP	Digital Signal Processor
DSU	Data Service Unit
DSX	Digital Signal Cross-connect
DTE	Data Terminal Equipment
DTP	Data Transfer Phase
DTP	Data Transport Process
DUP	Data User Part

EA	Extension Address
EBCDIC	Extended Binary Coded Decimal Information Code
EC	European Commision
EC	Error Control
ECC	Embedded Communications (Control) Channel
ECSA	Exchange Carrier Standards Association
ED	Ending Delimiter
EFS	End of Frame Sequence
EIA	Electronics Industry Association
EIB	Enterprise Information Base
EIR	Equipment Identity Register
EMA	Enterprise Management Architecture
EMS	Event Management Service
ENG	Enquiry
EOC	Embedded Operations Channel
EOF	End of File
EOR	Exclusive OR-gate
EOR	End of Record
EOT	End of Transmission
ESA	European Space Administrator
ESF	Extended SuperFrame
ESN	Electronic Series Number
E-TDMA	Extended TDMA
ETB	End of Transmission Block
ETSI	European Telecommunications Standard Institute
ETX	End of Text
EU	European Union
EURESCOM	European Institute for Research and Strategic Studies in Telecommunications
EVRC	Extended Variable-Rate Coding
EXM	Exchange Multiplexer

| F | Flag |
| FC | Frame Control |

FCC	Federal Communications Commission
FCS	Frame Check Sequence
FDD	Frequency Division Duplex
FDDI	Fiber Distributed Data Interface
FDM	Frequency Division Multiplexed
FDM or FDMA	Frequency Division Multiplexing
FDMA	Frequency Division Multiple Access
FDX	Full Duplex
FECN	Forward Explicit Congestion Control Notification
FED-STD	U.S. Federal Government Standards
FEP	Front-End Processor
FF	Form Feed
FFH-CDMA	Fast Frequency Hopping CDMA
FG	Feature Group
FIFO	first-in-first-out
FIPS	Federal Information Processing Standards
FM	Frequency Modulation
FoIP	Fax over Internet
FPLMTS	Future Public Land Mobile Telecommunications System
FRAD	Frame Relay Access Device
FRBS	Frame Relaying Bearer Services
FRMR	Frame Reject
FS	Frame Status
FSBS	Frame Switching Bearer Services
FSK	Frequency Shift Frequency
FTAM	File Transfer Access and Management
FTH-CDMA	Fast Time Hopping CDMA
FTP	File Transfer Protocol
GCF/GRJ	Gatekeeper Confirm/Reject
GDMF	Guideline for the Definition of TMN Management Function
GDMO	Guideline for the Definition of Managed Object
GF	Generic Flow
GNE	Gateway Network Element
GOL	Gigabit Optical Loop
GOS	Global Operating System
GOSIP	Government Open System Interconnection Profile
GPS	Global Positioning System
GRQ	Gatekeeper Request
GSM	Group Special Mobile
GSM	General Setup Message
HA	Hardware Address
HCS	Header Check Sequence
HDB3	High Density Bipolar 3
HDLC	High (level) Data Link Control
HDSL	High0bit rate Digital Subscriber Line
HDTV	High Definition TV
HDX	Half Duplex
HF	High Frequency

HL	Header Length
HLP	Higher Layer Protocol
HLR	Home Location Register
HPF	High Pass Filter
HPPI	High Performance Parallel Interface
HRC	Horizontal Redundancy Check
HS	High Speed
HT	Horizontal Tab
HTTP	Hypertext Transfer Protocol
I/G	Individual/Group address
I/O	Input/Output
I/P/V/S	Indoor/Pedestrain/Vehicular/Satellite
I/S	Information transfer/Supervisory
IAB	Internet Architecture Board
IANA	Internet Administrative Numbering Authority
ICF	Information Conversion Function
ICMP	Internet Control Message Protocol
ICO	Independent Company
IDLC	Integrated Digital Loop Carrier
IEC or IXC	Inter-Exchange Carrier
IEEE	Institute of Electrical and Electronics Engineering
IETF	Internet Engineering Task Force
IM&M	Information Movement and Management
IMSI	International Mobile Subscriber Identity
IMT-2000	International Mobile Telecommunications-2000
INE	Intermediate Network Element
INFO	Information
IOC	I/O Controller
IP	Internet Protocol
IPF	Information Processing Function
IR	Internet Register
IRTF	Internet Research Task Force
ISA	Integrated Service Architecture
ISDN	Integrated Service Digital Network
ISI	Inter Symbol Interference
ISO	International Standards Organization
ISOC	Internet Society
ISP	IP Service Provider
ISP	International Standardized Profile
ITB	Intermediate Transmission Block
ITF	Information Transport Function
ITSP	Internet Telephone Service Provider
ITU	International Telecommunications Union
ITU-R	ITU-Radio Communications Sector (Formally CCIR)
ITU-T	International Telecommunications Union-Telecommunications Standards Sector (formally CCITT)
IVD	Integrated Voice Data
IVDTE	Integrated Voice Data Terminal Equipment
IWU	Interworking Unit

JCG-TMN	Joint Coordination Group-TMN
JTC	Joint Technical Committee
LA	Local Area
LAN	Local Area Network
LAP	Link Access Procedure
LAPB	Link Access Procedure Balanced
LAPD	Link Access Procedure on the D channel
LAWN	Local Area Wireless Network
LBT	Listen Before Talk
LC	Logical Channel
LCF	Location Confirmation
LCI	Logical Channel Identifier
LDDI	Local Distributed Data Interface
LE	Local Exchange
LEC	Local Exchange Carrier
LED	Light Emitting Diode
LEO	Low Earth Orbit
LF	Line Feed
LF	Low Frequency
LLC	Logical Link Control
LME	Layer Management Entity
LMI	Layer Management Interface
LORAN	Long Range Navigation
LPC	Linear Predictive Coder
LPF	Low Pass Filter
LPF	Linear Predictive Filter
LR-CELP	Low-rate-CELP (Code Excited Linear Predictive)
LRC	Longitudinal Redundancy Check
LSB	Least Significant Bit
LSRR	Loose Source Route and Record
LU	Logical Unit
LWT	Listen While Talking
MA	My Address
MAM	Medium Access Method (or Connector?)
MAC	Media (or Medium) Access Control
MAE	Mobile Application Entity
MAF	Management Application Function
MAN	Metropolitan Area Network
MAP	Mobile Application Protocol
MAU	Medium Attachment Unit
MC	Multipoint Controller
MCF	Message Communications Function
MCF	Management Communications Function
MD	Mediation Device
MDAP	Management of Distributed Application Processing
MDI	Medium Dependent Interface
MEO	Medium Earth Orbit
MF	More Fragment

MF	Mediation Function
MGCP	Media Gateway Control Protocol
MHS	Message Handling System
MIB	Management Information Base
MIC	Medium Interface Connector
MIL-STD	U.S. Military Standards
MIME	Multipurpose Internet Mail Extension
MMUSIC	Multi-party Multimedia Session Control
MO	Managed Object
MOCS	Managed Object Confornance Statement
MOS	Mean Opinion Scale
MP	Multipoint Processor
MP-LPC	Multi-Pulse Linear Predictive Coder
MPLP	Multi-Pulse Linear Predictive
MS	Mobile Station
MSB	Most Significant Bit
MSC	Mobile Switching Center (see MTSO)
MSDSE	Master-Slave Determination Signaling Entity
MSISDN	Mobile Station ISDN Number
MSK	Minimum Shift Frequency
MTA	Message Transfer Agent
MTIE	Maximum Time Interval Error
MTSO	Mobile Telephone Switching Center (see MSC)
MTU	Maximum Transmission Unit
MVS	Multiple Virtual System
N(R)	Transmitter Receive sequence number
N(S)	Transmitter Send sequence number
NAK	Negative Acknowledgment
NAP	Network Access Point
NAU	Network Addressable Unit
NBS	National Bureau of Standards
NCC	Network Control Center
NCP	Network Control Program
NEF	Network Element Function
NETTBIOS	Network Basic Input Output System
NIC	Network Interface Card
NIC	Network Information Center
NICE	Network Information and Control Exchange
NIST	The National Institute for Standards and Technology
NIU	Network Interface Unit
NL	Network Layer
NLDM	Network Logical Data Management
NM	Network Management
NMF	Network Management Forum
NMPF	Network Management Productivity Facility
NMS	Network Management System
NMVT	Network Management Vector Transport
NNI	Network Node Interface
NOS	Network Operating System

NPDA	Network Problem Determination Application
NRZ	Non-Return-to-Zero
NSAP	Network Service Access Point
NT	Network Terminal
NW	Non Wireline
OA&M	Operation, Administration and Maintenance
OAM&P	Operation, Administration, Maintenance and Provisioning
OC	Option Class
OLC	Open Logical Channel
OME	OSI Management Environment
OMS	OSI Management Structure
ON	Option Number
OS	Operating System
OS	Operation System
OSF	Open Software Foundation
OSF	Operations Systems Function
OSI	Open System Interconnection
OSI-RM	Open System Interconnection Reference Model
OSPF	Open Shortest Path First
P	Primary
P/F	Poll/Final bit
PA	Preamble or Pre-arbitary
PABX	Private Automatic Branch Exchange
PAR	Positive Acknowledgment or Retransmission
PBX	Private Branch Exchange
PC	Personal Computer
PCI	Protocol Control Information
PCS	Personal Communications Service
PCS	Plastic Cladded Silica (fiber)
PCSC or MSC	Cellular or PCS Switching Center
P-MP	Point-to-Multipoint
pdf	probability density function
PDH	Plesiochronous Digital Hierarchy
PDU	Protocol Data Unit
PDN	Public Data Network
PDU	Protocol (or Packet) Data Unit
PhL	Physical Layer
PI	Protocol Interpreter
PID	Protocol ID
PIN	Personal Identification Number
PL	Presentation Layer
PLCF	Physical Layer Convergence Function
PLL	Phase Lock Loop
PLMN	Public Land Mobile Network
PLP	Packet Layer Protocol
PM	Phase Module
PMD	Physical (layer) Medium Dependent
PN	Pseudo Noise

POF	Plastic Optical Fiber
POH	Path Overhead
POL	Plain Old LAN
POTS	Plain Old Telephone Service
P-P	Point-to-Point
PPP	Point-to-Point Protocol
PRC	Primary Reference Clock (see PRS)
PRI	Primary Rate Interface
PRS	Primary Reference Source (see PRC)
PS	Personal Station
PSI	Performance System Incorporated
PSK	Phase Shift Frequency
PSN	Packet Switched Network
PSTN	Public Switched Telephone Network
PT	Payload Type
PTT	Posts, Telegrams and Telephone
PTTI	Precise Time and Time Interval
PU	Physical Unit
PVC	Permanent Virtual Circuit
Q/R	Query/Response
QA	Queue Arbitration
QA	Q-adapter
QAF	Q-Adapter Function
QAM	Quadrature Amplitude Modulation
QoS	Quality of Service
QPT	Queue PDU Timer
RA	Recursive Available
RACE	Research and Development in Advanced Communications in Europe
RARP	Reverse Address Resolution Protocol
RAS	Registration/Admission/Status
RBS	Radio Base Station
RD	Received Data
RD	Recursive Desired
RDN	Relative Distinguished Name
REJ	Reject
REL COMP	Release Complete
REQ	Request
REVAL	Radio Testing and Evaluation
RFC	Request for Comment
RI	Routing Information
RIP	Routing Information Protocol
RIPL	Remote Initial Program Load
RJ	Reject
RLSD	Received Line Signal Detect
RM	Reference Model
RNR	Receive Not Ready
ROM	Read-Only-Memory
RPE-LTP	Regular Pulse Excited Long Term Predictive coder

RPOA	Recognized Private Operating Agency
RQ	Request counter
RR	Receive Ready
RR	Resource Record
RRQ	Read Request
RRQ	Registration Request
RSVP	Resource Reservation Protocol
RTCP	RTP Control Protocol
RTP	Real-time Transport Protocol
RTS	Request-to-Sent
RTT	Radio Transmission Technologies
RU	Response Unit
RUI	Relay User Interface
RZ	Return-to Zero
S	Secondary
S/N	Signal-to-Noise ratio
SA	Source Address
SAA	System Application Architecture
SABME	Set Asynch Balanced Mode Extended
SAP	Service Access Point
SAU	Source Access Unit
SC6	Sub-Committee 6
SCE	Service Creation Environment
SCN	Service Creation Node
SCO	Santa Cruz Operation
SCP	Service Control Point
SD	Starting Delimiter
SDH	Synchronous Digital Hierarchy
SDLC	Synchronous Data Link Control
SDN	Software Defined Network
SDS3	Simplified DS3 (fiber to customer premises)
SDSL	Single-line (or symmetric) Digital Subscriber Line
SETS	Synchronization Equipment Timing Source
SF	Security Function
SFD	Start Frame Delimiter
SFS	Starting of Frame Sequence
SG	Study Group
SGCP	Simple Gateway Control Protocol
SGMP	Simple Gateway Monitor Protocol
SGND	Signal Ground
SIGDSM	Special Interest Group on Distributed System Management
SIM	Subscriber Identify Card
SIP	Session Initiation Protocol
SIT	Simple Internet Transition
SL	Session Layer
SLIP	Serial Line IP
SM	System Management
SMA	System Management Application

SMAE	System Management Application Entity
SMAP	System management Applications Process
SMB	Server Message Block
SMDS	Switched Multimegabit Data Service
SMDSI	System Management Data Service Interface
SMF	System Management Function
SMFA	Service Management Function Area
SMG2	ETSI Special Mobile Group 2 (includes 3G standards)
SMI	System Management Interface
SMI	Structure of Management Information
SMP	Standby Monitor Present
SMS	Short Message Service
SMS	Service Management System
SMT	Station Management
SMTP	Simple Mail Transport Protocol
SN/IP	Service Node/Intelligent Peripheral
SNA	System Network Area
SNAP	Subnet Access Protocol
SNMP	Simple Network Management Protocol
SOA	Start of a zone of Authority
SOH	Start-of-Header
SONET	Synchronous Optical Network
SP	Signaling Point
SPE	Synchronous Payload Envelope
SREJ	Selective Reject
SS7	Signaling System 7
SSAP	Source Service Access Point
SSCP	System Service Control Point
SSM	Synchronization Status Message
SSP	Service Switching Point
SSRR	Strict Source Route and Record
STM	Synchronous Transfer Mode
STM	Synchronous Transport Module
STP	Signal Transfer Point
STP	Shielded Twisted Pair
STS	Synchronous Transport Signal (SONET Signal)
STX	Start of Text
SVI	Subvector Identifier
SVL	Subvector Length
SVV	Subvector Value
Sync	Synchronization
T1	ANSI Telecomm Standards Committee
TA	Terminal Adapter
TABS	Telemetry Asynchronous Block Serial
TAM	Telecommunications Access Method
TASI	Time Assignment Speech Interpolation
TBOS	Telemetry Byte-Oriented Serial
TC	Truncation

TCAP	Transaction Capabilities Application Part
TCM	Trellis Coded Modulation
TCP/IP	Transmission Control Protocol/Internet Protocol
TCU	Trunk Coupling Unit
TD	Transmitted Data
TDM	Time Division Multiplexing
TDMA	Time Division Multiple Access
TE	Terminal Equipment
TEC	Toll (or trunk) Exchange Carrier
TEM	Transverse Electromagnetic (wave)
TFTP	Trivial File Transfer Protocol
TIA	Telecommunications Industry Association
TID	Transaction Identifier
TIE	Time Interval Error
TL	Transport Layer
TL	Transaction Language
TMN	Telecommunications Management Network
TMS	Time Monitoring System
TP	Transport Protocol
TR-45	TIA Committee for Mobile and Personal Comm at 800 MHz
TR-46	TIA Committee for Mobile and Personal Comm at 1800 MHz
TRG	Trunk Group
TSAP	Transport Service Access Point
TSG	Timing Signal Generator
TTA	Telecomm Technology Association (Korea)
TTC	Telecommunications Technology Committee
TTL	Transistor-to-Transistor Logic
TTL	Time to Live
TTU	Time Transfer Unit
TUP	Telephone User Part
TV	Television
U/L	Universally/Locally administered address
UA	Unnumbered Acknowledgment (or User Agent)
UART	Universal Asynchronous Receiver Transmitter
UDP	User Datagram Protocol
UI	Unacknowledged Information (or Unnumbered Information)
UIM	User Identity Module
UISF	User Interface Support Function
UM	User Module
UMTS	Universal Mobile Telecommunications Systems/services
UNI	User Network Interface
UP	User Part
UPT	Universal Personal Telecommunications
URI	Uniform Resource Identifier
URL	Uniform Resource Locator
URN	Uniform Resource Name
USNO	US Naval Observatory
UT	Universal Time

UTAM	Unlicensed PCS Ad-Hoc Committee for 2 GHz microwave transition and Management
UTC	Universal Time Coordinator (Coordinated Universal Time)
UTP	Unshielded Twisted Pair
UTRA	UMTS Terrestrial Radio Access
UWCC	Universal Wireless Communications Consortium
VC	Virtual Circuit
VCI	Virtual Channel Identifier
VCS	Virtual Circuit Services
VCXO	Voltage-controlled Crystal Oscillator
VDSL	Very (high bit-rate) Digital Subscriber Line
VER	Version
VF	Voice Frequency
VI	Vector Identifier
VL	Vector Length
VLF	Very Low Frequency
VLR	Visitor Location Register
VLSI	Very Large Scale Integration
VM	Virtual Machine
VNCA	VTAM Node Control Application
VoIP	Voice over Internet
VON	Voice on the Net
VRC	Vertical Redundancy Check
VT	Virtual Terminal
VT	Vertical Tab
VTAM	Virtual Telecommunications Access Method
VTF	Vocal Track Filter
WAN	Wide Area Network
WC	Wiring Concentrator
WDM	Wavelength Division Multiplexing
WG	Working Group
WIMS	Wireless Multimedia and Messaging Services
WIN	Wireless In-building Network
WL	Wire Line
WLL	Wireless Local Loop
WRQ	Write Request
WS	Workstation
WSCP	Wireless Service Control Point
WSF	Workstation Functional
WSSF	Workstation Support Function
WWW	World Wide Web
XID	Exchange Identification PDU
XTP	Xpress Transfer Protocol
1G	First Generation
3G	Third Generation

Index